ELEMENTARY ANALYSIS

a modern approach

PRENTICE-HALL MATHEMATICS SERIES

Dr. Albert A. Bennett, Editor

ELEMENTARY ANALYSIS
a modern approach

H. C. TRIMBLE

Head of the Department of Mathematics
Iowa State Teachers College

FRED W. LOTT, jr.

Associate Professor of Mathematics
Iowa State Teachers College

1960

Englewood Cliffs, N.J. PRENTICE-HALL, INC.

Library of Congress Catalog Card Number: 59–12432

Preface

This text grew out of a revision of the pre-calculus courses at Iowa State Teachers College. Its plan was a joint effort of the mathematics staff; the details are the responsibility of the two authors. A mimeographed edition was taught, from 1956 through 1958, to over three hundred students. The present text is a revision based upon experience with the preliminary edition.

A word about the plan of the text may help the prospective user to evaluate it in terms of his own thinking about the teaching of pre-calculus mathematics:

It is entirely possible to acquaint high school students with the elementary functions. Thus prepared, students should begin college mathematics with calculus or calculus and analytic geometry. In our experience only a minority of college freshmen, even of those who studied algebra, geometry, and trigonometry in high school, are ready to begin the study of calculus.

This text is planned to prepare entering freshmen for a course in calculus. Basically, its content is our interpretation of a modern approach to the elementary functions. This means that the concepts of set, and membership in a set, are fundamental. A condition is a set-builder; it defines a subset of a specified universe. A graph is a set of points; the graph of a condition in two variables is the set of points that corresponds to the set of ordered number-pairs that satisfy the condition. A relation is a subset of a Cartesian product, and a function is a special kind of relation. These simple ideas provide a coherent basis for a study of the elementary functions.

There are several reasons to recommend this modern approach:

1. Recent efforts of logicians and students of the foundations of mathematics to clarify mathematical concepts such as variable, parameter, unknown, condition, relation, function, and so forth have more than one reward. They yield more powerful mathematical tools, and they make mathematics easier to learn.

2. As the teacher tries to supplement the ideas that a college freshman brings from the high school, the student may feel that the teacher is merely repeating things he knows already. This may or may not be the case, but if he believes it, his belief is a barrier to progress. However, it is easy to establish the value of the modern approach demonstrated in this book.

3. Many college freshmen are deficient in manipulative techniques. In a

v

modern arrangement of elementary analysis, a capable college fresh-man who lacks background can learn some of the new ideas as quickly as many of his better-grounded classmates. Over a period of a year some of these students can be stimulated to make up for some, if not all, of their deficiency of technique. Not all students can overcome a lack of background, but even those who become drop-outs leave mathematics with a clearer idea of what constitutes the discipline. They have had a chance to learn where technique fits into the picture, as a means rather than as an end.

4. The study of pre-calculus mathematics may be viewed as an introduc-tion to mathematical structures. Few beginners are ready to handle the abstractions of a postutational approach to mathematical struc-tures. Yet, the study of mathematics can be organized to prepare students for such abstractions. In Chapter 11 the introductory treatment of mathematics as a study of structures is built upon the earlier chapters of the text.

Several topics usually included in college algebra courses have been omitted. We believe that work with the binomial theorem, permutations, combinations, and probability fits better into a pre-statistics course. These topics can be approached more powerfully and more understandably by modern methods. We hesitate to introduce them, rather artifically, into a course in elementary analysis; we prefer to treat them more thoroughly in a separate course. We also leave the treatment of mathematical induction for more advanced courses. It has been our experience that the very desirable rigor of proving such things as the laws of exponents by mathematical induction is misplaced in a freshman course.

Finally, this text is planned for use with a standard set of mathematical tables. To acquire a working knowledge of the elementary functions most students need to perform some calculations. Rather than include in the text excerpts from a few of the more familiar mathematical tables, we assume that the student has access to a standard set of tables and mathematical formulas. He is asked to make frequent use of these tables and to perform calculations with the mathematical formulas that accompany them.

In a word, the choice of topics and the emphasis upon each topic represents our considered judgment. We know from experience that the text is teachable. A teacher using the text for the first time may appreciate the following suggestions:

1. Covering the essential ideas in the text will require at least four class meetings per week for two semesters.
2. Students not ready for calculus but too advanced to begin the first semester course may join a second semester class. Such students, as they read the early portion of the text, will require a minimum of individual help to acquaint themselves with the novel features of the approach.

3. Certain topics may be omitted from a minimum course. These include most of Chapter 1, sections of Chapter 4 on arithmetic and geometric progressions, complex numbers in Chapter 5, matrices in Chapter 7, and sections of Chapters 9 and 10 that deal with elaboration of the basic ideas.

4. Many of the problems in the text are intended for the student who lacks the manipulative skills of algebra. Such problems should not be permitted to slow the pace of the course to accommodate the slowest student.

5. Other problems are intended to enrich the course for the best-prepared students. The teacher should make the scope of the course clear to each group of students.

We wish to thank our colleagues at Iowa State Teachers College for ideas and constructive criticism. Henry Van Engen and Dean Martin J. Nelson arranged time for study and writing. The Ford Foundation made it possible, through the Fund for the Advancement of Education, for Mr. Trimble to spend a year of study and to discuss desirable changes in the mathematics curriculum with mathematicians in universities and industries. Secretaries in the mathematics department and the printing room shared with Mrs. Trimble the task of preparing successive versions of the manuscript. Much credit and no blame is due these and others who influenced the text.

Contents

chapter **7**

CONDITIONS IN SEVERAL UNKNOWNS

chapter **8**

EXPONENTIAL AND LOGARITHMIC FUNCTIONS

chapter **9**

TRIGONOMETRY

chapter 10
COORDINATE GEOMETRY

chapter 11
MATHEMATICAL STRUCTURES

ELEMENTARY ANALYSIS

a modern approach

1

Numbers for Elementary Analysis

As you begin to study elementary analysis you should take a new look at numbers. Of course you have used numbers for a long time; but now you should reorganize what you know about numbers.

In this chapter you will learn to think of numbers as *members* of definite *sets*, or *families*. You will explore different ways to symbolize numbers. You will review operations like addition and multiplication and extend your ideas about such operations.

100. Natural numbers

Mary said, "I graduated third in a class of fifteen." Joe said, "In basketball, my number was 5." Jane said, "I belong to six clubs this year."

Notice that you can use a number-symbol, a word like "four," or a figure like 4, in either of two ways. Sometimes 4 tells how many. It means that there are as many of whatever you are discussing as there are circles below:

o   o

o   o

Sometimes 4 tells which one. It may be important to know that 4 comes after 3 and before 5.

When you say "There are five in my family," you mean that you could match the persons in your family, one by one, to the circles below:

o   o

o

o   o

There are as many people as there are circles. There are as many circles as there are people. You call this common property of the two sets (the set of people and the set of circles) the number five. You use a symbol like "five" or "V" to stand for the number five.

When you do not know how many things in a set, you *count* the set. What you really do is to match the set to the symbols

$$1, 2, 3, 4, 5, \ldots$$

Take the set

$$\begin{matrix} a & & p \\ & x & y \\ k & l & \end{matrix}$$

for example. Here is one way to match this set to the number-symbols:

a	k	x	l	y	p
1	2	3	4	5	6

There are other ways, like:

y	k	l	p	a	x
1	2	3	4	5	6

You always end up saying "six." You say, "There are six things in the set."

Notice how convenient counting is! Once you learn the words "one, two, three, ..." in their proper order, you can count any set. You can count very large sets because the counting words form an endless chain. You never run out of counting words.

When you want to *compare* two sets you can proceed in either of two ways. To answer the question "Are there more girls than boys?" you can match the groups of girls and boys, one girl to each boy. If there are some girls left over, you say there are more girls than boys. More often, though, you count the boys, count the girls, and compare the answers.

Notice how natural it is to develop an arithmetic of numbers that tell *how many*. You learned a long time ago to take short-cuts as you worked problems in counting. You called these short-cuts addition, subtraction, multiplication, and division. You called this whole subject arithmetic.

As you begin to study college mathematics it helps to have the simple, basic ideas of arithmetic clearly in mind. In algebra you take a careful look at these ideas. Then you generalize and extend them. For algebra, the simple, basic ideas of arithmetic are more important than the special tricks that a bookkeeper needs.

You should work through the exercises and examples that follow. They give you a chance to think about the meaning of numbers that tell *how many*. They remind you how the operations of adding, subtracting, multiplying, and dividing originate in counting. They illustrate the fact that all of these operations are short-cuts for counting.

EXERCISES §100

1. A fraternity house needed silverware. Jack contributed 3 spoons, and Pete contributed 5 spoons. How many spoons did the two boys contribute?

    (a) Represent spoons by circles. Make a diagram to show Jack's contribution, Jim's contribution, and their combined contribution.

    (b) Make up another example to illustrate the statement, "Adding groups is really *counting together.*"

    (c) What would be wrong with solving this problem by counting together? "The checks issued by waitress number 7 from 1:15 P.M. to 1:30 P.M. were: 1.03, .76, .31, 1.17, .68, .44, .87 (all in dollars). Total the checks."

    (d) Examine each number used in part (c) above. Which ones tell How many? Which ones tell Which one?

2. In each part of this exercise make a diagram to show the *action* of the problem. Each problem illustrates an everyday use of subtraction; but notice that subtraction is just a short-cut for counting.

    (a) Jack lost 4 of his 7 friends. How many friends did he have left? (Subtraction as take-away.)

    (b) Jack had 4 friends and Pete had 7 friends. How many more friends did Pete have than Jack? (Subtraction as comparison.)

    (c) Jack was assured of 4 votes. He needed 7 votes to win. How many votes did he need to get? (Subtraction to find what unknown number to add.)

    (d) I had $7 and lost some. Now I have $4. How much did I lose? (Subtraction to find how much was taken away.)

3. Make up three examples of everyday uses of subtraction. Choose examples that would be awkward to solve by diagrams and counting. Label each example as take-away, comparison, finding what to add, or what was taken away.

4. A case of cola has 6 bottles in each of 4 rows. How many bottles are in the case?

    (a) Make a diagram and solve by counting.

    (b) Visualize the problem as $4 + 4 + 4 + 4 + 4 + 4$. This is six 4's.

    (c) Visualize the problem as $6 + 6 + 6 + 6$. This is four 6's.

5. Make up another example of multiplication. Choose one that would be awkward to solve by counting or even by repeated adding (as in 4(b) or 4(c) above).

6. In each part of this exercise make a diagram to show the action of the problem. Each problem illustrates an everyday use of division; but notice that division is a short-cut for counting.

    (a) You go on a trip with $45. If you spend $5 a day, how many days will your money last? (Division as repeated subtraction of $5. In this example $45 \div 5$ means "Count the number of times you can subtract $5, beginning with $45, before you run out of money.")

    (b) You go on a trip with $45. You plan to stay 9 days. How much per day can you spend (on the average)? (Division as splitting a pile of 45 one-dollar bills into 9 equal piles. In this example, $45 \div 9$ means "Deal out 45 things into 9 equal piles and count the number in any one pile.")

7. The per capita income of a city is the average amount of income for each person (man, woman, or child) in the city.

(a) What is the per capita income in a city whose population is 126,000 if the total income for the city is $252,000,000? Would it work to split $252,000,000 into 126,000 equal piles?

(b) How many people live in a city where the per capita income is $1500 and the total income is $90,000,000? Would it work to count the number of times you can subtract $1500, beginning with $90,000,000, until you run out of money?

8. Make up two more everyday examples of division. Follow the pattern of Exercise 7.

Is there also an arithmetic of numbers that tell *which one*, numbers that locate a thing in an ordered system? The arithmetic of groups enables you to deal with a distance like 3 miles. You treat 3 miles as a group of 3 one-mile distances. Is there also an arithmetic that deals with mileposts like milepost number 3?

When you say "My room is 204," you use the symbol 204 to tell which room is yours. The symbol 204 is convenient because it has a special place among number-symbols. It comes after 203. It comes before 205. The person who plans the number system for a building can go even further. He can use numbers from 200 to 299 for second floor rooms. He can use odd numbers on one side of the hall and even numbers on the other side of the hall.

When you say "My phone number is COlfax 6–0835," you use a sequence of letters and numbers that distinguishes your phone from millions of others. People have invented ingenious ways to use number-symbols to tell *which one*. Often they make use of the position of a number in the counting sequence.

When number order is important mathematicians call these numbers *ordinal* numbers. They distinguish *ordinal* numbers (which tell *which one*) from *cardinal* numbers (which tell *how many*).

The arithmetic of ordinal numbers is often very crude. Take street numbers, for example. Joe lives at 305 West 5th Street. Mary lives at 507 West 5th Street. You know that Joe lives west of Mary on the same street. In some cities you could say "Mary lives about 2 blocks west of Joe," but in other cities the numbers do not go 100 to the block. It would be handy to say "Mary lives 507 − 305 = 202 houses west of Joe," but this would probably be wrong, because it is customary to skip some numbers in assigning addresses to buildings. Also, the other side of the street (the even-numbered houses) must be taken into account, since it is common practice to assign odd and even numbers to buildings on opposite sides of the street. About all you can say is, "Mary lives west of Joe on 5th Street."

In some situations you can treat ordinal numbers with greater confidence. Page 24 of a book is 5 pages beyond page 19, for example. Notice that saying "page 24" tells which page; hence 24 is an ordinal number. Of course you can visualize page 24 as the last of an ordered set of pages 1, 2, 3, ..., 24; you can visualize page 19 as the last of an ordered set of pages 1, 2, 3, ..., 19; hence you may think of subtracting 19 pages from 24 pages and conclude that 24 is 5 more than 19. Thus page 24 is 5 pages beyond page 19.

Many uses of numbers fall in this twilight zone between cardinal numbers and ordinal numbers. You can think of them either way. When you say "My desk is 24 inches wide," we have two good ways to visualize your desk:

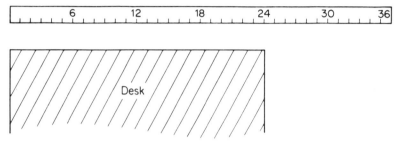

Fig. 1–1.

We can think of a pile of little pieces of wood each 1 inch long. We can think of laying these end-to-end. It will take 24 of them to reach across the desk. Hence 24 is a cardinal number; it tells *how many*. (Of course we would soon get tired of visualizing 24 inches this way. We learn to think of 24 inches as two ten-inch pieces and four one-inch pieces; or we learn to think of 24 inches as two twelve-inch pieces. These are just ways to help us visualize the number 24, to see how many 24 is.)

We can also think of a ruler. We have a mental image of a yardstick (Fig. 1–1). We imagine the yardstick laid on the desk with the proper end lined up with the back edge of the desk. Then we visualize the 24 mark as above the front edge of the desk. The 24 mark on the ruler gives us what we want to know. It locates a place on the yardstick. When we think of the position of the 24 mark (rather than of the collection of 24 inches), we are using 24 as an ordinal number. The number 24 tells us which one of the marks on the ruler. Hence it tells us the width of your desk.

The following exercises give you further examples of ordinal numbers. Then they pose problems that you can solve by thinking of the numbers as either cardinal or ordinal. It is important to be able to think both ways. The ordinal way of thinking, with its emphasis upon position, is especially convenient when you come to visualize negative numbers.

EXERCISES §100 (cont.)

9. People who visit the Pentagon building in Washington, D.C., like to make jokes about getting lost. Over 30,000 people, who work in the Pentagon, have no trouble finding their way. Once you know the system, the number of a room tells you exactly where the room is. A typical number is 4C267. To understand this number you should visualize the building (Fig. 1–2): It has 5 floors. Each floor has 5 rings, A, B, C, D, and E, and 10 corridors numbered clockwise from 1 to 10. Room 4C267 is on the 4th floor, in the C ring, between corridors 2 and 3. See the star in the figure.

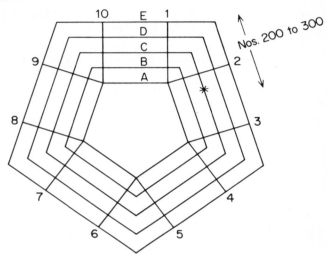

Fig. 1–2.

(a) How should you walk from 4C267 to 5E722?

(b) Does the fact $5 - 4 = 1$ mean anything here?

(c) Does it help to know that E is 2 letters after C in the alphabet?

(d) Does the fact that $722 - 267 = 455$ mean much here?

10. Describe another use of ordinal numbers.

11. A railroad numbers mileposts westward from Detroit to Chicago.

(a) How far is it from milepost 86 to milepost 128? How far from milepost 137 to milepost 95? Are these two answers really equal?

(b) A train travels west going 30 mph. At 9:00 A.M. the train is at milepost 100. Where is the train at 11 A.M.? Where is the train at 7 A.M.? What are you assuming in these calculations? Would it make sense to ask, "Where is the train at 9 P.M.?"

(c) A train travels east going 30 mph. At 9 A.M. the train is at milepost 100. Where is the train at 11 A.M.? Where is the train at 7 A.M.? What about the question, "Where is the train at 9 P.M.?"

Before you leave this section, look it over again. Notice several ways in which the examples are too narrow to meet the demands that modern living makes upon arithmetic.

What about the other kinds of numbers? So far we have discussed only counting numbers. We shall follow the common practice of calling them the *natural* numbers. But, if these are the natural numbers, surely people use a lot of "unnatural" numbers in everyday situations. How about fractions? How about negative numbers? You will need these, and still other kinds of numbers, to get along in the modern world.

101. Integers

"It was 10 *below* zero last night." "The market was *off* 2 points." "I went *in the hole* 5 points on that hand."

Notice that many of the numbers that people use are *directed* numbers. Contrast 10 *above* with 10 *below; off* 2 with *up* 2; 5 *ahead* with 5 *back.* People

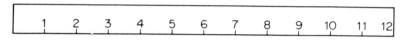

Fig. 1–3.

have learned to use *signed numbers* to make the number symbol tell what *direction* to associate with the number. They contrast $(+10)$ with (-10), (-2) with $(+2)$, and $(+5)$ with (-5).

This use of directed numbers, either *positive* or *negative*, is no surprise to you. Quite apart from your previous study of algebra, you have used directed numbers on measuring scales. On an ordinary ruler you use unsigned numbers. There is no need for numbers that carry either a positive or a negative sign (Fig. 1–3). Other familiar *scales* read both to the right and to the left of *zero.*

It is customary to label numbers to the right of zero $(+)$, numbers to the left of zero $(-)$ (Fig. 1–4). Often, as on the scales of the figure, the symbol $(+)$ is omitted. You write 10 as an abbreviation for $+10$.

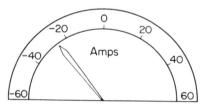

Fig. 1–4.

We shall use the symbol $N = \{1, 2, 3, 4, ...\}$ for the set of natural numbers. Notice how we list enough *members* of the set, 1, 2, 3, and 4 here, to give you a pattern; then we write ... for *and so forth* and enclose the list of members in braces: $\{1, 2, 3, 4, ...\}$.

We shall use the symbol $I = \{..., -3, -2, -1, 0, 1, 2, 3, ...\}$ for the set of *integers.* You should make it a habit to study the new symbols you meet as you read mathematics. Much of the power of mathematics comes from its use of convenient symbols.

We introduce one more symbol at this point. As you proceed, you will often want to make *statements* like "2 is a member of the set of natural numbers." We abbreviate this by saying "$2 \in N$." Notice that $5 \in N$, $176 \in N$, and $-1 \in I$ are *true* statements; notice that $0 \in N$, $-12 \in N$, and $\frac{1}{2} \in I$ are *false* statements. In mathematics we call a sentence a *statement* when it is either true or false. A sentence that is neither true nor false is not a statement.

To each statement, like $2 \in N$, there corresponds a second statement that *denies* the first one. To express the idea "2 is *not* a member of the set of natural numbers," we write "$2 \notin N$." Since $2 \in N$ is a true statement, its denial, $2 \notin N$, is a false statement. Notice that $5 \notin N$, $176 \notin N$, and $-1 \notin I$ are false statements; notice that $0 \notin N$, $-12 \notin N$, and $\frac{1}{2} \notin I$ are true statements.

Notice that, in mathematics, the truth of a statement may depend upon the definitions you have made. For example, we have called the statement $0 \in N$ false. For a long time people did not accept zero as a number. When they began to use zero as a number, they felt less sure about zero than about the then-familiar counting numbers. Hence, it became customary to exclude zero from the set N. In some modern treatments of number it is more convenient to call zero a natural number. A mathematician who finds it more convenient defines the set N to include zero; then he calls the statement $0 \in N$ true. Thus, in mathematics, the decision as to whether zero is a natural number is arbitrary. We shall follow the traditional scheme of classifying zero as an integer that is *not* a natural number.

We shall return, in Sections 105 and 106, to operations with integers. You already know that $5 - 7 \notin N$; perhaps you also know that $5 - 7 = -2 \in I$. Mathematically this is a big advantage of the set I over the set N; when you think of 5 and 7 as integers you can subtract 7 from 5, but when you think of 5 and 7 as natural numbers you can *not* subtract 7 from 5.

Here are a few exercises for further exploration of the sets N and I. They give you a chance to use the new symbols and to become familiar with them.

EXERCISES §101

1. Look at a Fahrenheit thermometer. Locate the points 68, -12, 17, -17. How are the numbers 17 and -17 alike? How are they different?

2. What does it mean to say, "The price of General Electric stock changed 1"? What does it mean to say, "The price of General Electric stock changed -1"? Are these changes equal?

3. Do you find it easier to think of *signed numbers* (numbers that are either positive or negative) as numbers that tell How many or as numbers that tell Which one?

4. Copy the number-scale shown below. On this scale place the numbers -3, $+2$ (abbreviated as 2), and -1. Can you place the number $+100$ on the scale? Can you picture in your mind where the number $+100$ belongs on the scale?

O   1

5. Decide whether each statement is true or false.

(a) $13 \in I$ (13 is an abbreviation for $+13$)

(b) $-3 \in N$ (c) $0 \notin N$

(d) $-5 \in I$ (e) $7 - 4 \in N$

(f) $3/4 \notin N$ (g) $2 + 5 \notin N$

(h) $2 \cdot 5 \in N$ (In algebra, $2 \cdot 5$ means multiply 5 by 2)

(i) $3 \cdot 7 \notin N$ (j) $28 \div 4 \in N$.

6. Consider the set $S = \{2, 4, 6, 8, 10\}$. Decide whether each statement is true or false.

(a) $5 \in S$ (b) $6 + 8 \notin S$

(c) $8 - 6 \in S$ (d) $7 \notin S$

(e) $2 \cdot 4 \notin S$ (f) $6/2 \notin S$.

102. Rational numbers

"The closet is $2\frac{1}{2}$ ft deep." "The diameter of the drive shaft is 1.487 in." "The washing machine sells for $229.88." "The galvanometer reads -4.83 amp."

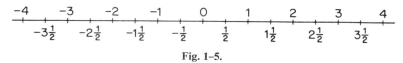

Fig. 1–5.

Notice that many of the numbers people use involve fractions. As before, you can use a number-scale to picture a set of numbers (Fig. 1–5). For some problems you need only the part of the scale from 0 to the right; you use the unsigned fractions of arithmetic or the positive fractions of algebra. For other problems you need the whole scale; you use the set of signed fractions that mathematicians call the *rational numbers*. You know how to place the rational numbers $1\frac{1}{2}$, $-2\frac{1}{3}$, 0.832, and -1.04 on the number-scale (see Exercise 4 below). You can picture in your mind where numbers like 74.8 and -427.3 belong on the scale, even though their positions are beyond the edge of the page.

It is easy to list a few natural numbers in a pattern that suggests the whole set of natural numbers. We write $\{1, 2, 3, ...\}$. Similarly, for the set I, we write $\{..., -2, -1, 0, 1, 2, ...\}$. When you try to list a few rational numbers in *order of size* you run into trouble. Suppose you begin with 1. What is the *next* rational number? If you answer "$1\frac{1}{2}$" I shall say, "What about $1\frac{1}{4}$?" If you answer "$1\frac{1}{4}$" I shall say, "What about $1\frac{1}{8}$?" and so forth. Hence, mathematicians say there is no *next-in-size* rational number after a given one.

We shall use the symbol R for the set of rational numbers, as we previously used the symbols N and I for the sets of natural numbers and integers.

Members of R are *quotients* of integers, like 3/4, $-18/32$, or 216/1. We rule out quotients with *divisor* zero because symbols like 5/0, $-3/0$, or 12/0 have no meaning in mathematics (see page 53). Hence *we call a number a rational number when and only when it can be written as the quotient of two integers with divisor not zero*. Examples are: 1/2 ($= \frac{2}{4} = \frac{3}{6} \ldots$), $12\frac{1}{3}$ ($= 37/3 = (-37)/(-3) = 74/6 \ldots$). This definition of a rational number enables you to identify rational numbers, even without a pattern for listing the set of rational numbers.

In Sections 103 and 104 you will meet real numbers that *can not* be written as the quotient of two integers. We shall call such numbers *irrational*, that is, *not ratios of integers*.

You should recall three ways to write rational numbers:

In mathematics it is often convenient to write quotients of integers as $\frac{3}{4}$, $5\frac{1}{4}$, $-7\frac{2}{3}$, and $-8/10$. In many calculations, and in much of the modern use of measures, you will find *decimals* instead: .75, 5.25, -7.667, and -0.8. Decimal representations of rational numbers often require *approximations*. We say $-7\frac{2}{3} \doteq -7.667$, using the symbol ($\doteq$) for the phrase *is approximately equal to*. Such approximations are permissible in practical problems where the measurements are themselves approximate. In most theoretical work mathematicians prefer to avoid approximations like $\frac{1}{3} \doteq .33$.

When fractions are used as *ratios* it is common to talk in rates per cent. We say $\frac{1}{4} = .25 = 25$ per cent. We mean that 1 of each 4 is 25 of each 100.

We shall return to operations with rational numbers in Sections 105 and 106. Meanwhile, Exercises §102 should remind you of some everyday applications of rational numbers.

EXERCISES §102

1. Locate the point $13\frac{5}{8}$ on an ordinary yardstick. Notice that $13\frac{5}{8}$ means $13 + \frac{5}{8}$. You move along the yardstick to the point 13; you break the interval from 13 to 14 into 8 equal parts; you move 5 of these $\frac{1}{8}$'s beyond 13.

2. Locate the points $3\frac{1}{2}$, $2\frac{3}{4}$, $5\frac{7}{16}$, and $9\frac{3}{8}$ on an ordinary ruler.

3. (a) Draw a number-scale that extends both to the right and to the left of zero. On this scale locate the points $5\frac{2}{3}$ and $-5\frac{2}{3}$. What do these two points have in common? How do the locations of these two points differ?

(b) How would you arrange to show the point $81\frac{3}{5}$ on a number-scale? What size units fit this problem?

(c) Notice the difference between *thinking about* the position of the point 146.93 and *actually placing* this point on a number-scale.

4. You may be interested in trying to place a fraction accurately on a number-scale. Here is a method that is theoretically exact. The only limitation upon the method is the practical difficulty of making a perfect drawing.

To place $3\frac{5}{7}$ on a number-scale, as a point between 3 and 4, proceed as follows (Fig. 1–6).

Through 3 draw a line like L; on L mark off 7 equal intervals (a compass is good here, but a ruler with equally spaced marks will work); join the seventh point on L to 4; through the fifth point on L draw a line parallel to this join; this locates the point $3\frac{5}{7}$ as a point $\frac{5}{7}$ of the distance from 3 to 4.

Use this technique to place:

    (a) $2\frac{3}{4}$ between 2 and 3
    (b) $-3\frac{1}{5}$ between -4 and -3
    (c) $-\frac{9}{13}$ between -1 and 0.

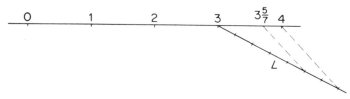

Fig. 1–6.

5. Label each number-symbol "$\in N$," "$\in I$," or "$\in R$" to identify it as a symbol for a natural number, an integer, or a rational number. Think of each element of N as an element of I and R also; for example, $3 = (+3) = +6/+2$. Think of each element of I as an element of R also; for example, $(-3) = -3/+1$.

    (a) 15   (b) -32

    (c) $3\dfrac{5}{16}$ (d) $-.0047$

    (e) -36.2 (f) $\dfrac{2146}{-10}$.

6. Complete the table to show the different ways to express a rational number:

Quotient of Integers	Decimal	Per cent
1/2		
3/8		
	.4	
		26
$3\frac{5}{12}$		
	9.125	
		148
		12.5

103. Real numbers: the line of numbers

So far we have used symbols like 5, $+3\frac{1}{4}$, and -2.8 to represent numbers. You may have noticed that we also used points to represent numbers. On the scale (Fig. 1–7) we labeled the points -4, -3, ..., 4; many other points are understood. You can visualize, although you may not be able to place accurately, the points that correspond to 10.62, -13, and $-.0046$. In this

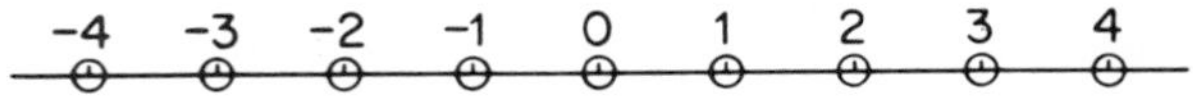

```
-4   -3   -2   -1   0    1    2    3    4
-⊕---⊕---⊕---⊕---⊕---⊕---⊕---⊕---⊕-
```

Fig. 1–7.

way many of the points on the scale correspond to, or represent, numbers.

The question arises, "Does every point on the scale represent a number?" This question leads to many complications in mathematics. It has worried some of the best mathematicians.

As you think about the set of rational numbers, it may seem "obvious" that "they fill the number-scale." For one thing, no matter how "close together" you pick two rational numbers, there are other rational numbers between them. For example, you may pick 1 and 2; $1\frac{1}{2}$ lies between 1 and 2. You may pick 1 and $1\frac{1}{2}$; $1\frac{1}{4}$ lies between 1 and $1\frac{1}{2}$. You can always pick a rational number midway between any two rational numbers. Hence it seems "evident" that the rational numbers "use up every point on the number-scale."

Mathematicians are not satisfied by such intuitive arguments. Slippery words and phrases like "obvious" and "fill up" make them start looking for a catch. The early Greek mathematicians found the catch as they tried to apply numbers to geometry.

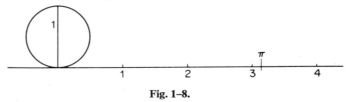

Fig. 1–8.

Perhaps you have been puzzled about some of the "numbers" you met in geometry. When you divide the distance around (*circumference* of) a circle by the longest distance across (*diameter* of) the circle, you get the number π. Remember that π is about 22/7; but not exactly 22/7. Sometimes you say $\pi \doteq 3.14$; but in a more exact problem you say $\pi \doteq 3.1416$. Remember that none of these number-symbols represents π exactly.

Of course it is easy to locate the point π on a measuring scale. Make a wheel of diameter 1 unit. The circumference of this wheel will be π units. Roll the wheel on the measuring scale (Fig. 1–8). As the wheel rolls (without slipping), you lay its circumference on the scale; hence the point π is one turn of the wheel from the point O.

This does not solve the problem of representing π exactly by a number-symbol. But you can build a very accurate machine to place the point that represents π on a number-scale.

Now recall another "number" from geometry. The figure shows a right triangle with sides *adjacent* to the right angle both equal to 1 (Fig. 1–9). Remember the words you use to describe such a triangle. You call it a *right* triangle because one of its angles is 90°. You call it an *isosceles* triangle because two of its sides are equal. You call the side opposite the right angle the *hypotenuse* (*h* in the figure).

The theorem of Pythagoras (c. 500 B.C.) says, "The square on the hypotenuse is the sum of the squares on the other two sides of a right triangle." Hence, in our triangle, $h^2 = 1^2 + 1^2$. This gives $h^2 = 2$, and we say h is the square root of 2 (written $h = \sqrt{2}$).

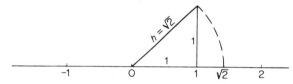

Fig. 1–9.

You may recall that $\sqrt{2}$ (like π) is a "number" that can not be expressed exactly as a fraction. When you work it out as a decimal you get $\sqrt{2} \doteq$ 1.4142; but you can always calculate more decimal places and never get an exact answer.

Of course it is easy to use a compass (see the dotted arc of a circle in the figure) to locate the point that corresponds to $\sqrt{2}$ on the measuring scale. Again this does not solve the problem of representing $\sqrt{2}$ exactly as a fraction. Again, it does provide a simple method to place the point that represents $\sqrt{2}$ on a number-scale.

These two examples show how to represent certain "numbers" (like π and $\sqrt{2}$) as points on a number-scale. Perhaps this is enough justification for calling them numbers. The symbol $\sqrt{2}$ expresses the length of a line even if you can not write down a fraction exactly equal to $\sqrt{2}$.

Pythagoras knew that it is impossible to represent $\sqrt{2}$ as the quotient of two integers. Lindemann (c. 1882 A.D.) showed that π can not be the solution of an algebraic equation, in particular, that it is impossible to represent π as the quotient of two integers. Euclid proved that $\sqrt{2}$ cannot be written as a quotient of two integers; his proof is as easy as the proofs of theorems in high school geometry. Lindemann's proof that π cannot be the solution of an algebraic equation requires advanced mathematical techniques. In effect, both proofs *imply* that there are points on the number-scale that *do not represent* rational numbers.

Now you have your choice. You can refuse to call $\sqrt{2}$ and π numbers; then there will be points on the number-scale that do not symbolize numbers. Or you can enlarge the set of things you call numbers; then each point on the number-scale will symbolize a number; each point will represent either a *rational* number (the quotient, or ratio, of two integers with the divisor not zero), or an *irrational* number (not the quotient of two integers) like $\sqrt{2}$ or π.

For the study of elementary analysis it is convenient to choose the second alternative. This gives you a *mathematical model* that we shall call the *line of real numbers*, or simply the *line of numbers*. This line is like the number-scales we have used so far; but it is more than an ordinary measuring scale. Since it is something you think about, rather than something you make of wood or metal, you do not need to restrict its length within practical limits; if you need a scale several million miles long, you can think about it even though you can not really construct one. Mentally you can cut a piece of the line of numbers into a billion equal parts; practically, it would be impossible to treat a ruler in this way.

We shall call the set of real numbers L. The members of L are the numbers that you can represent by points on the line of numbers. So each real number corresponds to a point on the line of numbers; and each point on the line of numbers corresponds to a real number.

The real numbers provide a powerful mathematical model. Theories about the measurement of length, like the theorem of Pythagoras, require all of the points on the line of numbers. They lead to number-symbols like $\sqrt{2}$, $\sqrt[3]{5}$, and π. The set L includes all such numbers because the line of numbers includes every possible length.

We shall return to the study of the real numbers as a *mathematical structure* in Chapter 2; then you will continue to learn more about real numbers as long as you study analysis. In the remainder of this section you should learn to classify numbers as members of one or more of the sets N, I, R, or L.

The numbers 1, 17, 4, and 66 are members of N. We call them natural numbers. The numbers $+1$, $+17$, $+4$, and $+66$ are members of I. We call them *positive integers*. The set I also includes *zero* and the *negative integers*. We shall think of the positive integers as a *subset* of the integers. That is, each member of the set of positive integers is a member of the set of integers. Although the natural numbers are unsigned numbers, and the positive integers are signed numbers, the arithmetic of these two sets of numbers is the same. Hence we shall speak of the set N as a *subset* of the set I; we really mean that each member of N *corresponds* to a positive integer that is a member of I. For example, 15 corresponds to $+15$, and $+15$ is a member of I.

Similarly, we shall speak of *I* as a subset of *R*; we mean that each member of *I* corresponds to a quotient of two integers, with divisor not zero. For example, 8 corresponds to 24/3 and 24/3 is a member of *R*.

It is convenient to abbreviate statements about subsets. We write

$$I \subset R$$

to mean that *I* is a subset of *R*. Similarly, we say $N \subset I$ and $N \subset R$.

Notice that $N \subset L$, $I \subset L$, and $R \subset L$. That is to say, each natural number corresponds to a point on the line of numbers; each integer corresponds to a point on the line of numbers; and each rational number corresponds to a point on the line of numbers. Hence you may think of natural numbers, integers, and rational numbers as examples, or *instances*, of real numbers.

Here are some examples of the special kinds of real numbers you have met so far; each is a real number because it corresponds to a point on the line of numbers:

(1) The number 3 is a real number. It is also a rational number (corresponding to 3/1 or 6/2, or the like), an integer (corresponding to +3), and a natural number (corresponding to 3).

(2) The number −11 is a real number. It is also a rational number $[(-11)/1 = (-22)/2 = ...]$ and an integer (−11). There is no natural number that corresponds to −11.

(3) The number −8/13 is a real number. It is also a rational number $[(-8)/13]$. It is not an element of *I* or *N*.

(4) The number $\sqrt{2}$ is a real number. Euclid proved that it is not a rational number, and hence is not an integer or a natural number. We call such real numbers *irrational*.

(5) Other examples of real numbers that are irrational are $\sqrt{5}$, $\sqrt[3]{2}$, $\sqrt{7}$, etc.; but $\sqrt{4} = 2$, $\sqrt{9} = 3$, $\sqrt{\dfrac{25}{36}} = \dfrac{5}{6}$, etc., are rational numbers.

EXERCISES §103

1. You can extend the ideas we used to place $\sqrt{2}$ on the number-scale. You can "construct" other numbers like $\sqrt{3}$, $\sqrt{4} = 2$, $\sqrt{5}$, etc. Here is a start (Fig. 1–10). You use the $\sqrt{2}$ that you had before. You draw a right triangle with sides $\sqrt{2}$ and 1. The hypotenuse is *h*, and $h^2 = (\sqrt{2})^2 + 1^2 = 2 + 1 = 3$. So $h = \sqrt{3}$. Generalize this procedure to construct $\sqrt{4} = 2$ and $\sqrt{5}$.

2. Place each of the following real numbers on a number-scale that represents the line of numbers. Use your book of mathematical tables to look up approximations for numbers like $\sqrt{5}$, $\sqrt[3]{17}$, and so forth. From a practical point of view these approximations are good enough for placing these numbers on the scale; but notice, again, the difference between the practical problem of placing a point and the theoretical problem of placing a point.

(a) $4\frac{3}{5}$ (b) $\sqrt[3]{18}$ (c) π (d) $-\sqrt{5}$ (e) $-\sqrt[3]{14}$.

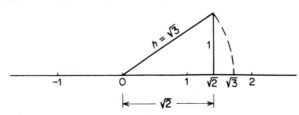

Fig. 1–10.

3. For each number, check the sets of which the number is a member. Use the first two lines of the table as examples:

Number	N	I	R	L	Other Sets (describe in words)
3 or +3	√	√	√	√	positive integers
$-\sqrt[3]{7}$				√	negative irrational numbers
3/8					
−14/9					
−10/5					
$\sqrt{16}$					
$\sqrt[3]{8/27}$					
$\sqrt{14}$					
$-\sqrt{16}$					
$-\sqrt{18}$					

4. Give one or more examples of numbers that fit each description:

(a) Negative integer
(b) Real, irrational, and negative
(c) Non-negative integer (that is, positive integer or zero)
(d) Natural number greater than 10
(e) Odd positive integer.

5. Decide whether each statement is true or false:

(a) $\sqrt{3}$ is positive
(b) $-4\frac{2}{3}$ is a negative real number
(c) $L \subset R$
(d) $\sqrt[3]{7}$ is a member of L
(e) π is a member of I
(f) 3.14 is a member of R
(g) $\pi = 3.14159$
(h) $I \subset R$ and $R \subset L$
(i) $I \subset R$ and $R \subset I$
(j) $1\frac{5}{16}$ is a member of I.

104. Complex numbers: vectors in the plane

The early Greek mathematicians were shocked to discover that there were lengths (and hence points on the line of numbers) that were not fractions of the unit of measurement (and hence numbers that were irrational). As the Arabs (c. 800 A.D.) and later the Italians (c. 1500 A.D.), worked with algebra they invented negative numbers and began to feel the need for yet another type of number. You can appreciate the problem by reviewing what you know about equations. You have the advantage over the early mathematicians of a convenient, modern way for writing algebraic sentences as equations.

An equation like $x + 5 = 8$ is easy to *solve*. You say, "What number added to 5 yields 8?" The answer, 3, is a natural number.

Early mathematicians found equations like $x + 8 = 5$ puzzling. There is no member of the set N that *satisfies* this equation; once you become familiar with the members of I, the *solution set* is $\{-3\}$. We shall review in Sections 105 and 106, the mathematical reasons why the statement $(-3) + 8 = 5$ is true. Notice that no member of the set N satisfies the equation $x + 8 = 5$; but one member, -3, of the set I satisfies this equation.

Equations like $3x = 5$ were easy for Arab mathematicians. The positive rational number, 5/3, satisfies this equation; the solution set is $\{5/3\}$. But an equation like $3x = -5$ requires the negative rational number, $-5/3$; some Arab mathematicians spoke of "false" solutions because they did not admit the existence of negative numbers.

The solution set for an equation may depend upon the set of numbers you use. In I, the solution set of the equation $x + 2 = 1$ is $\{-1\}$; in N, the solution set of this equation is the *empty* set, $\{\ \ \}$. That is, the member -1 of the set I satisfies the equation; and *no member of the set N satisfies this equation*. In N, the solution set of the equation $x^2 = 1$ is $\{1\}$; in I, the solution set of this equation is $\{1, -1\}$. That is, the member 1 of the set N satisfies this equation; and the members 1 and -1 of the set I satisfy this equation. We shall review, in Sections 105 and 106, the mathematical reasons why the statements $1^2 = 1$ and $(-1)^2 = 1$ are true. In *L*, the solution set of the equation $x^2 = 2$ is $\{\sqrt{2}, -\sqrt{2}\}$; in any of the sets, *N*, *I*, or *R*, the solution set of this equation is the empty set, { }.

We call the set { }, that has no members, the *empty set* or the *null set*. This idea of an empty set is a great convenience as we discuss mathematics.

When early mathematicians (before 1800 A.D.) thought about equations like $x^2 = -1$ they were puzzled and intrigued. In *L*, the solution set of the equation $x^2 = -1$ is { }. There is no real number whose product with itself (whose square) is negative. Perhaps you have already guessed what people did. For a time they spoke of *imaginary numbers*; then the mathematicians invented a new set of numbers with none of the mystery that the word "imaginary" suggests.

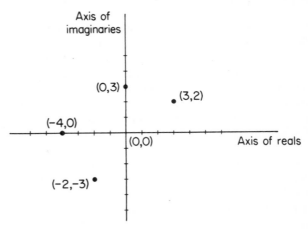

Fig. 1–11.

We shall study the set *C* of *complex numbers* in more detail in Chapter 5. Meanwhile we give you the picture that the German mathematician, Gauss, suggested (c. 1800 A.D.). There is no room on the line of numbers for a point that corresponds to a number whose square is negative. Gauss visualized a new set of numbers that correspond to points in the *plane* shown in Fig. 1–11. He placed the point (3,2) 2 units above the point 3 on the line of numbers. He placed the point (−2,−3) 3 units below the point −2 on the line of numbers. Notice that points like (−4,0) lie on the line of numbers that we now begin to call the *axis of reals*. Notice that points like (0,3) lie on a line *perpendicular* to the axis of reals at the point (0,0); we call this line the *axis of imaginaries*.

As you study Fig. 1–11 you will find that each point of the plane corresponds to an *ordered pair* of real numbers (order is important because (3,−2) and (−2,3) are different points of the plane); also, each ordered pair of real numbers corresponds to a point of the plane. We say there is a *one-to-one correspondence* between points of the plane and ordered pairs of real numbers.

We call these ordered pairs of real numbers *complex numbers*; we call the set C of ordered pairs of real numbers *the set of complex numbers*; we call the subset of C whose members lie on the axis of reals the real numbers; we call the subset of C whose members lie on the axis of imaginaries the set of *imaginary numbers*. It turns out that these imaginary numbers are the numbers whose squares are negative. They are the numbers you need to solve equations like $x^2 = -1$.

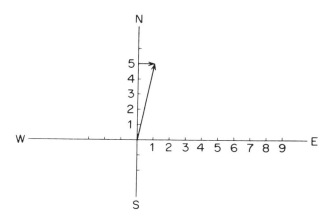

Fig. 1–12.

The invention of complex numbers, and of an algebra for complex numbers, made theoretical physics easier. People began to apply the algebra of complex numbers to study problems in navigation, mechanics, and electricity. We give you a simple example:

Suppose you want to describe the *velocity* of an airplane. The plane heads north and has an air speed of 500 mph. There is a 100-mph wind blowing from the west. Students of physics make a picture like Fig. 1–12. The arrow that points north is 5 units long, to represent 500 mph of air speed. The arrow that points east is 1 unit long, to represent 100 mph of wind. The slanting arrow represents the speed over the ground (the ground speed) of the plane.

Engineers call these arrows *vectors*. Notice that a vector has both length and direction. Of course real numbers have both length and direction too; $+5$ means 5 units to the right; -5 means 5 units to the left; $-\sqrt{13}$ means $\sqrt{13}$ units to the left; etc. Hence, we may speak of *vectors on the line of numbers*; but *vectors in the plane* have more freedom than vectors on the line of numbers. Vectors in the plane are not restricted to the axis of reals.

Notice that the ground-speed vector runs from 0 to the point $(1,5)$

(1 to the right and 5 up). Electrical engineers write $1 + 5j$ as a symbol for the number that measures this ground speed. They think of $1 + 5j$ as a number-symbol. You will use the symbol $1 + 5i$ when you study *quadratic equations*. You will think of this as a symbol for a complex number.

You may begin to wonder where this job of inventing new sets of numbers ends. For the purposes of elementary analysis we are finished. The set C enables us to do all that we shall need to do with numbers.

Notice that the real number -3 corresponds to the complex number $(-3,0)$. Each real number corresponds to a complex number that lies on the axis of reals. Hence $L \subset C$; that is, L is a subset of C (page 210).

The sentence $N \subset I \subset R \subset L \subset C$ may help you to recall some of the things we have said about numbers. Each new set of numbers that we talked about was an *extension* of the set that preceded it. Each new set of numbers that we talked about contained all the previous sets of numbers as subsets.

Exercises §104 will give you a chance to use the new words you have met. In Section 105 you will study the arithmetic of vectors.

EXERCISES §104

1. Write out the solution set for each equation. Work first in N, then in I, R, and L in order. Use (a) and (b) as samples.

(a) $x + 11 = 12$. In N: $\{1\}$; in I: $\{1\}$; in R: $\{1\}$; in L: $\{1\}$.

(b) $x + 12 = 11$. In N: $\{\ \ \}$; in I: $\{-1\}$; in R and L: $\{-1\}$.

(c) $x^2 = 4$ (d) $x^3 = 27$

(e) $x - 3 = 5$ (f) $x^2 = 3$

(g) $x^2 = -3$ (h) $x^2 = 81$

(i) $x^2 = -81$.

2. Draw the vectors from 0 to each of the following points:

(a) The point 5 miles east and 3 miles south

(b) The point 2 miles west and 6 miles north

(c) The point 3 miles west and 5 miles south

(d) The point 2 miles east and 7 miles north.

Instead of using the directions north, south, east, and west, we shall often use signed numbers. We have drawn the four vectors described above in Fig. 1–13.

3. A plane heads west with an air speed of 250 mph. The wind blows from the south at 75 mph. Lay these vectors end to end to find their sum, namely, the ground speed of the plane.

4. Use a vector to represent a wind blowing from the southwest at 10 mph. Then draw the vector that represents a wind from the same direction that is five times as strong. Notice the similarity to multiplication.

5. Draw the vector that corresponds to each ordered pair of real numbers:

(a) (2, −3)   (b) (5,2)
(c) (−3,2)   (d) (2,5)
(e) (−2,5)   (f) (−5,2)
(g) (0, −2)   (h) (3,0)
(i) (−2,0).

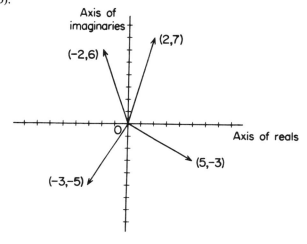

Fig. 1–13.

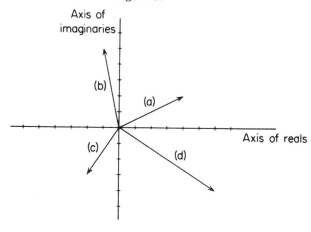

Fig. 1–14.

6. Write the ordered pair of real numbers that corresponds to each vector in Fig. 1–14.

7. Explain what it means to say $I \subset L$.

8. Explain what it means to say $N \subset C$.

105. Operations with vectors

Addition. (1) Jim read 28 pages Monday and 15 pages Tuesday. How many pages did he read in the two days?

Of course you can think of two groups of 28 and 15. You can combine these groups and count the combined group in any order you like. You always get the answer 43.

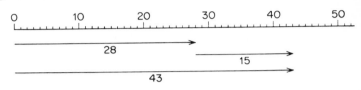

Fig. 1–15.

Another way to think is: Visualize a scale of the numbers in their usual order (Fig. 1–15). Go out to 28 and then go 15 more. You get 43.

(2) The temperature fell 20° and then rose 25°. How much did the temperature change? Notice in Fig. 1–16 that you begin with some temperature T; the temperature goes 20° one way; then it goes 25° the opposite way. The *net* effect is a 5° rise in temperature.

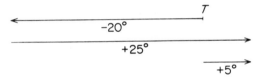

Fig. 1–16.

(3) A forest ranger walked from his camp 5 miles southeast, and then walked 3 miles northeast. How far from his camp was he?

In Fig. 1–17, the net effect is approximately 5.8 mi in a direction about 15 degrees south of east. This is the sum of the vectors 5 mi SE and 3 mi NE. The most efficient way to return to camp (unless there is an obstruction such as a lake) is to undo the vector 5.8 mi 15° S of E. The ranger should walk 5.8 miles in a direction 15° north of west.

Of course when the temperature falls 20° and then rises 25°, the total change is 45°; when you walk 5 miles in one direction and then 3 miles in a second direction, you have walked a total of 8 miles. Often the *vector sum*, the net change, is more interesting than the ordinary arithmetic sum. The two sums are the same when you add vectors that have the same direction. Recall, for example, that 28 pages + 15 pages = 43 pages is both a vector sum and an ordinary arithmetic sum.

To add two vectors, place the initial point of the second vector at the terminal point of the first vector. Then the sum is the vector from the initial point of the first vector to the terminal point of the second vector. In this sense, you *add vectors*, whether on the line of numbers or in the plane, *by laying them end to end.* Use the following exercises to explore further examples of vector addition.

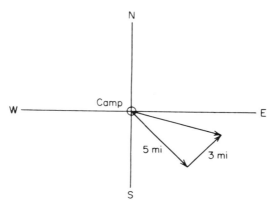

Fig. 1–17.

EXERCISES §105

1. At 8 A.M. the temperature was $-6°$. It rose $15°$ and then fell $10°$. What is the new temperature?

(a) Draw the scale. Mark the 8 A.M. temperature of $-6°$; go $15°$ to the right and then $10°$ to the left.

(b) Compute the sum $(-6) + (+15) + (-10)$.

2. Draw a number-scale to represent a railroad line. Label the zero point Columbus, Ohio. Interpret distances east of Columbus as $+$. Interpret distances west of Columbus as $-$.

(a) Where is the point $+45$? Where is the point -30?

(b) A train leaves Columbus and travels $(+45) + (-30)$. Where is the train then?

(c) Interpret $(-80) + (+50) + (+10) + (-15)$.

3. A stock listed at $16\frac{1}{4}$. It rose $\frac{1}{8}$, then fell $\frac{1}{2}$, then fell $\frac{1}{8}$, then rose $\frac{1}{4}$. Diagram this fluctuation in price and find the final price. You can represent this situation in figures as: $16\frac{1}{4} + (+\frac{1}{8}) + (-\frac{1}{2}) + (-\frac{1}{8}) + (+\frac{1}{4})$. Perhaps you can discover short-cuts for getting the answer.

4. A ship left its mooring and proceeded to a point 10 mi west and 3 mi south of the mooring; from this point the ship proceeded 4 mi east and 2 mi south. Find the final position of the ship with respect to its mooring.

Reproduce Fig. 1–18 on a sheet of graph paper; notice how the vectors (−10, −3) and (+4, −2) are laid end to end; notice that the vector sum is (−6, −5). Hence the final position of the ship is 6 mi west and 5 mi south of its mooring.

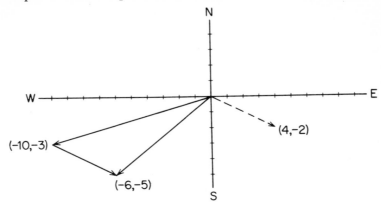

Fig. 1–18.

5. A plane cruises in level flight at 240 mph on a heading 135° (measure 135° *clockwise* from north; notice that the nose of the plane points southeast); the wind blows steadily from the west at 80 mph. Find the ground speed and *course* (direction over the ground) of the plane.

Subtraction. (4) Jane has $9. She needs $12.98 to buy a dress. How much more does she need?

Again you can think of this as a subtraction of cardinal numbers. You can also visualize it as a movement along a measuring scale (Fig. 1–19).

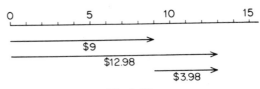

Fig. 1–19.

Jane goes from where she is ($9) to where she wants to be ($12.98). She goes (+$3.98).

(5) The temperature changed from 12 below zero at 4 A.M. to 6 above zero at 10 A.M. How much did the temperature change (Fig. 1–20)? From where the temperature was (−12°) to where it is (+6°) is +18°.

(6) How far is it from the point (−3,2) to the point (5,5)? As a movement in the plane (Fig. 1–21), the distance is the vector from (−3,2) to (5,5).

We shall define the *difference* of two numbers or vectors [12.98 − 9, or (+6) − (−12), or (5,5) − (−3,2), for example] to be the number, or vector, that you must add to the *subtrahend* [9, or (−12), or (−3,2), for example] to obtain the *minuend* [12.98, or (+6) or (5,5), for example].

The expression (−16) − (+18) means "How far is it from +18 to −16?" This is the problem: What is the change in temperature from 18° at noon to −16° at midnight?

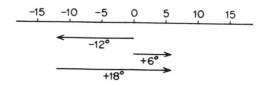

Fig. 1–20.

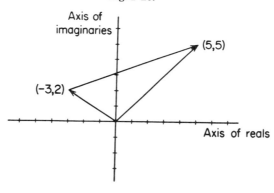

Fig. 1–21.

When you ask "What is the change in temperature from 20° at noon to 30° at midnight?" the answer is clear. The change is 30 − 20 = 10. In the same way a change from +18° to −16° is (−16) − (+18); but most people find it hard to visualize (−16) − (+18). On a scale (Fig. 1–22) the change is clearly −34°.

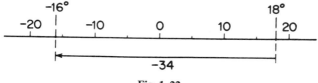

Fig. 1–22.

EXERCISES §105 (cont.)

6. "So far I have saved 6 pages of premium stamps. To get the premium that I want, I need 14 pages of stamps." Interpret the subtraction on a number-scale as the question "How far is it from the point 6 to the point 14?"

7. Interpret each of the following subtractions using the pattern: $a - b$ means "How far is it from the point b to the point a?"

(a) $-3 - 5 = (-3) - (+5) = $ _____
(b) $3 - (-5) = (+3) - (-5) = $ _____
(c) $3 - 5 = (+3) - (+5) = $ _____
(d) $-3 - (-5) = (-3) - (-5) = $ _____ .

8. An *ammeter* measures the current of electricity in a circuit. The ammeter on a car registers $(+)$ when current is flowing into the battery (when the battery is charging); it registers $(-)$ when current flows out of the battery (when the battery is discharging). Interpret each part of Exercise 7 as a change in reading on the ammeter. For example, part (a) asks "What is the change from charging 5 amp to discharging 3 amp?"

9. On a (railroad) line mark a convenient point 0 (zero). Call distances east of this point $(+)$. Call distances west of this point $(-)$. Calculate each answer and interpret it in words as a movement along the railroad:

(a) $7.6 - (-8.2) = $ (b) $13.1 - 6.3 = $
(c) $-8.2 - 1.8 = $ (d) $-8.2 - (-10.6) = $
(e) $-8.2 - (-6.6) = $.

10. Jim weighed 189 lb. He lost 16 lb. What does he weigh now? In this situation it seems natural to take 16 from 189; but it still works to say "How far is it from 16 to 189?" on a scale (Fig. 1–23). The answer 173 lb is correct.

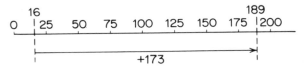

Fig. 1–23.

Now think of $(+189) + (-16)$ (Fig. 1–24): Notice that adding (-16) to $(+189)$ yields the same answer as subtracting $(+16)$ from $(+189)$. That is,

$$(+189) + (-16) = (+189) - (+16).$$

Sometimes it is easier to think of a subtraction as moving along a scale from the subtrahend to the minuend ($a - b$ means "How far is it from the point b to the point a?"); sometimes it is easier to think of a subtraction as adding the negative of the subtrahend to the minuend [$a - b$ means $a + (-b)$]. We shall prove, in Chapter 2, that these two ways of thinking yield the same number.

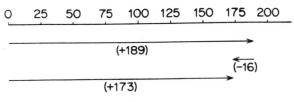

Fig. 1–24.

11. Repeat Exercises 7 and 9, thinking of each subtraction as adding the negative of the subtrahend to the minuend. For example:

$$-3 - 5 = (-3) + (-5) \quad \text{and} \quad 3 - (-5) = (+3) + (+5).$$

Think of the physical interpretation of each problem in the two ways we have suggested. For example, $3 - (-5)$ means "What is the change in amperage when the ammeter goes from -5 to 3?" $3 + 5 = 3 + [-(-5)]$ means to add the negative of -5 to 3.

12. Remember how we thought of the subtraction $a - b$ as the question "How far is it from b to a?" On a number-scale, we drew an arrow from the terminal point of the vector b to the terminal point of the vector a. We found, for vectors, that ground speed = air speed + wind. Now try the equation air speed = ground speed − wind. Interpret "ground speed − wind" as an arrow from wind to ground speed (Fig. 1–25).

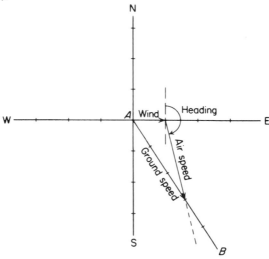

Fig. 1–25.

A pilot wants to fly from city A to city B (see figure). He wants to make a ground speed of 300 mph. The wind is 100 mph from the west. Find his air speed and the direction he should point his plane (his heading). In the figure the line AB fixes the direction of the ground-speed vector; on AB we marked off a distance of 300 mi (to scale) to represent the ground speed. We drew the wind vector with direction from west to east and length 100 mi (to scale). The air-speed vector is an arrow from the tip of the wind vector to the tip of the ground-speed vector. Measurement on the figure gives the air speed as 260 mph. To measure the heading you can measure an angle with a protractor. Pilots measure the heading as the number of degrees eastward from north. Measurement gives the heading as 167°.

As a check on your work notice that the figure says "Wind + air speed = ground speed."

13. City *B* lies northeast of city *A*. A pilot wants to fly from *A* to *B* and make a ground speed of 400 mph. The wind is 80 mph from the east. Find the air speed and heading the pilot must fly.

Multiplication. (7) When you lay sheets of aluminum foil one on top of another, the average thickness of the sheets is .003 in. What is the thickness of 24 sheets of this foil?

The measurement scale for this problem is like the ones we have used before; but, to make it fit the problem, we enlarge the scale (Fig. 1–26). When you lay .003 end to end 24 times you get 24 × .003 = .072. Hence the thickness of 24 sheets of the aluminum foil is .072 in.

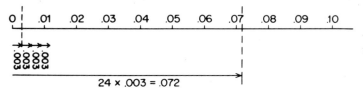

Fig. 1–26.

Notice how the picture helps you to visualize this problem and to check the reasonableness of the answer. It is easy to misplace a decimal point in a problem like this one.

(8) A boat moves through the water with speed 30 mph in the direction southwest. Picture a speed three times as great and in the same direction (Fig. 1–27). The speed is 90 mph toward the southwest.

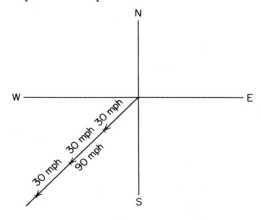

Fig. 1–27.

In Examples 7 and 8 you can think of multiplication as laying a length (like .003 in. or 30 mi) end-to-end a number of times. Many people get the idea that all multiplication problems are of this sort. You should study the examples that follow to see how wrong this notion is.

(9) A room is 30 ft long. Find the length of this room in a drawing whose *scale* is 1 : 120.

In the drawing you represent 120 ft by 1 ft, 240 ft by 2 ft, 60 ft by $\frac{1}{2}$ ft, etc. The *ratio* of lengths in the drawing to lengths in the building is 1/120. You multiply each measurement for the building by 1/120 to get the corresponding length for the drawing.

$$\tfrac{1}{120} \cdot 30 = \tfrac{30}{120} = \tfrac{1}{4}, \quad \text{and} \quad \tfrac{1}{4} \text{ ft is 3 in.}$$

This is a problem in multiplication; it takes quite a stretch of the imagination to think of laying the length 30 end-to-end 1/120 times. Yet the answer 1/4 ft, or 3 in., is sensible.

Multiplications like

$$\frac{2}{5} \cdot 15 = \frac{2 \cdot 15}{5} = 6 \quad \text{and} \quad \frac{3}{4} \cdot \frac{8}{10} = \frac{3 \cdot 8}{4 \cdot 10} = \frac{6}{10}$$

are something more than laying a length end-to-end a whole number of times. We shall discuss such multiplications further in Section 106.

The multiplications we have discussed changed the length, but not the direction of the vector that is multiplied. When you multiply by a directed number you may change not only the length, but also the direction of the vector that you are multiplying.

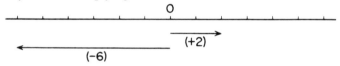

Fig. 1–28.

(10) For example (Fig. 1–28), $(-3)(+2) = (-6)$. Multiplication by (-3) multiplies the length of $(+2)$ by 3 *and reverses* its direction.

(11) In Fig. 1–29,

[vector to the point (3,4)] · [vector to the point (0,2)]

$$= [\text{vector to the point } (-8,6)].$$

We shall return in Section 106, and again in Chapters 5 and 9, to the multiplication of complex numbers. Then we shall justify our statement that this product is the vector $(-8,6)$. Meanwhile, you may want to experiment with the *definition*: The *product of two vectors* is the vector whose length is the product of the lengths of the two vectors, and whose *amplitude* is the sum of the amplitudes of the two vectors. The amplitude of a vector is the angle measured counterclockwise from the positive end of the axis of reals. Notice, in the figure, that the amplitude of $(-8,6)$ is the sum of the amplitudes of (3,4) and (0,2); the length of $(-8,6)$ $[\sqrt{64 + 36} = 10]$ is the product of the lengths of (3,4) [$\sqrt{9 + 16} = 5$] and (0,2) [$\sqrt{0 + 4} = 2$]. Notice also, in Example 10, that the amplitude of (+2) is zero, the amplitude of (−3) is 180°, and the amplitude of (−6) is $0 + 180° = 180°$; the length of (+2) is 2, the length of (−3) is 3, and the length of (−6) is $2 \cdot 3 = 6$.

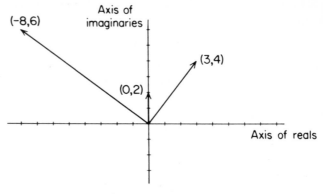

Fig. 1–29.

(12) See Fig. 1–30: $(-3)(-2) = (+6)$. The product of the vectors (−3) and (−2) is a vector whose length is $3 \cdot 2 = 6$, and whose amplitude is $180° + 180° = 360°$. A vector with amplitude 360° has the same direction as a vector with amplitude 0°.

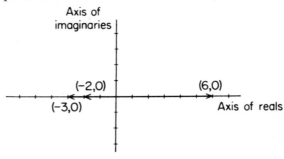

Fig. 1–30.

EXERCISES §105 (cont.)

14. Picture each of the following multiplications as laying a given vector end-to-end a whole number of times:

(a) $5 \cdot 3$ [Lay (+3) end-to-end 5 times]
(b) $5 \cdot \frac{1}{3}$
(c) $3 \cdot (.48)$
(d) $3 \cdot$ [vector to the point (2,3)]
(e) $5 \cdot (-2)$.

Notice, in each of these instances, that the product is a vector longer than the vector that is multiplied.

15. Picture each of the following multiplications as a multiplication of a given vector by a *proper* fraction of arithmetic (a fraction between 0 and 1):

(a) $\frac{1}{3} \cdot 6$ [In your figure, show the given vector ($+6$), the multiplier ($\frac{1}{3}$), and the product vector ($+2$)]

(b) $\frac{2}{3} \cdot \frac{6}{7}$

(c) $(.5) \cdot (7)$

(d) $(.5) \cdot (-6)$

(e) $.25 \cdot$ [vector to the point $(6, -4)$]   [Product vector is the vector to the point $(1.25, -1)$]

Notice, in each of these instances, that the product is a vector shorter than the vector that is multiplied.

16. Picture each of the following multiplications as a multiplication of a given vector by another vector. Recall that the length of the product vector is the product of the lengths of the given vector and the multiplier; the amplitude of the product vector is the sum of the amplitudes of the given vector and the multiplier.

(a) Rework Exercises 14 and 15. Notice in each instance that the amplitude of the multiplier is zero; hence the amplitude of the product is the same as the amplitude of the given vector.

(b) $(-3) \cdot (+2)$ (The product vector is -6)

(c) $(-2) \cdot (-3)$ (The product vector is $+6$)

(d) [Vector to the point $(0,2)$] · [vector to the point $(4,4)$] (The product vector has length $\sqrt{4} \cdot \sqrt{32}$, and amplitude $90° + 45° = 135°$).

(e) [Vector to the point $(0, -3)$] · [vector to the point $(-2,0)$] (The product vector has length 6 and amplitude $270° + 180° = 450°$. A vector with amplitude $450°$ has the same direction as a vector with amplitude $90°$).

Division. When you lay sheets of aluminum foil one on top of another, the average thickness of the sheets is .003 in. How many sheets of this foil are there in a pile .072 in. thick?

Contrast this problem with the one we used to introduce multiplication. Instead of adding 24 amounts each equal to .003, you subtract .003 from .072 and continue to subtract until you reach zero; or you add .003 to itself until you reach the known total, .072. You find out how many times .003 is contained in .072.

To each multiplication problem there is a corresponding problem in division. Especially when divisions get complicated, it may help to think of division as the process that reverses multiplication. So you use ideas about multiplication to visualize division.

It may help you to think again about how addition and subtraction are related. To find the *difference*, $a - b$, you ask "What number must I add to b to reach a?" Thus you solve a subtraction problem by asking a question about addition.

To find the *quotient, a/b,* you ask "By what number must I multiply *b* to reach *a*?" Thus you solve a division problem by asking a question about multiplication.

Sometimes you will find it easy to think of subtraction as a take-away process; often it will be easier to think of subtraction as finding what number to add. Sometimes you will find it easy to think of division as repeated subtraction; often it will be easier to think of division as finding the number to multiply by. We call subtraction the *inverse* of addition; we call division the *inverse* of multiplication. At least theoretically, this idea of *inverse* operations reduces the four operations of arithmetic to two. This saves a great deal of needless work as you proceed to study algebra.

The following exercises give you a chance to think of division problems both ways, as repeated subtractions *and* as inverses of multiplications.

EXERCISES §105 (cont.)

17. A box contains 24 bars of milk chocolate.

(a) To how many people can you give 8 bars each? First think "How many 8's in 24?" Then think "By what number do I multiply 8 to get 24?" Then lay the vector (+8) end-to-end until you reach vector (+24).

To how many people can you give

(b) 4 bars each?

(c) 2 bars each?

(d) 1 bar each?

(e) $\frac{1}{2}$ bar each?

(f) $\frac{1}{4}$ bar each?

Now complete the table:

N	32	16	8	4	2	1	$\frac{1}{2}$	$\frac{1}{4}$	$\frac{1}{8}$	$\frac{1}{16}$			
24 ÷ N			3	6	12								

Say each fact two ways. For example, say "24 divided by $\frac{1}{4}$ is 96"; then say "To get 24 I must multiply $\frac{1}{4}$ by 96."

18. Study the table in Exercise 17. Try to make general statements like: "When you divide 24 by one half as large a number your answer is _____."

When two numbers multiply to give the answer 24, making one number $\frac{1}{2}$ as large makes the other number _____.

Try to make several more general statements.

19. I need to save $25 in 5 days. How much must I save each day?

Notice how unnatural it is to think of subtracting 5 *days* from 25 *dollars*. Rather than ask "How many 5's in 25?" it seems more natural to ask "How much should I save on each of 5 days to get $25"; that is, "By what number do I multiply 5 to get 25?"

20. Compute each of the following:

(a) $18 \div 3 =$

(b) $18 \div (-3) =$

(c) $(-18) \div 3 =$

(d) $(-18) \div (-3) = .$

Picture each calculation as a vector division. For example, part (c) asks, "By what number must I multiply the length of $(+3)$ to get the length of (-18)?" and "What must I add to the amplitude of $(+3)$ to get the amplitude of (-18)?" These questions will lead you to the *quotient* vector (-6).

Interpret each of these calculations as a problem like Exercise 19. For example, part (c) becomes, "To spend \$18 in the *next* 3 days I must *spend* \$6 each day (a change of -6 dollars per day)."

Try both interpretations of division on each of the calculations. For example, part (c) asks either, "How many 3's in (-18)?" or "By what number do I multiply 3 to get (-18)?"

21. Solve the following divisions of vectors as the inverses of multiplications of vectors:

(a) $(-11)/(-2)$. [You must answer two questions: "By what number must I multiply the length of (-2) to get the length of (-11)?" (See Fig. 1–31.)

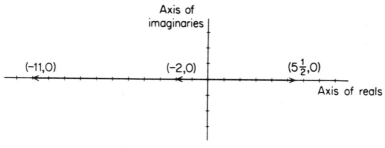

Fig. 1–31.

The answer to this question is $5\frac{1}{2}$. The second question is: "What must I add to the amplitude of (-2) to get the amplitude of (-11)?" The answer to this question is $0°$. Hence the *quotient* vector is $+5\frac{1}{2}$, a vector with length $5\frac{1}{2}$ and amplitude $0°$.]

(b) $(-14)/(+7)$ (c) $(+8)/(-3)$ (d) $(+10)/(-\frac{1}{2})$

(e) [Vector to the point (0,6)] / [vector to the point (3,0)]

(f) [Vector to the point $(-5,5)$] / [vector to the point (0,5)].

As you finish your reading of this section on operations with vectors, notice that adding vectors and the inverse operation of subtracting vectors are simpler than multiplying and dividing vectors. Pictures of vectors help you to visualize and interpret the algebraic operations with numbers that you will study in later sections. This is one important advantage of using algebra and geometry together. You go back and forth between the geometric picture and the algebraic formulation of a problem; each way of looking at the problem reinforces the other way of looking at the problem.

106. Operations with ordered number pairs

As you extend the set of natural numbers, and admit the integers, the rational numbers, the real numbers, and finally the complex numbers to full rights of "numbership," you must extend your ideas about operations upon numbers too. In Section 105 we used geometric pictures to help you do this. But geometric pictures are not enough. Each set of numbers has its own peculiar arithmetic.

In this section we point out that all calculations may be built upon calculations with natural numbers. As we extend the set of natural numbers, we define the operations of addition and multiplication in the enlarged set of numbers in terms of operations in the previous set of numbers. We define other operations, like subtraction, division, raising to powers, and extracting roots, in terms of addition and multiplication. Hence every calculation, however involved, goes back to additions and multiplications of pairs of natural numbers.

You should think of the work of this section as an exploratory exercise. Perhaps you can see the possibilities of doing much more with these ideas. It is possible to begin in somewhat this way and extend the system of natural numbers. One can define further number systems, and prove the properties of these new number systems from the assumed properties of the set of natural numbers.

Integers. First we take a new look at the members of the set I. Calculations like $(+4) + (+3) = (+7)$ and $(+2) \cdot (+3) = (+6)$ are nothing new. They correspond to the calculations $4 + 3 = 7$ and $2 \cdot 3 = 6$ with natural numbers. The question arises, "How can you treat calculations that involve zero or negative integers?"

You know how to deal with a difference like $5 - 3$. This is the number you add to 3 to reach 5. It is the natural number 2. You wish to deal also with differences like $5 - 5$ and $3 - 5$; these will correspond to the integers 0 and -2. We begin to experiment with the ordered pairs of natural numbers (5,5) and (3,5) as symbols for the integers 0 and -2.

Notice that the symbols for 0 and -2 are *not unique*. Instead of using (5,5) as a symbol for 0, we might have used (6,6) or (3,3); instead of using (3,5) as a symbol for -2, we might have used (4,6), or (17,19). This may remind you of the corresponding problem with fractions. The symbol $\frac{2}{3}$ is not unique; other symbols for the same rational number are $\frac{4}{6}$, $\frac{20}{30}$, etc.

You need a test for equality of integers; that is, you need a definition to tell you when two symbols represent the same integer. Notice that

$$(3,5) = (4,6) \quad \text{and} \quad 3 + 6 = 4 + 5$$
$$(17,19) = (7,9) \quad \text{and} \quad 17 + 9 = 7 + 19$$
$$(5,5) = (3,3) \quad \text{and} \quad 5 + 3 = 3 + 5.$$

To express the *definition of equality of integers* as a general rule we use letters as follows:

$$(a,b) = (c,d) \quad \text{if and only if} \quad a + d = c + b.$$

This is a concise way to make many statements all at once; instead of the letter a you may write any number of the set N; likewise you may *replace* the letters b, c, and d by natural numbers. If you choose natural numbers for which $a + d = c + b$, then $(a,b) = (c,d)$; if the symbols (a,b) and (c,d) represent the same integer, then $a + d = c + b$. Hence you know how to decide whether or not two ordered pairs of natural numbers symbolize the same integer.

To define addition of integers, you can generalize what you already know. Recall that $(5,3)$ is a symbol for $5 - 3 = 2$ and $(6,1)$ is a symbol for $6 - 1 = 5$; you know that $2 + 5 = 7$. Let

$$(5,3) + (6,1) = (5 + 6, 3 + 1).$$

Then $(5 + 6, 3 + 1) = (11,4) = 11 - 4 = 7$. *We define the addition of integers* by the formula

$$(a,b) + (c,d) = (a + c, b + d).$$

For example:

$$
\begin{aligned}
(3,2) + (12,8) &= (15,10), &\text{that is,}&& 1 + 4 &= 5; \\
(5,2) + (4,7) &= (9,9), &\text{that is,}&& 3 + (-3) &= 0; \\
(5,7) + (8,2) &= (13,9), &\text{that is,}&& (-2) + 6 &= 4; \\
(5,8) + (3,9) &= (8,17), &\text{that is,}&& (-3) + (-6) &= -9; \\
(6,9) + (5,5) &= (11,14), &\text{that is,}&& (-3) + 0 &= -3.
\end{aligned}
$$

Notice how we build our definition of the addition of integers upon calculations with ordered pairs of natural numbers.

We define multiplication of integers by the formula

$$(a,b) \cdot (c,d) = (ac + bd, ad + bc).$$

For example:

$$
\begin{aligned}
(3,2) \cdot (12,8) &= (3 \cdot 12 + 2 \cdot 8, 3 \cdot 8 + 2 \cdot 12) \\
&= (36 + 16, 24 + 24) \\
&= (52,48), &\text{that is,}&& 1 \cdot 4 &= 4; \\
(5,2) \cdot (4,7) &= (34,43), &\text{that is,}&& 3 \cdot (-3) &= -9; \\
(5,7) \cdot (8,2) &= (54,66), &\text{that is,}&& (-2) \cdot 6 &= -12; \\
(5,8) \cdot (3,9) &= (87,69), &\text{that is,}&& (-3) \cdot (-6) &= 18; \\
(6,9) \cdot (5,5) &= (75,75), &\text{that is,}&& (-3) \cdot 0 &= 0.
\end{aligned}
$$

Notice how we build our definition of the multiplication of integers upon calculations with ordered pairs of natural numbers. Of course we shall use the briefer notation of signed numbers in future chapters.

EXERCISES §106

1. Use the definition of equality of integers to decide whether each statement is true or false. Then rewrite the statement in the notation of signed numbers:

(a) $(3,5) \neq (5,3)$ [True because $3 + 3 \neq 5 + 5; 3 - 5 \neq 5 - 3$]

(b) $(4,1) = (44,41)$ (c) $(7,10) = (16,19)$

(d) $(421,421) = (1,1)$ (e) $(336,5) \neq (822,491)$.

2. Replace the letter by a natural number that makes each sentence a true statement:

(a) $(6,4) = (8,d)$ (b) $(3,7) = (c,5)$ (c) $(11,11) = (51,d)$

(d) $(19,29) = (c,26)$ (e) $(a,17) = (2,2)$ (f) $(3,b) = (7,11)$.

3. Use the definition of addition of integers to perform each addition with ordered pairs of natural numbers. Then write out the same addition in the notation of signed numbers:

(a) $(5,2) + (7,6) =$ (b) $(3,8) + (7,4) =$

(c) $(7,4) + (3,8) =$ (d) $(5,7) + (8,12) =$

(e) $(8,12) + (5,7) =$ (f) $(2,2) + (5,9) =$

(g) $(5,9) + (2,2) =$ (h) $(8,13) + (5,5) =$

4. To perform a subtraction, like $(3,6) - (7,1)$, you ask, "What integer can I add to $(7,1)$ to reach $(3,6)$?" Since there is no natural number that you can add to 7 to reach 3, you use another symbol for the integer $(3,6)$; for example, $(3,6) = (8,11)$. You ask the new question, "What integer can I add to $(7,1)$ to reach $(8,11)$?" The answer is $(1,10)$; hence $(3,6) - (7,1) = (8,11) - (7,1) = (1,10)$, that is, $(-3) - (+6) = -9$. Perform the following subtractions, first with ordered pairs of natural numbers and then in the notation of signed numbers:

(a) $(8,3) - (5,4) =$ [Notice that $(8,3) = (10,5)$]

(b) $(7,4) - (4,7) =$ [Notice that $(7,4) = (11,8)$]

(c) $(3,6) - (6,3) =$ [Notice that $(3,6) = (7,10)$]

(d) $(5,9) - (7,11) =$ [Notice that $(5,9) = (8,12)$].

5. Show that:

(a) $(7,3) + (2,2) = (9,5) = (7,3)$ (b) $(2,9) + (5,5) = (2,9)$

(c) $(4,1) + (4,4) = (4,1)$ (d) $(3,12) + (8,8) = (3,12)$.

Notice that a pair of the form (h,h) behaves like zero; that is, when you add it to any pair it leaves the pair unchanged. It is called the *additive identity* of *I*.

6. Show that:

(a) $(7,3) + (3,7) = (10,10) = (1,1)$ (b) $(2,9) + (9,2) = (1,1)$

(c) $(4,1) + (1,4) = (1,1)$ (d) $(3,12) + (12,3) = (1,1)$

(e) $(a,b) + (b,a) = (1,1)$.

The pair (b,a) is called the *additive inverse* of (a,b) because when you add it to (a,b) you get the additive identity (the zero) of *I*. What do you call the additive inverse of an integer in the language of signed numbers?

7. In I, every subtraction can be changed to an addition by replacing the subtrahend with its additive inverse, that is,

$$(a,b) - (c,d) = (a,b) + (d,c) = (a + d,b + c).$$

To show that this sum is the answer to the subtraction, we need to show that the sum of it and (c,d) is (a,b).

$$(a + d,b + c) + (c,d) = (a + d + c,b + c + d) \quad \text{(Def. of addition)}$$
$$(a,b). \quad \text{(Def. of equality)}$$

For example, in Exercise 4,

$$(3,6) - (7,1) = (3,6) + (1,7) = (4,13) = (1,10).$$

Perform the subtractions of Exercise 4 by this method.

8. Use the definition of multiplication of integers to perform the operation of multiplication with ordered pairs of natural numbers. Then write out the same multiplication in the notation of signed numbers. Do each part of Exercise 3, replacing addition by multiplication.

9. Use the definition of multiplication (and equality) to show that:

(a) $(9,4)(1,1) = (13,13) = (1,1)$
(b) $(2,6)(1,1) = (1,1)$
(c) $(8,3)(1,1) = (1,1)$
(d) $(a,b)(1,1) = (a + b,a + b) = (1,1)$.

What familiar property of integers is expressed above?

10. Use the definition of multiplication (and equality) to show that:

(a) $(9,4)(2,1) = (22,17) = (9,4)$
(b) $(2,6)(2,1) = (2,6)$
(c) $(8,3)(2,1) = (8,3)$
(d) $(a,b)(2,1) = (2a + b,a + 2b) = (a,b)$.

What familiar property of integers is expressed above?

Rational numbers. You probably know too much about fractions to enjoy spending much time on rational numbers as ordered pairs of integers. We shall treat rational numbers even more briefly than integers. In effect you learn to think of rational numbers as ordered pairs of integers, and hence as ordered pairs of ordered pairs of natural numbers.

You can express the rational number $\frac{2}{3}$ as the ordered pair of integers $(+2,+3)$; similarly $\dfrac{-3}{8}$ becomes $(-3,+8)$. Here are the definitions of equality, addition, and multiplication for rational numbers:

Agreement: When we use a symbol like (a,b), we agree that $b \neq 0$ (see Exercise 12, below).

Equality: $(a,b) = (c,d)$ if and only if $ad = bc$.

Addition: $(a,b) + (c,d) = (ad + bc,bd)$.

Multiplication: $(a,b) \cdot (c,d) = (ac,bd)$.

Again these mathematical sentences are brief ways to make many statements all at once; instead of the letter a you may write any member of the set I; likewise you may replace the letters b, c, and d by integers; by agreement, $b \neq 0$ and $d \neq 0$. If you choose integers for which $ad = bc$, then $(a,b) = (c,d)$; if the symbols (a,b) and (c,d) represent the same rational number, then $ad = bc$. Hence you know how to decide whether or not two ordered pairs of integers symbolize the same rational number, and you know how to add and multiply rational numbers.

The following exercises will guide you in an exploration of rational numbers as ordered pairs of integers.

EXERCISES §106 (cont.)

11. Use the definition of equality of rational numbers to decide whether each statement is true or false. Then rewrite the statement in the usual fraction notation:

(a) $(3,7) = (12,28)$ [True because $3 \cdot 28 = 7 \cdot 12$; $3/7 = 12/28$]

(b) $(-3,5) = (5,-3)$ [False because $(-3) \cdot (-3) \neq 5 \cdot 5$; $\dfrac{-3}{5} = \dfrac{5}{-3}$ is a false statement]

(c) $(-5,-2) = (5,2)$

(d) $(3,-12) \neq (-1,4)$

(e) $(0,4) = (0,7)$ $\left[\text{True because } 0 \cdot 7 = 4 \cdot 0; \dfrac{0}{4} = \dfrac{0}{7} = 0 \right]$

(f) $(4,0) = (7,0)$ [This is not a statement; that is, it is neither true nor false because we agreed not to use symbols like $(4,0)$ or $(7,0)$. The fact that $4 \cdot 0 = 0 \cdot 7$ is not important here. The symbols 4/0 and 7/0 are *not defined*. See Exercise 12, below].

12. We hope you are wondering why symbols like $(1,0)$ are not defined. Suppose you used the symbol $(1,0)$ as a symbol for a rational number. Then

$$(2,1) + (1,0) = (2 \cdot 0 + 1 \cdot 1, 1 \cdot 0) \quad \text{(Def. of addition)}$$
$$= (1,0). \quad \quad \text{(Calculation with integers)}$$

In the notation of fractions, $2/1 + 1/0 = 1/0$. If the symbol $(1,0)$ represented a rational number, this number would have the remarkable property that 2 more than the number is the number itself. From a vector point of view, there is no such number on the line of numbers.

Now try $(5,0) + (3,7)$. The sum turns out to be $(35,0)$. By the definition of equality of rational numbers, $(35,0) = (5,0)$. Hence $(5,0) + (3,7) = (5,0)$. When you add $(3,7)$ to $(5,0)$ you get $(5,0)$; that is, $\frac{3}{7}$ more than $(5,0)$ is $(5,0)$. There is no point on the line of numbers that behaves like $(5,0)$.

You may wish to experiment further with symbols of the form $(a,0)$, where a is an integer. We agree not to use such symbols; they do not represent rational numbers. We shall return to this question of "division by zero" in Chapter 2 (page 53).

13. Replace the letter by an integer that makes each sentence a true statement:

(a) $(6,12) = (1,d)$ [$6d = 12 \cdot 1$ yields $d = 2$]

(b) $(3,7) = (c,5)$ [$15 = 7c$ has no solution in the set I; hence you cannot rewrite $(3,7)$ in the form $(c,5)$]

(c) $(-2,-20) = (1,d)$

(d) $(4,-5) = (2,d)$.

14. Use the definition of addition of rational numbers to perform each addition with ordered pairs of integers. Then write out the same addition in the notation of rational numbers:

(a) $(3,5) + (2,3) = \left[(9 + 10,15) = (19,15); \dfrac{3}{5} + \dfrac{2}{3} = \dfrac{19}{15} \right]$

(b) $(-2,7) + (3,-7) = \left[(35,-49); \dfrac{-2}{7} + \dfrac{3}{-7} = \dfrac{-5}{7} \right.$.

$\qquad\qquad\qquad \text{Is } (35,-49) = (-5,7)? \Big]$

(c) $(-1,-2) + (5,-6) = \left[(-4,12); \dfrac{-1}{-2} + \dfrac{5}{-6} = \dfrac{-2}{6} = \dfrac{-1}{3} \right.$.

$\qquad\qquad\qquad \text{Is } (-4,12) = (-1,3)? \Big]$

(d) $(3,4) + (-1,8) =$

(e) $(-2,9) + (-5,12) =$

(f) $(0,4) + (5,11) = \left[(20,44); \dfrac{0}{4} + \dfrac{5}{11} = \dfrac{5}{11} \right]$.

15. You may wish to try your hand at subtraction; $(a,b) - (c,d)$ means to find a rational number that you can add to (c,d) to reach (a,b); but this is often hard to do. In Chapter 2 (page 65), we shall justify an easier procedure like $\dfrac{2}{3} - \dfrac{1}{2} = \dfrac{2}{3} + \dfrac{-1}{2}$, that amounts to changing a subtraction into an addition of the additive inverse (negative) of the subtrahend.

16. Use the definition of multiplication of rational numbers to perform each multiplication with ordered pairs of integers. Then write out the same multiplication in the notation of rational numbers. Do each part of Exercise 14, replacing addition by multiplication. For example:

$$(3,5) \cdot (2,3) = (6,15); \quad \dfrac{3}{5} \cdot \dfrac{2}{3} = \dfrac{6}{15} = \dfrac{2}{5}. \quad \text{Is } (6,15) = (2,5)?$$

Notice that the process of multiplication of rational numbers is simpler than the process of addition of rational numbers.

17. To perform a division, like $(3,5) \div (2,3)$, you ask "By what number can I multiply $(2,3)$ to reach $(3,5)$?" Such divisions (except by zero) are always possible in the set R. In this case,

$$(3,5) \div (2,3) = (18,30) \div (2,3) = (9,10).$$

You may wish to experiment with other examples of division, both in the notation of ordered numbered pairs and in the notation of rational numbers. (See also Exercise 20.)

18. Show that:

(a) $(7,3)(2,2) = (14,6) = (7,3)$ (b) $(-9,2)(1,1) = (-9,2)$
(c) $(-12,-5)(4,4) = (-12,-5)$ (d) $(1,-3)(8,8) = (1,-3)$
(e) $(a,b)(1,1) = (a,b)$.

Notice that a pair of the form (h,h) behaves like 1, that is, when you multiply it by any other pair it leaves that pair unchanged. It is called the *multiplicative identity* of the system of rational numbers.

19. Show that:

(a) $(7,3)(3,7) = (21,21) = (1,1)$ (b) $(-9,2)(2,-9) = (1,1)$
(c) $(-12,-5)(-5,-12) = (1,1)$ (d) $(1,-3)(-3,1) = (1,1)$
(e) $(a,b)(b,a) = (1,1)$.

The pair (b,a) is called the *multiplicative inverse* of (a,b) because, when you multiply it by (a,b), the product is the multiplicative identity. What do you call the multiplicative inverse of a rational number in the language of fractions?

20. In the system of rational numbers, every division (except by zero) can be changed to a multiplication by replacing the divisor with its multiplicative inverse, that is,

$$(a,b) \div (c,d) = (a,b)(d,c) = (ad,bc)$$

since
$$(ad,bc)(c,d) = (adc,bcd) = (a,b)$$

Carry out the following divisions:

(a) $(3,5) \div (2,3) =$ (b) $(-9,1) \div (1,-2) =$
(c) $(8,1) \div (4,-1) =$ (d) $(7,-6) \div (-2,-3) =$
(e) $(15,4) \div (3,4) =$

Answers: (a) $(3,5) \div (2,3) = (3,5)(3,2) = (9,10)$; (c) $(-8,4)$ or $(-2,1)$.

Real numbers. Recall that the set L includes all the points on the line of numbers; there are points on the line of numbers, like π and $\sqrt{2}$, that are irrational points; we cannot represent the numbers that correspond to these points exactly as fractions of the unit of measurement; that is, there is no way to represent these points exactly by rational numbers.

When we approximate an irrational number, we ordinarily use a rational approximation. For example: $\pi \doteq 3.14 = 314/100$; $\sqrt{2} \doteq 1.414 = 1414/1000$. With these approximations we use the arithmetic of rational numbers. You have learned that this arithmetic is based upon calculations with ordered pairs of integers, and hence upon calculations with ordered pairs of ordered pairs of natural numbers.

We shall return, in Chapter 5, to the arithmetic of roots. We shall perform calculations with numbers like $\sqrt{2}$, $\sqrt[3]{7}$, and the like. These calculations depend upon calculations with integers. Numerical calculations with irrational numbers like π are always approximate. We shall write numbers like

$3\sqrt{2}\pi$, meaning multiply 3 by $\sqrt{2}$ and multiply the result by π; but in numerical calculations we shall replace $\sqrt{2}$ and π by rational approximations.

Notice, on the one hand, that the step from rational numbers to real numbers is tricky. We skip over some points that careful mathematicians examine in great detail. Our only excuse for this is our desire to gain the important advantages that real numbers yield, without devoting a major part of our study to building this set of real numbers.

Notice, on the other hand, that the arithmetic of rational numbers can always be used to work with decimal approximations to irrational numbers. These decimal approximations can be chosen close enough to fit any particular applied problem. This has the effect of reducing all the calculations that arise in applied mathematics to decimal calculations. Decimal calculations involve only the numerals 0, 1, 2, ..., 9 and their positions in reference to the decimal point. For example, 42.037 means $4(10) + 2(1) + 0(\frac{1}{10}) + 3(\frac{1}{100}) + 7(\frac{1}{1000})$. The work of actually performing decimal calculations is frequently turned over to calculating machines. This is possible because all calculations are built upon calculations with natural numbers, and all calculations with natural numbers (in a numeral system based upon ten) are built upon calculations with the digits 0, 1, 2, ..., 9.

Complex numbers. We shall deal, in Chapter 5, with the arithmetic of complex numbers. You will not be surprised to hear that all such calculations are built upon calculations with ordered pairs of real numbers.

REFERENCES

Some students find it interesting and enlightening to trace the history of counting, the origins of the counting words, the choice of a number base (like our base ten), and of figure symbols. Other students want to read more of man's efforts to extend his early ideas about numbers. We list the following references for your convenience.

1. Courant, R., and Robbins, H., *What is Mathematics?* New York: Oxford University Press, 1947. Pages 77–85 are on infinite cardinal numbers.
2. Dantzig, T., *Number, the Language of Science.* New York: The Macmillan Co., 1939. This book presents a most interesting account of the development of the concept of number.
3. Davis, H. M., "Mathematical Machines," *Scientific American*, Vol. 180, No. 4, April 1949. This article discusses numbers to the base 2 (binary numbers) and how they are used in high-speed computing machines.
4. Johnston, J. H., *The Reverse Notation.* London: Blackie and Son, Ltd., 1937. An unusual proposal for number notation.
5. Karpinski, L. C., *The History of Arithmetic.* New York: Rand McNally and Co., 1925. Includes early forms of numerals.
6. Kasner, E. and Newman, J., *Mathematics and the Imagination.* New York:

Simon and Schuster, 1940. Pages 27–104 discuss large natural numbers, transfinite numbers, and extensions of number in an interesting fashion.

7. Logsdon, M. I., *A Mathematician Explains*. Chicago: The University of Chicago Press, 1936. Number notation and number bases, pages 12–20. Systems of numeration used by other civilizations, pages 36–46.

8. Merriman, G. M., *To Discover Mathematics*. New York: John Wiley and Sons, 1942. Chapter 1 discusses the development of the fundamental concepts of number and number bases. The idea of number is extended in Chapter 4.

9. Richardson, M., *Fundamentals of Mathematics*. New York: The Macmillan Co., 1941. Finite and transfinite cardinal numbers, pages 404–413. Systems of notation, pages 165–173.

10. Sanford, V., *A Short History of Mathematics*. Boston: Houghton Mifflin Co., 1930.

11. *Solar Ephemeris*. New York: Keuffel and Esser Co., published yearly. Here you will find positive and negative numbers used to measure time and angles.

12. Terry, G. S., *Duodecimal Arithmetic*. London: Longmans, Green and Co. 1938. A brief discussion of numbers to the base 12 is given, including addition and multiplication tables, techniques of converting numbers, etc. Most of the book is devoted to standard mathematical tables with the entries given in the duodecimal system.

2

The Set of Real Numbers:
A Structure

Whether in everyday affairs, or in your study of mathematics, you deal constantly with *sets of elements*: the set of pupils in your mathematics class; the set of sentences in Chapter 1 of this text; the set of natural numbers; the set of odd numbers from 5 to 13 inclusive, {5, 7, 9, 11, 13}.

In Chapter 1 you worked with sets of numbers: the natural numbers, the fractions of arithmetic, the negative integers, and the like. In this chapter we begin to discuss the algebra of the set of real numbers.

We shall think of the real numbers as a *mathematical structure*. The elements, or members, of the set of real numbers are the building blocks; our assumptions about the behavior of the real numbers are the cement that holds the blocks together and gives form to the structure.

When we speak of the properties of real numbers, we use *mathematical sentences*. It is important to get together on the form and meaning of these sentences. Hence we begin with a discussion of sentences in mathematics.

200. Sentences in mathematics

The simplest sentences in mathematics are *statements*. *To be a statement, a sentence must be either true or false.* Examples are:

$$8 + 5 = 13 \quad \text{(a true statement)}$$
$$3 - 7 = -2 \quad \text{(a false statement)}.$$

Notice, however, that each statement has a certain *context*. As you read the statement "$8 + 5 = 13$," you take it for granted that you are working in the set N, or in a set like L that contains the natural numbers as a subset; you assume the familiar arithmetic based upon ten; you assume that the figure symbols have their usual meaning. Hence you should recognize that a mathematical statement says something about mathematical objects (numbers, triangles, or the like) that is either true or false in a certain context.

In Chapter 1 we found it convenient to use sentences that contained letters. For example, we defined the multiplication of rational numbers by the sentence

$$(a,b) \cdot (c,d) = (ac,bd), \quad b \neq 0 \text{ and } d \neq 0.$$

Such sentences enabled us to make many statements all in one. By agreement, you may replace the letters a, b, c, and d by integers; only those *replacement instances* for which $b = 0$ or $d = 0$ are prohibited. Examples of permissible replacement instances are:

$$(3,5) \cdot (1,-5) = (3,-25);$$
$$(0,4) \cdot (-3,-7) = (0,-28).$$

By agreement, $(3,0) \cdot (2,2) = (6,0)$, and $(5,4) \cdot (2,0) = (10,0)$ are *not* permissible replacement instances; they are not statements at all because you cannot decide whether they are true or false; the symbols $(3,0)$, $(6,0)$, $(2,0)$ and $(10,0)$ are *not defined*.

Many people think of algebra as a subject where you work with letters. Certainly you will use letters constantly in your study of algebra; but this use of letters is incidental rather than fundamental. Let us take a closer look at the way mathematicians use letters in algebra.

First you have a definite set, like N or L. Let us use the set $\{1,3,5,7,9\}$ of odd *digits* for purposes of illustration. You construct a mathematical sentence like

$$x + 2 = 5,$$
$$a + b = b + a,$$
$$r > 5,$$

or $\qquad\qquad q \cdot 3 = 0.$

The letters in these sentences *hold open* a place where you may insert the name of a member of the set you are discussing. For example, in the sentence $x + 2 = 5$, you may replace the letter x by 1, 3, 5, 7, or 9. Suppose you replace x by 7; you get the statement

$$7 + 2 = 5;$$

this is a false statement. If you replace x by 3, you get the true statement

$$3 + 2 = 5.$$

When mathematicians use letters in this way they call the letters *variables*. This word "variable" comes from an earlier period in mathematics when men like Isaac Newton (c. 1750) used mathematics to describe the physical world. These mathematicians used letters, like T for temperature or t for time, and thought of these letters as taking "values" that flowed along from one number to another. Later mathematicians found that this idea of variable led to very serious logical difficulties. You will recall the discussion, in Section 102 (page 9), of the fact that there is no rational number that comes "next in order of size" after a given rational number. Modern mathematicians still use the word "variable." But they do not think of a variable as a "quantity that varies." To them, and to us, a variable is much simpler, much less mysterious. *A variable is a letter that holds open a place in a sentence that you may fill by the name of a member of the set you are discussing.*

Now try all the replacement instances of each sentence, choosing replacements for the variables from the set $\{1,3,5,7,9\}$:

For the sentence $x + 2 = 5$, notice that the replacement of x by 3 yields a true statement, but the other four replacements yield false statements.

For the sentence $a + b = b + a$, notice that there are twenty-five different replacements. The statement $7 + 1 = 1 + 7$ is one of these replacement instances. Notice that each of these twenty-five statements is true.

For the sentence $r > 5$, there are five possible replacements: $1 > 5$, $3 > 5, 5 > 5, 7 > 5$, and $9 > 5$. These replacement instances of the sentence $r > 5$ will make no sense to a person who is unfamiliar with the *connective phrase* ">"; but once you read the symbol ">" to mean "greater than,"

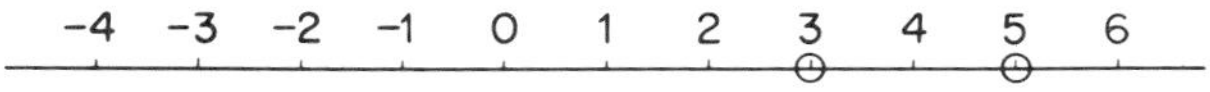

-4 -3 -2 -1   0   1   2   3   4   5   6

Fig. 2–1.

each of these replacements becomes a statement. The statements $1 > 5$, $3 > 5$, and $5 > 5$ are false; the statements $7 > 5$ and $9 > 5$ are true. Much of the difficulty of the beginner in mathematics is a result of not learning the exact meaning of each new symbol. It is the same in any field of study. To understand a plumber, you must first learn what he means by the words he uses.

For the sentence $q \cdot 3 = 0$, there are five possible replacements: All of the statements $1 \cdot 3 = 0, 3 \cdot 3 = 0, 5 \cdot 3 = 0, 7 \cdot 3 = 0$, and $9 \cdot 3 = 0$ are false.

The following exercises give you a chance to explore replacement instances of sentences that contain variables. Besides the connective phrases, "$=$" and "$>$," which you have met already, you need the phrase "$<$," which means "less than." Notice the geometric meaning of some sample statements: $5 > 3$ means "5 is greater than 3"; that is, the point 5 lies to the right of the point 3 on the line of numbers (see Fig. 2–1); this is a true statement.

Similarly, $5 \le 3$ means "5 is *less than or equal to* 3"; that is, the point 5 lies to the left of or in the same position as the point 3 on the line of numbers; this is a false statement.

EXERCISES §200

1. Consider the set $\{0, 2, 4, 6, 8\}$ of even digits:

(a) Write the 5 replacement instances of the sentence $x + 4 = 10$. Which of these 5 statements are true?

(b) Write the 25 replacement instances of the sentence $x + 2 = 4 + y$. Which of these 25 statements are true?

(c) Write the 25 replacement instances of the sentence $a + b = b + a$. Which of these 25 statements are true?

(d) List only the true replacement instances of each sentence:

(i) $y + 5 = 9$	(ii) $y + 5 = 8$	(iii) $y \geq 7$
(iv) $y + 3 \leq 5$	(v) $y + 3 < 5$	(vi) $4y = 24$
(vii) $4y = 20$	(viii) $4y \not\leq 20$	(ix) $xy \neq yx$
(x) $xy = yx$	(xi) $x + 5 = 3 + y$	(xii) $0 \cdot y = 0$.

2. The ideas of Exercise 1 apply to sets whose members are not numbers. Consider the set of colleges in the Big Ten. This is the set {Michigan, Michigan State, Wisconsin, Ohio State, Purdue, Indiana, Illinois, Iowa, Minnesota, Northwestern}. Notice that each element of this set is a college.

(a) Write the 10 replacement instances of the sentence "It lies west of the Mississippi river." Which of these 10 statements are true? Notice that the pronoun "it" behaves like a variable. You can express the idea of the sentence by saying "x lies west of the Mississippi river."

(b) List only the true replacement instances of each sentence:

(i) In the year 1950, the enrollment of x was over 15,000. (Notice that you need facts, beyond the field of mathematics, to decide about the truth of the replacement instances.)

(ii) In the year 1958 the football team of x defeated the football team of y. (Mathematically there are 100 replacement instances possible. Some of these statements contradict one another. For example, "Michigan defeated Wisconsin" contradicts "Wisconsin defeated Michigan." You may have to deal with tie games. If team A tied team B, both of the statements "A defeated B" and "B defeated A" are false. If team A did not play team B in 1958, the replacement instances "A defeated B" and "B defeated A" are both false.)

3. You may wish to experiment further with sets whose members are not numbers. Pronouns like *he, she, they*, etc., may be used as variables in sentences. Use the set of people enrolled in your mathematics class. A sentence like "He has red hair" becomes a statement when you replace the variable *he* by the name of a *man* in your class. Notice the difference between the sentences "x has red hair" and "He has red hair." We restrict variables like *he* and *she* to refer to only those members of a set who are of the appropriate sex. We shall not follow up these non-mathematical examples here. For the most part we shall deal with sets whose elements are real numbers.

4. Consider the set L. It is, of course, impossible to write all of the replacement instances of a sentence that contains one or more variables. Write replacement instances of each of the following sentences. If possible, choose three replacements to yield true statements. If this is not possible, make as many true statements as you can.

(a) $x + 2 \geq 5$	(b) $x < -5$	(c) $(x - 1)(x + 2) = 0$
(d) $r - s = s - r$	(e) $r + s = s + r$	(f) $a + 5 = 3 + b$
(g) $3x \neq 7$	(h) $3x = 7$	(i) $3x \leq 7$.

To continue our discussion of mathematical sentences, it is convenient to use the idea of set to express ourselves briefly and clearly.

We shall have occasion to use sentences that are true of every number of a set. For example, we shall say: For every pair of real numbers, a, and b,

$$a + b = b + a.$$

It is not appropriate to replace a by a wall and b by a roof. It may be all wrong to "add" a wall to a roof and all right to "add" a roof to a wall. In this discussion we limit replacements of a and b to symbols for elements of the set of real numbers. We say the *range* of a and b is the set of real numbers. You may *substitute* for a a symbol for any real number. You may substitute for b a symbol for any real number. Then you get a true statement, like $2 + \sqrt{3} = \sqrt{3} + 2$.

We shall also have occasion to use sentences that are true for only certain select members of a set. For example, we shall say: Find all the replacements of x, from the set L, that make the sentence

$$x + 5 = 8$$

a true statement. It is *not* appropriate to replace x by a saxophone player. It is appropriate to replace x by a symbol for a real number, like 6. We say, the range of x is the set of real numbers. When you replace x by 6, you get the *false* statement

$$6 + 5 = 8.$$

Many other choices of x yield false statements. For example, try -3, $2\frac{1}{2}$, and $\sqrt{2}$. Then try 3; this choice of x yields a *true* statement, namely,

$$3 + 5 = 8.$$

You may be able to convince yourself that 3 is the *only* value of x that makes the sentence $x + 5 = 8$ a true statement. In the language of Chapter 1 (page 17), the *solution set* of the sentence $x + 5 = 8$, in the set L, is $\{3\}$.

We call the letters a, b, and x in these sentences *variables*. They *stand for*, or *represent*, elements of a definite set of numbers. When you see a variable like a you should think: "a represents one of the members of the set of numbers I am discussing. I can substitute for a the name of any one of the numbers of this set." Hence a variable really holds a place open in a sentence until you make up your mind what value of the variable (from its range) you want to use. Students of logic call sentences like $a + b = b + a$ and $x + 5 = 8$ *open sentences*. When you substitute definite values for the variables, you get sentences like $3 + (-2) = (-2) + 3$ and $4 + 5 = 8$, which are either true or false. You may call these *closed sentences*, or statements.

Open sentences in mathematics may be rather complicated. For example, "A triangle belongs to the set of right triangles if and only if the sum of the squares on the two shorter sides of the triangle is equal to the square on the longest side of the triangle." In this sentence the word *triangle* is a variable whose range is the set of all triangles in the plane; the sides of each definite triangle have definite lengths. Our present need is for comparatively simple open sentences like the ones you have met in this section. We shall call such sentences *conditions*.

Notice that some conditions, like $a + b = b + a$, yield true statements for each replacement of a and b. We call such conditions *identities*. They are true for each replacement instance from the range of the variables they contain.

Other conditions, like $x + 5 = 8$, yield both true statements ($3 + 5 = 8$) and false statements ($4 + 5 = 8$). When you insist that $x + 5 = 8$, you impose a "condition" upon the real numbers that you may substitute for x. As it turns out, the condition $x + 5 = 8$ is a strong one. Only the replacement 3 satisfies this condition. A condition may be less restrictive than this one and still not be an identity. For example, the sentence $x > 3$ (x is greater than 3) becomes a true statement for many values of x. The values 4, $7\frac{1}{2}$, and 10 all *satisfy* this condition. When you substitute them in the sentence $x > 3$ they yield true statements. But the values 3, 0, and $1\frac{1}{4}$ do *not* satisfy this condition. When you substitute them in the sentence $x > 3$ they yield *false* statements.

Still other conditions are even more restrictive than $x + 5 = 8$. For example, the sentence $x - x = 2$ imposes a condition that *no* real number fulfills. There is no real number that you can subtract from itself to get 2. The condition ($x > 0$ *and* $x = 0$ *and* $x < 0$) also rules out every real number.

You can use your everyday experiences with sets to help you think about these mathematical ideas. Consider, then, a set of elements that we shall call S. By a *subset* of S, we mean a set each of whose elements is an element of S. For instance, let S stand for the set of pupils in a mathematics class, and B for the set of boys in the class. Then B is a subset of S. We write $B \subseteq S$ to abbreviate the sentence "B is a subset of S." If every member of the class is a boy, then $B = S$; if some members of the class are boys and some members of the class are girls, then $B \subset S$ (recall sentences like $N \subset I$ from Chapter 1).

Now you can make up conditions that are true for every member of the mathematics class. The sentence "x is either a boy or a girl" contains the variable x. The range of x is the set S of pupils in the mathematics class. Each value of x (each member of the class) makes this a true statement. Hence the sentence "x is either a boy or a girl" is an identity. It defines a subset of S that equals the set S. If we denote the subset of S, for which x is either a boy or a girl, by the symbol T, then $T = S$.

As a second example, take the sentence "x has red hair or x does not have red hair." If you use R for the subset of S that makes this sentence true, then it is clear that $R = S$.

Of course you must be careful of the meanings of sentences when you define subsets of S. If you say, "x has red hair or x has hair that isn't red," you can not be sure that this sentence always yields true statements. Perhaps there is a member of the class who is bald; then this condition defines a subset of S that is unequal to S.

You can also make up conditions that are true for some, but not all, members of your mathematics class. For example, "x sits in the front row" is, for most classes, such a condition. It is true of some values of x and false of other values of x. If you name the subset of S, for which x sits in the front row, by the symbol F, then $F \subset S$.

Finally, you can make up conditions that are true for no members of the mathematics class. For example, "x is over 80 years of age" is, for most classes, such a sentence. It is false for every value of x. Hence it defines a subset of S that has no members. We call a set with no members an *empty* set or a *null* set. The conditions "$x - x = 2$" and "x is over 80 years of age" both define a null set. There seems to be no point in distinguishing between the set that contains no numbers and the set that contains no persons. We shall call both of these sets, and every other set that contains no elements, *the* null set. Since each member of the null set (there being no such elements) is a member of every set, the null set is a subset of every set. Recall the symbol { } which you used for the empty set in Chapter 1.

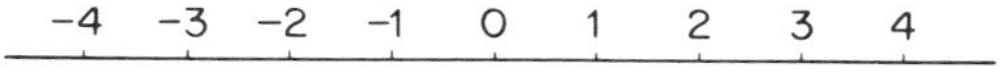

Fig. 2–2.

In our study of algebra, we begin with the set L of real numbers. These are, as you saw in Chapter 1, the numbers that correspond to points on the line of numbers (Fig. 2–2). To each point on the line of numbers, there corresponds a real number. To each real number, there corresponds a point on the line of numbers. The set L includes the numbers 0, 1, -2, $7\frac{1}{3}$, $-3\frac{1}{8}$, $\sqrt{2}$, $\sqrt[3]{7}$, and many others. It does *not* include those complex numbers like $3 + 2i$, which correspond to points in the plane but not on the line of numbers.

Often the set of real numbers is more extensive than you need for special problems. For problems that require only counting, the natural numbers suffice. This set,

$$N = \{1, 2, 3, \ldots\},$$

is a subset of the set of real numbers, $N \subset L$. Much work in business arithmetic requires, besides, the number zero and the fractions of arithmetic. Again this set of numbers is a subset of the real numbers. Sometimes we require the set of *integers*,

$$I = \{\ldots -3, -2, -1, 0, 1, 2, 3, \ldots\},$$

or the set R of *rational* numbers (which includes 0 and all of the positive and negative fractions). In measuring gasoline, people usually use the set with elements 0 and the positive decimal numbers expressed *to the nearest tenth.* You buy 8.6 gallons of gasoline. Really, you may get a little more or a little less, depending upon the accuracy of measurement. Technically, the number symbol 8.6 gal, used in this way, means an amount between 8.55 gal and 8.65 gal. It is *rounded off* to the nearest tenth. All of these sets of numbers, which we shall use, are subsets of *L.*

When you learn the *structure* of the set *L,* you can apply what you know about the set *L* to subsets of *L.* A sentence that is true for each real number is automatically true for each member of a subset of the real numbers. Hence it saves a lot of time and work to study the general properties of real numbers first.

EXERCISES §200 (cont.)

5. What are the members of the following sets?

(a) The possible grades in this course.
(b) The days of the week this class meets.
(c) The automobiles registered in this state.
(d) The state capitals in the United States.
(e) The odd integers between 3 and 5.
(f) The natural numbers between 3 and 5.
(g) The rational numbers between 3 and 5.
(h) The replacements of x that make the statement $x + 5 = 1$ true.

6. Name two sets that have a *finite* number of members. Name two sets that have an *infinite* number of members. Describe a set that contains no elements.

7. Let x be a variable whose range is the set of integers. What is the range of y if:

(a) $y = 2x$?   (b) $y = 2x + 1$?
(c) $y = 10x$?   (d) $y = x + \frac{1}{2}$?

8. If b is a variable whose range is the set of real numbers L, describe the subset of L for which each of the following conditions is satisfied; that is, find the solution set of the condition. Use a line of numbers whenever it helps you to visualize a sentence:

(a) $\frac{1}{2}b = 3$ (b) $2b + 3 = 12$
(c) $2b + 3 = 3 + 2b$ (d) $(b - 2)(b - 3) = 0$
(e) $7(b + 5) = b(b + 5)$ (f) $1 < b < 5$
(g) $2/b = 0$ (h) $b^2 = 9$
(i) $b^2 = 5$ (j) $b^2 < 5$
(k) $b^2 < 0$ (l) $b^2 > 0$
(m) $b^2 + 4 = 0$ (n) $4 \cdot b = b \cdot 4$
(o) $2(3 - b) = 6 - 2b$ (p) $b = 3 + b$.

Answers: (a) $\{6\}$; (c) L; (e) $\{7, -5\}$; (g) null set.

9. Repeat Exercise 8 using the set of natural numbers for the range of *b*.

Answers: (a) {6}; (c) *N*; (e) {7}; (f) {2, 3, 4}; (g) null set.

10. Let *S* be the set of numbers {1, 2, 3}. Find all possible subsets of *S*. (Do not forget that the null set is a subset of every set.) Do the same with the set *T*: {John, Mary, Sam}. Is there any similarity between these two exercises?

11. Repeat Exercise 10 with $S = \{0, 1, 2, 3\}$.

12. Let *S* be the set {John, Henry} and *T* the set {Mary, Betty, Sue}. List the elements of a new set, *C*, that contains all the possible ordered pairs that can be formed by taking one element from *S* and then one element from *T*.

13. Repeat Exercise 12 with $S = \{0, 1, 2, 3\}$ and $T = \{31, 35, 39\}$. Could you have predicted the number of elements in *C* before you listed them?

14. You often use words as variables. In each of the following sentences indicate a word that is used as a variable and name a set that you might reasonably assume to be the range of the variable.

(a) If he is willing to study, he can pass mathematics.
(b) Man is mortal.
(c) A triangle with two equal sides is said to be isosceles.
(d) To graduate with honors a student needs a grade point index of 3.5 or more.

15. A theorem in mathematics may have the form: If *A*, then *B*. For example, "If a triangle has two equal sides, then it has two equal angles" is a theorem from geometry. Here *A* has been replaced by the statement "a triangle has two equal sides," and *B* by "a triangle has two equal angles," to make a true statement.

(a) State two theorems in this form from geometry and two from algebra. What replacements for *A* and *B* are you making in each case?
(b) What is the range of the variable *A*?

16. Consider the sentence: The sum of the first *n* even natural numbers is $n(n + 1)$. Is it permissible to replace *n* with -6? π? 3? What is the range of *n*? Make several different replacements for *n* from its range. Do they yield true statements?

17. Consider the sentence: a^n is defined to be the product of *n* factors of *a*. What is the range of *n*? of *a*?

201. Special properties of 0 and 1

Before we state the general properties of operations with real numbers, we pause to study some special properties of the numbers 0 and 1. This is worth while because many of the exceptions to the rules for operations with real numbers involve either 0 or 1 or both of these numbers. Hence the numbers 0 and 1 have special importance as you study the structure of the set *L*.

Recall the following properties of addition of real numbers:

I $$a + 0 = 0 + a = a.$$

II $$a + (-a) = (-a) + a = 0.$$

These are identities. You should say in words what they mean. For example, "When you add 0 to a real number, or add a real number to 0, the sum is the real number with which you began." You should also look at several *instances* of each identity. For example: $5 + 0 = 0 + 5 = 5$, $(-3) + 0 = 0 + (-3) = (-3)$, $0 + 0 = 0 + 0 = 0$, $\sqrt{2} + 0 = 0 + \sqrt{2} = \sqrt{2}$, etc.

When you study property II in this manner, you see that adding a real number to its negative always gives you 0; also, $3 + (-3) = (-3) + 3 = 0$, $(-2\frac{1}{8}) + [-(-2\frac{1}{8})] = [-(-2\frac{1}{8})] + (-2\frac{1}{8}) = 0$, $0 + (-0) = (-0) + 0 = 0$, etc. Of course $[-(-2\frac{1}{8})] = 2\frac{1}{8}$, and $(-0) = 0$; hence you can write many of the instances of II more simply.

Now recall the following facts about multiplication:

III $\qquad\qquad a \cdot 0 = 0 \cdot a = 0$.

IV $\qquad\qquad a \cdot 1/a = 1/a \cdot a = 1$, provided a is not 0 ($a \neq 0$).

V $\qquad\qquad a \cdot 1 = 1 \cdot a = a$.

Again you should say these identities in words, and look at several instances of each identity. You will find that identities III and V are straightforward. But notice the exception in IV. Why must $a \neq 0$?

In Chapter 1, you learned that subtraction and division are the *inverses* of addition and multiplication. You learned that $x = a - b$ meant $b + x = a$. You learned that $x = a/b$ meant $bx = a$. We shall use these ideas to work with subtraction and division. Consider, in particular, $1/0$, or $1 \div 0$. If you find a replacement of x, such that $x = 1/0$, then $0 \cdot x = 1$. But III states that $0 \cdot a = 0$, for every value of a. Hence it is impossible to find a replacement of x from L, such that $0 \cdot x = 1$.

We say the fraction $1/a$ is not defined (and hence is meaningless) when $a = 0$. When we write the fraction $1/a$ we agree that $a \neq 0$.

Compare the argument that the symbol $1/0$ is meaningless with the one we gave in Chapter 1. In Section 106 (page 38), we argued that the symbol $1/0$ [the ordered number pair $(1,0)$] would have the property $1/0 + 2/1 = 1/0$ [$(1,0) + (2,1) = (1,0)$]; but no real number is left unchanged by the addition of 2.

There are still other ways to argue that the symbol $1/0$ is meaningless. Try to give a sensible answer to the question "How many zeros are there in 1?" That is, "How many times must I subtract 0, beginning with 1, to reduce 1 to 0?" "To how many persons must I give 0 dollars to give away a total of 1 dollar?"

You may or may not find such arguments convincing. From our point of view, division by zero is forbidden because, when you apply the definition of division as the inverse of multiplication, the result contradicts property III.

Even though subtraction and division reduce to addition and multiplication, it is convenient to explore subtractions and divisions that involve 0, or 1, or both 0 and 1. These operations come up frequently. So the following properties are worth knowing.*

For subtraction:

VI $a - 0 = a.$

VII $0 - a = (-a).$

For division:

VIII $a \div 0$ is not defined.

When $a \neq 0$, $a \div 0 = x$ requires $0 \cdot x = a \neq 0$. This contradicts III.

When $a = 0$, $0 \div 0 = x$ requires $0 \cdot x = 0$; but $0 \cdot x = 0$ is an identity (III), true for every replacement of x from the set L. Hence $0 \div 0$ may represent any real number; the division $0 \div 0$ does *not* yield a *unique* quotient.

Hence either $a \div 0$ is impossible ($a \neq 0$), or so ambiguous as to be useless ($a = 0$). In either case, $a \div 0$ is not defined; we say division by zero is forbidden.†

IX $0 \div a = 0,$ provided $a \neq 0.$

X $a \div 1 = a.$

XI $1 \div a = 1/a,$ provided $a \neq 0.$

EXERCISES §201

1. Rewrite properties I, II, III, V, VI, VII, VIII, and X with a replaced by

(a) 7   (b) -7 (c) $3/4$ (d) $2x$
(e) $a + 6$ (f) $2b - 5$ (g) r/t (h) $m^2 + n^2.$

2. Make the same replacements for a (as in Exercise 1) in IV, IX, and XI. In each case indicate values of the variable that must be excluded.

3. Is there a replacement for x such that $5/x = 0$ yields a true statement? Explain.

4. Indicate whether each of the following statements is true or false:

(a) $0 \div 4 = 0$ (b) $2 + (-2) = 0$ (c) $2 - 2 = 0$
(d) $7 \div 0 = 7$ (e) $7 \div 0 = 0$ (f) $5/5 = 0/0$
(g) $0/3 = 3.$

(h) If x is replaced by an element of L, then $x[3 + (-3)] = 0.$

(i) If x is replaced by an element of L, not 2, $(x - 2)\dfrac{1}{x - 2} = 1.$

(j) For each value of b from L, $\dfrac{0}{b + 4} = 0.$

* In the exercises of Section 202 (page 61), you will meet properties VI and VII as logical consequences of the definition of subtraction and other properties of real numbers.

† In the exercises of Section 202 (page 61), you will meet properties IX, X, and XI as logical consequences of the definition of division and of other properties of real numbers.

(k) For each value of m from L, and $n = 1$, $\dfrac{m}{n-1} = 0$.

(l) If x and a are replaced by elements of L, $3x + (2a - 2a) = 3x$.

Answers: (a) T; (d) F; (e) F; (g) F; (i) T; (j) F.

5. Since division by zero is not permitted, a division with variables in the divisor may be possible for some replacements of the variables and not possible for others. Give the range of the variables for which each of the following sentences yields a true statement:

(a) $\dfrac{2a}{a} = 2$

(b) $\dfrac{17d}{d} = 17$

(c) $\dfrac{5(x - 4)}{(x - 4)} = 5$

(d) $\dfrac{a(x - 4)}{(x - 4)} = a$

(e) $5 \div \dfrac{m}{n} = \dfrac{5n}{m}$

(f) $\dfrac{-2(y + 3)}{(y + 3)} = -2$

(g) $\dfrac{0}{a} = 0$

(h) $\dfrac{0}{x - 2} = 0$

(i) $\dfrac{0}{x - 2} = x - 2$

(j) $\dfrac{x - 2}{0} = x - 2$

(k) $\dfrac{1}{2} \div a = \dfrac{1}{2a}$

(l) $a \div \dfrac{1}{2} = 2a$

(m) $\dfrac{(x - 2)(x + 3)}{4(x - 2)(x + 3)} = \dfrac{1}{4}$

(n) $\left(\dfrac{y - 2}{y + 5}\right)\left(\dfrac{y + 5}{2y}\right) = \dfrac{y - 2}{2y}$

(o) $\dfrac{ay + 3}{y} = a + 3$

(p) $\dfrac{0 \cdot x}{0} = x$.

Answers: (a) L, excluding 0; (c) L, excluding 4; (h) L, excluding 2.

202. Basic properties of real numbers

You already know how to calculate with real numbers. When you can express real numbers as fractions, you know how to find sums, differences, products, and quotients. Even real numbers like π and $\sqrt{2}$ that you cannot express exactly as quotients of integers do not cause you much trouble. You can express these numbers *approximately* as decimals. You use 3, or 3.1, or 3.14, or 3.142, or 3.1416 for π. You choose a rational approximation for π that is accurate enough for the problem in hand. Then you perform a decimal calculation.

Now we write sentences that express the basic properties of real numbers. From one point of view, these sentences summarize what you already know about calculations with real numbers. From another point of view, these sentences express the basic *assumptions* that you make as you perform calculations with real numbers. Beginning with these assumptions, you can prove that the familiar rules for calculations with real numbers are correct. From this point of view, the assumptions *determine the structure* of the set of real numbers.

We shall use the letters a, b, c, etc., as variables whose range is the set L. We shall introduce convenient symbols to shorten our sentences and make the meaning clear. Each time we use a new symbol, we explain its meaning. Soon you will find algebraic sentences like "$(a = b) \Rightarrow (ac = bc)$" easier to understand than equivalent, wordy sentences, like "When each of two equal real numbers is multiplied by the same real number, the products are equal real numbers."

The symbol $p \Rightarrow q$ is a convenient one which we shall frequently use. You may read it in words, "If the condition p is true, then the condition q is true." Similarly, $p \Leftarrow q$ is read, "If the condition q is true, then the condition p is true. Combining these symbols, $p \Leftrightarrow q$ is read, "The condition p is true if and only if the condition q is true"; that is, "If p, then q, *and* if q, then p."

When a property has a common name, we give it this name. You will often find it convenient to refer to a property by name.

For equality of real numbers:

P 1. The sentence $a = b$ means that a and b are symbols for the same real number. For example: 2/3 and 4/6 are symbols for the same real number; when, in an investigation, you find $a = 2/3$ and $b = 4/6$, you may say $a = b$; likewise .25 and 1/4 are symbols for the same real number.; $\sqrt{9}$ and 3 are symbols for the same real number; etc.

For addition of real numbers:

P 2. *Closure for addition:* For each choice of a and b, there is a real number c such that $a + b = c$. This says that a *sum* of two real numbers is a real number.

P 3. *Uniqueness for addition:* A sum of two real numbers is unique; that is, for each pair of real numbers there is exactly one sum. The statement

$$(a = c \text{ and } b = d) \Rightarrow (a + b = c + d)$$

is a useful way to express the uniqueness of addition. For example, $1/2 + 1/3 = 3/6 + 2/6$ because $1/2 = 3/6$ and $1/3 = 2/6$. Moreover, if $x = y$ and $a \in L$, then $x + a = y + a$.

People who say, "When equal real numbers are added to equal real numbers, the sums are equal real numbers"; or, as a special case, "When the same real number is added to each of two equal real numbers, the sums are equal real numbers," mean that addition is unique.

P 4. *Commutative law of addition:* $a + b = b + a$. For example: $2 + 3 = 3 + 2$; $(-5) + \sqrt{2} = \sqrt{2} + (-5)$; etc.

P 5. *Associative law of addition:* $(a + b) + c = a + (b + c)$. For example: $(2 + 3) + 4 = 2 + (3 + 4)$, that is, $5 + 4 = 2 + 7$; $[(-\sqrt{2}) + 3] + 5 = (-\sqrt{2}) + (3 + 5)$, that is, $[(-\sqrt{2}) + 3] + 5 = (-\sqrt{2}) + 8$; etc.

P 6. There is a unique real number (which we shall call 0), such that $a + 0 = a$ for each real number, a. Notice that P 6 is a restatement of property I of Section 201 (page 51). We know that $a + 0 = 0 + a$ by replacing b by 0 in P 4. We shall call 0 the *identity for addition*.

P 7. For each real number a there is one and only one corresponding real number [which we shall call $(-a)$] such that

$$a + (-a) = 0.$$

Notice that P 7 is a restatement of property II of Section 201 (page 51). We know that $a + (-a) = (-a) + a$ by replacing b by $(-a)$ in P 4. We shall call $(-a)$ the *inverse of a for addition*.

For multiplication of real numbers:

P 8. *Closure for multiplication:* For each choice of a and b, there is a real number c such that

$$ab = c.$$

This says that a *product* of two real numbers is a real number.

P 9. *Uniqueness for multiplication:* A product of two real numbers is unique; that is, for each pair of real numbers there is exactly one product. The statement

$$(a = c \text{ and } b = d) \Rightarrow (ab = cd)$$

is a useful way to express the uniqueness of multiplication. For example, $5 \cdot 3/5 = 5/1 \cdot 3/5$ because $5 = 5/1$. Moreover, if $x = y$ and $a \in L$, then $xa = ya$.

P 10. *Commutative law of multiplication: $ab = ba$*. For example: $5 \cdot 7 = 7 \cdot 5$; $2 \cdot \sqrt{3} = \sqrt{3} \cdot 2$, etc.

P 11. *Associative law of multiplication: $(ab)c = a(bc)$*. For example: $(2 \cdot 4) \cdot 9 = 2 \cdot (4 \cdot 9)$, [that is, $8 \cdot 9 = 2 \cdot 36$]; $(\sqrt{7} \cdot 5) \cdot 2 = \sqrt{7} \cdot (5 \cdot 2)$, [that is, $(\sqrt{7} \cdot 5) \cdot 2 = \sqrt{7} \cdot 10$]; etc.

P 12. There is a unique real number (which we shall call 1), such that $a \cdot 1 = a$ for each real number, a. Notice that P 12 is a restatement of property V of Section 201 (page 52). We know that $a \cdot 1 = 1 \cdot a$ by replacing b by 1 in P 10. We shall call 1 the *identity for multiplication*.

P 13. For each real number a, $a \neq 0$, there is one and only one corresponding real number (which we shall call $1/a$) such that

$$a \cdot 1/a = 1.$$

Notice that P 13 is a restatement of property IV of Section 201 (page 52). We know that $a \cdot 1/a = 1/a \cdot a$ by replacing b by $1/a$ in P 10. We shall call $1/a$ the *inverse of a for multiplication*. But notice that 0 *has no* inverse for multiplication.

For working with algebraic expressions that involve both addition and multiplication of real numbers:

P 14. *Distributive law for multiplication over addition:*

$$a(b + c) = ab + ac.$$

For example: $2(3 + 5) = 2 \cdot 8 = 16,$
and $2(3 + 5) = 2 \cdot 3 + 2 \cdot 5 = 6 + 10 = 16;$
                        $3(x + 2) = 3x + 6;$
                        $\sqrt{2}(1 + y) = \sqrt{2} \cdot 1 + \sqrt{2} \cdot y = \sqrt{2} + \sqrt{2}y$

We shall call the operation of replacing $a(b + c)$ by $ab + ac$ *expanding the expression* $a(b + c)$.

Used in reverse, **P 14** enables you to *factor* certain expressions. Thus **P 14** states that $ab + ac = a(b + c)$.

For example: $2x + 2y = 2(x + y);$
                              $3y + 2y = y \cdot 3 + y \cdot 2$ (P 10)
                                      $= y(3 + 2)$ (P 14)
                                      $= 5y;$ (P 10)
                        $p + .25p = p(1) + p(.25)$ (P 10 and P 12)
                                      $= p(1 + .25)$ (P 14)
                                      $= 1.25p.$ (P 10)

We use **P 14** to illustrate how the rules for calculations with real numbers can be proved from the basic properties of real numbers. The question of calling the product of two negative numbers positive bothers a great many people. Suppose you want to show that $(-3)(-5) = (+15)$:

Consider $(-3)[5 + (-5)] = (-3)(0)$ (P 7)
                                  $= 0.$ (III, page 52)
Also, $(-3)[5 + (-5)] = (-3) \cdot 5 + (-3)(-5)$ (P 14)
                                  $= -15 + (-3)(-5).$

$[(-3) \cdot 5 = -15$ is a fact that many people find reasonable; you can prove it from the basic identities (see Exercise 16).]

Hence $-15 + (-3)(-5) = 0$ (P 1)
and $15 + [-15 + (-3)(-5)] = 15 + 0$ (P 3)
                 $[15 + (-15)] + (-3)(-5) = 15$ (P 5 and P 6)
                              $(-3)(-5) = (+15).$ (P 7 and P 6)

Notice, then, that **P 14** becomes an important link between the operations of addition and multiplication in the set L.

For subtraction of real numbers:

P 15. $a - b = a + (-b).$

For division of real numbers:

P 16. $b \neq 0 \Rightarrow a \div b = a/b = a \cdot (1/b).$ Notice, again, that division by 0 is not defined.

We pause now, in our listing of the basic properties of real numbers, to let you use the properties of real numbers that you have met thus far.

EXERCISES §202

1. Rewrite the commutative properties, P 4 and P 10, with a and b replaced by

(a) 5, 7   (b) 4, -3
(c) $-\frac{1}{4}$, -2 (d) 3, x
(e) r, t (f) $y + 3, c$
(g) $(r + u), (2m + t)$.

2. Rewrite the associative properties, P 5 and P 11, with a, b, and c replaced by

(a) 2, 3, -4 (b) $\dfrac{1}{3}, \dfrac{-2}{3}, \dfrac{9}{4}$

(c) $x, 3, -2$ (d) $(r + 4), 3, w$

(e) $(2y - 1), b, 4$ (f) $4, -5, (x + u)$.

3. The additive inverse of a, in P 7, can always be found by multiplying (-1) and a. For example, if $a = -3$, then $-a = -(-3) = (-1) \cdot (-3) = 3$. You are probably familiar with

P 17: $-a = (-1)a;$

you can prove it from the distributive law and the fact that (-1) is the additive inverse of 1. Using the following outline, write out a formal proof. Give a reason for each step.
    To prove $-a = (-1)a$, let $x = (-1)a$. Then

	Statement	*Reason(s)*
(1)	$a + x = a + (-1)a$	
(2)	$\quad\;\; = a \cdot 1 + a(-1)$	
(3)	$\quad\;\; = a[1 + (-1)]$	
(4)	$\quad\;\; = a \cdot 0 = 0$	

Since $a + x = 0$, x is the additive inverse of a by property (?). Hence $(-1)a = -a$.

4. Determine the inverse of a for addition and the inverse of a for multiplication for each of the following replacements of a:

(a) 2   (b) -5 (c) $-\frac{1}{4}$

(d) $x + 2$ (e) $-y$ (f) $v - 3$

(g) $x - y$ (h) $\dfrac{1}{4 - t}$ (i) $\dfrac{r}{s}$

(j) $\dfrac{3}{m - 2}$ (k) $\dfrac{x - 1}{x + 1}$ (l) $2 - \dfrac{1}{x}$.

Answers: (c) $1/4$, -4; (f) $3 - v$, $\dfrac{1}{(v - 3)}$; (i) $-r/s$, s/r.

5. Rewrite the distributive property, P 14, with a, b, and c replaced by

(a) 4, -3, 5 (b) $-\frac{1}{2}$, 7, -3

(c) m, -6, 2 (d) 3, x, 5

(e) x, y, 2 (f) r, r, 5

(g) a, x, 2 (h) $(m + 4)$, x, 2

(i) $(r - 2)$, t, 3 (j) $(z - y)$, x, u

(k) $(a + b)$, c, d (l) $(a + b)$, a, b

(m) $(a - b)$, a, b (n) a, $(b + c)$, d.

6. Replacements for a, b, and c in the distributive law, $a(b + c) = ab + ac$, are the basis for factoring sums and expanding products. However, it is often convenient to use further identities that are proved from the properties given above. Fill in the reasons for each step in the proof of

P 18: $$(a + b)c = ac + bc.$$

Statement	*Reason(s)*
(1) $(a + b)c = c(a + b)$	
(2) $c(a + b) = ca + cb$	
(3) $(a + b)c = ca + cb$	
(4) $ca = ac$ and $cb = bc$	
(5) $ca + cb = ac + bc$	
(6) $(a + b)c = ac + bc$	

7. Do as in Exercise 6 for the proof of

P 19: $$a(b - c) = ab - ac.$$

Statement	*Reason(s)*
(1) $a(b - c) = a[b + (-c)]$	
(2) $\quad\quad\quad = ab + a(-c)$	
(3) $\quad\quad\quad = ab + a[(-1)c]$	
(4) $\quad\quad\quad = ab + (-1)(ac)$	
(5) $\quad\quad\quad = ab - ac$	

8. Complete the following proof that

P 20: $$(a + b)(c + d) = ac + bc + ad + bd$$

$$(1) \quad (a + b)(c + d) = (a + b)c + (a + b)d$$

$$\text{etc.}$$

9. Other identities that are useful in changing the form of an algebraic expression are listed below. Outline a brief proof of each.

P 21: $(a + b)^2 = a^2 + 2ab + b^2$.

P 22: $(a - b)^2 = a^2 - 2ab + b^2$.

P 23: $(a + b)(a - b) = a^2 - b^2$.

P 24: $a(b + c + d) = ab + ac + ad$.

P 25: $-(a + b + c) = (-a) + (-b) + (-c)$.

[*Suggestions:* For P 21 use P 20 with c and d replaced by a and b. For P 22, try P 21 with b replaced by $-b$.]

10. Rewrite P 18 through P 25 with a, b, c, and d replaced by

(a) 3, 2, 5, 7   (b) 5, -3, -2, 4
(c) 2, 6, x, $-y$ (d) x, 2, x, 3
(e) y, 5, $(y - 2)$, 4   (f) $2x$, 1, $3x$, -2
(g) $\frac{1}{2}x$, 6, $4x$, 3   (h) $(a + b)$, c, 0, 5
(i) $2x$, $2x$, c, 4   (j) $(x - y)$, 2, $(x - y)$, 4.

11. Use the distributive law, or an identity that you can prove from it, to expand the following expressions; tell the identities you use in each case:

(a) $r(x + 2)$ (b) $(s + t)x$

(c) $3(x - 4)$ (d) $-2(y - 5)$

(e) $4a(x + y + z)$ (f) $-(a - 3)$

(g) $-2[4 - (2 - x)]$ (h) $(u - 3)(u + 3)$

(i) $(t - 3)(t - 2)$ (j) $(2x + 3)^2$

(k) $(4u - t)^2$ (l) $\frac{1}{3}(6r + 9)$

(m) $\dfrac{1}{m}(m^2 - mn)$ (n) $\left(\dfrac{3}{x} - 1\right)\left(\dfrac{3}{x} + 1\right)$

(o) $\left(2y + \dfrac{1}{y}\right)^2$ (p) $a(x - y) - y(x - a)$

(q) $2(x - 2) - 3(x + 1) + 4(x + 2)$ (r) $(4 + bx)(bx - 4)$
(s) $(2ay + 3)(ay - 1)$ (t) $(-x - y)(x - y)$.

Answers: (a) $rx + 2r$;   (d) $-2y + 10$;   (g) $-8 + 4 - 2x$;   (h) $u^2 - 9$;
(l) $2r + 3$;   (o) $4y^2 + 4 + 1/y^2$;   (p) $ax - yx$.

12. Use the distributive law, or an identity that you can prove from it, to factor the following expressions; tell the identities you use in each case.

(a) $3a + 6b$ (b) $16x - 2y$
(c) $10ax + 6ay - 8ak$ (d) $x^2 - a^2$

(e) $4x^2 + 4x + 1$ (f) $\dfrac{a^2 x^2}{4} - \dfrac{a^2 y^2}{9}$

(g) $b(y - a) + c(y - a)$ (h) $9h^2 - 12hk + 4k^2$
(i) $y^2 + 3y + 2$ (j) $x^2 + x - 12$
(k) $2r^2 - rt - 3t^2$ (l) $sb + 3b - 2s - 6$
(m) $2a(a - b) + 3(a - b)^2$ (n) $(a^2 - b^2) - (a - b)^2$
(o) $(a - b)^2 - (a + b)^2$ (p) $(r - t)^2 + 2(r - t)(x + y) + (x + y)^2$

(q) $5y^2 - 5x^2$ (r) $\dfrac{3x}{g} + \dfrac{3y}{g}$

(s) $\dfrac{2a}{x^2} + \dfrac{2a}{xy}$ (t) $x^2 + \dfrac{2x}{y} + \dfrac{1}{y^2}$.

Answers: (a) $3(a + 2b)$;   (c) $2a(5x + 3y - 4k)$;   (f) $a^2\left(\dfrac{x}{2} + \dfrac{y}{3}\right)\left(\dfrac{x}{2} - \dfrac{y}{3}\right)$;
(g) $(y - a)(b + c)$;   (j) $(x + 4)(x - 3)$;   (k) $(2r - 3t)(r + t)$;   (l) $(b - 2)(s + 3)$;
(n) $2b(a - b)$;   (p) $(r - t + x + y)^2$.

13. Prove property VI of Section 201 (page 53). Suggested outline:

To prove
$$a - 0 = a,$$

Statement	Reason(s)
(1) Suppose $a - 0 = x$	Definition of the symbol x
(2) $0 + x = a$	Definition of subtraction
(3) $x = a$	P 6
(4) $a - 0 = a$	P 1

14. Prove property VII of Section 201 (page 53). Suggested outline:

To prove
$$0 - a = (-a),$$

Statement	Reason(s)
(1) Suppose $0 - a = x$	
(2) $a + x = 0$	
(3) $x = (-a)$	

15. Prove properties IX, X, and XI of Section 201 (page 53). Suggested outline for proof of IX:

To prove
$$a \neq 0 \Rightarrow 0 \div a = 0,$$

Statement	Reason(s)
(1) $a \neq 0$	Given
(2) Suppose $0 \div a = x$	Definition of the symbol x
(3) $ax = 0$	Definition of division
(4) $1/a \cdot (ax) = 1/a \cdot (0)$	There is a real number $1/a$ (P 13) and a product is unique (P 9)
(5) $(1/a \cdot a) \cdot x = 0$	etc.
(6) $x = 0$	
(7) $0 \div a = 0$	

16. Use the distributive law and other properties of real numbers to prove each of the following "facts of calculation with integers."

(a) $(5)(-3) = -15$.

Proof: Consider

$$5[3 + (-3)] = 5[0] = 0 \qquad \text{(P 7 and III, page 52)}$$
$$5[3 + (-3)] = (5)(3) + 5(-3) \qquad \text{(P 14)}$$
$$= 15 + 5(-3).$$

Hence
$$0 = 15 + 5(-3);$$
and
$$5(-3) = -15. \qquad \text{(P 7)}$$

(b) $(-3)(5) = -15$.

(c) $(-5)(-3) = 15$.

(d) $(7)(21) = 147$.

Proof:

$$7(21) = 7(2 \cdot 10 + 1) \qquad (21 \text{ means } 2 \cdot 10 + 1)$$
$$= 7(2 \cdot 10) + 7(1) \qquad \text{(P 14)}$$
$$= 14 \cdot 10 + 7$$
$$= 147.$$

Notice what you accomplish in parts (a) through (d). In effect, you reduce calculations with integers to calculations with natural numbers; and you reduce calculations with natural numbers to calculations with numbers from the set $\{0, 1, 2, ..., 9\}$.

With these ideas in mind, prove each of the following facts of calculation with integers:

  (e) $5(146) = 730$.
  (f) $(22)(35) = 770$.
  (g) $(-7)(15) = -105$.

We conclude this section on basic properties of real numbers with five *order assumptions* for real numbers. These assumptions enable us to deal with the connective phrases greater than ($>$), less than ($<$) and equal to ($=$), which we use to place the real numbers "in order" on the line of numbers. They fix the *order structure* of the real numbers, and tie together this order structure with the *algebraic structure* of the real numbers that is fixed by the previously assumed properties.

For ordering of real numbers:

P 26. For each replacement of *a* and *b*, one and only one of the following sentences becomes a true statement:

$$a < b, \qquad a = b, \qquad a > b.$$

In words, either *a* is less than *b*, or *a* equals *b*, or *a* is greater than *b*. On the line of numbers, either *a* lies to the left of *b* ($a < b$), or *a* coincides with *b* ($a = b$), or *a* lies to the right of *b* ($a > b$).

P 27. $\hspace{3cm} (a < b \text{ and } b < c) \Rightarrow (a < c)$.

On the line of numbers, if *a* is to the left of *b*, and *b* is to the left of *c*, then *a* is to the left of *c*.

P 28. $\hspace{3cm} (a < b) \Rightarrow (a + c < b + c)$.

For example: $\hspace{1.5cm} (3 < 7) \Rightarrow [(3 + 5) < (7 + 5)];$

$$(-6 < -4) \Rightarrow [(-6) + (-3) < (-4) + (-3)],$$

that is, $\hspace{3cm} -9 < -7.$

On the line of numbers, when *a* lies to the left of *b* and you move the same distance *c* (to the right or to the left, depending upon the sign of *c*) from each point, $a + c$ lies to the left of $b + c$. Of course $c = 0$ is a possibility. Then you move 0 units to the right, or to the left. It does not really matter in which direction you choose to move 0 units.

P 29. $\hspace{2cm} (a < b \text{ and } c > 0) \Rightarrow (ac < bc)$.

Notice the restriction, $c > 0$, here. When $c < 0$, you use

P 30. $\hspace{2cm} (a < b \text{ and } c < 0) \Rightarrow (ac > bc)$.

For example: $\hspace{0.5cm} [3 < 5 \text{ and } -1 < 0] \Rightarrow [3(-1) > 5(-1)],$

that is, $\hspace{4cm} -3 > -5.$

For your convenience, we summarize the basic properties of real numbers.

Notice that we have grouped the properties as properties of order (O), properties of addition (A), properties of multiplication (M), and properties for combining addition and multiplication (D). We have relabeled the properties for convenient future reference.

PROPERTIES OF ORDER

O 1: $a = b$ means that a and b are symbols for the same real number.

O 2: For each replacement of a and b, one and only one of the following sentences becomes a true statement:

$$a < b, \qquad a = b, \qquad a > b.$$

O 3: $(a < b \text{ and } b < c) \Rightarrow (a < c)$.

PROPERTIES OF ADDITION	PROPERTIES OF MULTIPLICATION

Closure

A 1: For each a and b, there is a real number c, such that $a + b = c$.

M 1: For each a and b, there is a real number c, such that $ab = c$.

Uniqueness

A 2: $(a = c \text{ and } b = d) \Rightarrow$ $(a + b = c + d)$.

M 2: $(a = c \text{ and } b = d) \Rightarrow (ab = cd)$.

Commutative

A 3: $a + b = b + a$.

M 3: $ab = ba$.

Associative

A 4: $(a + b) + c = a + (b + c)$.

M 4: $(ab)c = a(bc)$.

Identity

A 5: There is a unique identity for addition, that we call 0, such that $a + 0 = a$ for every real number a.

M 5: There is a unique identity for multiplication, that we call 1, such that $a \cdot 1 = a$ for every real number a.

Inverse Element

A 6: For each real number a, there is a unique inverse for addition, that we call $(-a)$, such that $a + (-a) = 0$.

M 6: For each real number a, $a \neq 0$, there is a unique inverse for multiplication, that we call $1/a$, such that $a \cdot 1/a = 1$.

Inverse Operation

A 7: $a - b = a + (-b)$.

M 7: $b \neq 0 \Rightarrow a \div b = a/b = a \cdot (1/b)$.

Order

A 8: $(a < b) \Rightarrow (a + c < b + c)$.

M 8: $(a < b \text{ and } c > 0) \Rightarrow (ac < bc)$
$(a < b \text{ and } c < 0) \Rightarrow (ac > bc)$.

Properties for Combining Addition and Multiplication

D 1 : $a(b + c) = ab + ac$.
D 2 : $-a = (-1)a$.
D 3 : $(a + b)c = ac + bc$.
D 4 : $a(b - c) = ab - ac$.
D 5 : $(a + b)(c + d) = ac + bc + ad + bd$.
D 6 : $(a + b)^2 = a^2 + 2ab + b^2$.
D 7 : $(a - b)^2 = a^2 - 2ab + b^2$.
D 8 : $(a + b)(a - b) = a^2 - b^2$.
D 9 : $a(b + c + d) = ab + ac + ad$.
D 10 : $-(a + b + c) = (-a) + (-b) + (-c)$.

From one point of view, this list of properties of real numbers is too long. Recall that D 2 through D 10 can be proved from the preceding identities. Mathematicians like to shorten the list of properties and eliminate some of them by proving them from the remaining ones. See Exercise 21 for the proofs of A 7 and M 7.

From another point of view, this list of properties of real numbers is too short. There are other convenient identities that can be proved from the ones we have listed. See your book of mathematical tables for other identities; for example,

$$(a + b)^3 = a^3 + 3a^2b + 3ab^2 + b^3.$$

EXERCISES §202 (cont.)

17. Insert the appropriate symbol ($<$, $=$, or $>$) between each pair of real numbers:

(a) -4, -6 (b) $\sqrt{3}$, $\sqrt{2}$ (c) $5\sqrt{2}$, $3\sqrt{3}$
(d) 0, 4 (e) 0, -4 (f) -100, -1.

18. Replace the a, b, and c of O 3 by the given numbers or variables. Choose the replacements to make $a < b$ and $b < c$:

(a) -5, -2, 3 (b) 2, 3, -4
(c) -3, 1, 4 (d) -5, -4, -2
(e) x, 2, 3 (f) x, y, -1
(g) $(2x + 3)$, 7, -3 (h) $4x$, 8, $\frac{1}{2}$.

19. Repeat Exercise 18 for A 8 and M 8. Choose appropriate replacements for a, b, and c.

20. Notice how A 6 enables you to prove the *converse* of A 8. Thus

A 8: $(a < b) \Rightarrow (a + c < b + c)$

has as its converse

$$(a + c < b + c) \Rightarrow (a < b).$$

You obtain the converse of an if-then statement by interchanging the *hypothesis* and the *conclusion*.

To prove $(a + c < b + c) \Rightarrow (a < b)$,

Statement	Reason(s)
$a + c < b + c$	Given
$(a + c) + (-c) < (b + c) + (-c)$	
$a + [c + (-c)] < b + [c + (-c)]$	
$a < b$	

Recall the convenient way to express a theorem and its converse in a single statement. We write

$$(a < b) \Leftrightarrow (a + c < b + c).$$

In words, $a < b$ *if and only if* $a + c < b + c$.

21. (a) Prove A 7. To prove $a - b = a + (-b)$,

Statement	Reason(s)
Suppose $a - b = x$	Definition of symbol x
$b + x = a$	Definition of subtraction
$(-b) + [b + x] = (-b) + a$	
$[(-b) + b] + x = a + (-b)$	
$x = a + (-b)$	
Hence $a - b = a + (-b)$	

(b) Prove M 7.

22. Expand the following expressions:

(a) $-3(x + 2y - z)$
(b) $(x + y)^3$ [means $(x + y) \cdot (x + y) \cdot (x + y)$]
(c) $(x - y)^3$
(d) $(x - y)(x^2 + xy + y^2)$
(e) $(3x^2 - 1)^2$.

Answers: (b) $x^3 + 3x^2y + 3xy^2 + y^3$; (d) $x^3 - y^3$.

23. Factor the following expressions:

(a) $-2x + 3x^3$
(b) $x^3 - y^3$
(c) $a^2 - (b - a)^2$
(d) $6rs - 2s^2 + 8r^2s$
(e) $4/x^2 - 9/y^2$.

Answers: (a) $x(3x^2 - 2)$; (c) $b(2a - b)$; (d) $2s(3r - s + 4r^2)$.

203. Conditions that define subsets of the real numbers

Now we take a further look at conditions that define subsets of L, and at ways of representing these conditions geometrically.

The line of numbers will help you to visualize subsets of L. As examples, study the following conditions and their graphs:

(1) $$x + 2 = 7.$$

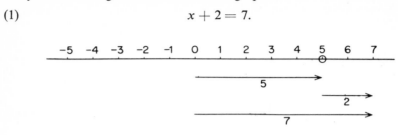

Fig. 2–3.

The graph of condition (1) is the circled point. Clearly, condition (1) defines a subset, $\{5\}$, with just one element (Fig. 2–3).

(2) $$x \geq 1.$$

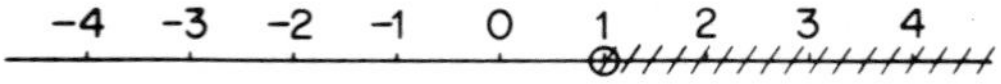

Fig. 2–4.

The graph of condition (2) is the point 1 and all of the points to the right of 1 on the line of numbers. Notice that condition (2) defines a subset with infinitely many elements (Fig. 2–4).

(3) $$x^2 = 16.$$

The graph of condition (3) is the two circled points. Clearly, condition (3) defines a subset, $\{-4, 4\}$, with just two elements (Fig. 2–5).

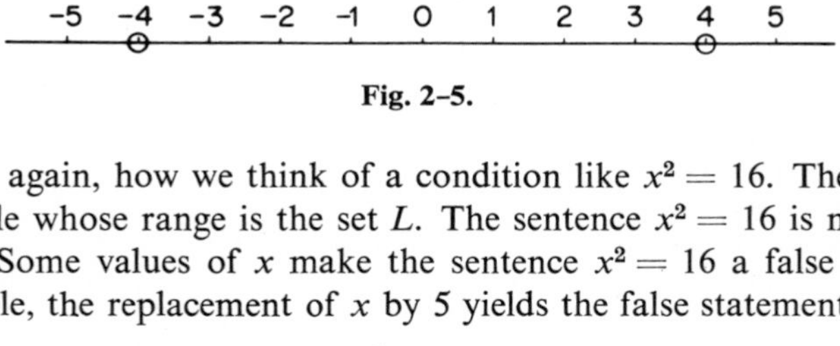

Fig. 2–5.

Notice, again, how we think of a condition like $x^2 = 16$. The symbol x is a variable whose range is the set L. The sentence $x^2 = 16$ is neither true nor false. Some values of x make the sentence $x^2 = 16$ a false statement. For example, the replacement of x by 5 yields the false statement

$$5^2 = 16.$$

Some values of x make the sentence $x^2 = 16$ a true statement. For example, the replacement of x by 4 yields the true statement

$$4^2 = 16;$$

also the replacement of x by -4 yields the true statement

$$(-4)^2 = 16.$$

Hence the condition $x^2 = 16$ defines a subset of L, namely, the set of elements from L that can be used as replacements for x to make the sentence $x^2 = 16$ a true statement. It turns out that this subset contains just two elements, namely, 4 and -4. It is the set $\{-4, 4\}$.

The problem of finding the subset of L that a condition defines is one of the central problems of algebra. The condition $x + 2 = 7$ is comparatively simple. As you examine this condition, and use the line of numbers to help you visualize what it means, you conclude that 5 is the only value of x that makes the sentence, $x + 2 = 7$ a true statement. Other conditions, like $x^3 - 3x = 15$, are much harder to analyze. We shall study the question of "solving equations" (that is, of finding the subset of a given set of numbers that an equation defines) in later chapters. We shall also study *inequalities*: $2x - 3 < 5$, $x^2 + 2x - 1 \geq 0$, and the like.

It will be convenient to have a brief way to express this problem of finding the subset of a given set that a condition defines. We shall write

$$\{x \mid x + 2 = 7\}$$

to mean the set of all replacements of x such that $x + 2 = 7$. Similarly,

$$\{x \mid x \geq 1\}$$

means the set of all replacements of x such that $x \geq 1$, and

$$\{x \mid x^2 = 16\}$$

means the set of all replacements of x such that $x^2 = 16$. In each of these expressions, the range of the variable x must be stated or understood from the context. Unless we specify another range for the variable x, you may take the range of x as the set L.

We have said that $\{x \mid x + 2 = 7\} = \{5\}$, $\{x \mid x \geq 1\} = \{$real numbers greater than or equal to 1$\}$, and $\{x \mid x^2 = 16\} = \{-4, 4\}$. Each of these sets is a subset of L; each is called the *solution set* of the given condition.

The following exercises give you a chance to read, write, and talk this new language of conditions.

EXERCISES §203

1. Use the line of numbers to represent graphically the subset of L determined by each of the following conditions. That is, graph the solution set of each condition:

(a) $x + 4 = 6$	(b) $x + 6 = 3$	(c) $x < 7$
(d) $x < -5$	(e) $x + 4 < 6$	(f) $2x = 5$
(g) $2x < 5$	(h) $x^2 = 9$	(i) $x^2 = 3$
(j) $(x - 2)(x - 5) = 0$	(k) $x^2 \leq 9$	(l) $x^2 > 3$
(m) $2x^2 - 10 < 0$	(n) $x^2 \geq 16$	(o) $x^2 < 16$.

2. In each part of this exercise you are given the range of the variable and a symbol for the solution set of a condition. List the members of this solution set if possible; if the solution set has too many elements to list, describe the set in words or use a graph.

(a) N; $\{x \mid x - 3 = 5\} =$

The only replacement from the set N that satisfies the condition $x - 3 = 5$ is 8.

Hence $\{x \mid x - 3 = 5\} = \{8\}$.

(b) R; $\{x \mid 5x = -12\} =$ *Ans.* $\{-12/5\}$

(c) I; $\{x \mid x^2 = 49\} =$ *Ans.* $\{-7, 7\}$

(d) N; $\{x \mid x^2 = 49\} =$ *Ans.* $\{7\}$.

(e) L; $\{x \mid x^2 = 17\} =$

(f) N; $\{x \mid x > -5\} =$

Ans. $\{1, 2, 3, ...\} = N$. The condition $x > -5$ is an identity in N.

(g) R; $\{x \mid x > -5\} =$

Ans. {all rational numbers greater than -5}. This set *does not* include every point on the line of numbers to the right of the point -5. It includes only the points that correspond to rational numbers to the right of the point -5.

(h) L; $\{x \mid x > -5\} =$ (Describe in words and show the graph.)

(i) L; $\{x \mid x + 5 > -3\} =$

(j) L; $\{x \mid x - 5 > -3\} =$

(k) N; $\{x \mid x < 0\} =$ *Ans.* { }. This is the null set.

(l) R; $\{x \mid x^2 = 3\} =$

(m) N; $\{x \mid x + 5 < 2\} =$

(n) N; $\{x \mid x^2 < 10\} =$ *Ans.* $\{1, 2, 3\}$.

204. Equivalent conditions for real numbers

Consider now the question of finding the solution set of the condition $x + 2 = 7$; that is, how can you find the elements of $\{x \mid x + 2 = 7\}$? Of course you already know that the solution set is $\{5\}$. But how can you reach this conclusion mathematically, using the properties of real numbers? It is worth your while to examine this question carefully. We shall use similar methods to find the solution sets of more difficult conditions in later chapters.

To prove: $\{x \mid x + 2 = 7\} = \{x \mid x = 5\}$.

First we prove: $x + 2 = 7 \Rightarrow x = 5$.

Statement	*Reason(s)*
$x + 2 = 7$	Given
$-2 = -2$	O 1
$(x + 2) + (-2) = 7 + (-2)$	A 2
$x + [2 + (-2)] = 5$	A 4
$x + 0 = 5$	A 6
$x = 5$	A 5

Second we prove: $x = 5 \Rightarrow x + 2 = 7$

Statement	*Reason(s)*
$x = 5$	Given
$2 = 2$	O 1
$x + 2 = 7$	A 2

We conclude: $x + 2 = 7 \Leftrightarrow x = 5.$

In words, $x + 2 = 7$ *if and only if* $x = 5$; hence

$$\{x \mid x + 2 = 7\} = \{x \mid x = 5\}.$$

That is, the conditions $x + 2 = 7$ and $x = 5$ have the same solution set. We shall call two conditions that have the same solution set *equivalent* conditions. Hence we say the conditions $x + 2 = 7$ and $x = 5$ are equivalent.

The condition $x = 5$ is especially convenient. Its solution set is obviously $\{5\}$. Thus the question of finding the solution set of a condition (like $x + 2 = 7$) reduces to the question of finding an equivalent condition whose solution set is known.

As a second example, we take $\{x \mid x + 2 < 7\}$. First we prove:

$$x + 2 < 7 \Rightarrow x < 5.$$

$x + 2 < 7$	(given)
$(x + 2) + (-2) < 7 + (-2)$	(A 8)
$x < 5$	(A 4, A 6, A 5)

Second we prove: $x < 5 \Rightarrow x + 2 < 7.$

$x < 5$	(given)
$x + 2 < 7$	(A 8)

We conclude: $x + 2 < 7 \Leftrightarrow x < 5;$

and hence $\{x \mid x + 2 < 7\} = \{x \mid x < 5\};$

the conditions $x + 2 < 7$ and $x < 5$ are equivalent.

The condition $x < 5$ is convenient because its solution set is obvious; it is the subset of L whose elements lie to the left of the point 5 on the line of numbers. The statement $\{x \mid x + 2 < 7\} = \{x \mid x < 5\}$ clearly describes the set $\{x \mid x + 2 < 7\}$; you could also describe it as follows:

$\{$elements of L that are less than 5$\}$; or (Fig. 2–6).

Fig. 2–6.

A further property of real numbers is often convenient as you seek the solution set of a given condition. We prove this property as a *theorem* about real numbers:

T 1: $ab = 0 \Leftrightarrow (a = 0 \text{ or } b = 0)$.

First we prove: $(a = 0 \text{ or } b = 0) \Rightarrow ab = 0$.

$(a = 0 \text{ or } b = 0)$ means a is 0, b is 0, or both a and b are 0. If at least one of the factors, a or b, is zero, then $ab = 0$ (III, page 52).

Next we prove: $ab = 0 \Rightarrow (a = 0 \text{ or } b = 0)$.

$ab = 0$ (given). Either $a = 0$ or $a \neq 0$. If $a = 0$, the theorem holds. If $a \neq 0$, then there is a real number $1/a$ (by M 6), and

$$ab = 0 \qquad \text{(given)}$$

$$\frac{1}{a} \cdot (ab) = \frac{1}{a} \cdot 0 \qquad \text{M 2}$$

$$\left(\frac{1}{a} a\right) \cdot b = 0 \qquad \text{M 4 and III, page 52.}$$

$$b = 0 \qquad \text{M 6 and M 5}$$

Thus if the first factor is not zero, the second is zero. Hence

$$ab = 0 \Rightarrow (a = 0 \text{ or } b = 0).$$

We apply T 1 to find the solution set of the condition $x^2 = 16$, namely $\{x \mid x^2 = 16\}$:

$x^2 = 16$ (given)
$x^2 + (-16) = 16 + (-16)$ A 6 and A 2
$x^2 - 16 = 0$ A 7 and A 6
$(x + 4)(x - 4) = 0$ D 8
$x + 4 = 0 \text{ or } x - 4 = 0$ T 1
$x = -4 \text{ or } x = 4$ $\{x \mid x + 4 = 0\} = \{x \mid x = -4\}$
                                        and $\{x \mid x - 4 = 0\} = \{x \mid x = 4\}$

Since the above steps are clearly reversible, $\{x \mid x^2 = 16\} = \{x \mid x = -4 \text{ or } x = 4\} = \{-4, 4\}$.

Notice, in the statement and proof of T 1, the use of the words "and" and "or." These are important words in mathematical, as in everyday, discourse. We agree to use them as follows:

To assert "*A* and *B*" is to assert *both A* and *B*. For example, "$x > 0$ and $x < 3$" means x is greater than zero and x is less than 3; that is, x lies *between* 0 and 3 on the line of numbers.

To assert "*A* or *B*" is to assert either *A*, or *B*, or both *A* and *B*. For example, "$x > 0$ or $x < 3$" means x may be greater than zero, or may be less than 3, or may be both greater than zero and less than 3. Every real number has at least one of these properties. Hence the sentence "$x > 0$ or $x < 3$" is an identity in L. As a further example, "$x > 0$ or $x < -3$" restricts replacements of x to real numbers that are positive, or less than -3, or both positive and less than -3; that is, it excludes values of x from -3 to 0 inclusive.

The following exercises provide further opportunities to explore equivalent conditions for real numbers.

EXERCISES §204

1. Rewrite T 1 with a and b replaced by

(a) $2, x$ (b) $-4, y$
(c) $x - 1, x - 4$ (d) $x + 2, x - 3$
(e) $y + 5, y - 1$ (f) $x - r, x - t$.

2. By factoring, and applying T 1, show that

$$\{x \mid x^2 - 5x + 6 = 0\} = \{x \mid x = 2 \text{ or } x = 3\} = \{2, 3\}.$$

3. Repeat Exercise 2 to show that the condition

(a) $x^2 - 25 = 0$ is equivalent to $(x - 5 = 0 \text{ or } x + 5 = 0)$
(b) $x^2 - 7x + 12 = 0$ is equivalent to $(x - 4 = 0 \text{ or } x - 3 = 0)$
(c) $x^2 + x - 12 = 0$ is equivalent to $(x + 4 = 0 \text{ or } x - 3 = 0)$.

4. Prove that:

(a) $3x < 9 \Leftrightarrow x < 3$ (you must prove $3x < 9 \Rightarrow x < 3$ *and* $x < 3 \Rightarrow 3x < 9$)
(b) $2x + 3 < 7 \Leftrightarrow x < 2$
(c) $(-2x + 1 < 5) \Leftrightarrow (-2 < x)$
(d) $(4 - 2y < 2y) \Leftrightarrow (1 < y)$
(e) $(2y + 10 < 2) \Leftrightarrow (y < -4)$
(f) $(x + 4 < 3 - x) \Leftrightarrow (x < -\frac{1}{2})$.

5. Restate each part of Exercise 4 in the language of solution sets. For example, in part (c),

$$\{x \mid -2x + 1 < 5\} = \{x \mid -2 < x\} = \{\text{elements of } L \text{ to the right of the}$$
$$\text{point } -2 \text{ on the line of numbers}\}$$

6. For each of the following conditions, use the properties of the structure of the real number system to write an equivalent condition in simpler form; then draw the graph of the condition on the line of numbers.

(a) $x + 5 = 9$ (b) $x + 5 < 9$
(c) $x - 3 = 4$ (d) $x - 3 < 4$
(e) $3x + 4 = 9$ (f) $3x + 4 < 9$
(g) $2x - 7 = 1$ (h) $6 - 2x = 8$
(i) $1 - 3x < 7$ (j) $\frac{1}{2}x + \frac{1}{4} = 2$.

Partial answers: (a) $x = 4$; (b) $x < 4$; (f) $x < 5/3$; (i) $-2 < x$.

7. Graph each of the following conditions as a subset of L on the line of numbers:

(a) $x < 4$ *and* $x > 1$. Notice that each member of the subset defined by this statement must satisfy both conditions. This is conveniently expressed by the *continued inequality* $1 < x < 4$.

(b) $x \leq 3$ and $x \geq -1$ (the same as $-1 \leq x \leq 3$).

(c) $-7 < x < -5$.

(d) $x < 5$ and $x > 7$.

(e) $x < 5$ or $x > 7$. Here an element of L will be in the subset if it satisfies $x < 5$ or $x > 7$. There is no way to express this condition as a continued inequality.

(f) $x < -3$ or $x > 3$.

(g) $x < 2$ or $x > -2$.

8. Use the structure of the number system (i.e., the properties of Section 202, page 63) to prove that the following conditions are equivalent.

(a) $(x + 6 = 9) \Leftrightarrow (x = 3)$

(b) $(x + 6 < 9) \Leftrightarrow (x < 3)$

(c) $(2x < -10) \Leftrightarrow (x < -5)$

(d) $(4x + 6 = 8) \Leftrightarrow (x = \frac{1}{2})$

(e) $(5 - 2x < 4) \Leftrightarrow (-2x < -1) \Leftrightarrow (x > \frac{1}{2})$.

3

Relations as Sets of Ordered Pairs

When you think of applying mathematics to solve everyday problems, you will recall that tables of numbers, graphs, and formulas play an important part. You use all of these aids to study and display number *relations*. In this chapter we explore number relations. We hope to answer questions like: "Just what is a relation?" "How can you use tables, graphs, and sentences that involve variables to express relations?"

300. More about sets

In Chapters 1 and 2, you used the phrase *set of elements* without saying exactly what it means. Of course, you can use other phrases like "collection of things," "class of distinct entities," or the like. This is what a dictionary does. It defines words by using other words. You hope to come, eventually, to words you understand.

We continue to use the phrase "set of elements" as an *undefined term*. As you work with sets your ideas about them will become richer. The phrase *set of elements* will mean more to you.

We shall think of the phrase "set of elements" as a *primitive term* in mathematics. We make no attempt to define it. Rather, we use it to define other mathematical words. In particular we shall define a relation as a special kind of set of elements.

First, recall some things you know about sets: A set has *elements*, or *members*. These elements may be numbers, or triangles, or names of baseball teams. The elements of a set need not to be all of a kind. You can think of the set {John, chair, eraser, John's dog Pluto}. But we shall usually work with sets of elements of one kind, like the set of real numbers.

In mathematics, as in all logical discourse, we begin by making clear the set of things we want to discuss. We use *variables*. We specify the *range* of these variables. This amounts to specifying a *universe of discourse*. We shall often use the set L, of real numbers, as our universe of discourse.

We define *subsets* of our universe of discourse in several ways. For example, in the set L, we can speak of the subset

$$S = \{1, 3, 5, 7, 9\}.$$

This technique of *listing* the elements of a set leads us to make *tables* of various kinds. In the universe of cities of the United States, we list the subset of state capitals. Sometimes we *order* the listing. We arrange a list alphabetically; or we arrange a list of numbers in order of size.

Sometimes we define a subset by a *verbal phrase* or *sentence*. We speak of the odd integers from 1 to 9 inclusive; or we speak of the cities of the United States that are state capitals.

Sometimes we use *graphs* or *pictures*. We speak of the circled points on the line of numbers, or we speak of the cities on a map of the United States that are marked ★.

Very often we use algebraic *conditions* like $x > 3$, $x + 3 = 7$, or $x^2 = 25$ to define subsets. Recall the notation, $\{x \mid x > 3\}$, for the solution set of the condition $x > 3$; such solution sets are subsets of the universe of discourse. A condition may define the universe of discourse (and hence be an identity, like $1 + x = x + 1$ in L); or it may define a subset of the universe that contains some but not all of the elements of the universe (and hence be a *proper* condition like $x > 3$ in L); or it may define the null set (and hence be a condition like $x = x + 2$ in L).

When we wish to specify a universe of discourse, or a subset of the universe, it is important to know whether a thing *belongs to* this set. Hence we use lists, or words, or graphs, or algebraic conditions to express rules of membership.

It is convenient to write $a \in A$ to abbreviate the statement "*a* is an element of the set *A*." Thus $5 \in N$ says 5 is a natural number; $\sqrt{7} \in L$ says $\sqrt{7}$ is an element of the set L of real numbers; etc. To say, "*a* is not an element of the set *A*," we write $a \notin A$. Thus $3\frac{1}{2} \notin N$, $\sqrt{2} \notin N$, and $5 + 2i \notin L$.

EXERCISES §300

1. We have mentioned four ways to define a set: list, verbal statement, graph, and algebraic condition. Decide which way is most convenient to define each set:
  (a) The telephone subscribers in your community.
  (b) The even (natural) numbers.
  (c) The odd integers (includes numbers like -5).
  (d) The real numbers less than -2.
  (e) The rational numbers, (positive and negative integers and fractions, and zero), greater than or equal to $-2\frac{1}{2}$.

(f) The natural numbers that are 3 less than 10. (Notice that this set contains just one member, namely, the number 7.)

(g) The set I of integers.

(h) The rational numbers that satisfy the condition $x^2 = 3$. (Notice that this set contains no members.)

2. Write an algebraic condition to define each of the following sets:

(a) The real numbers such that their doubles equal 9 [$x \in L$ and $2x = 9$].

(b) The natural numbers such that their triples equal 7. [The condition is $n \in N$ and $3n = 7$. Of course, for $n \in N$, $\{n \mid 3n = 7\} = \{\ \ \}$.]

(c) The real numbers such that their squares are 12.

(d) The integers such that twice their squares are 4 more that 14.

(e) The real numbers which, when divided into 5, yield a quotient of 0.

(f) The integers such that their triples are less than -5.

(g) The rational numbers whose products with $-3/4$ are at least 2 more than -10.

(h) The real numbers whose products with -5 are at most 3 less than -6. Notice how complicated the description in verbal language of these sets becomes; yet the algebraic conditions are rather simple.

3. Draw a line of numbers for each part of this question. On your line, indicate the points that belong to the set.

(a) $x \in L$ and $x + 1 = 5$.

(b) $x \in L$ and $x > -1$.

(c) $x \in L$ and $x < 7$.

(d) $x \in N$ and $x^2 = 9$.

(e) $x \in I$ and $x^2 = 9$.

(f) $x \in L$ and $-\sqrt{2} < x < -1$.

(g) $x \in R$ and $5x = 13$.

(h) $i \in I$, $\{i \mid i - 5 \le -8\}$.

(i) $t \in L$, $\{t \mid t^2 - 4 = 5\}$.

(j) $x \in L$, $\{x \mid x^2 \ge 16\}$.

(k) $x \in L$, $\{x \mid x^2 < 16\}$.

(l) $x \in L$, $\{x \mid x^2 \le 0\}$.

4. Write a condition (equation or inequality) that defines the subset of the given set. Then graph the subset on the line of numbers.

(a) The rational numbers that are at least $1\frac{1}{2}$ (i.e., greater than, or equal to, $1\frac{1}{2}$).

(b) The real numbers whose squares are at most 5 ($x^2 \le 5$).

(c) The natural numbers whose doubles are equal to the sum of the numbers with themselves. ($2x = x + x$. Notice that every natural number has this property. Hence this is an instance of a subset of the natural numbers that is the set of natural numbers itself. We called a condition like $2x = x + x$ an identity.)

(d) The real numbers that are greater than -3 *and* less than 5 ($-3 < x < 5$).

(e) The real numbers whose squares are at least zero.

5. Let N be the set of natural numbers, I the set of integers, R the set of rational numbers, and L the set of real numbers. Identify each of the following statements as true or false.

(a) $6 \in R$ (b) $-\sqrt{2} \in L$

(c) $\pi \in R$ (d) $29.7 \notin L$

(e) $\frac{1}{4} \notin I$ (f) $(\sqrt{10} + \sqrt{6}) \in R$

(g) $3.1416 \notin R$ (h) $(x \in N) \Rightarrow (1/x \in R)$

(i) $(x \in N) \Rightarrow (x - 5 \in N)$ (j) $(x \in R) \Rightarrow (x \in L)$.

301. The cartesian product of two sets

So far we have dealt with single sets of numbers. Practical problems commonly deal with two or more sets of numbers. For example, the height-weight "relation" for college girls involves the set of heights of college girls (a set of numbers found by measuring) *and* the set of weights of college girls (a second set of numbers found by measuring). People speak of a *relation* between the heights and weights of college girls. It is this notion of relation that we now wish to make precise.

When you begin with two sets, say $\{1, 2, 3\}$ and $\{4, 8, 12\}$, you can always build a third set by pairing members of the first set with members of the second set. Thus, for the sets $\{1, 2, 3\}$ and $\{4, 8, 12\}$ the list of possible *ordered pairs* is:

(1,4)	(2,4)	(3,4)
(1,8)	(2,8)	(3,8)
(1,12)	(2,12)	(3,12)

Notice that we began with two sets of numbers, $\{1, 2, 3\}$ and $\{4, 8, 12\}$; we built a third set whose members are ordered number-pairs; we paired each member of the set $\{1, 2, 3\}$ with every member of the set $\{4, 8, 12\}$; the first element of a number-pair is a member of $\{1, 2, 3\}$; the second element of a number-pair is a member of $\{4, 8, 12\}$. We call the set of number-pairs formed in this way the *cartesian product* of the two given sets.

You should study other examples of cartesian products to fix this idea in your mind:

(1) $S_1 = \{2, 3\}$, $S_2 = \{4, 6, 8\}$. If we designate the cartesian product of S_1 and S_2 by $S_1 \times S_2$, then

$$S_1 \times S_2 = \{(2,4), (2,6), (2,8), (3,4), (3,6), (3,8)\}$$

(2) $S_1 = \{a, b, c\}$; $S_2 = \{w, x, y, z\}$.

$$S_1 \times S_2 = \{(a,w), (a,x), (a,y), (a,z), (b,w), (b,x),$$
$$(b,y), (b,z), (c,w), (c,x), (c,y), (c,z)\}.$$

Notice, in each instance, that the number of elements in $S_1 \times S_2$ is the number of elements in S_1 times the number of elements in S_2. In (1), $S_1 \times S_2$

contains $2 \times 3 = 6$ elements. In (2), $S_1 \times S_2$ contains $3 \times 4 = 12$ elements. Hence the word *product* fits.

(3) S_1 is the set of real numbers. S_2 is the set of rational numbers. $S_1 \times S_2$ is the set of number-pairs $\{(x,y)\}$, where x is a variable whose range is the set L, and y is a variable whose range is the set R. Thus $(-3,2\frac{1}{4}) \in S_1 \times S_2$, $(\sqrt{2},-3\frac{1}{8}) \in S_1 \times S_2$, but $(-3\frac{1}{8}, \sqrt{2}) \notin S_1 \times S_2$.

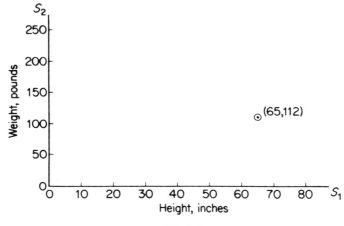

Fig. 3–1.

It is often convenient to represent the cartesian product of two sets by a graph. When you represent a single set of numbers by a graph, you plot points on the line of numbers to correspond to the members of the set. A convenient way to represent the cartesian product of two sets of numbers is to draw two lines at right angles. René Descartes contributed this idea to mathematics about 1637, hence the name *cartesian* product.

Suppose you are studying the heights and weights of college girls. S_1 is the set of heights of college girls, and S_2 is the set of weights of college girls. To represent the set $S_1 \times S_2$, you arrange two lines of numbers as in Fig. 3–1.

You represent heights in inches along the S_1 *axis*. You represent weights in pounds along the S_2 axis. You represent the number-pair (h,w) [where h is a variable whose range is the set of heights of college girls, and w is a variable whose range is the set of weights of college girls] by a point in the plane. Thus the number-pair $(65,112)$ corresponds to a girl 65 in. tall who weighs 112 lb; a point 65 units along the S_1 axis (to the right of the S_2 axis), and 112 units along the S_2 axis (above the S_1 axis) also corresponds to this girl.

Notice that Fig. 3–1 provides a place for every possible girl. There is a place for the girl $(25,190)$. It is unlikely that you will find such a girl. But the system of axes provides a place for such a girl if you should happen to find one.

Now consider the graphic representation of the other examples of cartesian products that we gave you:

(1) $\qquad\qquad S_1 = \{2, 3\}; \qquad S_2 = \{4, 6, 8\}.$ $\qquad$ (Fig. 3–2)

The six circled points represent $S_1 \times S_2$.

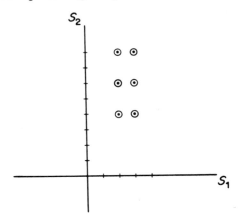

Fig. 3–2.

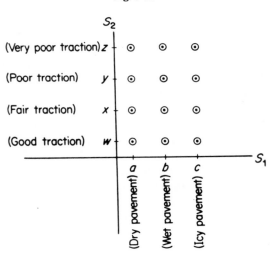

Fig. 3–3.

(2) $\qquad\qquad S_1 = \{a, b, c\}; \qquad S_2 = \{w, x, y, z\}.$ $\qquad$ (Fig. 3–3)

[Recall that we have not assigned meanings to the letter symbols. One possibility would be $a = $ dry pavement, $b = $ wet pavement, $c = $ icy pavement; $w = $ good traction, $x = $ fair traction, $y = $ poor traction, $z = $ very poor traction (i.e., very slippery). We restrict most of our discussion to numbers. But you should notice that much of what we say applies to sets of objects other than numbers]. The twelve circled points represent $S_1 \times S_2$.

(3) S_1 is the set L. S_2 is the set R.   (Fig. 3–4)

You cannot plot and circle *all* the points that represent $S_1 \times S_2$. Each real number (from S_1) is paired with each rational number (from S_2) to yield a

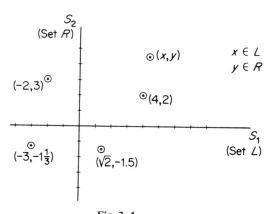

Fig. 3–4.

number-pair (x,y), and hence a point (x,y) that is x units from the S_2 axis and y units from the S_1 axis. The points $(4,2)$, $(-2,3)$, $(-3,-1\frac{1}{3})$, and $(\sqrt{2},-1.5)$ are instances of the members of $S_1 \times S_2$.

An especially useful system of axes results from taking both S_1 and S_2 as the set L of real numbers. This is the system we shall use most. It is the one that Descartes suggested originally.

EXERCISES §301

1. Write out the cartesian product of each pair of sets as a list of number-pairs:

(a) $S_1 = \{-1, 1\}$, $S_2 = \{\sqrt{2}, \sqrt{3}, 2\}$; $S_1 \times S_2 =$
(b) $S_1 = \{5\}$, $S_2 = \{1, 2, 3, 4, 5\}$; $S_1 \times S_2 =$
(c) $S_1 = \{7, 6, 5\}$, $S_2 = \{5, 4, 3, 2, 1\}$; $S_1 \times S_2 =$

2. Is the number of members of the set $S_1 \times S_2$ always the product of the number of members of S_1 and the number of members of S_2?

3. Prepare a system of axes for each part of Exercise 1 and represent the set $S_1 \times S_2$ by a set of circled points.

4. Is $S_1 \times S_2 = S_2 \times S_1$? Write the elements of $S_2 \times S_1$ for each part of Exercise 1.

5. We have agreed that every point on the line of numbers corresponds to a real number, and every real number corresponds to a point on the line of numbers. We say more briefly there is a one-to-one correspondence between the set of real numbers and the set of points on the line of numbers. Consider now the cartesian product of the set L with itself. Prepare an appropriate system of axes where both S_1 and S_2 are the set L of real numbers. Give an informal argument that there is a one-to-one correspondence between the points of the plane and the elements of $L \times L$.

6. Let S_1 be the set of automobiles registered in your state and S_2 the set of numbers (or combinations of letters and numbers) on auto license tags that have been issued. What is the set $S_1 \times S_2$? Rather than the entire set $S_1 \times S_2$, the state police would be more concerned with a special subset of $S_1 \times S_2$. Which subset?

7. Let $S_1 = \{0, 1, 2, 3\}$ and $S_2 = \{0, 1, 2\}$.
(a) List the elements of $S_1 \times S_2$.
(b) On a system of axes, represent the set $S_1 \times S_2$ by a set of points.
(c) Let x be a variable whose range is S_1, and y a variable whose range is S_2. List the subset of elements, $\{(x,y)\}$, of $S_1 \times S_2$ that satisfy the condition $x = y$. Locate the corresponding points on the system of axes.
(d) List the elements of $S_1 \times S_2$ that satisfy the condition $x < y$. Represent this subset graphically.
(e) Repeat with the condition $x + y = 3$.

302. Relations as subsets of cartesian products

We return now to the example of heights and weights of college girls. Suppose you measure the heights of 1000 college girls. Use H to designate this set of measurements. Suppose you measure heights to the nearest tenth of an inch. Suppose the shortest girl is 54.1 in. tall and the tallest girl is 74.8 in. tall. You expect to get other heights between these extremes, and perhaps to find several girls who are 65.5 in. tall.

Suppose you also measure each girl's weight and use W to designate this set of measurements. Suppose you measure weights to the nearest tenth of a pound. Suppose the lightest girl weighs 77.4 lb, and the heaviest girl weighs 196.8 lb. You expect to get other weights between these extremes, and perhaps to find several girls who weigh 124.6 lb.

In Section 301, we described the cartesian product, $H \times W$. The graph of $H \times W$ (Fig. 3–5) is a set of points that lie in a rectangle in the plane.

The actual measurements of the 1000 girls give you 1000 points (not necessarily all different) in the rectangle. These 1000 points are a subset of all of the points in the rectangle. Or, to say the same thing in another way, the 1000 number-pairs, $\{(h,w)\}$, are a subset of the cartesian product $H \times W$. The figure suggests a set of points that is a subset of $H \times W$. We call a subset of $H \times W$ a *relation* in $H \times W$.

Some subsets of $H \times W$ have little or no practical interest. A subset like the 1000 points $\{(h,w)\}$ may have much practical interest. For one thing. it gives a factual account of the heights and weights of the 1000 girls. Beyond this, a person who studies the graph of the relation (that is, the 1000 points) can see a *trend*. He can see how weight increases with height for the 1000 girls. If, now, he begins to think of the 1000 ordered number-pairs as a *sample* of the heights and weights of all college girls, he can begin to make statements about the weights that are *typical* of different heights and the

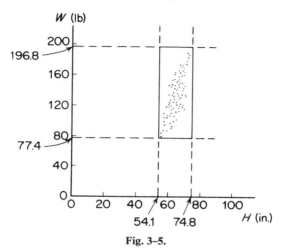

Fig. 3–5.

heights that are typical of different weights. This is the kind of thinking that statisticians do when they prepare height-weight charts to define such terms as "overweight" and "underweight" for a group of people.

From a mathematical point of view, *every subset of H × W is a relation in H × W.* From a practical point of view not all of these subsets of *H × W* are *useful* relations. In most of our future work we shall be concerned with only the simplest relations, but we shall devote the rest of this section to giving you examples of a variety of mathematical relations.

You have learned to think of subsets of a given set, like the set *L*; you called *L* the universe of discourse. Now you begin to think of subsets of cartesian products, like *L × L*; hence *L × L* is the universe of discourse. You will use conditions, expressed by tables, graphs, verbal or algebraic sentences, to define subsets of cartesian products.

EXERCISES §302

1. Form each cartesian product as directed. Then graph the indicated relation as a subset of the cartesian product.

(a) $S_1 = \{1, 2, 3, 4\}, \qquad S_2 = \{1, 2, 3, 4, 5\}.$

Prepare a system of axes for $S_1 \times S_2$, but plot only the points

$$\{(1,1), (1,3), (2,2), (3,3), (3,4), (4,4), (4,5)\}.$$

This set of number-pairs (or points) is a relation in $S_1 \times S_2$.

(b) S_1 is the set I of integers. S_2 is the set I of integers. Prepare a system of axes for $S_1 \times S_2$, but plot only the points, $\{(x,y)\}$, such that $y = x$. The points such that $y = x$ form a subset of $I \times I$. We shall write "$(x,y) \in I \times I$ and $\{(x,y) \mid y = x\}$" to describe this subset of $I \times I$. Here are some members of $\{(x,y) \mid y = x\}$, that is, of the set of ordered number-pairs, $\{(x,y)\}$, such that $y = x$ in $I \times I$: $\{\ldots, (-2,-2), (-1,-1), (0,0), (1,1), (2,2), \ldots\}$. The set of all these number-pairs is a relation in $I \times I$.

(c) In the cartesian product $L \times L$, plot the points $\{(x,y)\}$, such that $y = x^2$. That is, graph the relation $\{(x,y) \mid y = x^2\}$ in $L \times L$.

Here are some members of this subset of $L \times L$:

$$\{\ldots, (-2,4), (-1,1), (0,0), (1,1), (2,4), \ldots\}.$$

The set of all these number-pairs is a relation in $L \times L$. Does the number $(\sqrt{2},2)$ belong to this relation? Does the number-pair $(9,3)$ belong to this relation?

(d) Graph the relation $\{(x,y) \mid y > x\}$ in $R \times R$. Where do all the points of this subset of $R \times R$ lie? [Notice that each point of the relation is farther from the x-axis than it is from the y-axis (directed distances); but not all such points belong to the relation because some such points are in $L \times L$ and not in $R \times R$.]

(e) Graph the relation $\{(x,y) \mid y = \sqrt{x}\}$ in $N \times N$. This is the relation $\{(1,1), (4,2), (9,3), \ldots\}$. Is $(3,\sqrt{3})$ an element of the relation? What about $(4,16)$? $(100,10)$?

(f) Graph the relation $\{(x,y) \mid y < \sqrt{x}\}$ in $L \times L$.

(g) Graph the relation $\{(x,y) \mid x \text{ and } y \text{ are odd numbers}\}$ in $N \times N$.

(h) Graph the relation $\{(x,y) \mid x \le 0 \Rightarrow y = 2 \text{ and } x > 0 \Rightarrow y = 1\}$ in $L \times L$.

2. Six essays submitted in a contest were read by two judges and ranked according to merit. The following table shows the results of the rankings.

Contestant	Rank by First Judge (x)	Rank by Second Judge (y)
Smith	2	3
Brown	4	6
Kelly	1	1
Miller	3	2
Owens	6	5
Jones	5	4

Let x be a variable whose range, S_1, is the set of possible ranks assigned by the first judge and y a variable whose range, S_2, is the set of ranks that could be given by the second judge.

(a) How many elements are there in $S_1 \times S_2$? On a system of axes, draw a rectangle to enclose the points of $S_1 \times S_2$.

(b) In $S_1 \times S_2$ plot the points that correspond to the results given in the table. Mark each point with the corresponding contestant's name. Notice that this relation in $S_1 \times S_2$ has a practical interpretation.

3. Let S_1, $\{1, 2, 3, ..., 50\}$, be the set of ticket numbers in a raffle, and S_2 be the set of names of the 20 people who purchase one or more of the tickets.
(a) Describe $S_1 \times S_2$.
(b) The record of ticket sales defines a relation in $S_1 \times S_2$. Describe several possible relations that fit the facts given above.

4. The table below gives the scores of 30 students on placement tests in English and mathematics.

Student	Mathematics (x)	English (y)	Student	Mathematics (x)	English (y)
1	18	11	16	44	34
2	25	19	17	45	33
3	28	25	18	46	25
4	29	22	19	46	30
5	31	17	20	47	32
6	31	21	21	52	24
7	31	25	22	52	24
8	35	19	23	52	33
9	37	20	24	54	26
10	37	27	25	55	35
11	42	25	26	57	29
12	43	31	27	57	32
13	44	17	28	60	35
14	44	22	29	68	37
15	44	26	30	75	43

The possible scores on the mathematics test are the integers from 0 through 100; and for English, from 0 through 50.
(a) Draw the graph of the relation expressed by this table.
(b) What is the set S_1? The set S_2? How many points are there in the cartesian product of S_1 and S_2? How many of the points of $S_1 \times S_2$ belong to the relation of part (a)?

303. Types of relations

Perhaps you are beginning to see how broad the concept of relation is. In its general, mathematical form, we shall speak of a relation in $S_1 \times S_2$ as any subset of $S_1 \times S_2$. This includes the rather loose correspondence of height to weight for college girls. Although girls of the same height may have different weights, the set of number-pairs for a large sample of college girls will not include all the number-pairs in the cartesian product $H \times W$. There is a definite *trend* for taller girls to weigh more than shorter girls.

Other relations show stronger trends. For example, suppose you pay 4 cents for each ounce, or fraction of an ounce, when you send first-class mail. Graphically (Fig. 3–6), the cartesian product $W \times P$ has elements like $(2\frac{1}{4},4)$ corresponding to 4 cents postage on $2\frac{1}{4}$ oz. But such elements do *not*

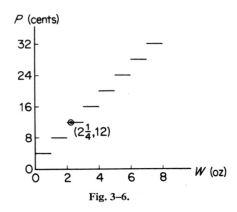

Fig. 3–6.

belong to the first-class postage relation in $W \times P$. Only elements like $(2\frac{1}{4},12)$, corresponding to 12 cents postage on $2\frac{1}{4}$ ounces, belong to the first-.class postage relation. Notice how definite the trend, more-weight-requires-more-postage, is for the first-class postage relation. Yet an increase in weight does not always lead to an increase in postage. The relation contains elements, like $(2\frac{1}{4},12)$ and $(2\frac{1}{2},12)$, corresponding to an increase in weight with no increase in postage.

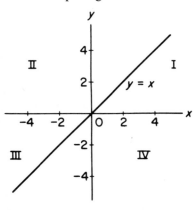

Fig. 3–7.

Still other relations show even stronger trends. For example, the subset of $L \times L$ that contains the number-pairs $\{(x,y)\}$, such that $y = x$, is a relation in $L \times L$. This is the relation $\{(x,y) \mid y = x\}$ in $L \times L$. Graphically, this relation is the set of points on the straight line of Fig. 3–7. Hence we say this relation has a *linear* trend.

Notice another feature of this relation. Values of x are not limited to the non negative numbers; the range of x is the set L. The x- and y-axes divide the plane into four quarters or *quadrants*. Mathematicians label these quadrants counterclockwise from the positive x axis. Notice that the graph lies in quadrants I and IV.

If you plot the relation $\{(x,y) \mid y = x\}$ in $N \times N$, the graph (Fig. 3–8) is a set of isolated points in the first quadrant; but, again, these points "line up." We say this relation also has a linear trend.

The word *linear* is important. For, consider the relation $\{(x,y) \mid y = x^2\}$ in $L \times L$. The graph (Fig. 3–9) lies in quadrants I and II. Again each change in x yields a definite change in y; there is a definite trend, but the trend is not linear.

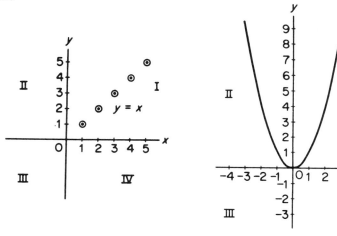

Fig. 3–8.   Fig. 3–9.

In the study of statistical data, the concept of trend (weak trends versus strong trends, linear trends versus *curvilinear* trends, etc.) is a central idea. For our present purposes, we are more concerned with two other characteristics of relations.

First, we are interested in whether the graph of a relation is *continuous* or *discontinuous*. We shall limit ourselves to an intuitive interpretation of these words. The first-class postage relation has a broken graph; we call such a graph discontinuous. The graph of the relation $\{(x,y) \mid y = x\}$ in $N \times N$ is a set of isolated points; we call such a graph discontinuous. By contrast, the graphs of the relations $\{(x,y) \mid y = x\}$ and $\{(x,y) \mid y = x^2\}$ in $L \times L$ are continuous.

Roughly speaking, a continuous graph is one that you can draw without lifting your pencil from the paper. We leave the question of a more precise definition of continuity for Chapter 6 (page 263).

Second, we are interested in *uniqueness*. In some relations, $\{(x,y)\}$, the first element of an ordered number-pair is repeated; for example, in the relation $\{(1,2), (1,3), (2,5), (3,4)\}$ in $N \times N$, the first element, 1, appears twice. In other relations the first element of an ordered number-pair is not repeated; for example, in the relation $\{(1,3), (2,4), (3,3), (4,5)\}$ in $N \times N$ none of the first elements, 1, 2, 3, or 4, is repeated.

Recall the relation $\{(h,w)\}$ in $H \times W$ for 1000 college girls. When you measure heights to the nearest 0.1 in., you expect to find several girls of the same height who have different weights; the same value of h is paired with different values of w.

By contrast, in the first-class postage relation, $\{(w,p)\}$, you do not find two packages of the same weight that require different amounts of postage. This fact has an important practical meaning. To each weight, there corresponds a definite, unique postage. Of course you cannot reverse this statement. When you know the postage you do not know the weight exactly, but only within an ounce. From a practical point of view, the important thing is to have a unique postage for each definite weight.

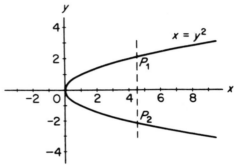

Fig. 3–10.

Consider each pair of elements, (x_1,y_1) and (x_2,y_2), of a relation, $\{(x,y)\}$: If $(x_1 = x_2) \Rightarrow (y_1 = y_2)$, we call the relation a *function*; conversely, if a relation $\{(x,y)\}$ is a function, for each two elements (x_1,y_1) and (x_2,y_2), $(x_1 = x_2) \Rightarrow (y_1 = y_2)$. That is, for each value of x for which there is a corresponding value of y, there is exactly one value of y. Functions have great practical usefulness, and are mathematically simpler than other relations. You will study them further in Chapter 4 and throughout the remainder of your work in mathematics.

The simplest functions are *one-to-one correspondences*. Consider each pair of elements (x_1,y_1) and (x_2,y_2) of a relation $\{(x,y)\}$: If $(x_1 = x_2) \Leftrightarrow (y_1 = y_2)$, we call the relation a one-to-one correspondence; conversely, if a relation is a one-to-one correspondence, for each two elements (x_1,y_1) and (x_2,y_2), $(x_1 = x_2) \Leftrightarrow (y_1 = y_2)$. That is, for each value of x for which there is a corresponding value of y, there is exactly one value of y, and, for each value of y that occurs in the set of number-pairs there is exactly one value of x to which it corresponds.

As examples:

(1) The relation $\{(x,y) \mid x = y^2\}$ in $L \times L$ is not a function, and hence is not a one-to-one correspondence. It contains the members $(1,1)$ and $(1,-1)$; these ordered number-pairs have the same first element $(x_1 = x_2 = 1)$, and different second elements $(y_1 = 1$ and $y_2 = -1)$.

(2) The relation $\{(x,y) \mid y = x^2\}$ in $L \times L$ is a function, but is not a one-to-one correspondence. It contains members like $\{(1,1), (-1,1), (\sqrt{2},2), (-\sqrt{2},2), ...\}$; it is a function because if $x_1 = x_2$ then $y_1 = y_2$; it is not a one-to-one correspondence because members like $(1,1)$ and $(-1,1)$ have $y_1 = y_2$ and $x_1 \neq x_2$.

(3) The relation $\{(x,y) \mid y = 2x\}$ in $L \times L$ is a one-to-one correspondence, and hence is a function. It contains members like $\{(-3,-6), (-\sqrt{2},-2\sqrt{2}), (5,10), (\pi,2\pi), ...\}$; it is a one-to-one correspondence because $x_1 = x_2 \Leftrightarrow y_1 = y_2$.

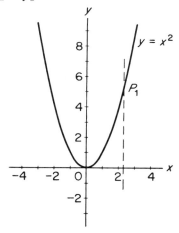

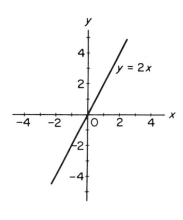

Fig. 3–11.   Fig. 3–12.

Perhaps you find it hard to keep all these ideas about uniqueness in mind. Perhaps you begin to feel overwhelmed by so many words. If so, you will appreciate the simple graphic interpretation of the preceding definitions:

In Example (1): There are *vertical* lines, like the dotted line in Fig. 3–10, that *intersect* the graph at two points, like P_1 and P_2; that is, the *same* value of x corresponds to 2 different values of y. Hence the relation is *not* a function.

In Example (2): A vertical line, like the dotted line in Fig. 3–11, cannot intersect the graph at more than one point; that is, to each value of x there corresponds at most one value of y. Hence the relation is a function. Notice that a *horizontal* line may intersect the graph in 2 points; that is, the same value of y may correspond to 2 different values of x. Hence the function is not a one-to-one correspondence.

In Example (3): Neither a vertical line nor a horizontal line can intersect the graph (Fig. 3–12) at more than one point; that is, to each value of x there corresponds at most one value of y, and to each value of y there corresponds at most one value of x. Hence the relation is a one-to-one correspondence.

EXERCISES §303

1. Plot the relation that consists of number-pairs $\{(x,y)\}$ such that $y = 2x$ in $N \times N$. Describe the trend in this relation. Is the relation continuous? Is the relation a function? Is the relation a one-to-one correspondence? In what quadrants does the graph lie?

2. Repeat Exercise 1 for the following relations in $L \times L$:

(a) $\{(x,y) \mid y = 3x\}$ (b) $\{(x,y) \mid y = x^3\}$

(c) $\{(x,y) \mid y > x\}$ (d) $\{(x,y) \mid y > x^2\}$

(e) $\{(x,y) \mid y = \frac{1}{2}x^2\}$ (f) $\{(x,y) \mid x = \frac{1}{2}y^2\}$

(g) $\{(x,y) \mid y = 1/x\}$ (h) $\{(x,y) \mid y \leq x^2\}$.

In parts (c), (d), and (h), the idea of continuity involves new difficulties; ignore it. In part (g), y is not defined when $x = 0$. This makes the graph discontinuous at $x = 0$. The relation $\{(x,y) \mid y = 1/x\}$ is a one-to-one correspondence in $L \times L$, provided $x \neq 0$ and $y \neq 0$.

3. A taxicab company charges fares according to the rule: 25 cents for the first quarter mile, 10 cents for each additional $\frac{1}{4}$ mile or fraction thereof. Let M represent the set of miles ridden, and F the set of fares paid. Prepare a system of axes for the cartesian product $M \times F$. Plot the relation in $M \times F$ that is defined by the rule. Comment on the following characteristics of this relation: type of trend, continuity, uniqueness. Is the relation a function? Is it a one-to-one correspondence?

4. The following table defines a subset of the set of ordered pairs of real numbers:

x	2	3	4
y	-3	0	1

Graph this relation. The graph consists of 3 isolated points in the *cartesian plane*. Label each point with its x and y *coordinates* in the proper order, $(2, -3)$ for example. Is this relation a function?

5. The condition $x = 5$ defines a relation in the set of ordered pairs of real numbers. Notice that this condition places no restriction on the values (from the real number system) that you can assign to the variable y. So the number-pairs $(5, -4)$, $(5,0)$, $(5,3)$, etc., all belong to the relation defined by this condition. What is the graph of $\{(x,y) \mid x = 5\}$? That is, what is the graph of the relation that the equation $x = 5$ defines? Is this relation a function?

6. Graph the condition $y = -2$ for every value of x. Notice that each value of x corresponds to a definite value of y, namely $y = -2$. Is the relation defined by the condition $y = -2$ a function?

7. Here are two conditions: $y > 3$ and $y < 5$. Graph the condition $y > 3$. Graph the condition $y < 5$. Now what is the graph of the condition $y > 3$ *and* $y < 5$?

8. Graph the following relations in $L \times L$:

(a) $\{(x,y) \mid x = 1 \text{ and } y = -2\}$ (b) $\{(x,y) \mid y = 3x \text{ or } x = 5\}$

(c) $\{(x,y) \mid y = x^2 \text{ or } y = -x\}$ (d) $\{(x,y) \mid y = 2x \text{ and } x = 3\}$

(e) $\{(x,y) \mid y = x^3 \text{ and } y = -2\}$ (f) $\{(x,y) \mid x = y^3 \text{ and } y = 2\}$.

Which of these relations are functions? One-to-one correspondences?

304. Graphs of relations

Before you go on studying relations, you should stop to reexamine what you already know about graphs. We want to help you to organize the things you already know. This will give you a powerful thinking-aid as you explore relations.

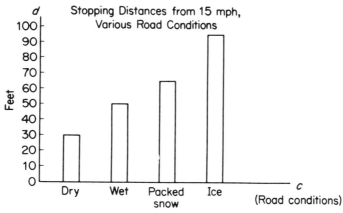

Fig. 3–13.

(1) Figure 3–13 displays a simple graph that consists of 4 isolated points: (*dry*,30), (*wet*,50), (*packed snow*,65), (*ice*,95).

People often use bars, and sometimes combine these with pictures and color arrangements, to make a graph more dramatic. We are not concerned with these artistic touches here. They tend to conceal the basic mathematical structure of a graph.

In the language of Section 301,

$$S_1 = \{\text{dry, wet, packed snow, ice}\},$$
$$S_2 = \{\text{the positive real numbers}\}.$$

(By the sense of the problem, a stopping distance of $d = 0$ ft is excluded. Certainly, negative values of d are meaningless in the problem. You are not apt to use real numbers like $\sqrt{2}$ or π to describe your measurements of stopping distances. The approximate nature of the measurements probably limits your use of real numbers to the integers. That is, you will probably round off your measurements to the nearest foot. If so, the set S_2 is, for practical purposes, the natural numbers.)

The cartesian product, $S_1 \times S_2$, is the set of ordered pairs of elements $\{(c,d)\}$. A typical pair is (packed snow,254). The coordinate system we set up provides a place for every possible ordered pair of elements. The graph displays just four ordered pairs. These four ordered pairs of elements are a relation. Since no value of c is paired with more than one value of d, this relation is a function.

Now notice the advantages of expressing this function by means of a graph. Your eye tells you, at a glance, that it takes more than twice as much distance to stop on packed snow as it takes to stop on dry road. You use visual skills to help you think about the function.

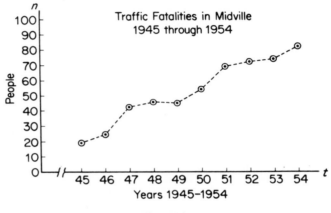

Fig. 3–14.

(2) In Fig. 3–14,

$$S_1 = \{1945, 1946, 1947, ..., 1954\},$$

$$S_2 = \{\text{zero and the positive integers}\}.$$

Notice that it is inconvenient to use the same unit of measure on the two axes; the lengths that correspond to one year and one fatality are unequal in the graph. With equal units the graph would take on a clumsy shape. It would not tell its story nearly so well.

Notice that it is impractical to include the useless section of the graph from $t = 0$ to $t = 1944$. Sometimes graph-makers show a break in the axis (see graph) to call your attention to the fact that they have omitted part of the graph.

Notice that the graph consists of ten isolated points in the cartesian product $S_1 \times S_2$. We joined these points by dotted lines to help your eye follow the trend in traffic fatalities from 1945 to 1954; but only the plotted points belong to the graph.

Notice how easy it is to see the upward trend in traffic fatalities in the ten-year period; but notice that there were fewer fatalities in 1949 than in 1948; notice how sharply the fatalities rose from 1946 to 1947.

(3) In Fig. 3–15,

$$S_1 = \{\text{zero and the positive real numbers}\},$$
$$S_2 = \{\text{zero and the positive real numbers}\},$$
$$S_1 \times S_2 = \{\text{ordered pairs of real numbers from the sets } S_1 \text{ and } S_2\}.$$

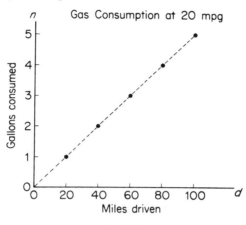

Fig. 3–15.

Notice that numbers like 18.3 mi make sense; the odometer on your car registers numbers like this, but it would be hard to make practical use of a number like 18.346 mi. The approximations you make, when you measure miles driven, ordinarily rule out measuring to the nearest thousandth of a mile.

Notice that numbers like 3.8 gal make sense; modern gas pumps display measurements to the nearest tenth of a gallon.

Between the plotted points there are other points whose coordinates belong to the function. For example, the points $(10, \frac{1}{2})$, ten miles on half a gallon, $(45, 2\frac{1}{4})$, 45 miles on $2\frac{1}{4}$ gal, etc., belong to the function. All these points lie on the straight line that joins the plotted points. Of course, there are points on the line that have little practical application. The point $(20.760, 1.038)$ is an example. When you use gasoline at the rate of 20 mi per gallon, you go 20.760 mi on 1.038 gal of gasoline; but this theoretical statement has little practical usefulness.

In Chapter 4 we shall discuss the *linear function*. In one sense, the straight line of this example is the graph of the condition: "I get 20 mi per gallon." Each point of the graph *satisfies* this condition. No other points, except the ones on the graph, satisfy this condition. But, of course, the straight line contains points you do not need for practical purposes.

(4) The graph of $y < 3$ (Fig. 3–16) is the set of points less than 3 units above the x-axis. This graph is shaded vertically. The graph of $y > x$ is the set of points whose y-coordinates are greater than their x-coordinates. This graph is shaded horizontally. Where the two types of shading overlap, we have $y < 3$ *and* $y > x$.

Notice how natural it is, in this theoretical problem, to take $S_1 = S_2 = L$. Then $S_1 \times S_2$ is the set of ordered pairs of real numbers. The condition, $y < 3$ and $y > x$, defines a relation in $L \times L$. Graphically, this relation corresponds to the points in the area where the shading overlaps.

$$\{(x,y) \mid y < 3 \text{ and } y > x\}$$

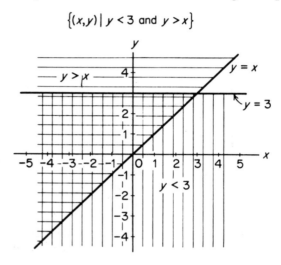

Fig. 3–16.

The relation that the condition $y < 3$ and $y > x$ defines is *not* a function. You can see from the graph that some values of x correspond to several different values of y; for example, the ordered pairs $(0,2)$, $(0,1\frac{1}{2})$, and $(0,1)$ all satisfy the condition $y < 3$ and $y > x$.

EXERCISES §304

1. The following table shows the per capita consumption of electric power in selected countries for 1953.

(a) Construct a graph in the manner of Example 1.

(b) What is the set S_1? The set S_2? The set $S_1 \times S_2$?

(c) Is the set of nine ordered pairs of elements displayed in the table a relation in $S_1 \times S_2$? Is it a function?

Country	Kilowatt hours
Norway	5,847
Canada	4,925
United States	3,244
Switzerland	2,592
United Kingdom	1,498
Australia	1,471
Belgium	1,124
Italy	668
Russia	605

2. Suppose the following table shows the population (in thousands of people) of a town at ten-year intervals.

Year	1890	1900	1910	1920	1930	1940	1950
Population (thousands)	6.5	8.5	11.9	15.2	19.0	24.3	32.6

(a) Make a graph of these data in the manner of Example 2.
(b) Notice that the population is always rounded off to the nearest 100 people. What does this suggest as a possible set for S_2?
(c) Is the relation expressed by this table a function?
(d) Estimate the population for 1935 from the graph. Can the population for 1955 be estimated? What assumptions do you make for such an estimate?

3. In an experiment in probability, a student plans to toss 5 pennies and count the number of heads that appear. He will then repeat the operation 200 times, keeping count of the number of heads that turn up each time. Let x be a variable whose range is the set of possible numbers of heads on each toss, and y a variable whose range is the set of numbers of times that a given value of x may occur when the experiment is performed.

(a) What numbers are in the range of x? What numbers are in the range of y? What is the cartesian product of these two sets?
(b) Suppose the table below gives the outcome of such an experiment. Make a graph to display these results. If the plotted points are joined by dotted lines, do the points on the dotted lines have any interpretation for the experiment?

x (number of heads)	0	1	2	3	4	5
y (frequency of occurrence)	6	30	62	55	38	9

4. A plane travels at the constant rate of 200 mph for 4 hr. Using d for distance traveled and t for time elapsed, give six number-pairs, $\{(t,d)\}$, of the relation that this statement suggests. Draw the graph of the relation. Is it a function? Is it a continuous function?

5. Let x and y be variables whose range is the set of real numbers.

(a) Find some number-pairs that satisfy the relation $y > 3x$. Show the graph of this relation.

(b) Graph the relation $y < -2x$.

(c) What is the graph of $y > 3x$ *and* $y < -2x$?

(d) Graph the relation $y = -2x$ and $y > x$. Is this relation a function?

6. Suppose the rate for electric power is 5 cents per KWH (kilowatt hour) for the first 50 KWH, 4 cents per KWH for the next 50 KWH, and 2 cents per KWH for all over 100 KWH. This relation can be expressed in symbols as:

$$y = 5 \quad \text{for} \quad 0 < x \le 50$$
$$y = 4 \quad \text{for} \quad 50 < x \le 100$$
$$y = 2 \quad \text{for} \quad 100 < x$$

Draw the graph of the relation. Is it a function? Is it continuous?

7. Let x represent the number of kilowatt hours that may be used in a home in a month's time, and C the cost of the electricity. Using the rates of Exercise 6 together with the additional information that the minimum monthly bill is 75 cents, draw the graph of the relation {(amount of electricity consumed, monthly bill)}.

8. Express the relation of Exercise 7, using algebraic conditions.

Answer: $C = 75$ for $0 < x \le 15$, $C = 5x$ for $15 < x \le 50$, $C = 50 + 4x$ for $50 < x \le 100$, $C = 250 + 2x$ for $100 < x$.

4

Introduction to Functions

In this chapter we shall introduce you to the functions that mathematicians call *elementary*. We shall deal with functions that are subsets of the cartesian product $L \times L$. This is convenient because, in the set of real numbers, you can add, subtract, multiply, divide, and find square roots, cube roots, and the like. You can also perform some other operations that you met if you studied trigonometry. These are the operations of finding the sine, cosine, tangent, etc., of a number; also the operation of finding the logarithm of a number.

First you will study *linear* functions; then more general *power* functions; then *exponential* functions that lead to *logarithms;* then, finally, *periodic* or *circular* functions. Thus you will become acquainted with the elementary functions as you study this chapter. But you should think of this as an introduction to these functions; we shall postpone the detailed study of the functions for later chapters.

400. A set of linear functions—slope

When you graph the relation $\{(x,y) \mid y = 2x\}$, it is convenient to begin with a table:

x	-3	-2	-1	0	1	2	3
y	-6	-4	-2	0	2	4	6

Of course the table displays only a few of the number-pairs of the relation $\{(x,y)\}$. Other number-pairs, like $(-2\frac{1}{2}, -5)$, $(1\frac{1}{4}, 2\frac{1}{2})$, and $(15,30)$, also belong to the relation.

The circled points of Fig. 4–1 correspond to the number-pairs in the table. Each point on the straight line corresponds to an ordered number-pair that belongs to the relation. Each ordered number-pair (x,y) that belongs to the relation has, as its graph, a point on the straight line. Hence the straight line corresponds to the set of ordered number-pairs that belong to the relation.

We shall call the straight line the *graph* of the relation $\{(x,y) \mid y = 2x\}$ or $\{(x,2x)\}$. It is also convenient to call the straight line the graph of the condition $y = 2x$. In the graph, just one value of y corresponds to each value of x (each vertical line crosses the graph just once). Hence the relation is a function; and the relation is linear. We shall call it a *linear function*.

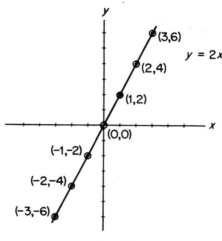

Fig. 4–1.

Notice, in the table, that y increases by 2 when x increases by 1. Also on the graph: when you start from any point on the line and move one unit to the right and two units up, you reach a new point on the line (Fig. 4–2).

This is an example of the property that distinguishes linear functions from other functions. When you say, "Another day another dollar," you are describing a linear function. When you say, "I get 20 mi per gallon," you are describing another linear function. In the first instance, the *rate of change* is 1 to 1; one more day, one more dollar. In the second instance, the rate of change is 20 to 1; 1 more gallon, 20 more miles.

You are familiar with linear functions because you have used them intuitively all your life. Suppose a baby gains 6 oz per week. If he weighs 7 lb 4 oz at birth, you can tabulate his weight in successive weeks as follows:

Age in weeks	0	1	2	3
Weight in oz	116	122	128	134

Of course, if this is a practical problem, you must not continue your table indefinitely. In 20 yr (1040 wk), he would gain $6 \times 1040 = 6240$ oz $=$

390 lb. Then he would weigh 7 lb 4 oz + 390 lb = 397 lb 4 oz. This answer is ridiculous for at least two reasons. First, the growth pattern of a baby does not continue to follow a simple law of 6-oz gain per week. Second, even if it did, it would not be exactly 6 oz per week, and a better answer would be, "In 20 yr he would weigh about 400 lb."

As you begin to study functions, then, it is important to contrast mathematical models and their applications to describe the world of experience. The functions you study in mathematics are simplified models. Experience has shown that these models help people describe their observations of the

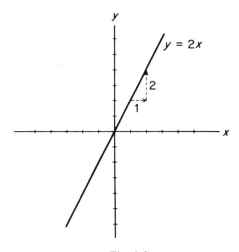

Fig. 4–2.

physical world. But the models must be applied with caution. A rule, like "The baby gains 6 oz a week," applies approximately for a time interval of several weeks. Then the law of growth may change to another, quite different one.

The simplest linear functions are *direct proportions*. We say, the distance-you-travel at 40 mph is *directly proportional* to the time-you-travel. Thus

Time (hr)	1	2	3
Distance (mi)	40	80	120

Notice, again, the distinguishing property of a linear function; another hour, another 40 miles. When you express this condition as an algebraic sentence,

$$d/t = 40/1, \quad \text{or} \quad d = 40t.$$

When y is directly proportional to x (or y *varies* directly as x), the *ratio* of y to x, y/x, is the same number for each pair (x,y). If you know that *the constant of proportionality* is 2, then $y/x = 2$, or $y = 2x$. Recall the graph of the function $\{(x,y) \mid y = 2x\}$. Recall how y "changes twice as fast as x changes."

It is important to ask how the constant of proportionality affects the graph. Figure 4–3 helps you to investigate this question.

On the line $y = \frac{1}{2}x$, when x changes by 1, y changes by $\frac{1}{2}$;
On the line $y = x$, when x changes by 1, y changes by 1;
On the line $y = 5x$, when x changes by 1, y changes by 5;
On the line $y = -3x$, when x changes by 1, y changes by -3;
On the line $y = -\frac{1}{5}x$, when x changes by 1, y changes by $-\frac{1}{5}$.

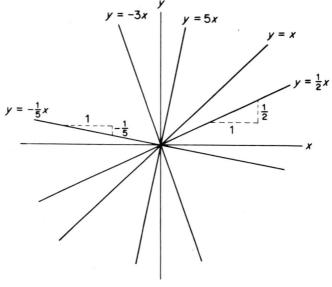

Fig. 4–3.

We shall call the change in y that corresponds to a change of 1 unit in x the *slope* of the line. Thus the line $y = 5x$ has slope 5; the line $y = -\frac{1}{5}x$ has slope $-\frac{1}{5}$, etc.

We use the equation $y = mx$ to define a *set of straight lines* through the origin. The letter m is a variable whose range is the set L of real numbers. When you give m a value, you determine a straight line through the origin. For example: when $m = 3$ you determine the straight line, $y = 3x$, of slope 3; when $m = -2$ you determine the straight line, $y = -2x$, of slope -2.

As we continue our discussion of the elementary functions, it will often be convenient to speak of a set of straight lines, or set of curves. This is an extension of your previous ideas. You have already learned to think of a condition, like $y = 2x$, that defines a set of points. These points lie on a definite straight line, of a slope 2, through the origin. Now you must think of a condition like $y = mx$. To each value of m, there corresponds a straight line through the origin, that is, a definite set of points like $y = 2x$. Hence the equation $y = mx$ defines a *set of sets* of points.

When we use a variable, like m, in this way, we call it a *parameter*. Each value of the parameter corresponds to one element of a set of sets. In the equation $y = mx$, each value of m determines one element of a set of lines (each of which is a set of points).

Students of geometry call a set of lines, like $y = mx$, a *family* of lines. They speak of the *one-parameter* family of lines, $y = mx$. This means that you must assign a value to one parameter, m, to get a particular member of the family.

The parameter m is especially convenient because it represents the slope of a line. You can learn to visualize a straight line through the origin by thinking of its slope. As you study the following table, sketch the graphs of the corresponding linear functions:

Slope	*Equation*	*Line*
-10	$y = -10x$	Slopes steeply, downward to the right
-1	$y = -x$	Drops 1 as you move 1 to the right
$-\frac{1}{10}$	$y = -\frac{1}{10}x$	Slopes gently, downward to the right
0	$y = 0 \cdot x$	The x-axis; y changes by 0 when x changes
	or $y = 0$	by 1
$\frac{1}{10}$	$y = \frac{1}{10}x$	Slopes gently, upward to the right
1	$y = x$	Rises 1 as you move 1 to the right
10	$y = 10x$	Slopes steeply, upward to the right

Notice that negative values of m correspond to lines that slope downward to the right; positive values of m correspond to lines that slope upward to the right. When

$m < -1$	the line *drops* sharply, less and less sharply for values of m closer to -1.
$m = -1$	the line *drops* 1 to 1.
$-1 < m < 0$	the line *drops* gradually, more and more gradually for values of m closer to zero.
$m = 0$	the line is horizontal.
$0 < m < 1$	the line *rises* gradually, less and less gradually for values of m closer to 1.
$m = 1$	the line *rises* 1 to 1.
$m > 1$	the line *rises* sharply, more and more sharply for larger values of m.

Each value of m (from the set L) determines a straight line through the origin. But there is one line through the origin that does *not* correspond to any value of m. The vertical line is an exceptional case. Study Fig. 4-4 as you try to answer the question, "How much does y change when x changes by 1?"

When you increase (or decrease) x by 1, and then try to get back to the vertical line through the origin (the y-axis), you find that this is impossible. Hence the vertical line does *not* have a slope.

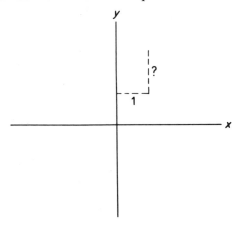

Fig. 4–4.

We assume that every other line through the origin corresponds to a definite value of m. We say that the equation $y = mx$ defines the family of lines through the origin, except that the vertical line through the origin does not correspond to any value of m from the set L. To each value of m, there corresponds a definite member of the family of lines through the origin. To each member of the family of lines through the origin (except the vertical line), there corresponds a definite value of m.

Recall that the vertical line through the origin is *not* the graph of a function; it contains points, like (0,0), (0,5), (0,−5), etc., whose x-coordinates are equal and whose y-coordinates are not equal. Every other line through the origin is the graph of a function; on these lines, if two points have the same x-coordinates, they have the same y-coordinates.

To each value of m there corresponds a linear function $\{(x,y) \mid y = mx\}$; to each linear function $\{(x,y) \mid y = mx\}$ there corresponds a definite value of m. Hence there is a one-to-one correspondence between the set of linear functions that contain the element (0,0) (whose graphs pass through the origin) and the set of values of m (the set L).

In summary, direct proportions, and statements like "y varies directly as x," lead to linear conditions like

$$y/x = m/1 \quad \text{or} \quad y = mx.$$

The parameter m is called the constant of proportionality. The graphs of these conditions are non-vertical straight lines through the origin. The constant of proportionality corresponds to the slope of the line. The mathematical model is the set of linear functions that contain the element (0,0);

each element, $\{(x,y) \mid y = mx\}$, of this set corresponds to a value of m from the set L.

EXERCISES §400

1. Find the constant of proportionality for each of the following direct proportions. Write the algebraic condition, and express the corresponding linear function in the notation of sets. Then graph the function, and identify the slope of the straight line.

(a) Sample: y varies directly as x, and
$y = 30$ when $x = 6$.
Since $y/x = 30/6$, $m = 5$.
Hence $y = 5x$.
The corresponding linear function
is $\{(x,y) \mid y = 5x\}$ or $\{(x,5x)\}$.
Its graph is Fig. 4–5.
The line has slope 5.

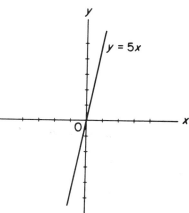

(b) The distance travelled d is directly proportional to the time of travel t; in 15 min the distance travelled is 10 mi.

(c) The weight w varies directly as the volume v; when $v = 50$ gal, $w = 350$ lb.

(d) The voltage E varies directly as the current I; when $I = 15$ amp, $E = 300$ v.

Fig. 4–5.

(e) The total cost C is directly proportional to the unit cost c; when $c = \$0.12$, $C = \$30$.

2. If a home-movie camera is operated at the standard speed of 16 pictures per second, the length of film passed through the camera is directly proportional to the time that has elapsed. This means that $L/T = m$, where m is the constant of proportionality.

(a) Determine m, if a 10-sec scene uses 4 ft of film.
(b) Make a table to show how many feet of film are used for scenes that last $T = 1, 2, 3, ..., 12$ sec.
(c) Draw the graph of the corresponding function. What is the slope of the straight line?

3. If (x_1,y_1) and (x_2,y_2) are two number-pairs of the function $\{(x,kx)\}$, where k is a parameter, and $k \neq 0$, prove that

(a) $\dfrac{y_1}{x_1} = \dfrac{y_2}{x_2}$ (b) $\dfrac{y_2}{y_1} = \dfrac{x_2}{x_1}$.

(These proportions are the basis for the expression "y is directly proportional to x.")

4. If x_2 is three times as large as x_1, what do the proportions of Exercise 3 state about y_2 and y_1?

5. Use the idea of Exercise 4 to decide how many feet of film the camera of Exercise 2 will use for a 30-sec scene; for a 20-sec scene; for a 5-sec scene.

6. The condition $y = mx$ defines a family of straight lines through the origin. Prepare a set of axes and graph the members of this family that correspond to the following replacements of m: $\{0, \frac{1}{3}, 1, 3, -3, -\frac{1}{3}\}$.

7. Does the statement "a line has no slope" mean the same as "a line has zero slope"? Explain.

8. On one set of axes, sketch the graphs of $y = 3x$, $y > 3x$, and $y < 3x$. How would you use the graph of $y = 3x$ to describe the graphs of $y > 3x$ and $y < 3x$?

9. Use the ideas of Exercise 8 to describe the graphs of each condition:

(a) $y < \frac{1}{5}x$ (b) $y \geq -2x$ (c) $y < -\frac{1}{3}x$
(d) $y < 4x$ and $y > \frac{1}{4}x$
(e) $y \leq \frac{3}{2}x$ or $y > \frac{2}{3}x$.

401. The set of all linear functions—slope and y-intercept

Each element of the set of linear functions of Section 400 contained the number-pair $(0,0)$; each corresponding straight line passed through the origin. There are other linear functions that do not contain the number-pair $(0,0)$; the corresponding straight lines do not pass through the origin.

To see how these linear functions arise, compare the equations

$$y_1 = 2x;$$

$$y_2 = 2x + 3.$$

To calculate the first y (y_1), you select a value of x and double it; to calculate the second y (y_2), you select a value of x, double it, and then add 3. Hence, for each value of x, y_2 is 3 more than y_1.

Figure 4–6 shows the graphs of $y = 2x$ and $y = 2x + 3$. Each point on the graph of $y = 2x + 3$ is 3 units above the corresponding point on the graph of $y = 2x$. The graph of $y = 2x + 3$ passes through the point $(0,3)$, whereas the graph of $y = 2x$ passes through the point $(0,0)$ (the origin); the graph of $y = 2x + 3$ passes through the point $(2,7)$, whereas the graph of $y = 2x$ passes through the point $(2,4)$; etc.

Recall the relation that we used in Section 400 to describe the weight of a baby in successive weeks. Each element of this function is a number-pair, (a,w), where a corresponds to age in weeks and w corresponds to weight in ounces. Here are the number-pairs we tabulated:

$$(0,116), \quad (1,122), \quad (2,128), \quad (3,134).$$

The condition $w = 6a + 116$ is satisfied by these four number-pairs $[128 = 6(2) + 116$, for example], and by many others $[140 = 6(4) + 116,$

for example]. We have already emphasized the importance of limiting the range of *a*, and recognizing the approximations that are involved.

Notice that the baby was born weighing 116 oz. He did not start (at time of birth) from weight zero. His weight is not directly proportional to his age.

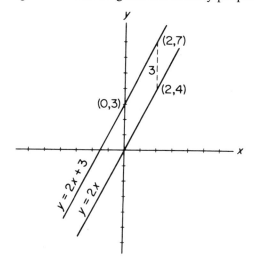

Fig. 4–6.

Now tabulate the relation $\{(a,g)\}$, where *a* corresponds to age in weeks and *g* corresponds to the excess in weight above 116 oz:

$$(0,0), \quad (1,6), \quad (2,12), \quad (3,18).$$

You find that *g* varies directly with *a* ($g = 6a$), that is, the excess in weight of the baby, above 116 oz, is directly proportional to his age.

Many everyday relations, like the average age-weight relation for the baby, obey a law of the form

$$y = mx + b.$$

Notice that when $x = 0$, $y = m \cdot 0 + b = b$. Hence the graph passes through $(0,b)$ rather than through $(0,0)$. *y* is *not* proportional to *x*; but $y - b = mx$, or $(y - b)/x = m/1$, means that $y - b$ is proportional to *x*. That is, the *excess* in *y*, above the value $y = b$, is proportional to *x*.

We drop the idea of proportion now, because it is no longer simple and convenient. But notice that it is still proper to think of the parameter *m* as the slope. It is the amount that *y* changes when *x* changes by 1. We have, besides, a new parameter *b*, which has a useful interpretation. We have seen that the graph passes through the point $(0,b)$; for $x = 0$, $y = b$. We call *b* the *y-intercept* of the graph. It is the directed distance from the origin (positive or negative, depending upon the value of *b*) to the point where the graph crosses the *y*-axis.

The equation $y = mx + b$ defines a *two-parameter* family of lines. This means that you must assign values to two parameters, m and b, to get a member of the family of lines. For example: $m = 3$ and $b = -2$ yields the line $y = 3x + (-2)$, which has slope 3 and crosses the y-axis at $(0,-2)$ (see Fig. 4–7).

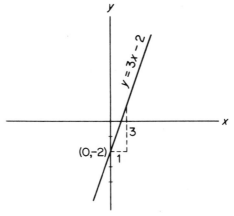

Fig. 4–7.

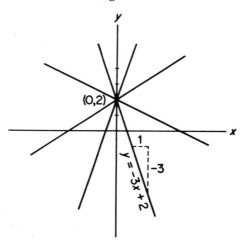

Fig. 4–8.

Suppose you assign a value to b, but not to m. For example, $b = 2$ yields the family of lines $y = mx + 2$ (see Fig. 4–8). Each of these lines has y-intercept 2; that is, it passes through the point $(0,2)$. When you assign a value to m, you get a member of this family of lines. For example, $m = -3$ yields $y = -3x + 2$.

When you replace b by 0, the result is the family of lines $y = mx$ through the origin. Hence this one-parameter family of lines through the origin is a special instance of the two-parameter family of lines, $y = mx + b$.

Suppose now you assign a value to m, but not to b. For example, $m = \frac{1}{2}$ yields the family of lines $y = \frac{1}{2}x + b$ (Fig. 4–9). Each of these lines

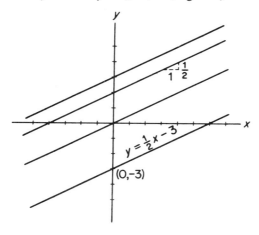

Fig. 4–9.

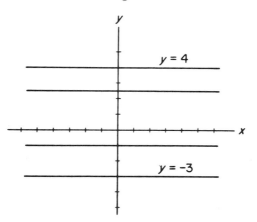

Fig. 4–10.

has slope $\frac{1}{2}$. When you assign a value to b you get a member of this family of lines. For example, $b = -3$ yields $y = \frac{1}{2}x + (-3)$, or $y = \frac{1}{2}x - 3$.

When you replace m by 0, the result is the family of lines $y = 0x + b$, or $y = b$. This is the family of lines parallel to the x-axis (see Fig. 4–10). Hence the one-parameter family of lines parallel to the x-axis, $y = b$, is a special instance of the two-parameter family of lines, $y = mx + b$.

In summary, the equation $y = mx + b$ defines a two-parameter family of lines. When you choose a value of b you get a one-parameter family of lines through $(0,b)$. When you choose a value of m you get a one-parameter family of lines with slope m. When you assign values to both b and m, you get a particular straight line that goes through $(0,b)$ and has slope m.

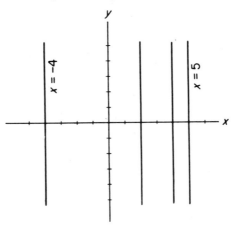

Fig. 4–11.

Finally, recall the exceptional case. Vertical lines do not have slopes, so their equations are *not* instances of $y = mx + b$. The equation $x = a$ defines a family of lines parallel to the y-axis. The parameter a corresponds to the *x-intercept*; that is, the line $x = a$ passes through the point $(a,0)$. When $a = 5$, you get the line $x = 5$ as one member of the family of vertical lines (Fig. 4–11).

Of course the line $x = 5$ is *not* the graph of a linear function. The same value of x, namely $x = 5$, corresponds to many different values of y. The number-pairs $(5,0)$, $(5,-4)$, $(5,8)$, and $(5,56)$ all satisfy the condition $x = 5$. Vertical lines are not the graphs of functions, because the same value of x corresponds to more than one distinct value of y.

As you review what we have said thus far about linear functions, the following statements should seem reasonable:

If a function is linear, the corresponding equation takes the form $y = mx + b$, and, conversely, if an equation takes the form $y = mx + b$, the corresponding relation is a linear function.

Every non-vertical straight line has an equation of the form $y = mx + b$.

Vertical straight lines have equations of the form $x = a$. These lines are not graphs of functions, because several values of y correspond to the same value of x.

Use the following example to apply these ideas, to help fix them in your mind. Then use the exercises that follow to assimilate these ideas.

It costs $10 to buy a set of water colors and a pack of drawing paper; it costs $5 for the labor of painting each picture. Express the relation

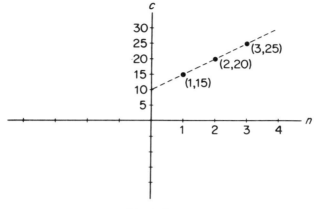

Fig. 4–12.

{(number of pictures painted, cost of producing the pictures)} by preparing a table, a graph, and an equation.

First the table:

(n) Number of pictures painted	0	1	2	3
(c) Cost of production (dollars)	10	15	20	25

You can continue the table until the paints needed to produce more pictures, or the drawing paper, are used up. This limits the range of *n* and hence limits the range of *c*.

Second the graph (Fig. 4–12): Notice that (1) negative values of *n* are meaningless here; (2) the amount that you can extend the straight line to the right and upward is limited by your supply of paints or paper; (3) fractional values of *n* are meaningless. Hence the function really consists of a set of isolated points (0,10), (1,15), (2,20), (3,25), etc., until the supplies run out. We drew a dotted line to show the trend; but only points in $N \times N$ belong to the function.

Third the equation: Notice that this example is of the "another picture, another $5" kind; hence the relation is a linear function. The equation will take the form $y = mx + b$. Clearly, $b = 10$ and $m = 5$. So the equation is $y = 5x + 10 \ (x \in N)$.

Finally, notice a peculiarity of this graph as compared with previous graphs. Previously we used the same units of measure along the *x* and *y* axes. In this graph, the units along the *n* axis are numbers of pictures; the units along the c axis are dollars. We used about the same distance to represent one picture as to represent $5; so it is no longer convenient to *visualize* the slope as 5 to 1 in the graph. The graph does not appear to rise 5 for each step of one to the right. The reason is, of course, the way we chose our units of measurement on the x and y axes.

EXERCISES §401

1. Draw the line through each of the following points with slope as indicated

(a) $(0,0)$; $m = 2$ (b) $(0,-5)$; $m = 4$
(c) $(4,2)$; $m = -3/2$ (d) $(-3,3)$; $m = -1$
(e) $(-4,-1)$; $m = 1/3$ (f) $(-2,-4)$; $m = 0$
(g) $(-6,5)$; $m = 1/8$ (h) $(1,6)$; $m = -8$.

2. In each of the following equations, identify the slope and the y-intercept. Draw the line.

(a) $y = \frac{1}{2}x + 4$ (b) $y = -3x + 5$
(c) $y = 9x - 5$ (d) $y = .4x$
(e) $y = 30x$ (f) $y = 3$
(g) $y = -(3/2)x + 2$ (h) $2y = 5x - 7$.

3. Suppose P_1 $(2,1)$ and P_2 $(4,7)$ are two points on a line.

(a) Draw the line.
(b) In moving from P_1 to P_2, how much does y change? How much does x change?
(c) Starting at P_1, if x is increased only 1 unit, what change is needed in y to remain on the line? What, then, is the slope of this line?

Answers: (b) 6, 2;   (c) 3.

4. Repeat Exercise 3 with the following points for P_1 and P_2.

(a) $(0,2)$; $(3,8)$ (b) $(1,4)$; $(5,5)$ (c) $(2,5)$; $(6,1)$
(d) $(1,1)$; $(3,-5)$ (e) $(-2,-3)$; $(2,3)$ (f) $(-4,1)$; $(2,1)$
(g) $(3,2)$; $(1,4)$ (h) $(5,1)$; $(-2,-1)$ (i) $(-2,2)$; $(-3,-2)$.

Answers: (a) 2;   (c) -1;   (d) -3;   (f) 0.

5. Draw the line with x-intercept -2 and y-intercept 6. What is the slope of this line? What is its equation?

Answers: 3; $y = 3x + 6$.

6. Write the equations of each of the following lines. Then express the corresponding linear function, using the notation of sets.

(a) Sample: A line has slope 2 and y-intercept -3.
Equation of this line: $y = 2x - 3$.
Corresponding linear function: $\{(x,y) \mid y = 2x - 3\}$ or $\{(x, 2x - 3)\}$.
(b) A line has y-intercept 4.08 and slope -0.8.
(c) A line passes through the origin and has slope $-3/5$.
(d) A line passes through the point $(0,-11)$ and has slope 4.5.
(e) A line of slope -2 cuts the y-axis at the point $(0,-1)$.

7. Draw the graphs of the following instances of the condition $x = a$.

(a) $a = 6$ (b) $a = -2$ (c) $a = 0$.

8. What value of m in the equation $y = mx + b$ results in a horizontal line? What value of m results in a vertical line?

9. Of two *integers* (call them x and y), the second is 3 less than twice the first. Write an equation to express this condition. Graph the set of number-pairs that satisfy the condition.

10. A retail salesman receives a weekly salary of $60. In addition, he gets a 5% commission on the amount of merchandise he sells each week.

(a) Using A for the dollar value of the merchandise he sells during the week and I for his total weekly income, make a table of number-pairs to illustrate this relation. Use $A = 0, 100, 200, 300, \ldots, 1000$.
(b) Make a graph to display this relation. It will be necessary to choose the units carefully to make the graph fit the page.
(c) Write an equation to express this relation. [*Answer:* $I = .05A + 60$.]
(d) What is an appropriate set of numbers for the range of the variable A?

11. To change a given temperature from the centigrade (C) scale of measurement to the Fahrenheit (F) scale, you can use the formula $F = \frac{9}{5}C + 32$.

(a) Make a table of about six number-pairs $\{(C,F)\}$ of this relation.
(b) Draw the graph of the relation. What is the slope? The F intercept?
(c) Scientists say that absolute zero (the lowest possible temperature) is -273.13 on the centigrade scale. How does this restrict the range of C? The range of F?

12. Graph the conditions $y = 2x - 3$, $y > 2x - 3$, and $y < 2x - 3$ on one set of axes. How does the graph of $y = 2x - 3$ help you to describe the graphs of $y > 2x - 3$ and $y < 2x - 3$?

13. Graph each condition:

(a) $y > 2x$ (b) $y > 3x - 1$
(c) $y > -\frac{1}{2}x + 4$ (d) $y < \frac{3}{4}x - 2$.

14. Graph each condition:

(a) $y < 2x + 1$ *and* $x < 2\frac{1}{2}$
(b) $y > -\frac{1}{2}x + 4$ *and* $x > -1$
(c) $y < -\frac{1}{2}x + 4$ *or* $x > 3$
(d) $y < -\frac{1}{2}x + 4$ *or* $y > 3x - 1$
(e) $y > -\frac{1}{2}x + 4$ *and* $y < 3x - 1$ *and* $x < 3$
(f) $1 < y < 3$ *and* $-4 < x < -2$.

402. Special lines

It is easy to write the equation of a non-vertical straight line when you know its slope and y-intercept. By definition, the equation of a straight line of slope 3 and y-intercept -2 is $y = 3x + (-2)$. This is an instance of the equation $y = mx + b$, with the replacements $m = 3$ and $b = -2$. In this section you will learn to write the equations of straight lines that satisfy other conditions.

(1) To write the equation of a straight line of slope 2 through the point (3,5), you can proceed as follows:

Since this is a non-vertical straight line, its equation is an instance of $y = mx + b$; since $m = 2$, its equation is an instance of $y = 2x + b$; since it passes through the point (3,5), you know that $5 = 2 \cdot 3 + b$; hence $b + 6 = 5$, and $b = -1$. The required equation is $y = 2x + (-1)$ or $y = 2x - 1$.

It is easy to generalize this result, and to write the equation of a straight line of slope m, through the point (x_1, y_1). We need to find the y-intercept, b, in terms of the slope m, and the coordinates of the point (x_1, y_1). Since the line $y = mx + b$ passes through the point (x_1, y_1), we know that $y_1 = mx_1 + b$; hence $b = y_1 - mx_1$. The required equation is $y = mx + (y_1 - mx_1)$; the equivalent equation

I
$$y - y_1 = m(x - x_1)$$

is more convenient.

Equation I enables you to write down the equation of a line when given its slope and one point on the line. For example, the line of slope 2, through (3,5), is $y - 5 = 2(x - 3)$. This is equivalent to the equation $y = 2x - 1$, which we found previously. As a second example, the line of slope $-2/3$, through $(-4,7)$, is $y - 7 = \dfrac{-2}{3}(x + 4)$.

(2) To write the equation of a straight line through the points $(-2,3)$ and $(4,5)$, you can proceed as follows:

Since the x-coordinates of the two points are unequal $(-2 \neq 4)$, the line is not vertical; hence its equation is an instance of $y = mx + b$. Since the line passes through $(-2,3)$,
$$3 = m \cdot (-2) + b.$$

Since the line passes through (4,5),
$$5 = m \cdot (4) + b.$$

By uniqueness of subtraction,
$$5 - 3 = [m(4) + b] - [m(-2) + b]$$

Hence $2 = 6m$

and $m = 1/3.$

From Equation I, the line of slope 1/3, through $(-2,3)$, is $y - 3 = \frac{1}{3}(x + 2)$; the line of slope 1/3, through (4,5), is $y - 5 = \frac{1}{3}(x - 4)$. Both of these equations are equivalent to $y = \frac{1}{3}x + \frac{11}{3}$. It should not surprise you that the two lines have equivalent equations; that is, that two points *determine* a straight line.

It is easy to generalize this result, and to write the equation of a straight line through (x_1, y_1) and (x_2, y_2), provided $x_1 \neq x_2$. Since the x-coordinates of the two points are unequal $(x_1 \neq x_2)$, the line is not vertical; hence its equation is an instance of $y = mx + b$. As before,

$$y_1 = mx_1 + b \quad \text{and} \quad y_2 = mx_2 + b.$$

Hence
$$y_2 - y_1 = m(x_2 - x_1).$$

Since $x_1 \neq x_2$, $x_2 - x_1 \neq 0$.

Hence
$$m = \frac{y_2 - y_1}{x_2 - x_1}.$$

From Equation I, the line of slope $\dfrac{y_2 - y_1}{x_2 - x_1}$, through (x_1, y_1), is $y - y_1 = \dfrac{y_2 - y_1}{x_2 - x_1}(x - x_1)$; the line of slope $\dfrac{y_2 - y_1}{x_2 - x_1}$, through (x_2, y_2), is $y - y_2 = \dfrac{y_2 - y_1}{x_2 - x_1}(x - x_2)$. We prove that

$$\left[y - y_1 = \frac{y_2 - y_1}{x_2 - x_1}(x - x_1) \right] \Leftrightarrow \left[y - y_2 = \frac{y_2 - y_1}{x_2 - x_1}(x - x_2) \right].$$

That is, any two points (x_1, y_1) and (x_2, y_2), such that $x_1 \neq x_2$, determine a straight line.

$$y - y_1 = \frac{y_2 - y_1}{x_2 - x_1}(x - x_1) \text{ is equivalent to}$$

$$y = \frac{y_2 - y_1}{x_2 - x_1} \cdot x + y_1 - \frac{y_2 - y_1}{x_2 - x_1} \cdot x_1.$$

$$y - y_2 = \frac{y_2 - y_1}{x_2 - x_1}(x - x_2) \text{ is equivalent to}$$

$$y = \frac{y_2 - y_1}{x_2 - x_1} \cdot x + y_2 - \frac{y_2 - y_1}{x_2 - x_1} \cdot x_2.$$

We shall prove that $\quad y_1 - \dfrac{y_2 - y_1}{x_2 - x_1} \cdot x_1 = y_2 - \dfrac{y_2 - y_1}{x_2 - x_1} \cdot x_2.$

$$y_1 - \frac{y_2 - y_1}{x_2 - x_1} \cdot x_1 = \frac{y_1(x_2 - x_1) - (y_2 - y_1)x_1}{x_2 - x_1}$$

$$= \frac{y_1 x_2 - y_2 x_1}{x_2 - x_1}$$

$$= \frac{(y_2 x_2 - y_2 x_1) - (y_2 x_2 - y_1 x_2)}{x_2 - x_1}$$

$$= \frac{y_2(x_2 - x_1) - (y_2 - y_1)x_2}{x_2 - x_1}$$

$$= y_2 - \frac{y_2 - y_1}{x_2 - x_1} \cdot x_2.$$

We write

II
$$y - y_1 = \frac{y_2 - y_1}{x_2 - x_1}(x - x_1)$$

as the equation of *the* straight line through (x_1, y_1) and (x_2, y_2), $x_1 \neq x_2$.

Equation II enables you to write the equation of a line when given two points not on the same vertical line. For example, the line through $(-2,3)$ and $(4,5)$ is

$$y - 3 = \frac{5 - 3}{4 - (-2)}(x + 2), \quad \text{or} \quad y - 3 = \frac{1}{3}(x + 2).$$

As a second example, the line through $(-4,0)$ and $(-3,-5)$ is

$$y - 0 = \frac{-5 - 0}{(-3) - (-4)}(x + 4), \quad \text{or} \quad y = -5(x + 4).$$

(3) To write the equation of a straight line through the points $(3,-2)$ and $(3,5)$, you can proceed as follows:

Since the x-coordinates of the two points are equal $(3 = 3)$, the line is vertical; hence its equation is an instance of $x = a$. Since the line passes through $(3,-2)$,

$$3 = a.$$

The required equation is $x = 3$.

It is easy to generalize this result to write the equation of a straight line through (x_1, y_1) and (x_2, y_2), when $x_1 = x_2$. The required equation is

III
$$x = x_1.$$

EXERCISES §402

1. Write the equations of the straight lines that satisfy the given conditions:
(a) Slope -1 and through $(-4,3)$ (b) Through $(2,3)$ and $(5,7)$
(c) Slope 4 and through $(5,0)$ (d) Slope -3 and through $(0,-2)$
(e) Through $(-1,2)$ and $(3,10)$ (f) Through $(0,6)$ and $(6,0)$
(g) Through $(-4,7)$ and $(-4,6)$.
Answers: (a) $y = -x - 1$;   (b) $y = \frac{4}{3}x + \frac{1}{3}$.

2. Write the equation of a one-parameter family of lines each member of which satisfies the given condition:
(a) Slope 5   (b) Through $(-2,3)$ (c) Through $(-4,5)$
(d) Through $(-1,-2)$ (e) Through $(-7,0)$ (f) Through $(0,-4)$.
Answers: (a) $y = 5x + b$;   (c) $y = m(x + 4) + 5$.

3. What member of the family of lines from the corresponding part of Exercise 2 satisfies the additional condition given below?
(a) Through $(-1,1)$ (b) Slope $1/5$ (c) Through $(2,2)$
(d) Through $(0,0)$ (e) Through $(-7,5)$ (f) Slope 23.
Answers: (a) $v = 5x + 6$;   (c) $y = -\frac{1}{2}x + 3$.

4. (a) The cost of setting up production for a manufactured item is $12,500; once production is set up it costs $.30 to turn out each item. Write the equation that gives the cost c of producing n items. [*Hint:* When $n = 0$, $c = $12,500$. The change in c that corresponds to a change of 1 in n is $.30.]

(b) Express the corresponding linear function, using the notation of sets.

(c) Sketch the corresponding graph, choosing the units on the n-axis and the c-axis to yield a well-balanced graph. What is the range of n? Is this graph continuous?

Answer: (a) $c = .3n + 12,500$, $n \in N$.

5. Repeat Exercise 4 with these data:

(a) A metal bar is 10 cm long when measured at $0°C$. The expansion of the bar is proportional to temperature with a coefficient of expansion of .0004 cm/degree C. Explore the relation $\{(t,l)\}$ where t is measured in degrees centigrade and l in centimeters. Is the graph continuous? Do negative values of t mean anything here?

(b) The population of a town in 1950 was 8500. Suppose the town grows at a steady rate of 500 persons per year. Explore the relation $\{(t,p)\}$, where t is the number of years after 1950 and p is the population of the town. Is the graph continuous? Do negative values of t mean anything here?

6. (a) Write the equation of the two-parameter family of lines through $(0,b)$ and $(a,0)$, that is, with y-intercept b and x-intercept a.

(b) Assume that $a \neq 0$ and $b \neq 0$. Write the equation of part (a) in the form $x/a + y/b = 1$. This is called the *intercept* form of the equation of a line.

7. With the help of Exercise 6(b), write the equation of the line that crosses the axes at:

(a) $(3,0)$ and $(0,5)$	(b) $(2,0)$ and $(0,-4)$	(c) $(1,0)$ and $(0,1)$
(d) $(-6,0)$ and $(0,-1)$	(e) $(h,0)$ and $(0,h)$	(f) $(-h,0)$ and $(0,2h)$.

Answer: (a) $\dfrac{x}{3} + \dfrac{y}{5} = 1$ or $y = \dfrac{-5}{3}x + 5$.

8. Explain why vertical and horizontal lines cannot be written in the intercept form.

403. Arithmetic progressions

Of the many applications of the mathematical model that we have called the linear function, one of the simplest and most useful is to *arithmetic progressions*. An ordered set, or *sequence*, of numbers is called an arithmetic progression when each number of the sequence, after the first, differs from the preceding one by a fixed *increment*. For example, in the sequence

$$4, 7, 10, 13, \ldots,$$

each number differs from the preceding one by the increment 3.

Consider the function $\{(n,y_n)\}$, where $n \in N$, $1 \leq n \leq k$, and, for $n > 1$, $y_n - y_{n-1} = d$. It is easy to write down the values of y_n beginning with y_1.

Since $y_n = y_{n-1} + d$,

$$y_2 = y_1 + d$$
$$y_3 = y_2 + d = y_1 + 2d$$
$$y_4 = y_3 + d = y_1 + 3d$$

. . .

. . .

. . .

$$y_k = y_{k-1} + d = y_1 + (k-1)d.$$

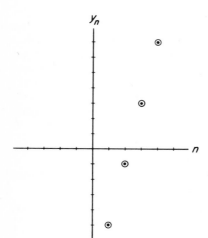

Fig. 4–13.

To each value of n, $1 \leq n \leq k$, there corresponds an element

$$(n,y_n) = (n,y_1 + (n-1)d)$$

of the function $\{(n,y_n)\}$.

The equation $y_n = y_1 + (n-1)d$, or $y_n = dn + (y_1 - d)$, is of the form $y = mx + b$. You make the following replacements: $y = y_n$, $x = n$, $m = d$, and $b = y_1 - d$. Hence the function $\{(n,y_n)\}$ is a linear function in $N \times L$ [$n \in N$ and $y_n = y_1 + (n-1)d \in L$, provided y_1 and d are real numbers].

Consider the instance in which $y_1 = -5$ and $d = 4$. The function $\{(n,y_n)\}$ is $\{(n,(-5) + (n-1)4)\} = \{(n,4n-9)\}$. This is a linear function in $N \times L$. Its graph is a set of isolated points on the line of slope 4 and y-intercept -9 (see Fig. 4–13).

We shall call the parameter y_1 the *first term*, and the parameter d the *common difference* of the arithmetic progression

$$\{y_1, y_2, y_3, \ldots, y_{k-1}, y_k\}.$$

You have learned to express the kth term of the progression,

I $$y_k = y_1 + (k-1)d,$$

in terms of the parameters y_1, d, and k.

Since $y_n - y_{n-1} = d$, $y_{n-1} = y_n - d$. Hence

$$y_{k-1} = y_k - d$$
$$y_{k-2} = y_{k-1} - d = y_k - 2d$$

. . .

. . .

. . .

$$y_1 = y_2 - d = y_k - (k-1)d.$$

The formula

II $$y_1 = y_k - (k - 1)d$$

expresses the first term of an arithmetic progression in terms of the kth term of the progression, and the parameters k and d. For example, given that the tenth term of an arithmetic progression is 37 and the common difference is 4, the first term is

$$y_1 = 37 - 9(4) = 1.$$

It is often useful to have a formula for the *sum* of an arithmetic progression. Let

$$S_k = y_1 + y_2 + \ldots + y_{k-1} + y_k$$

represent the sum of a sequence of k numbers in arithmetic progression. By reversing the order of the terms,

$$S_k = y_k + y_{k-1} + \ldots + y_2 + y_1.$$

Hence, by addition,

$$2S_k = (y_1 + y_k) + (y_2 + y_{k-1}) + \ldots + (y_{k-1} + y_2) + (y_k + y_1).$$

Notice that

$$y_2 + y_{k-1} = (y_1 + d) + (y_k - d) = y_1 + y_k$$
$$y_3 + y_{k-2} = (y_1 + 2d) + (y_k - 2d) = y_1 + y_k$$

$$\begin{array}{ccc} \cdot & \cdot & \cdot \\ \cdot & \cdot & \cdot \\ \cdot & \cdot & \cdot \end{array}$$

$$y_{k-1} + y_2 = [y_1 + (k - 2)d] + [y_k - (k - 2)d] = y_1 + y_k$$
$$y_k + y_1 = \qquad\qquad\qquad\qquad = y_1 + y_k.$$

Hence $$2S_k = (y_1 + y_k) + (y_1 + y_k) + \ldots + (y_1 + y_k) \quad (k \text{ addends})$$
$$= k(y_1 + y_k).$$

The formula

III $$S_k = \frac{k(y_1 + y_k)}{2}$$

expresses the sum of k numbers in arithmetic progression in terms of the first term, y_1, the kth term, y_k, and the number of terms, k.

Since $y_k = y_1 + (k - 1)d$, Formula III may be written

IV $$S_k = \frac{k}{2}[2y_1 + (k - 1)d].$$

Formula IV expresses S_k in terms of the parameters y_1, d, and k. Notice that the corresponding relation $\{(n, S_n)\}$ is *not* linear. The equation

$$S_n = \frac{n}{2}[2y_1 + (n - 1)d] = \frac{d}{2}n^2 + \left(y_1 - \frac{d}{2}\right)n$$

is *not* of the form $y = mx + b$. It is of the form $y = ax^2 + bx$. We shall return to such *quadratic expressions* in Section 404, and again in Chapter 6.

Exercises 403 give you an opportunity to use the complicated-looking Formulas I through IV. We hope that the simplicity of their applications will remove some of the first shock you naturally get when you meet such formulas. We hope you can begin to relax and accept the need for mathematical notation that helps you express your thoughts more exactly.

EXERCISES §403

1. A man has saved $30. He adds $5 to his savings each week.

(a) Write the sequence of numbers that represents his savings at the beginning of each week for the next ten weeks.

Answer: 30, 35, 40, ..., 75.

(b) Is this sequence of numbers an arithmetic progression?

(c) List the elements of the corresponding linear function.

Answer: {(1,30), (2,35), ..., (10,75)}.

(d) Graph this linear function.

(e) Find the 60th term of the arithmetic progression in which $y_1 = 30$ and $d = 5$.

Answer: Using I, $y_{60} = 30 + 59 \cdot 5 = 325$.

(f) Find the 52nd term of this same arithmetic progression.

2. In a question that involves paying a debt by monthly installments, you meet the sum $1 + 2 + 3 + ... + 11 + 12$. Of course you can write these numbers down and add them up. Can you use Formula III to get the sum more easily?

Answer: Let $y_1 = 1, y_2 = 2, ..., y_{12} = 12$ in the model. Since $y_n - y_{n-1} = 1$, $1 < n \le 12$, then 1, 2, 3, ..., 12 is an arithmetic progression. Formula III yields

$$S_{12} = \frac{12(1 + 12)}{2} = 6(13) = 78.$$

3. Use the given parameters of an arithmetic progression to find other parameters of this arithmetic progression:

(a) If $y_1 = 19$ and $d = -3$, find y_{11} and S_{11}.

Answers: $y_{11} = 19 + 10(-3) = -11$ (I);

$$S_{11} = \frac{11[19 + (-11)]}{2} \qquad \text{(III)};$$

$$S_{11} = \frac{11}{2}[38 + 10(-3)] \qquad \text{(IV)}.$$

(b) If $y_{15} = 108$ and $d = 6$, find y_1 and S_{15}.

Answers: $y_1 = 108 - 14(6) = 24$ (II)

$$S_{15} = \frac{15(24 + 108)}{2} \qquad \text{(III)}$$

(c) If $y_1 = 10$ and $y_7 = 32$, find d.

Answer: Formula I yields $32 = 10 + 6d$. Hence $d = 11/3$.

(d) If $y_1 = 6$, $y_n = 22$, and $d = 2$, find n and S_n.

Answers: $n = 9$; $S_n = 126$.

(e) If $y_1 = 15$ and $d = 1/4$, find y_{100} and S_{100}.

(f) If $y_1 = 18$ and $y_{49} = -54$, find d and S_{49}.

(g) If $y_1 = 12$ and $S_{16} = 48$, find y_{16} and d.

Answers: $y_{16} = -6$; $d = -1.2$.

(h) If $y_{20} = 54.2$ and $d = 2.4$, find y_1, y_{10}, and S_{10}.

4. The terms of an arithmetic progression between the first and last terms are called *arithmetic means*.

(a) Insert three arithmetic means between 7 and 15.

Answer: Take $n = 5$, $y_1 = 7$, and $y_5 = 15$. Hence $d = 2$, and the required means are $y_2 = 9$, $y_3 = 11$, $y_4 = 13$.

(b) Insert five arithmetic means between 8 and -7.

Answer: 5.5, 3, .5, -2, -4.5.

(c) Insert four arithmetic means between 59 and 137.

(d) Insert two arithmetic means between 59 and 137.

5. Show that $1 + 2 + 3 + ... + n = \frac{1}{2}n(n + 1)$; that is, the sum of the first n natural numbers is $\frac{1}{2}n(n + 1)$. [*Hint:* Think of this sum as the sum of an arithmetic progression with $y_1 = 1$ and $d = 1$.] Test the statement with $n = 3$; 5; 10.

6. Show that $1 + 3 + 5 + ... + (2n - 1) = n^2$; that is, the sum of the first n odd natural numbers is equal to the square of n. Test the statement with a few selected values of n.

7. Show that $2 + 5 + 8 + 11 + ... + (3n - 1) = \dfrac{n(3n + 1)}{2}$. This is the sum of the first n natural numbers that leave a remainder of 2 when divided by 3.

8. Find a formula for the sum of the first n natural numbers that leave a remainder of 1 when divided by 4.

Answer: $S_n = n(2n - 1)$.

9. How many natural numbers between 100 and 400 are divisible by 7? Determine the sum of these numbers.

Answer: $n = 43$; $S_n = 10,836$.

10. A man takes a job with the understanding that his beginning salary is to be $4200 per year and that he will receive a yearly increase of $300. Under this agreement, what will his salary be during the eighth year? What will be the amount of his total earnings from this job for the first eight years?

Answers: $6300; $42,000.

11. A man must decide between two jobs which are judged to be equivalent except for salary arrangements. Job *A* pays $4200 the first year with salary raises of

$200 each year. Job *B* pays $2100 for the first six months period with salary raises of only $50 each six months. At the end of *n* years, which arrangement will result in more total income? [*Hint:* Determine y_n for each job; then find S_n for job *A* and compare with S_{2n} for job *B* (since there are 2*n* six-month periods in *n* years). It may surprise you to discover that $50 raises at the end of each six months period amounts to $50 more each year than $200 raises at the end of each year.]

12. A triangular pile of logs has one log on the top, two logs in the second row, three in the third, etc. If there are twenty rows of logs, how many are in the entire pile?

Answer: 210.

13. A man plans to invest $500 at the end of each year for the next 10 years. If his investment earns at the rate of 4% simple interest each year, how much money will he have at the end of the 10 years? [*Hint:* Write the terms of the progression in reverse of their natural order, i.e., $500, $520, $540, ...]

14. A free-falling object drops 16 ft during the first second, 48 ft during the second second, etc. In each second it falls 32 ft more than the previous second. How far will it fall during the tenth second? What is the total distance it will have fallen in the first 10 seconds? In the first *n* seconds?

15. In setting up reserve funds for depreciation, a manufacturer decides that a $50,000 machine will depreciate $12,000 the first year, $10,400 the second year, and $1600 less depreciation each succeeding year. Accordingly he puts these amounts in a reserve fund. How much will he place in this fund in the seventh year? At the end of the eighth year the machine will probably be worn out and will need to be replaced. How much will the reserve fund amount to at this time?

Answers: $2400; $51,200.

404. Parabolic-type functions

When you restrict yourself to linear functions, you restrict yourself to equations of the form $y = mx + b$. Now what about equations like $y = x^2$, $y = x^3$, $y = 1/x$, $y = 1/x^2$, etc.? In this section, and the next two, you will investigate the graphs of some of these other algebraic functions; we shall give you examples of how these mathematical models are applied to the world of experience; we shall preview some of the possible generalizations of these functions.

Parabolas. Look first at the equation $y = x^2$. You should check the entries in the table of the relation $\{(x,y) \mid y = x^2\} = \{(x,x^2)\}$:

x	-6	-4	-2	0	2	4	6
y	36	16	4	0	4	16	36

You should extend this table in both directions. You should also fill in some of the gaps. For example, the number-pair $(-5,25)$ is an element of the function. What other ordered pair can you match with $(-5,25)$? Notice that $(-5)^2 = 25$ and $5^2 = 25$; more generally, $(-a)^2 = a^2$. What property of the function corresponds to this fact? Now examine the graph (Fig. 4–14).

Notice that the graph is *symmetrical* with respect to the y-axis. If you think of the y-axis as a mirror, the portion of the curve to the right of the y-axis is a mirror image of the portion of the curve to the left of the y-axis.

Notice also that the graph fulfills the basic requirement for being the graph of a function. No vertical line crosses the graph more than once. So no value of x corresponds to more than one value of y. Hence the relation $\{(x,x^2)\}$ is a function. It is not, however, a one-to-one correspondence; some values of y correspond to *two* distinct values of x. For example, $y = 4$ corresponds to both $x = -2$ *and* $x = 2$.

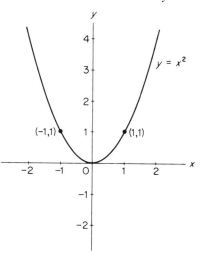

Fig. 4–14.

We call the function $\{(x,y) \mid y = x^2\}$ a *quadratic* function; we say the expression x^2 has *degree* 2. The general quadratic expression in the variable x is $ax^2 + bx + c, a \neq 0$; it is of degree 2 in x because the highest *power* of x in the expression is x^2; that is, the greatest *exponent* of x is 2.

We call the graph of an element of the set of quadratic functions, $\{(x,y) \mid y = ax^2 + bx + c\}$, a *parabola*. For example, we call the graph of $\{(x,y) \mid y = 2x^2 - 3x - 1\}$, or the corresponding condition $y = 2x^2 - 3x - 1$, a parabola. We postpone the general discussion of this three-parameter family of parabolas until Chapter 6; but there are three special instances that are useful, and easy, at this point in our discussion:

First, each instance of

$$y = ax^2$$

resembles $y = x^2$. Both curves pass through $(0,0)$. Compare the graph of $y = 5x^2$ with the graph of $y = x^2$ (Fig. 4–15). Notice that, for each value of x, the equation $y = 5x^2$ yields a value of y 5 times as great as the equation $y = x^2$. For example, when $x = 1$, the two values of y are 5 and 1; when $x = 2$, the two values of y are 20 and 4; etc.

Now compare the graphs of $y = 2x^2$ and $y = -2x^2$ (Fig. 4–16). For a particular value of x, the equation $y = -2x^2$ yields the negative of the value of y that the equation $y = 2x^2$ yields. That is, the graph of $y = -2x^2$ is the reflexion in the x-axis of the graph of $y = 2x^2$.

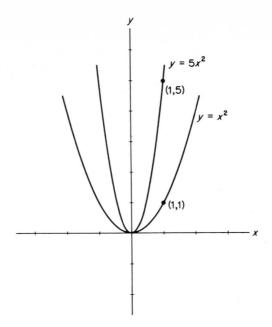

Fig. 4–15.

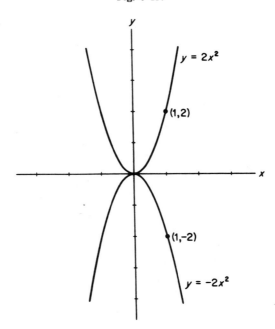

Fig. 4–16.

When you study these examples and plot a few more instances of $y = ax^2$ for yourself, you should conclude that:

When $a \neq 0$, $y = ax^2$ represents a family of parabolas through the origin. (Of course, when $a = 0$ the graph is not a parabola. The equation becomes $y = 0x^2$, or $y = 0$. The graph becomes the x-axis.)

When $a > 0$, the graphs are *concave* as seen from above (like a dish in a position to hold water). When $a < 0$, the graphs are concave as seen from below.

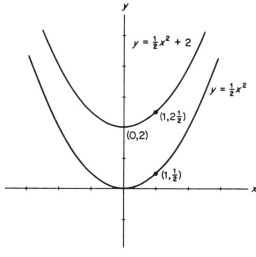

Fig. 4–17.

When $a > 1$, the graphs rise more and more steeply for larger values of a.

When $0 < a < 1$, the graphs are more and more flat for values of a closer to 0.

When $-1 < a < 0$, or when $a < -1$, you can make corresponding statements about the parabolas that are concave as seen from below.

Second, each instance of

$$y = ax^2 + c$$

resembles $y = ax^2$; but the graph of $y = ax^2 + c$ passes through $(0,c)$ instead of $(0,0)$. Compare the graphs of $y = \frac{1}{2}x^2$ and $y = \frac{1}{2}x^2 + 2$ (Fig. 4–17).

Notice that the graph of $y = \frac{1}{2}x^2 + 2$ is the graph of $y = \frac{1}{2}x^2$ shifted 2 units upward. For each value of x, the y of the graph of $y = \frac{1}{2}x^2 + 2$ is 2 more than the y of the graph of $y = \frac{1}{2}x^2$.

In general, the graph of $y = ax^2 + c$ is the graph of $y = ax^2$ shifted c units vertically. When $c > 0$, the curve is shifted upward; when $c < 0$, the curve is shifted downward; when $c = 0$, the curve is shifted 0 units (either up or down; it makes no difference).

To fix this idea in your mind, you may compare the conditions $y_1 = ax^2$ and $y_2 = ax^2 + c$. Clearly, y_2 is $y_1 + c$. Hence you can think of the graph of $y = ax^2 + c$ as the graph of $y = ax^2$ shifted c units vertically. Some students of geometry use the word *alibi* to describe this. When a person has an alibi, he says, "I fit the description of the man you are looking for but I was somewhere else when the crime was committed." When you visualize the graph of $y = ax^2 + c$, you think of it as the graph of $y = ax^2$ shifted to another place.

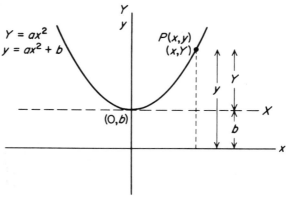

Fig. 4–18.

There is another good way to think of the graph of $y = ax^2 + c$. Rewrite this equation as $y - c = ax^2$. Then replace $y - c$ by the new variable Y. The condition $Y = ax^2$ has the same form as the condition $y = ax^2$. To interpret the new variable Y, study Fig. 4–18. The parabola has two "names," $y = ax^2 + c$ and $Y = ax^2$; any point P on the parabola has two names, (x,y) and (x, Y). We chose the variable Y to make $Y = y - c$. Notice, in the figure, that Y is the vertical distance from the dashed line to the point P. This amounts to using the dashed line as a new horizontal axis, and measuring vertical distances (called Y) from this X-axis.

We shall call this second way of thinking *alias*. When a person takes an alias he is the same person known by another name. When you think of the graph of $y = ax^2 + c$ as the graph of $Y = ax^2$, you give it an alias. You re-name each point of the curve by making $y - c = Y$. This amounts to measuring vertical distances from a new X-axis. You *translate* the x-axis a directed distance c in the vertical direction; you call the new horizontal axis the X-axis.

Third, each instance of

$$y - k = a(x - h)^2$$

resembles $y = ax^2$. Use Fig. 4–19, and the idea of alias, as you think about this. Each point of the parabola has two names, (x,y) and (X, Y).

We take
$$X = x - h$$
$$Y = y - k$$

Then the parabola has two equations, $y - k = a(x - h)^2$ and $Y = aX^2$.

We use the word *vertex* to stand for the lowest point $(a > 0)$, or highest point $(a < 0)$, of the parabola. Then we think of the parabola as having its vertex at (h,k) when we use the x- and y-axes; or we think of the parabola as having its vertex at $(0,0)$ when we use the X- and Y-axes. Thus the parabola

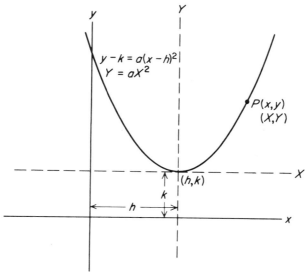

Fig. 4–19.

$y - k = a(x - h)^2$ is the parabola $Y = aX^2$ with an alias. We know about parabolas whose equations take the form $y = ax^2$; hence we know about parabolas whose equations take the form $y - k = a(x - h)^2$.

When we return, in Chapter 6, to the three-parameter family of parabolas, $y = ax^2 + bx + c$, you will learn to rewrite the condition $y = ax^2 + bx + c$ in the form $Y = aX^2$. This amounts to translating the x-axis into a new X-axis, and the y-axis into a new Y-axis, to make the new origin the vertex of the parabola.

Before continuing your study of parabolic-type functions, you should work some exercises.

EXERCISES §404

1. Write the instance of $y = ax^2$ with $a = \frac{1}{3}$. Compare the graphs of $y = \frac{1}{3}x^2$ and $y = x^2$.

2. Repeat Exercise 1 with (a) $a = 3$; (b) $a = -1/3$; (c) $a = -3$.

3. Write the instance of $y = ax^2 + c$ with $a = -5, c = 3$. Compare the graphs of $y = -5x^2$ and $y = -5x^2 + 3$. Compare the graphs of $y = x^2$ and $y = -5x^2 + 3$.

4. Repeat Exercise 3 with (a) $a = -5$ and $c = -3$; (b) $a = 5$ and $c = 3$; (c) $a = 5$ and $c = -3$.

5. Repeat Exercise 3 with (a) $a = 1/5$ and $c = 3$; (b) $a = -1/5$ and $c = 3$; (c) $a = 1/5$ and $c = -3$; (d) $a = -1/5$ and $c = -3$.

6. Write the instance of $y - k = a(x - h)^2$ with $a = 1/2$, $h = 2$, and $k = 3$. Compare the graphs of $y - 3 = \frac{1}{2}(x - 2)^2$ and $y = \frac{1}{2}x^2$.

7. Repeat Exercise 6 with (a) $a = 1/2$, $h = -2$, and $k = 3$; (b) $a = 1/2$, $h = -2$, and $k = -3$; (c) $a = 2$, $h = 2$, and $k = -3$.

8. When you graph a condition, like $y = 2x^2 - 3x + 5$, for each replacement of x, you can find a number-pair (x,y) that belongs to the function $\{(x,y) \mid y = 2x^2 - 3x + 5\}$. For example, for $x = 7$, $y = 2 \cdot 7^2 - 3 \cdot 7 + 5 = 82$; hence $(7,82)$ belongs to the function. Find the number-pair that corresponds to each of the following replacements of x: (a) -8; (b) -2; (c) 0; (d) 2; (e) 8.

9. In Exercise 8 we call the value of y that corresponds to $x = 0$ the y-intercept of the graph. Since the number-pair $(0,5)$ belongs to the function, the y-intercept of the graph is 5. Find the y-intercept of each of the following parabolas: (a) $y = 3x^2 - 2x + 17$; (b) $y = -3x^2 + 2x - 17$; (c) $y = -x^2 + 17x - 32$.

10. Make a table of number-pairs that belong to the function $\{(x,.3x^2)\}$. Choose values of x in the range $0 \le x \le 4$; begin with $x = 0$, and use the increment 0.5 to get successive values of x. Plot these points and locate other points, using your knowledge of the symmetry of the graph. Draw the graph.

11. Make a table of six selected number-pairs that belong to the function $\{(x,y) \mid y = \frac{1}{4}x^2 - 3\}$. Sketch the graph of this function.

12. Graph the condition $y = \frac{1}{4}x^2$, and use the idea of alibi to graph the condition $y = \frac{1}{4}x^2 - 3$.

13. Using the idea of alibi, sketch the following parabolas:

(a) $y = 2x^2 + 4$ (b) $y = -3x^2 + 8$
(c) $y = \frac{1}{3}x^2 - 2$ (d) $y = -\frac{1}{5}x^2 - 5$
(e) $y = \frac{1}{100}x^2 - 1$.

14. Graph the parabola $y = -\frac{1}{3}x^2$, and use the idea of alias to graph the parabola $y - 4 = -\frac{1}{3}(x - 2)^2$.

15. Using the idea of alias, sketch the following parabolas:

(a) $y + 3 = 2(x - 1)^2$ (b) $y - 3 = 2(x + 1)^2$
(c) $y + 4 = \frac{1}{2}(x + 3)^2$ (d) $y = -\frac{1}{2}(x - 2)^2$
(e) $y + 2 = \frac{1}{10}x^2$.

16. Graph the following inequalities:

(a) $y > \frac{1}{3}x^2 - 5$ (b) $y \le 2x^2 + 1$ (c) $y - 1 > \frac{1}{3}(x + 3)^2$.

Other, parabolic-type curves. Figure 4–20 shows a table and a graph for $y = x^3$. Use this opportunity to work with signed numbers. Extend the table and fill in some of the gaps. For example, when $x = -.5$, $y = (-.5)^3 = -.125$. Hence the number-pair $(-.5, -.125)$ is an element of the function $\{(x, x^3)\}$. What about the number-pair $(.5, .125)$?

Notice that the graph of $y = x^3$ is *symmetrical with respect to the origin*.

Figure 4–21 shows a table and a graph for $y = x^4$. Notice that $y \geq 0$ for each value of x. Compare the graphs of $y = x^4$ and $y = x^2$. Both graphs

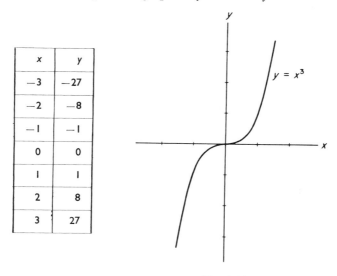

x	y
−3	−27
−2	−8
−1	−1
0	0
1	1
2	8
3	27

Fig. 4–20.

are symmetrical with respect to the y-axis. The graph $y = x^4$ rises more sharply for $x > 1$ and is flatter near $x = 0$.

We could go on to discuss the graphs of $y = ax^3 + d$ and $y = ax^4 + e$ as we discussed the graph of $y = ax^2 + c$. We could also discuss $y = x^5$, $y = x^6$, etc. We prefer to leave these generalizations for exercises at the end of this section. We proceed, instead, to some applications of parabolic-type functions.

Extensions of direct variation. In Section 400 we used the sentence "y varies directly as x" as equivalent to the algebraic condition $y = mx$. We interpreted m as a parameter, and the condition $y = mx$ as the family of non-vertical lines through the origin. We now proceed to study sentences like "y varies directly as x^2," "y varies directly as x^3," and the like.

We interpret "y varies directly as x^2," "y varies as x^2," or "y varies as the square of x" to mean $y = ax^2$. We picture the condition $y = ax^2$ as a family of parabolas through the origin. You have already explored the effect of the parameter a.

Similarly, "*y* varies directly as x^3," or the like, means $y = ax^3$. Graphically, $y = ax^3$ is a family of curves that resemble $y = x^3$.

Scientists make extensive use of the language of variation. The following examples, and the exercises at the end of this section, illustrate this fact:

(1) The lifting-force of an airplane wing varies directly as its area. For wings of the same shape, the area varies as the square of the length. A model plane with wing span 1.00 ft has a lift of 1.50 lb. Find the lift of a similar plane flying at the same airspeed, but with wing span 110 ft.

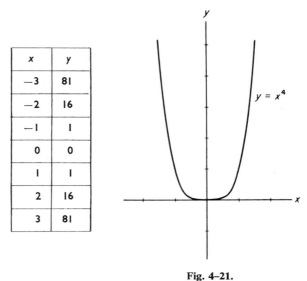

x	y
−3	81
−2	16
−1	1
0	0
1	1
2	16
3	81

$y = x^4$

Fig. 4–21.

We use the *quadratic* function $\{(L, kL^2)\}$ as a mathematical model. The area (A), and hence the lifting-force (F), vary directly with the square of the length (L^2).

The corresponding condition is $F = kL^2$, where k is a parameter that depends upon wing design, airspeed, etc. We know the number-pair (1.00, 1.50) belongs to the function $\{(L, F)\}$. Hence $1.50 = k(1.00)^2$, and $k = 1.50$. The condition for the given design, airspeed, etc., is

$$F = 1.50L^2.$$

When $L = 110$, $F = 1.50(110)^2 = 1.50(12,100) = 18,150.$

In practice, you might *round off* the number 18,150 and say the lifting force is approximately 18,200 lb. Errors in measurement of the length, 1.00 ft, and lifting-force, 1.50 lb, of the model plane affect the accuracy of the value $k = 1.50$, and hence of the value $F \doteq 18,150$ lb.

(2) In a given culture, the number of babies per year (B) varies as the number of women of childbearing age (W). The condition is $B = kW$,

where k is a parameter that depends upon the culture. This corresponds to the *linear* function $\{(W,kW)\}$.

(3) The weight (W) of silt carried by a cubic foot of flood water varies directly as the sixth power of the speed (S) that the water moves. The condition is $W = kS^6$, where k is a parameter that depends upon the type of silt, the type of water, etc. This corresponds to a *sixth-degree* function $\{(S,kS^6)\}$.

Suppose the number-pair $(10,.002)$ belongs to the function; That is, at 10 ft per second (ft/sec) of speed, the water carries .002 oz of silt per cubic foot. Notice that $.002 = k \cdot 10^6$ gives $k = .000,000,002$. When $S = 30$ ft/sec, $W = k(30^6) = (k)729,000,000 \doteq 1.5$ oz; when $S = 60$ ft/sec, $W = k(60^6) \doteq 93$ oz. You can prove that when the water travels 10 times as fast it carries 1,000,000 times as much silt.

EXERCISES §404 (cont.)

17. Write the instance of $y = ax^3$ with $a = \frac{1}{3}$. Compare the graphs of $y = \frac{1}{3}x^3$ and $y = x^3$.

18. Repeat Exercise 17 with (a) $a = 3$; (b) $a = -\frac{1}{3}$; (c) $a = -3$.

19. Write the instance of $y = ax^3 + d$ with $a = \frac{1}{2}$ and $d = 4$. Compare the graphs of $y = \frac{1}{2}x^3 + 4$ and $y = \frac{1}{2}x^3$. Compare the graphs of $y = \frac{1}{2}x^3 + 4$ and $y = x^3$.

20. Repeat Exercise 19 with (a) $a = 2$ and $d = -4$; (b) $a = -\frac{1}{2}$ and $d = 4$; (c) $a = -2$ and $d = -4$.

21. Write the instance of $y - k = a(x - h)^3$ with $a = \frac{1}{2}$, $h = 3$, and $k = -1$. Compare the graphs of $y + 1 = \frac{1}{2}(x - 3)^3$ and $y = \frac{1}{2}x^3$.

22. Repeat Exercise 21 with (a) $a = 2$, $h = -3$, and $k = 1$; (b) $a = 2$, $h = -3$, and $k = -1$.

23. Write the instance of $y = ax^4 + e$ with $a = \frac{1}{4}$ and $e = 0$. Compare the graphs of $y = \frac{1}{4}x^4$ and $y = x^4$.

24. Do exercises like 18 through 22, replacing x^3 by x^4, and d by e.

25. For the function $\{(x,y) \mid y = 2x^3 - 3x^2 + x - 7\}$, find the number-pair that corresponds to each of the following replacements of x: (a) -2; (b) 0; (c) 2.

26. Repeat Exercise 25 for the function $\{(x,y) \mid y = 7x^4 - 2x + 3\}$.

27. Find the y-intercept of the graph of each function:
(a) $\{(x,y) \mid y = 4x^3 - 2x^2 + 11\}$
(b) $\{(x,y) \mid y = 3x^5 - 2x^4 + x\}$
(c) $\{(x,y) \mid y = 5x^8 - 3x^4 + 2x^3 - 7x^2 + x - 1\}$.

28. Using the idea of alibi, sketch the following graphs:
(a) $y = \frac{1}{4}x^3 - 7$ (b) $y = \frac{1}{2}x^4 + 3$ (c) $y \leq 2x^3 + 1$
(d) $y > x^3 - 1$ (e) $y < \frac{1}{4}x^5$.

29. Using the idea of alias, sketch the following graphs:

(a) $y - 3 = \frac{1}{2}(x - 2)^3$ (b) $y + 2 = \frac{1}{6}(x - 3)^3$

(c) $y + 1 = \frac{1}{5}(x + 2)^4$ (d) $y - 5 \geq 2(x + 4)^4$

(e) $y - 2 < \frac{1}{3}x^4$ (f) $y > \frac{1}{4}(x - 3)^3$.

30. If (x_1,y_1) and (x_2,y_2) are two elements of the function $\{(x,y) \mid y = ax^2\}$, prove that $\dfrac{y_2}{y_1} = \dfrac{x_2{}^2}{x_1{}^2}$. If x_2 is 3 times x_1, what does this proportion say about y_2 and y_1? What about the element $(0, 0)$?

31. The area of a projected slide varies as the square of the distance from the slide-projector to the screen. When the projector is 8 ft from the screen the area of the picture is 15 sq ft. Find the area of the picture corresponding to each of the following projector distances: (a) 16 ft; (b) 4 ft; (c) 10 ft; (d) 20 ft.

Answers: (a) 60 sq ft;   (c) 23.4 sq ft.

32. The thrust of an airplane propeller varies as the square of the number of revolutions per minute. How will the thrust change if the speed of rotation is (a) doubled; (b) tripled; (c) increased by 50%; (d) decreased by 50%?

Answers: (a) quadrupled;   (c) increased by 125%.

33. The distance that a ball, starting at rest, rolls down an inclined plane is proportional to the square of the time. If it travels 2 ft in the first second, how far will it travel in (a) 2 sec; (b) 2.5 sec; (c) 1.2 sec; (d) 0.5 sec.

Answers: (a) 8 ft;   (c) 2.88 ft.

405. Hyperbolic-type functions

Hyperbolas. Look first at the equation, $y = 1/x$. You should check the entries in the table of the relation $\{(x,1/x)\}$:

x	-6	-4	-2	0	2	4	6
y	$-1/6$	$-1/4$	$-1/2$	undefined	$1/2$	$1/4$	$1/6$

You should extend this table in both directions. You should also fill in some of the gaps. For example, the number-pair (1,1) is an element of the relation. So is the number-pair $(-1,-1)$. Study Fig. 4–22 to discover its symmetry.

Notice that the graph is symmetrical with respect to the origin. You can imagine that the point $(0,0)$ is a tiny mirror. The image of each point, such as $(3,\frac{1}{3})$, is a second point, such as $(-3,-\frac{1}{3})$, also on the curve.

Notice that when $x = 0$ the equation $y = 1/x$ does not define a value of y. Thus we cannot include the value $x = 0$ in the range of x. For all other replacements of x by real numbers, just one value of y corresponds to each value of x. Hence the relation $\{(x,1/x)\}$ is a function. Notice that the relation is also a one-to-one correspondence (except that no value of y corresponds to $x = 0$, and no value of x corresponds to $y = 0$).

When we express the condition $y = 1/x$ in words, we say "y is the

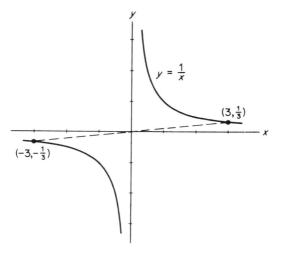

Fig. 4–22.

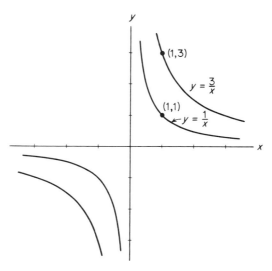

Fig. 4–23.

reciprocal of x." We describe the more general condition, $y = k/x$, by saying "*y varies inversely as x*," or "*y is inversely proportional to x*." Scientists make frequent use of this language of *inverse variation*. They call k the constant of proportionality. In Fig. 4–23, notice that for each value of x the equation

$y = 3/x$ yields a value of y three times as great as the equation $y = 1/x$. In other words, the graph of $y = 3/x$ is, at each of its points, three times as far from the x-axis as the graph of $y = 1/x$.

Consider the following application of the relation $\{(x,k/x)\}$: In a simple electric circuit, the current I varies inversely as the resistance R. Given that $I = 10$ amp when $R = 11$ ohms, find I when $R = 55$ ohms.

Since I varies inversely as R, you know that

$$I = k/R, \quad \text{or} \quad I \cdot R = k.$$

where k is a parameter. Since $I = 10$ when $R = 11$, you know that

$$10 \cdot 11 = k.$$

Hence $k = 110$. (Electricians would say that this circuit carries 110 volts.) Now that you have determined the parameter k, you have

$$I = 110/R \quad \text{or} \quad IR = 110.$$

When $R = 55$ ohms, $I = 110/55 = 2$ amp.

We call the family of functions $\{(x,y) \mid y = k/x\}$ *hyperbolic* functions. We call the graph of a member of this family a *hyperbola*.

EXERCISES §405

1. Write the instance of $y = k/x$ with $k = 2$. Compare the graphs of $y = 2/x$ and $y = 1/x$.

2. Repeat Exercise 1 with (a) $k = 1/2$; (b) $k = -2$; (c) $k = -1/2$.

3. (a) The number of items (n) a producer sells varies inversely as the price per item (p). Given that $n = 100$ when p is \$.20, find n when p is \$.40.

(b) Repeat part (a) when p is \$.60, \$.80, \$1.00.

(c) What is the effect upon n of doubling p? of multiplying p by 5? of multiplying p by 10?

Answers: (a) 50; (c) n is 1/2 as large, 1/5 as large, 1/10 as large.

4. If (x_1,y_1) and (x_2,y_2) are elements of the function $\{(x,y) \mid y = k/x\}$, prove that $y_2/y_1 = x_1/x_2$. If x_2 is 3 times x_1, what does this proportion say about y_1 and y_2?

5. For a given length of movie film, the viewing time (T) is inversely proportional to the speed (S) that the projector is operated. This means that $T = k/S$.

(a) Determine k if T is 30 min when S is 16 pictures per second.

(b) Make a table to show how many minutes the film will last if $S = 8, 12, 16, 24, 32,$ and 64 pictures per second.

(c) Graph the function $\{(S,T)\}$. (Choose the units carefully so that the graph will fit on the graph paper. The units need not be the same on the two axes.)

6. Suppose that a roll of film will last 60 min when the projector is operated at 16 pictures per second. Use the ideas of Exercise 4 and determine, without first finding k, how long the film will last if the projector is operated at 48 pictures per second; at 64 pictures per second; at 8 pictures per second.

Answers: 20 min;   15 min;   120 min.

7. The volume of a given amount of gas is inversely proportional to the pressure applied. If the pressure is doubled what will happen to the volume? If the pressure is only 1/3 the original pressure, how will the volume change?

8. Using the idea of alibi, sketch the following graphs:

(a) $y = \dfrac{3}{x} - 2$;   (b) $y = -\dfrac{2}{x} + 3$.

9. Using the idea of alias, sketch the following graphs:

(a) $y - 4 = \dfrac{2}{x - 2}$;   (b) $y + 4 = \dfrac{2}{x + 2}$.

Other hyperbolic-type curves. Figure 4–24 presents a table and a graph for $y = 1/x^2$. You should begin to associate symmetry about the y-axis with

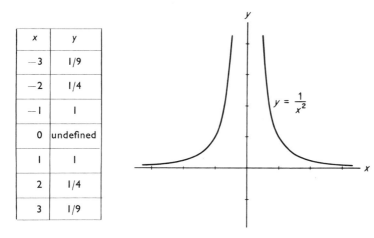

x	y
-3	$1/9$
-2	$1/4$
-1	1
0	undefined
1	1
2	$1/4$
3	$1/9$

$y = \dfrac{1}{x^2}$

Fig. 4–24.

even powers of x (the expression $1/x^2$ here). Compare the graphs of $y = 1/x^2$ and $y = 1/x$ to notice the different types of symmetry they involve. Also notice that both curves pass through $(1,1)$, but that $y = 1/x^2$ *approaches* the x-axis more quickly than $y = 1/x$ does. For example, the point $(2,\frac{1}{4})$ on $y = 1/x^2$ contrasts with the point $(2,\frac{1}{2})$ on $y = 1/x$.

We call the generalization $\{(x,k/x^2)\}$ of the relation $\{(x,1/x^2)\}$ "inverse variation as the *square*." Thus the equation $y = k/x^2$, or $x^2y = k$, is an algebraic translation of the sentence, "y varies *inversely as the square* of x," or "y is *inversely proportional to the square* of x."

Compare the graphs of $y = 3/x^2$ and $y = 1/x^2$ (Fig. 4–25). For each replacement of x, the y of $y = 3/x^2$ is three times the y of $y = 1/x^2$.

Consider the following application of the relation $\{(x,y) \mid y = k/x^2\}$: The brightness I of the picture on a screen varies inversely as the square of distance

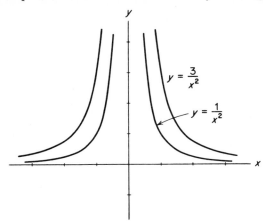

Fig. 4–25.

x	y
−3	−1/27
−2	−1/8
−1	−1
0	0
1	1
2	1/8
3	1/27

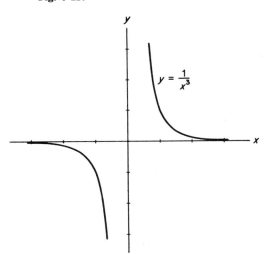

Fig. 4–26.

d from the projector to the screen. Given that $I = 2$ when $d = 5$, find I when $d = 10$. Since I varies inversely as d^2, you know that

$$I = k/d^2,$$

where k is a parameter. Since $I = 2$ when $d = 5$,

$$2 = k/5^2.$$

Hence $k/25 = 2$, and $k = 50$. Now that you have determined the value of k, you have

$$I = 50/d^2.$$

When $d = 10$, $I = 50/10^2 = 1/2$. It is characteristic of this relation that doubling d (from $d = 5$ to $d = 10$) makes I one fourth as great (from $I = 2$ to $I = 1/2$).

Figure 4–26 shows a table and a graph for $y = 1/x^3$. You should begin to associate symmetry about the origin with *odd* powers of x (the expression $1/x^3$ here). Compare the graphs of $y = 1/x^3$ and $y = 1/x$. Notice that they have the same sort of symmetry. But notice that $y = 1/x^3$ approaches the x-axis more quickly than $y = 1/x$ does. For example, the point $(2,\frac{1}{8})$ on $y = 1/x^3$ contrasts with the point $(2,\frac{1}{2})$ on $y = 1/x$.

EXERCISES §405 (cont.)

10. (a) Is the family of relations $\{(x,k/x^2)\}$ a family of functions?

(b) If $k > 0$, what can you say about the quadrants in which the graphs of the members of the family of curves lie?

(c) If $k < 0$, what can you say about the quadrants in which the graphs of the members of the family of curves lie?

11. (a) Is the family of relations $\{(x,k/x^3)\}$ a family of functions?

(b) In what quadrants does the graph lie for a replacement of k such that $k > 0$?

(c) In what quadrants does the graph lie for a replacement of k such that $k < 0$?

12. Are the relations of Exercise 10 one-to-one correspondences? How about the relations of Exercise 11?

13. Write the instance of $y = k/x^2$ with $k = 1/2$. Compare the graphs of $y = 1/2x^2$ and $y = 1/x^2$.

14. Repeat Exercise 13 with (a) $k = 2$, (b) $k = -2$, (c) $k = -1/2$.

15. Write the instance of $y = k/x^3$ with $k = 2$. Compare the graphs of $y = 2/x^3$ and $y = 1/x^3$.

16. Repeat Exercise 15 with (a) $k = -2$, (b) $k = 1/2$, (c) $k = -1/2$.

17. (a) The weight (W) of an object varies inversely as the square of its distance (d) from the center of gravity of the earth. Given that W is 10 lb when d is 4000 mi, find W when d is 5000 mi.

(b) Repeat part (a) when d is 8000 mi, 10,000 mi, 16,000 mi, 20,000 mi.

(c) What is the effect upon W of doubling d? of multiplying d by 5? of multiplying d by 10?

(d) What happens to the weight of a rocket that travels 500 mi up from the earth's surface?

18. If $y = k/x^2$, prove that $y_2/y_1 = (x_1)^2/(x_2)^2$. If x_2 is twice as great as x_1, what does this proportion state about y_2 and y_1?

19. The force of attraction of a magnet is inversely proportional to the square of the distance of the object from the magnet. If the distance is doubled, what is the effect on the force? (See Exercise 18.) What happens when the distance is tripled? When it is halved?

20. The distance that a free-falling object travels varies as the square of the elapsed time. If a stone falls 64 ft in 2 sec, how far will it fall in 3 sec? Caution: This is direct, *not* inverse, variation.

21. Using the idea of alibi, sketch the following graphs:

(a) $y = \dfrac{1}{x^2} - 3$ (b) $y = \dfrac{1}{3x^3} + 2$.

22. Using the idea of alias, sketch the following graphs:

(a) $y - 2 = \dfrac{4}{(x + 1)^2}$ (b) $y + 2 = \dfrac{4}{(x - 1)^2}$

(c) $y = \dfrac{3}{(x - 2)^2} + 5$ $\left(Hint\text{: Write the equivalent condition, } y - 5 = \dfrac{3}{(x-2)^2} \right)$

(d) $y = \dfrac{1}{3x^2} - 2$.

23. Graph the following inequalities:

(a) $y \geq 2/x$ (b) $y - 1 < \dfrac{1}{x + 3}$

(c) $y \leq \dfrac{1}{3x^2}$ (d) $y > \dfrac{4}{x^2} - 3$

(e) $y + 5 \geq 2/x^3$ (f) $y < 2/x$ and $x > 0$

(g) $y < 1/x^2$ and $y > 0$ (h) $y > 2/x$ or $y > x$

(i) $y > 5/x + 2$ and $y < -x + 8$.

406. Algebraic functions

All the functions you have met in this chapter are examples of *algebraic* functions. Now is a good time to take a fresh look at these functions. As you read this section, you should try to separate details from key ideas; you should look back, and you should look ahead.

We call expressions like $ax^2 + bx + c$, $\dfrac{ax^3 + bx}{cx + d}$, and the like, *algebraic*

expressions in the variable x. These expressions involve *powers* of x like $x^1 = x$, $x^2 = x \cdot x$, $x^3 = x \cdot x \cdot x$, etc. They also involve parameters, which do not depend upon x, like a, b, and c in the expression $ax^2 + bx + c$.

We call these expressions algebraic because you can construct them by algebraic additions and multiplications of real numbers and the variable x.

Of course, algebraic subtractions and divisions are included as inverses of additions and multiplications. Thus, you construct the expression

$$\frac{3x^2 - 2x + 5}{x^3 - \sqrt{2}}$$

from the real numbers 3, -2, 5, and $-\sqrt{2}$, and the variable x, by algebraic additions and multiplications.

There are still other expressions that we shall call algebraic. Besides additions and multiplications, algebra includes other operations like square root, cube root, etc. Thus we call expressions like $\sqrt{3x - 1}$ (the square root of $3x - 1$), $1/\sqrt[3]{x^2 + a}$, etc., algebraic expressions. We shall return to algebraic expressions that involve *radicals* in Chapter 5. Meanwhile we ignore such expressions in the variable x.

The simplest algebraic expressions are *polynomials*. As their name suggests, polynomials may have many terms. Examples are $3x^2 - 2x + 5$, $ax^3 + bx^2 + cx + d$, and $2x^{16}$. The expression $2x^2 - 3/x^3$ is *not* a polynomial, because it contains the term $3/x^3$ involving division by a power of x. We shall return, in Chapter 6, to a formal definition of the word polynomial.

Next come the *rational* algebraic expressions, like $\dfrac{3x - 2}{x^2 + 7}$, $\dfrac{ax^2 + bx + c}{x - k}$, and the like. These expressions have the form of fractions whose numerators and denominators are polynomials.

Finally, there are non-rational expressions that involve roots of polynomials.

It is convenient to introduce new symbols to make it easier to talk about algebraic functions. We shall use the symbol $a(x)$ to represent any element of the set of algebraic expressions; we shall use $p(x)$ to represent any element of the set of polynomials; and we shall use $r(x)$ to represent any element of the set of rational algebraic expressions. These symbols are read "a of x," "p of x," etc.

With these new symbols it is easy to explain what an *algebraic relation* in the variable x is. It is a set of number-pairs $\{(x,a(x))\}$ in $L \times L$. Similarly, a polynomial relation is a set of number-pairs $\{(x,p(x))\}$, and a rational algebraic relation is a set of number-pairs $\{(x,r(x))\}$.

We make one more agreement about these new symbols. An example with polynomials will make this clear: Suppose

$$p(x) = x^3 - 2x + 1.$$

Then

$$p(3) = (3)^3 - 2(3) + 1 = 22$$

$$p(-2) = (-2)^3 - 2(-2) + 1 = -3$$

$$p(a) = a^3 - 2a + 1, \text{ etc.}$$

That is, you may replace x by any number from its range to obtain a corresponding value of $p(x)$. The symbol $p(x)$ is, then, a variable whose value depends upon the value you assign to x. It does *not* mean "p times x."

In a particular problem the variable x has a definite range; we shall define each algebraic expression $a(x)$ that we use, to give it exactly one value corresponding to each replacement of x. Hence the relation $\{(x,a(x))\}$ is an *algebraic function*.

We shall speak of $\{(x,a(x))\}$ as a function from the range of the *independent variable* x to the range of the *dependent variable* $a(x)$. This language is convenient. You think of choosing a replacement for x first; you make a free choice of a value of x from the range of x; that is, x is the *independent* variable. To each replacement of x there corresponds a unique value of $a(x)$; that is, $a(x)$ is the *dependent* variable.*

EXERCISES §406

1. Given $p(x) = 2x^3 - x^2 + 4$, calculate $p(-2)$, $p(-1)$, $p(0)$, $p(1)$, and $p(2)$. Tabulate the corresponding ordered number-pairs of the function $\{(x,p(x))\}$.

Answer: $\{..., (-2,-16), (-1,1), (0,4), (1,5), (2,16), ...\}$.

2. Repeat Exercise 1 for $r(x) = \dfrac{3x^2 - 2}{x + 5}$. Notice that you must exclude the value -5 from the range of x. Why?

3. Repeat Exercise 1 for $a(x) = x^2 + 9$. Notice that $a(x)$ is an algebraic expression that is also a rational algebraic expression and a polynomial.

4. Recall the terminology you used to describe sets of numbers, in particular the sets N, R, and L. Compare this with the new terminology of algebraic functions. What special algebraic functions correspond to natural numbers, to rational numbers, and to irrational numbers?

5. Classify each of the following algebraic expressions as a polynomial, a rational algebraic expression, or a non-rational algebraic expression.

(a) $3x^5 - 2x^2 + 7$

(b) $\dfrac{2x^3 - 3x^2 + x}{2}$ $\quad \left[\text{*Hint:* equivalent to } x^3 - \dfrac{3}{2}x^2 + \dfrac{1}{2}x \right]$

(c) $\dfrac{3x - 1}{2x^2 + 3x + 7}$

(d) $\dfrac{\sqrt[3]{x - 1}}{\sqrt{x^2 + 3x + 7}}$.

* Many writers speak of the *domain* and *range* of a function. The domain of $\{(x,y)\}$ is the set from which you may pick replacements for x; the range of $\{(x,y)\}$ is the set of values of y that corresponds to all the replacements of x. We shall speak more simply of the range of x and the range of y as we discuss the function $\{(x,y)\}$.

6. Use the notation of sets to express the algebraic function that corresponds to each algebraic expression in Exercise 5. For example, corresponding to part (a) is $\{(x,y) \mid y = 3x^5 - 2x^2 + 7\}$ or the equivalent symbol $\{(x, 3x^5 - 2x^2 + 7)\}$.

7. Let $p(x) = 2x$. The corresponding polynomial function is $\{(x, p(x))\} = \{(x, 2x)\} = \{(x,y) \mid y = 2x\}$. Suppose the range of x is N. What is the range of y?

8. Repeat Exercise 7 for (a) $p(x) = -2x$; (b) $p(x) = x^2$; (c) $p(x) = \frac{1}{2}x$; (d) $p(x) = -x^3$.

9. If (x_1, y_1) is a number-pair of the function $\{(x,y) \mid y = 3x^4 - 2x^2 + 7 + 5/x^2\}$, show that the number-pair $(-x_1, y_1)$ also belongs to the same function. What can you conclude about the symmetry of the graph of this function?

10. With the help of the graph of $y = x^2$, shade the part of the coordinate plane for which $y > x^2$.

11. Graph the set of points that satisfy each condition:

(a) $y > 2x^2$

(b) $y > -2x^2$

(c) $y < \dfrac{1}{x^2}$

(d) $y > \frac{1}{2}x^2$ and $y < 4$

(e) $y < \dfrac{1}{x}$ and $y > 0$ and $x > 0$

(f) $y < -\frac{1}{2}x^2 + 4$

(g) $y > \frac{1}{4}x^4$ and $y < \frac{1}{2}x + 3$.

12. (a) Make a table of eight number-pairs of the function $\{(x,y) \mid y = \frac{1}{2}x^2 + 2$ and $x > 0$, or, $y = x + 2$ and $x \leq 0\}$. Choose x to be positive for about half of the number-pairs and negative for the others.

(b) Draw the graph of this function.

407. Exponential functions

In previous sections, we gave you some examples of algebraic functions. Then we suggested ways to generalize these examples. Perhaps you began to wonder whether it would be possible to construct algebraic functions to fit any demand that might arise. It might be. But it would take a very complicated algebraic function to describe some everyday things that are much easier to describe in other ways.

Americans who watch quiz programs have become familiar with games where you may double your money. Thus, the table

Number of successive questions correctly answered (n)	1	2	3	4	5	6	7
Pay off (P dollars)	1	2	4	8	16	32	64

describes such a game. The range of n is the set $\{1, 2, 3, 4, 5, 6, 7\}$. The range of P is the set $\{1, 2, 4, 8, 16, 32, 64\}$. The set of ordered pairs, $\{(n,P)\}$, displayed in the table is a function.

Consider, now, the function $\{(n,S) \mid S = 2^n\}$. If the range of n is the set of positive integers, the range of S is the set of powers of 2 with positive integral exponents. The table,

n	1	2	3	4	...
S	2	4	8	16	...

lists a few of the elements of this function. You can calculate the value of S that corresponds to any value of n (from its range). For example, when $n = 6$, $S = 2^6 = 2 \times 2 \times 2 \times 2 \times 2 \times 2 = 64$.

People are usually surprised when first they realize what large values of S correspond to comparatively small values of n. For example, when $n = 12$, $S = 2^{12} = 2^6 \times 2^6 = 64 \times 64 = 4096$; when $n = 24$, $S = 2^{24} = 2^{12} \times 2^{12} = (4096)(4096) = 16{,}777{,}216$; etc. When a number that represents a population, price, or monthly sale of yo-yos, increases very rapidly, people say it increases "almost exponentially."

Except in quiz programs, it is unusual to double your money on each successive try. For example, when you invest money, you may increase the amount of your investment by 5% per year (rather than double it, or increase it by 100% per year). When you begin with a *principal* of $1, and increase your amount by 5% per year, you get:

After 1 year, $S_1 = 1 + .05(1) = 1.05$
After 2 years, $S_2 = 1.05 + .05(1.05) = (1 + .05)1.05 = (1.05)^2$
After 3 years, $S_3 = (1.05)^2 + .05(1.05)^2 = (1 + .05)(1.05)^2 = (1.05)^3$
After n years, $S_n = (1.05)^n$.

You can use the equation $S = (1.05)^n$ to calculate the amount at the end of n years when you invest $1 at 5% *compound interest*. It is more convenient to use a compound interest table. In the 5% column of your table, you will find:

$$(1.05)^{14} \doteq 1.9799$$

$$(1.05)^{15} \doteq 2.0789$$

Thus it takes between 14 and 15 yr to accumulate $2 by investing $1 at 5% compound interest.

The variable S, in the equation $S = (1.05)^n$, grows much more slowly than the variable S in the equation $S = 2^n$. But, as n becomes greater, $S = (1.05)^n$ grows more and more rapidly. In your table you will find

$$(1.05)^{50} \doteq 11.4674.$$

Hence $(1.05)^{100} = (1.05)^{50}(1.05)^{50} \doteq (11.4674)(11.4674) \doteq 131.50,$

and $(1.05)^{200} = (1.05)^{100}(1.05)^{100} \doteq (131.50)(131.50) \doteq 17{,}292.$

It may surprise you to realize that $1, invested for 200 years at 5% compound interest, amounts to over $17,000.

About 350 years ago a Swiss named Bürgi and a Scotsman named Napier were trying to invent ways to simplify arithmetical calculations. Both men hit upon an ingenious way to convert multiplications into additions. We shall describe Bürgi's method because it seems easier to us; but Napier's method really amounts to the same thing.

Bürgi's idea is really there for anyone to see in the examples we have been using. It is easy to understand, too, after a man like Bürgi points it out. When you see how easy it is you may want to take a closer look at some things you "know" to try to discover new ways to look at them. Many inventions and discoveries seem to come about when people do just this.

From your compound interest table,

$$(1.05)^8 \doteq 1.4775 \quad \text{and} \quad (1.05)^{12} \doteq 1.7959.$$

Now look at these statements backward. To multiply

$$1.4775 \times 1.7959$$

means to multiply $(1.05)^8 \times (1.05)^{12}$. This is easy to do. 8 factors of 1.05 multiplied by 12 factors of 1.05 yield 20 factors of 1.05. That is,

$$(1.05)^8 \times (1.05)^{12} = (1.05)^{20}.$$

Now use the compound interest table again to get

$$(1.05)^{20} \doteq 2.6533.$$

Hence $1.4775 \times 1.7959 \doteq 2.6533.$

Of course this last statement is only approximate; at best your answer is precise to the nearest 1/10,000. But this precision is often satisfactory for practical problems; and, once you have the compound interest table, you can multiply 1.4775×1.7959 by adding $8 + 12$.

You may very well ask What about numbers not in the table? For example, How could you multiply 1.5775×1.7959? The number 1.5775 is not in the table.

Bürgi faced this problem and solved it well enough to satisfy the practical people of his time. He used the *base* 1.0001 instead of the base 1.05. This gave him a much longer table to work with; so it included many more numbers. Thus

n	1	2	3	...
$(1.0001)^n$	1.0001	1.0002	1.0003	...

Really, $(1.0001)^3$ is not exactly equal to 1.0003; but this answer is correct to the nearest 1/10,000,000. (Try it, if you wish.) You can see how Bürgi could extend his table to include most of the rounded numbers from 1.0001 to 9.9999. With such a table, you can multiply most of the numbers that arise in the natural sciences to find products with a satisfactory degree of accuracy. You add the values of n that correspond to the numbers you want to multiply. Then you use the table to find the product that corresponds to this sum.

This is the historical origin of *logarithms* as an aid to calculation. We shall return to this topic in later chapters, and you will learn to perform logarithmic calculations in a practical, modern way. Now we shall examine the function $\{(x,y) \mid y = b^x\}$. Mathematicians call it an *exponential function*.

Think of the variable b as a parameter. In previous examples we used $b = 2$, then $b = 1.05$, and finally $b = 1.0001$. As usual, x and y are the variables in the mathematical model. They replace the variables n and S of the examples.

First, consider the need to restrict the values that b, x, and y may take.

When $b = 1$, you get the trivial function, $\{(x,y \mid y = 1^x\}$. You know that $1^2 = 1^3 = 1^4 = \ldots = 1$. Thus, if x ranges over the positive integers, the range of y is $\{1\}$. When $b = 0$, you get another trivial function, namely, $\{(x,y) \mid y = 0^x\}$. When x takes positive integral values, y always takes the value 0. When b is negative, new complications arise. For example, when $b = -2$ you get:

x	1	2	3	4	...
$y = (-2)^x$	-2	4	-8	16	...

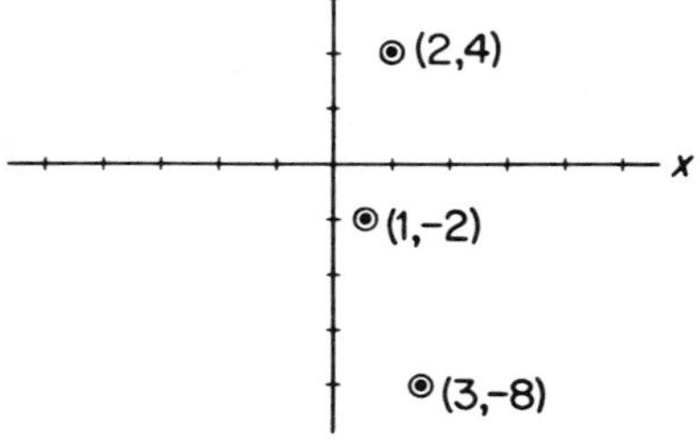

Fig. 4–27.

Thus $(-2)^1 = -2, (-2)^2 = (-2)(-2) = 4$, $(-2)^3 = (-2)(-2)(-2) = -8$, etc. The values of y alternate between positive and negative. The corresponding graph (Fig. 4–27) is very jumpy. We shall restrict b to be a positive number $(b > 0)$ different from 1 $(b \neq 1)$.

Now notice that we have used only the natural numbers for the range of x. As yet we have given no meaning to symbols like b^{-2}, b^0, or $b^{1/2}$. Until we define negative, zero, or fractional exponents, we must restrict the range of x to the set N.

Here, then, are two instances of the function $\{(x, b^x)\}$:
(1) When $b = 1.5$,

x	1	2	3	4	...
$y = (1.5)^x$	1.5	2.25	3.375	5.0625	...

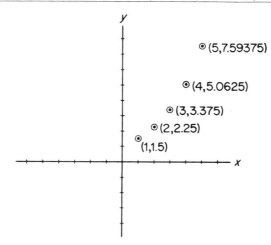

Fig. 4–28.

(2) When $b = 0.5$,

x 1	1	2	3	4	...
$y = (0.5)^x$	0.5	0.25	0.125	0.0625	...

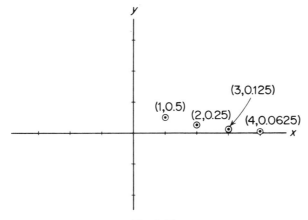

Fig. 4–29.

Notice, in Example (1), how the increments in y (corresponding to an increment of 1 in x) are greater for greater values of x. Notice, in Example (2), that the increments in y are negative; the points of the graph *approach* the x-axis less rapidly for greater values of x.

In Chapter 5 we shall assign meaning to symbols like $(1.5)^{-3}$, $(0.5)^{3/4}$, $(1.5)^{2.6}$, etc. Then you can fill the gaps to make exponential functions *continuous*. Meanwhile we close this section with a contrast of two types of *growth*. This permits us to compare and contrast linear functions (with which we began Chapter 4) with exponential functions.

(3) Growth by equal increments: A young man, on his first job, decides to save \$10 a week and lay it aside until he can get married. He hopes to be married soon; so he decides to keep the cash in a safety deposit box, ready for use. Here is his plan:

End of week number n	1	2	3	...
Amount saved S	10	20	30	...

$\{(n,S)\}$ is a linear function, characterized by the phrase, "another week another \$10." The graph is a set of isolated points, all of which lie in the first quadrant. You can also think of the graph as a set of stair treads.

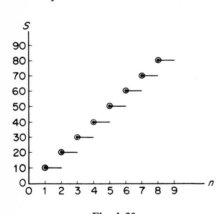

Fig. 4–30.

Thus, all during the second week the amount of the young man's savings is \$10, all during the third week the amount of the young man's savings is \$20, etc. (Fig. 4–30).

The equation is $S = 10n$, where the range of n is the natural numbers, broken off at the point where the young man stops saving \$10 a week (corresponding to the time of his marriage). In Section 403 we called the sequence of values of S an arithmetic progression.

(4) Growth at a *constant rate*: The young man of Example (3) saves his money for 50 wk, and accumulates \$500 in cash. He deposits the \$500 with a Building and Loan Company that pays 3% interest, compounded semiannually. This means that each half-year, the Building and Loan Company adds $1\frac{1}{2}\%$ interest to the young man's accumulated capital. Here is what happens.

End of half-year number h	0	1	2	3	4
Capital invested C	500	507.50	515.12	522.85	530.69

$\{(h,C)\}$ is a exponential function, characterized by the phrase, "another half-year another $1\frac{1}{2}\%$." The graph is a set of isolated points, all of which lie in the first quadrant. If (as is common practice) the Building and Loan Company pays interest only at the end of each half-year, you can also think of the graph as a set of stair treads. But notice that the treads are not evenly spaced. The distance you step up keeps increasing exponentially (Fig. 4–31).

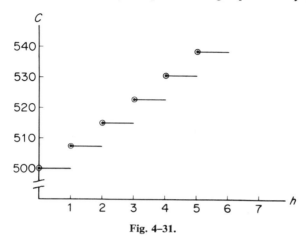

Fig. 4–31.

The equation is $C = 500(1.015)^h$, where the range of h is the natural numbers broken off at the point where the young man draws upon his capital.

In Section 408 we shall call the sequence of values of C a *geometric progression*.

Some of the exercises at the end of this section give you further opportunities to compare and contrast growth by equal increments and growth at a constant rate.

EXERCISES §407

1. (a) Draw the graph of the "double your money" function, $\{(x,y) \mid y = 2^x\}$.
(b) Use the same axes to graph the "another question answered, another two dollars" function, $\{(x,y) \mid y = 2x\}$.

2. Graph $y = b^x$ for the following values of b. Use the set of natural numbers as the range of x.

      (a) $b = 1.2$ (b) $b = 3$ (c) $b = 5$
      (d) $b = 2/3$ (e) $b = 1/4$ (f) $b = 0.1$.

3. Comment on the appearance of the graph of $y = b^x$ for $0 < b < 1$; for $b > 1$. (Use the graphs of Exercise 2 for illustrations.)

4. How would the graph of $y = a(b^x)$, $a \neq 0$, be related to the graph of $y = b^x$? Illustrate by graphing $y = (1.5)^x$, $y = 2(1.5)^x$, and $y = -\frac{1}{2}(1.5)^x$ on the same coordinate axes.

5. The formula $S = A(1 + i)^n$ gives the amount at the end of n years when A dollars are invested at an interest rate of i, compounded yearly. Using $A = \$100$ and $i = .06$ (that is, 6% per year, compounded yearly), graph $\{(n,S)\}$. What is the range of n?

6. If provided with sufficient food and an ideal environment, a colony of a certain type of bacteria will, in a day's time, increase its number by 50%. Suppose the colony begins with 128 bacteria. Make a table of the number y of bacteria at the end of x days, for the first eight days. Graph the relation $\{(x,y) \mid y = 128(1.5)^x\}$. Show that this relation is a function.

7. A ping-pong ball is dropped from a height of 10 ft. Each time it bounces, it reaches a height 0.8 of the distance it last fell. Make a table of the function $\{(n,H)\}$, to show the height of rebound, H, corresponding to a number of bounces, n. What is the range of n? Graph the function. Write a formula for H in terms of n.

    Answer: $H = 10(0.8)^n$.

408. Geometric progressions

An ordered set, or sequence, of numbers is called a *geometric progression* when each number of the sequence, after the first, is a fixed multiple of the preceding one. For example, in the sequence

$$3, 6, 12, 24, \ldots,$$

each number is 2 times the preceding one.

Consider the function $\{(n,y_n)\}$ where $n \in N$, $1 \leq n \leq k$, and, for $n > 1$, $y_n/y_{n-1} = r$. It is easy to write down values of y_n beginning with y_1. Since $y_n = r \cdot y_{n-1}$,

$$y_2 = ry_1$$
$$y_3 = ry_2 = r^2 y_1$$
$$y_4 = ry_3 = r^3 y_1$$
$$\cdot \quad \cdot \quad \cdot$$
$$\cdot \quad \cdot \quad \cdot$$
$$y_k = ry_{k-1} = r^{k-1} y_1$$

To each value of n, $1 \leq n \leq k$, there corresponds an element

$$(n,y_n) = (n, r^{n-1} y_1)$$

of the function $\{(n,y_n)\}$. When $n = 1$, we define $r^0 y_1$ to be y_1.

The equation $y_n = r^{n-1} y_1$, or $y_n = y_1 r^{n-1}$, is of the form $y = ab^x$. You make the following replacements: $y = y_n$, $x = n - 1$, $b = r$, and $a = y_1$. Recalling the restrictions $b > 0$, and $b \neq 1$, the function $\{(n,y_n)\}$ is an exponential function in $N \times L$ provided $r > 0$ and $r \neq 1$.

Consider the instance in which $y = 1$ and $r = 2$. The function $\{(n,y_n)\}$ is $\{(n,2^{n-1})\}$. This is the exponential function $\{(x,y) \mid y = 2^{x-1}\}$ in $N \times L$. For $x > 1$, 2^{x-1} is a positive integral power of 2; when $x = 1$, we define $2^{x-1} = 2^{1-1} = 2^0$ to be 1. This yields the quiz-program function $\{(1,1), (2,2), (3,4), (4,8), \ldots\}$ with which we introduced Section 407.

We now remove the restrictions $r > 0$ and $r \neq 1$, and consider the general geometric progression:

$$\{y_1, y_2, y_3, \ldots, y_{k-1}, y_k\}.$$

We shall call y_1 the *first term*, r the *common ratio*, and

I $$y_k = y_1 r^{k-1}$$

the kth term, or *last term*, of the progression.

Here are some examples of the application of Formula I:

(1) Find the last term of a progression in which $y_1 = 81$, $r = -1/3$, and $k = 7$:

$$y_7 = 81 \cdot \left(-\frac{1}{3}\right)^6 = 81\left(\frac{1}{729}\right) = \frac{1}{9}.$$

(2) Find the first term of a progression in which $y_k = 1/64$, $r = 1/6$, and $k = 9$:

$$y_k = y_9 = \frac{1}{64} = y_1\left(\frac{1}{6}\right)^8,$$

$$\frac{y_1}{6^8} = \frac{1}{64},$$

$$y_1 = \frac{6^8}{64} = \frac{36 \cdot 36 \cdot 36 \cdot 36}{64} = 26{,}244.$$

(3) A boy who understands geometric progressions agrees to work for 20 days and to be paid as follows: 5 cents for the first day; each day twice as much as the preceding day. Find his pay for the 20th day.

$$y_{20} = 5 \cdot 2^{19};$$

$$2^5 = 32; \quad 2^{10} = 32 \cdot 32 = 1024; \quad 2^{20} = 1024 \cdot 1024 = 1{,}048{,}576;$$

$$2^{19} = \frac{1{,}048{,}576}{2} = 524{,}288.$$

$$y_{20} = 5 \cdot 524{,}288 = 2{,}621{,}440.$$

His pay for the 20th day is $26,214.40.

It is often useful to have a formula for the sum of a geometric progression; such a formula enables you to answer a question like "What total pay did the boy of Example (3) receive in 20 days?"

Let $$S_k = y_1 + y_2 + \ldots + y_{k-1} + y_k$$

represent the sum of a sequence of k numbers in geometric progression. Then

$$S_k = y_1 + y_1 r + y_1 r^2 + \ldots + y_1 r^{k-2} + y_1 r^{k-1}.$$

Also, $$rS_k = y_1 r + y_1 r^2 + \ldots + y_1 r^{k-2} + y_1 r^{k-1} + y_1 r^k.$$

First, suppose $r \neq 1$; subtracting the second equation from the first,

$$S_k(1 - r) = y_1(1 - r^k).$$

This yields formula

II $$S_k = \frac{y_1(1 - r^k)}{1 - r}.$$

However, if $r = 1$

III $$S_k = y_1 + y_1 + y_1 + \ldots + y_1 \quad (k \text{ addends})$$
$$= ky_1.$$

In this special case, where $r = 1$, the geometric progression *degenerates* into a sequence of equal numbers.

When you know the kth term, $y_k = y_1 r^{k-1}$, of a geometric progression, you can rewrite Formula II in a more convenient form. Then you replace $y_1 r^k$ by $ry_k = r(y_1 r^{k-1}) = y_1 r^k$.

IIa $$S_k = \frac{y_1 - y_1 r^k}{1 - r} = \frac{y_1 - ry_k}{1 - r}.$$

These formulas have much mathematical interest. In practice, they lead to tedious arithmetical calculations. For example,

(4) Find the total wages of the boy of Example (3). Formula II yields:

$$S_{20} = \frac{5(1 - 2^{20})}{1 - 2} = \frac{5(-1,048,575)}{-1}$$
$$= 5,242,875.$$

Since you already know y_{20}, it is more convenient to use Formula IIa:

$$S_{20} = \frac{5 - 2(2,621,440)}{1 - 2}$$
$$= 5,242,875.$$

The boy's total wages are $52,428.75.

When the ratio, r, is a less-convenient number, say 1.05, the calculations are correspondingly laborious.

You will appreciate the theory of logarithms as an aid to calculation when you work with geometric progressions. Exercises 408 give you further illustrations of simple geometric progressions.

EXERCISES §408

1. Find y_k and S_k, when given:

(a) $y_1 = 30$, $r = 1/5$, and $k = 4$;
(b) $y_1 = -6$, $r = -3$, and $k = 5$;
(c) $y_1 = 1$, $r = -1/3$, and $k = 7$.

Answers: (a) .24, 37.44; (b) -486, -366.

2. Show that Formulas II and IIa can be written as

$$S_k = \frac{y_1(r^k - 1)}{r - 1} = \frac{ry_k - y_1}{r - 1}.$$

These forms are more convenient when $r > 1$.

3. An ancient Hindu problem calls for placing one grain of wheat on the first square of a chess board, 2 grains on the second square, 4 grains on the third square, etc. There are 64 squares on a chess board.

(a) How many grains belong on the 10th square?
(b) Write an expression that tells how many grains belong on the 64th square. Estimate this number.
(c) Write an expression that tells how many grains belong on the chess board. Estimate this number.

Answers: (a) 512; (b) $2^{63} \doteq 9,223,000,000,000,000,000$;
(c) $2^{64} - 1 \doteq 18,447,000,000,000,000,000$.

4. (a) In Exercise 6 of Section 407, identify y_1, y_8, and r.
(b) In Exercise 7 of Section 407, identify y_1, y_{10}, and r. Find S_{10}. Remembering that the ball travels both up and down in one bounce, find the distance that the ball travels from the time you release it 10 ft above the floor until it strikes the floor the tenth time.

Answer: (b) 79.263 ft.

5. In a geometric progression $y_1 = 24$ and $y_7 = 2187/8$. Find y_2, y_3, ..., y_6. Mathematicians call this inserting 5 geometric means between 24 and 2187/8. [*Hint:* $y_7 = 24r^6 = 2187/8$. Hence

$$r^6 = \frac{2187}{24 \cdot 8} = \frac{27 \cdot 81}{3 \cdot 8 \cdot 8} = \frac{3^6}{2^6};$$

$r = 3/2$ is one solution and $r = -3/2$ is another. Try them.]

6. The radiator of a car holds 15 qt of liquid, of which 5 qt are alcohol. The radiator has a leak, losing 3 qt of liquid each week. Every week 3 qt of water are added. Write a geometric progression to show the amount of alcohol remaining at the beginning of each week. Write an expression giving the amount of alcohol remaining at the beginning of the nth week.

Answer: 5, 4, 3.2, 2.56, ..., $5(.8)^{n-1}$.

7. A bacteria culture increased from 8100 on the first day to 25,600 on the fifth day. Find the daily rate of increase if it is assumed to be constant.

8. Each swing of a pendulum is .9 as long as the preceding swing. If the pendulum travels 10 in. on the first swing, how far will it travel on the sixth swing? What is the total distance traveled in the first five swings?

Answers: 5.9040, 40.951.

9. A design is formed by series of squares. Each square has its vertices at the midpoints of the sides of the preceding square. The length of one side of the largest square is 10 in.

(a) Show that the area of each square is 1/2 the area of the preceding square.
(b) What is the area of the eleventh square?
(c) What is the sum of the areas of the first ten squares?
(d) Show that the sum of the areas, no matter how many are included, is always less than 200 sq in.

Answers: (b) 25/256 sq in.; (c) 199.8 sq in.; (d) $S_n = 200 - 100(\frac{1}{2})^{n-1}$.

10. A design is formed with a series of equilateral triangles, each with its vertices at the midpoints of the preceding triangle. The area of the first is 1024 sq in. Find the area of the sixth triangle. Find the sum of the areas of the first six triangles.

Answers: 1 sq in., 1365 sq in.

409. Circular functions

There are two more sets of closely associated functions that mathematicians call *elementary*. Like algebraic functions, and exponential functions, these *circular* and *inverse circular*, functions are mathematical models. They were invented to describe events in the physical world. Early Greek astronomers and surveyors learned to use what we call *trigonometric ratios* to *solve triangles*; that is, they learned to find unknown sides and angles of triangles in which they knew certain other sides and angles. Modern scientists use these same trigonometric ratios to describe what they call *periodic* phenomena.

You should study Fig. 4–32 for an example of a simple periodic event. AOB represents a plank 2 yd long lying in a horizontal position on the ground. The points, S_0, S_1, S_2, ..., S_6 represent positions of the sun from sunrise until sunset.

When the sun is at:

S_0 the line AB receives no radiation
S_1 the line AB receives some radiation
S_2 the line AB receives more radiation
S_3 the line AB receives maximum radiation
S_4 the line AB receives the same radiation as for the position S_2
S_5 the line AB receives the same radiation as for the position S_1
S_6 the line AB receives no radiation.

The next day the cycle is repeated, in essentially the same way if you ignore the secondary effect of summer-to-winter differences in the elevation of the sun.

To each position of the sun, there corresponds a definite, unique amount of radiation on the plank. If we learn to represent positions of the sun by a set of numbers $\{a\}$, and amounts of radiation by a set of numbers $\{r\}$, we can study the function, $\{(a,r)\}$.

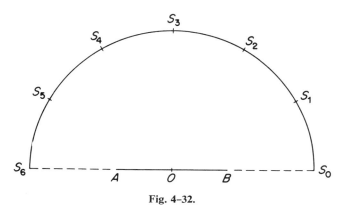

Fig. 4–32.

In Fig. 4–33, we drew a circle of radius 1 with center at 0. Since $OB = OA = 1$, the circle passes through A and B; since its radius is 1, we call it a *unit* circle. To each position of the sun there corresponds a value of a, that is, an *arc length* of the unit circle. The correspondence between values of a and positions of the sun is one-to-one. The set of values of a is a subset of

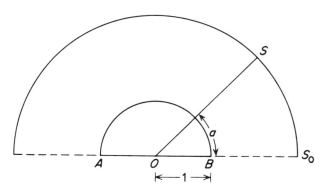

Fig. 4–33.

L; clearly, $a \geq 0$; since the *circumference* of a circle of radius 1 is $C = 2\pi$, the half-circumference is $C/2 = \pi$; hence $0 \leq a \leq \pi$.

Each amount of radiation r on the plank AB is an element of a second set.

We leave it to the physicists to devise a way to measure values of r that correspond to particular values of a.

Now consider the set of elements $\{(a,r)\}$. To each value of a, $0 \leq a \leq \pi$, there corresponds a unique value of r. Hence the set $\{(a,r)\}$ is a function. But, despite its everyday (!) origin, the task of representing it as an algebraic

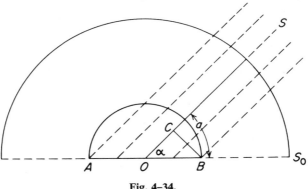

Fig. 4–34.

function is not at all simple. Fortunately, it is easy to represent the function $\{(a,r)\}$ in another way.

In Fig. 4–34, the line CB receives the maximum radiation of a beam of parallel rays of the sun that strikes it at right angles. The line OB receives

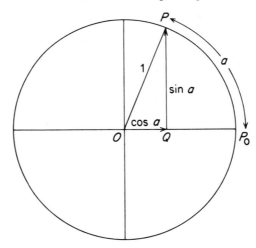

Fig. 4–35.

the same amount of radiation as the line CB; but this radiation is spread over a longer line segment.

Recall that AOB is 2 yd long. So OB is 1 yd long. The triangle OBC has a right angle at C; the *hypotenuse OB* is the longest side of the triangle; the side *CB* is shorter than the hypotenuse. The same amount of radiation falls on *CB* and *OB*; but the radiation is more concentrated on *CB* than on *OB*.

For each value of *a*, the line *CB* has a definite length. This length receives maximum radiation, since the sun is directly above it. As *a* takes different values, the total radiation on *CB* is proportional to the length of *CB*; hence the total radiation on *OB* is proportional to the length of *CB*.

Notice how simple this is! For each arc-length *a*, there is a definite right triangle *OBC*, and a definite side *CB* of this triangle. The amount of radiation on *OB* is proportional to the length of *CB*. (If you want the total radiation on *AB*, you double the radiation on *OB*.)

This method of using the length of *CB*, to represent the radiation on *OB* that corresponds to a particular value of *a*, is an example of how the so-called *circular* functions arise in everyday problems. Now we build a mathematical model that makes it convenient to discuss such examples.

In Fig. 4–35, the unit circle has centre at *O*. To each position of a point *P* on the unit circle, there corresponds a unique real number *a*. The geometric interpretation of *a* is the arc-length along the unit circle, measured from P_0.

To each value of *a* corresponds a unique *directed distance*, or *vector*, *QP*. When *P* lies above OP_0, $QP > 0$; when *P* lies below OP_0, $QP < 0$; when *P* lies on OP_0, $QP = 0$. The mathematical name of the variable *QP* is "sin *a*." The letters *sin* are a shortened form of the word *sine* (pronounced like *sign* but meaning something quite different). This is a very old mathematical word that we use to follow an ancient tradition. Custom has given it meaning. People who know mathematics will understand you when you talk about sin *a* (the sine of the real number *a*).

To each value of *a* corresponds a unique vector *OQ*. The mathematical name of the variable *OQ* is "cos *a*." The letters *cos* are a shortened form of the word *cosine*. Again, this is a mathematical word of ancient origin, that has definite meaning for people initiated into the language and customs of mathematics. Again you can speak of cos *a* (the cosine of the real number *a*).

Use Fig. 4–36 to study the expression sin *a*.

Recall how the *x*- and *y*-axes divide the plane into 4 quarters, or quadrants, labeled I, II, III, and IV in the figure.

In quadrant I, sin *a* is a positive number between 0 and 1. When *P* is close to P_0, sin *a* is a positive number close to 0. When P is close to the *y*-axis, sin *a* is a positive number close to 1.

In quadrant II, sin *a* is a positive number between 1 and 0. When *P* is close to the *y*-axis, sin *a* is close to 1. When *P* is close to the *x*-axis, sin *a* is close to 0.

In quadrants III and IV, sin *a* is a number between −1 and 0. When *P*

is close to the x-axis, sin a is a negative number close to 0. When P is close to
the y-axis, sin a is a negative number close to −1.

When P lies on the x-axis, sin a = 0. When P lies on the y-axis, sin a = 1
or sin a = −1.

A similar study of the expression cos a yields the following conclusions.
In quadrants I and IV, 0 < cos a < 1; in quadrants II and III, −1 < cos a < 0;
on the x-axis, cos a = 1 or cos a = −1; on the y-axis, cos a = 0.

The graphs of y = sin x and y = cos x illustrate the periodic character
of the functions {(x,sin x)} and {(x,cos x)} (Fig. 4–37).

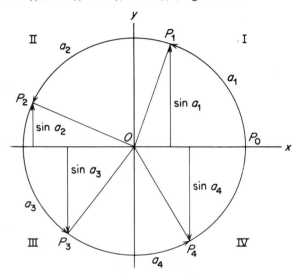

Fig. 4–36.

We divided the circumference of a circle of radius 1 unit into 24 equal
parts. Recall that the circumference, C = 2πr = 2π · 1. So each arc is
C/24 = 2π/24 = π/12 units long. Now π ≐ 3.1416; so each arc is 3.1416/12 ≐
.2618 ≐ .26 units long. We drew vertical lines at intervals of .26 unit. Then
we located points on each of these vertical lines as shown for four points
in each figure.

For the graph of y = sin x, each point has y-coordinate equal to the vector
sin x; hence you measure the vector sin x that corresponds to an arc-length
x of the unit circle; then you transfer this vector to the corresponding vertical
line of the graph. It is convenient to do this with a compass or a pair of
dividers.

For the graph of y = cos x, each point has y-coordinate equal to the
vector cos x; hence you measure the vector cos x that corresponds to an arc-
length x of the unit circle; then you transfer this vector to the corresponding
vertical line of the graph.

Notice how the variable sin x goes through a cycle as x increases from 0 to 2π (corresponding to arcs from 0 to one circumference of the unit circle). As x increases from 2π to 4π, sin x repeats its cycle (corresponding to arcs from one to two circumferences of the unit circle). Points of the graph to the left of the y-axis correspond to negative values of x, that is, to arcs measured clockwise from P_0.

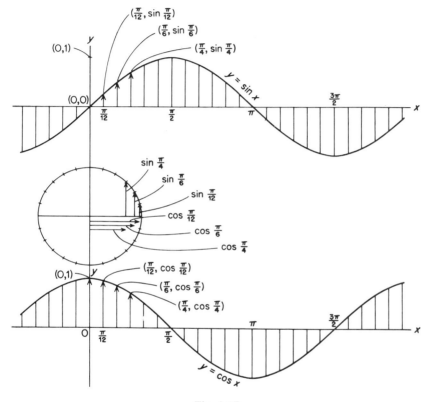

Fig. 4–37.

Similarly, the variable cos x goes through a cycle as x increases from 0 to 2π; then it repeats this cycle as x increases from 2π to 4π; etc. Again, points of the graph to the left of the y-axis correspond to negative values of x, that is, to arcs measured clockwise from P_0.

We say the circular functions $\{(x,\sin x)\}$ and $\{(x,\cos x)\}$ are *periodic*; they repeat themselves in *periods* of 2π. When the range of x is the subset of L, $0 \leq x < 2\pi$, the range of sin x is $-1 \leq \sin x \leq 1$ and the range of cos x is $-1 \leq \cos x \leq 1$. In general, $\sin x = \sin (x + 2k\pi)$, and $\cos x = \cos (x + 2k\pi)$, $k \in I$.

When you want to use sin x or cos x, it is convenient to have a table that lists values of $\sin x$ and $\cos x$ that correspond to selected values of x. Here is an excerpt from such a table:

x	$\sin x$	$\cos x$	x	$\sin x$	$\cos x$	x	$\sin x$	$\cos x$
0.0	.0000	1.0000	0.6	.5646	.8253	1.2	.9320	.3624
0.1	.0998	.9950	0.7	.6442	.7648	1.3	.9636	.2675
0.2	.1987	.9801	0.8	.7174	.6967	1.4	.9854	.1700
0.3	.2955	.9553	0.9	.7833	.6216	1.5	.9975	.0707
0.4	.3894	.9211	1.0	.8415	.5403	1.6	.9996	$-.0292$
0.5	.4794	.8776	1.1	.8912	.4536			

It would be difficult to achieve such a precise result as $\cos 0.6 = .8253$ by drawing and measuring. The people who make the tables use methods of calculus that are not yet available to you. For the time being, you may use the tabulated values of $\sin x$ and $\cos x$ without being concerned about how these values are calculated. You can always make a scale drawing of a unit circle and measure the vectors $QP = \sin x$ and $OQ = \cos x$ that correspond to a particular arc-length x; but the precision of your drawing will limit the precision of your results. Still more precise tables are available if you need them. The calculations, upon which the tables are based, can be carried to any desired precision.

You should examine the several tables of trigonometric ratios of your book of tables. We shall return, in Section 410, to the question of angle-measurement. Then you will be better prepared to read and use these tables.

We return now to the function $\{(a,r)\}$ that expresses the radiation r on the plank AB, corresponding to a position of the sun measured by the arc-length a of the unit circle. Figure 4–38 presents the essential data.

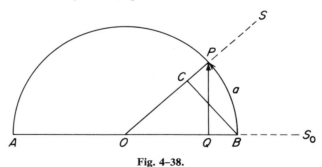

Fig. 4–38.

Recall that the radiation on OB, that corresponds to a, is proportional to CB. Notice that $CB = QP$. (Triangles BCO and PQO are right triangles in which $OB = OP = 1$; angles BOC and POQ are equal; the triangles are *congruent* right triangles, in which the corresponding sides, CB and QP, are equal.) Hence the radiation on OB that corresponds to a is proportional to QP. By definition, $QP = \sin a$.

This means that $r/\sin a = k$, or $r = k \sin a$, where k is the constant of proportionality. When $a = \pi/2$ (corresponding to an arc-length of 1/4 the circumference of the unit circle), $\sin a = 1$; then $r = k$. Hence k represents the maximum radiation on OB, achieved when the sun is directly above OB. We set $k = r_{max}$ to remind ourselves that k represents the maximum radiation on OB. Then the condition

$$r = r_{max} \sin a$$

yields the value of r that corresponds to each replacement of a, $0 \le a \le \pi$. For example, use your set of tables to check the following facts:

a	0	.3	.6	.9
$r = r_{max} \sin a$	0	$.2955r_{max}$	$.5646r_{max}$	$.7833r_{max}$

Once you find a physicist to measure r_{max}, you can calculate the value of r that corresponds to each replacement of a.

EXERCISES §409

1. Suppose OB receives 50 units of energy per second when the sun is at its greatest elevation above the horizon; that is, $r_{max} = 50$.
  (a) What is the radiation on AB at this time? ($2 \times 50 = 100$)
  (b) On this same day what is the radiation on OB for each of the following values of a? $a = 0, 0.1, 0.4, 0.7, 1.1, 1.4, 1.5, 1.6$. (*Hint:* Use the table on page 154.)

2. As you examine the table on page 154, you can tell that $a = 1.5$ places the sun in quadrant I and $a = 1.6$ places the sun in quadrant II. How?

3. (a) Use the methods of this section to construct graphs of $y = \sin x$ and $y = \cos x$. Check your graphs with the ones given on page 153.

(b) You may be interested in making the construction of these graphs still more mechanical. You can divide the circumference of a circle into six equal arcs by a simple geometric construction (Fig. 4–39). Call the radius of the circle 1 unit. Draw the circle with a compass; then draw the horizontal diameter of the circle with a ruler; then use your compass to locate P_1 on the circle at a distance of 1 from P_0, P_2 on the circle at a distance 1 from P_1, etc. Notice that triangle OP_0P_1

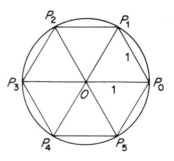

Fig. 4–39.

is *equilateral*, since each of its sides is 1 unit long. Hence angle $P_0OP_1 = 60°$, and arc P_0P_1 is one sixth of the circumference of the circle. The circumference of the circle is $C = 2\pi \cdot 1$; hence the arc, $P_0P_1 = 2\pi/6 = \pi/3$, is $\pi/3$ units long.

Now you can *bisect* angle P_0OP_1 to get a 30° angle and an arc that is $\frac{1}{2} \cdot \pi/3 = \pi/6$ unit long. Finally, you can bisect this 30° angle to get a 15° angle and an arc that is $\frac{1}{2} \cdot \pi/6 = \pi/12$ unit long.

If, now, you cut a unit circle from a piece of thin cardboard, you can roll your circle along a line and mark the points on the line at distances $\pi/12$, $2\pi/12$, $3\pi/12$, ..., 2π from the starting point.

This drawing procedure eliminates approximations like calling $\pi \doteq 3.1416$, $\pi/12 \doteq .26$, etc. It introduces another kind of approximation, which depends upon how well you construct the 15° angles, cut out a unit circle, and roll it (without slipping) along a straight line.

If you have a mechanical flair, you may want to think about ways to improve this graphical procedure by using metal cylinders (like half dollars) instead of cardboard ones; rolling these wheels along metal bars instead of straight lines; etc.

(c) It is also feasible to draw the sine curve electrically. We discuss this briefly to indicate the possibilities, and to point to another everyday application of the circular functions. Modern work in electronics depends very heavily upon the circular functions as mathematical models.

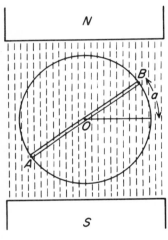

Fig. 4–40.

Figure 4–40 represents a simplified dynamo (for changing mechanical energy into electrical energy). The electric motor (for putting electrical energy to work) is very similar. In the dynamo, you supply power to turn the coil of wire; then you get electricity in the coil of wire. In the motor you supply electricity to the coil of wire; then you get power to turn the coil of wire.

Think of AB as representing an end view of a rectangular loop of wire that turns on an axle through O. The dashed lines in the figure represent lines of force that pass between the north and south poles of a magnet. The wire (vertical to the plane of the diagram) forming the side of the rectangular loop at B moves through the lines of force as the coil rotates about O.

According to the laws of physics, a voltage is induced that is proportional to the rate at which the wire is cutting the lines of force. Now let the angular rotation be constant. This rate of cutting lines of force will be zero when $a = 0$, and will build up to a maximum when $a = \pi/2$. As a increases from $\pi/2$ to π, the rate at which the lines of force are cut decreases to zero again. Continuing in its rotation, the wire at B now begins to cut the lines of force in the opposite direction, which reverses the induced voltage. We take this direction to be negative, and the cycle continues in a similar fashion from π to 2π, but with negative voltages.

The sine function, $\{(a,E)\}$, provides a mathematical model for the behavior of the voltage that the dynamo generates, with

$$E = E_{\max} \sin a.$$

E is the induced voltage that corresponds to the position of the coil as measured by a, and $E_{\max}$ is the value of E that corresponds to $a = \pi/2$.

Figure 4–41, which might appear in a text on electricity, may help you to visualize one cycle of voltage-output for a dynamo. The physicist, who works with alternating currents, pictures an alternating current as a *sine wave*. He uses an instrument called a cathode-ray oscilloscope, which looks and acts somewhat like a TV picture-tube, to display variations in voltage with time. Perhaps you can find some one to demonstrate an oscilloscope. Physics laboratories and television repair shops are good sources.

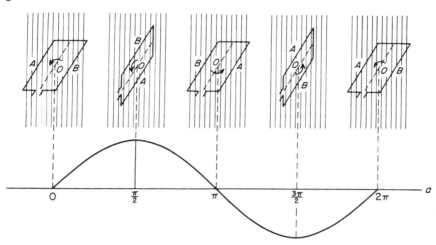

Fig. 4–41.

4. Use the condition of Exercise 3(c), $E = E_{max} \sin a$, to tabulate values of E that correspond to several replacements of a, assuming that $E_{max} = 155$ v.

5. As you examine the graphs of $y = \sin x$ and $y = \cos x$ you should notice a simple connection between them:

$$\cos x = \sin \left(\frac{\pi}{2} - x \right).$$

Use the graphs to check the correctness of this identity for several replacements of x.

6. As you examine the graph of $y = \sin x$, notice that

$$\sin x = \sin (\pi - x).$$

Use the graph to check the correctness of this identity for several replacements of x.

There are several more *circular* (sometimes called *trigonometric*) functions. We mention one other function and then postpone further study of circular functions and their applications until Chapter 9.

Figure 4–42 shows a unit circle with a *tangent line* drawn at P_0. The mathematical name of the vector $P_0 T$ is tan a. The letters *tan* are an abbreviation of

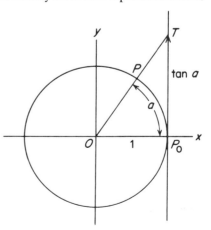

Fig. 4–42.

the word tangent. To each position of P, except two, there corresponds a definite position of T, and hence a definite vector P_0T; but when P is vertically above O, or vertically below O, OP is parallel to the tangent line. Hence, when $a = \pi/2$, $3\pi/2$, $5\pi/2$, ..., tan a is *not* defined.

You should check the following statement about the function $\{(a,\tan a)\}$:

$$\tan 0 = 0;$$

$$0 < a < \frac{\pi}{2} \Rightarrow 0 < \tan a.$$

As a takes a value close to $\pi/2$, tan a takes a large positive value; you can make the value of tan a exceed any previously chosen real number N by selecting a value of a less than $\pi/2$ and sufficiently close to $\pi/2$.

$$\tan \frac{\pi}{2} \text{ is not defined};$$

$$\frac{\pi}{2} < a < \pi \Rightarrow \tan a < 0.$$

The point T that corresponds to a lies below P_0; hence P_0T is negative. When a takes a value close to $\pi/2$, tan a takes a small value. You should avoid the confusion of speaking of a "large" negative number; say, rather, that the value of tan a is small.

$$\tan \pi = 0$$

$$\pi < a < \frac{3\pi}{2} \Rightarrow 0 < \tan a;$$

$$\tan \frac{3\pi}{2} \text{ is not defined};$$

$$\frac{3\pi}{2} < a < 2\pi \Rightarrow \tan a < 0; \text{ etc.}$$

The graph of $y = \tan x$ tells this whole story at a glance. Moreover it reveals the periodic character of the function $\{(x,\tan x)\}$. Notice in Fig. 4–43 that the period is π (rather than 2π as for $y = \sin x$ and $y = \cos x$). Points on the graph to the left of the y-axis correspond to arcs measured clockwise from P_0.

It is common practice to say "*y becomes infinite as x approaches* the values

$$\ldots, -\frac{3\pi}{2}, -\frac{\pi}{2}, \frac{\pi}{2}, \frac{3\pi}{2}, \ldots,"$$

This way of speaking may describe the behavior of the graph better than the flat statement that y is not defined for these values of x. But you should keep it in mind that the symbols tan $(-\pi/2)$, tan $\pi/2$, tan $3\pi/2$, etc., are not real numbers; that is, they are not defined. In effect, the range of x *does not include* the values

$$\ldots, \ -\frac{3\pi}{2}, \ -\frac{\pi}{2}, \frac{\pi}{2}, \frac{3\pi}{2}, \ldots$$

when we discuss the function $\{(x, \tan x)\}$.

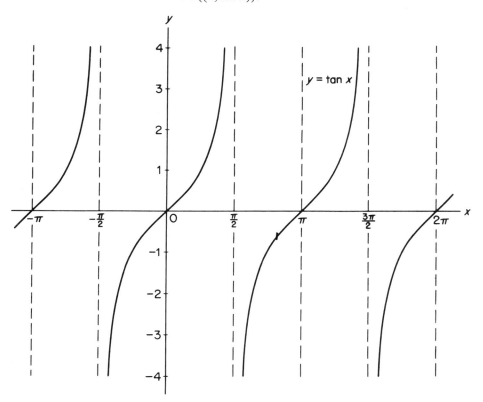

Fig. 4–43.

The tangent function is an example of a function that is continuous except for certain isolated values of x. Recall the hyperbola, $y = 1/x$, as a second such example. For the hyperbola, y is defined *except* for $x = 0$. Hence the range of x does not include the value 0 when we discuss the function $\{(x, 1/x)\}$.

We shall return, in Section 410, to applications of the tangent function $\{(x, \tan x)\}$.

As you think over what you have learned in this section, notice that we have associated to each real number, x, other real numbers, $\sin x$, $\cos x$, and $\tan x$. We have called the corresponding functions, $\{(x, \sin x)\}$, $\{(x, \cos x)\}$, and

$\{(x,\tan x)\}$, circular functions. Convenient tables are available to look up the approximate value of sin x, cos x, or tan x that corresponds to a replacement of x by a real number.

The *inverse* process is also important. Given a real number x, and $-1 \leq x \leq 1$, it is always possible to find a real number y, with $-\pi/2 \leq y \leq \pi/2$, such that sin $y = x$. For example, if $x = .2955$, $y \doteq 0.3$ (see the table on page 154). In Section 905 you will study the inverse-circular functions, such as $\{(x,\text{Arcsin } x)\}$ (read x, principal value whose sine is x); besides this inverse-sine function you will study the inverse cosine and inverse tangent functions.

EXERCISES §409 (cont.)

7. Apply the methods of Exercise 3 to graph $y = \tan x$. Check your graph with the one given on page 159. The methods of Exercise 3, parts (a) and (b), can be readily adapted to Fig. 4–42.

8. As you examine the graph of $y = \tan x$, notice that

$$\tan x = \tan (\pi + x);$$

that is, the function $\{(x,\tan x)\}$ has period π.

9. Draw the unit circle with an arc a and the vectors sin a, cos a, and tan a. Using similar triangles, explain why you would expect tan $a = (\sin a)/\cos a$. From tables, check this identity for $a = 0$; 0.5; 1.0; 1.6.

10. Use your book of mathematical tables to find a decimal approximation to each of the following real numbers:

(a) Given $x = 1.3$, cos $x \doteq$
(b) Given $x = .8912$, Arcsin $x \doteq$
(c) Given $x = 0.64$, tan $x \doteq$
(d) Given $x = 1.072$, Arctan $x \doteq$

410. Angles and trigonometric ratios

First, review the measurement of *directed arc-lengths* from Section 409. You draw an arbitrary circle; you choose a point P_0 on the circle; you use the radius of the circle as a unit of measurement; you measure directed arc-lengths from P_0.

Compare this with our previous measurement of *directed distances* on the line of numbers. You draw an arbitrary line; you choose a zero point (0) on the line; you choose a unit of measurement; you measure directed distances from 0.

To each real number there corresponds a unique directed distance, and hence a unique point on the line of numbers. To each directed distance, or point on the line of numbers, there corresponds a unique real number.

To each real number there corresponds a unique directed arc-length, and hence a unique point on the unit circle. To each directed arc-length there corresponds a unique real number; but, to each point on the unit circle there corresponds *a set* of real numbers, whose elements correspond to arc-lengths that differ by multiples of 2π; that is, for a given replacement of a, the set of arc-lengths, $\{a + k(2\pi) \mid k \in I\}$, all correspond to the same point on the unit circle.

There is a one-to-one correspondence between points on the unit circle and "directions" in the plane from the point 0. In Section 409 we used directed arc-lengths of the unit circle to specify "directions" in the plane from the point 0.

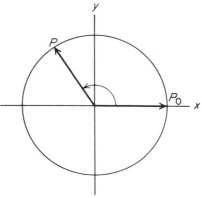

We come now to the concept of *angle*. It is customary to think of an angle as a rotation of a vector OP from an *initial position OP_0* to a *terminal position* like OP in Fig. 4–44. We call counterclockwise rotations *positive*; we call clockwise rotations *negative*; we speak of the angle P_0OP generated

Fig. 4–44.

by rotating the vector OP in a counterclockwise direction from the initial position OP_0 to the terminal position OP.

There are several commonly used ways to measure angles. The one with which you are most familiar is *degree measure*. You divide the circumference of a circle into 360 equal arcs. Each of these arcs corresponds to 1/360 of a complete revolution of the vector OP; we call 1/360 of a complete revolution of the vector OP one *degree* (1°). We speak of a 90° angle (a *right* angle) as

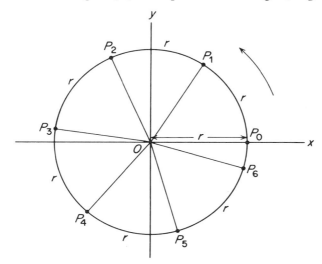

Fig. 4–45.

1/4 of a complete revolution; we speak of a 180° angle (a *straight* angle) as 1/2 of a complete revolution; etc.

Arcs of the unit circle provide a second way to measure angles. The circumference of a unit circle is 2π. Hence an arc of $2\pi/360 = \pi/180$ corresponds to a 1° angle; an arc of $\pi/4$ corresponds to a 45° angle; an arc of $\pi/2$ corresponds to a 90° angle; an arc of π corresponds to a 180° angle, etc.

Arcs of a circle of radius r provide a third way to measure angles. The circumference of a circle of radius r is $2\pi r$. Hence an arc of $2\pi r/360 = \pi r/180$ corresponds to a 1° angle, etc. Mathematicians call the measure of an angle that corresponds to an arc-length r in a circle of radius r one *radian*. Figure 4–45 illustrates "walking around a circle of radius r." Measure of angle $P_0OP_1 = 1$ radian; measure of angle $P_0OP_2 = 2$ radians; etc. One revolution is $2\pi \doteq 6.28$ radians.

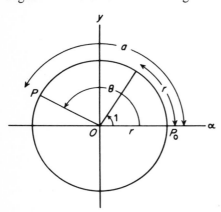

Fig. 4–46.

We shall use the symbol θ for the radian measure of an angle P_0OP. From Fig. 4–46, $\theta/a = 1/r$, that is, $\theta = a/r$. In a unit circle, $\theta = a/1 = a$. Hence you may think of the radian measure θ of an angle as the ratio of the corresponding arc-length to the radius of the circle; or you may think of the radian measure θ of an angle as the corresponding arc-length in a unit circle.

Study Fig. 4–47 as you try to visualize angles measured in radians. Each of these angles is in *standard position*, that is, it is measured from OP_0.

It is convenient to have a simple formula to calculate the arc of a circle when you know a measure of the corresponding angle. The formulas $\theta = a/r$, $a = r\theta$, etc., are especially useful. In theoretical work, it is customary to measure angles in radians. Then it is an easy step to convert the number of radians into the corresponding number of revolutions (for purposes of practical work in fields like mechanical engineering), or into the corresponding number of degrees (for practical work in fields like surveying and navigation). The following proportions summarize the important relations:

$$\frac{\alpha \text{ (degrees)}}{\theta \text{ (radians)}} = \frac{180}{\pi},$$

$$\frac{N \text{ (revolutions)}}{\alpha \text{ (degrees)}} = \frac{1}{360},$$

$$\frac{N \text{ (revolutions)}}{\theta \text{ (radians)}} = \frac{1}{2\pi}.$$

We give you some examples to illustrate the application of these pro-portions:

(1) A flywheel rotates 3000 revolutions per minute (rpm). How many radians per second (rps) is this?

$$\frac{3000}{\theta} = \frac{1}{2\pi} \text{ yields } \theta = 6000\pi \text{ radians.}$$

The flywheel rotates 6000π radians in 1 min, which is 100π rps.

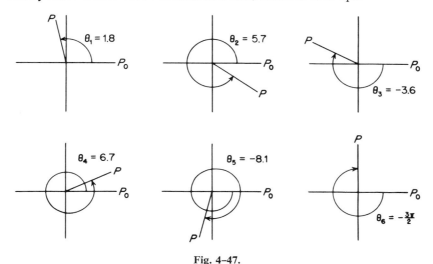

Fig. 4–47.

(2) A planet revolves about the sun in an elliptical path that is approxi-mately circular. It sweeps out an angle of 8° in 1 month. Express this angle in radians and in revolutions.

$$\frac{8}{\theta} = \frac{180}{\pi} \text{ yields } \theta = \frac{8\pi}{180} = \frac{2\pi}{45} \text{ radians.}$$

$$\frac{N}{8} = \frac{1}{360} \text{ yields } N = \frac{8}{360} = \frac{1}{45} \text{ revolutions.}$$

If this planet is at an average distance of 8.2×10^9 mi from the sun during the month, how far does it move in its orbit? Figure 4–48 will help you to visualize this question.

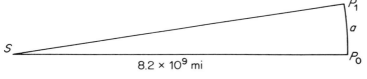

Fig. 4–48.

Notice that we replace the elliptical orbit of the planet by the arc of a circle of radius 8.2×10^9 mi; we express the angle of $8°$ as $2\pi/45$ radian; then we estimate the distance P_0P_1, that the planet moves, by calculating the arc a of this circle.

$$\theta = \frac{a}{r} \text{ yields } \frac{2\pi}{45} = \frac{a}{8.2 \times 10^9}, \quad \text{and} \quad a = \frac{16.4\pi(10^9)}{45} \doteq 1.1 \times 10^9 \text{ mi.}$$

Many practical problems in astronomy and physics are treated in somewhat the way we treated Example (2). You replace the arc of an ellipse by the arc of a circle, or you replace a straight line by the arc of a circle. Such replacements are justified when the precision of your measurements makes them harmless. We illustrate this point further by using some of the ideas of Section 409.

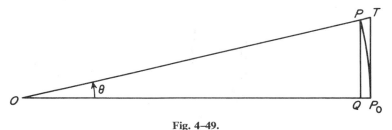

Fig. 4–49.

Figure 4–49 shows a *sector* of a circle of radius $OP_0 = 1$. Recall that $QP = \sin \theta$, and $P_0T = \tan \theta$. The arc P_0P, which we called a in Section 409, corresponds to a central angle whose measure is θ radians in a circle of radius 1; hence $\theta = a/1 = a$. Of course θ is measured in radians, and a is measured in the unit of length OP_0; but the numbers that θ and a represent are the same.

You should look now at a table of natural trigonometric functions. It is most convenient to use a table that shows angles in degrees and in radians, and includes the sines and tangents of these angles. Here is an excerpt from such a table.

(Deg.)	θ (rad.)	Sin θ	Tan θ
0	0.0000	0.0000	0.0000
1	0.0175	0.0175	0.0175
2	0.0349	0.0349	0.0349
3	0.0524	0.0523	0.0524
4	0.0698	0.0698	0.0699
5	0.0873	0.0872	0.0875
6	0.1047	0.1045	0.1051

Notice that, according to the table, $\theta = \sin \theta = \tan \theta$ when θ is the measure of a small angle. Of course this is untrue. In Fig. 4–49, it is clear that $QP \neq P_0T$, and that the arc P_0P is not equal to either QP or P_0T. The explanation is, of course, that the table gives approximate values of the arc

a and the directed line segments QP and P_0T. For a small angle, of measure θ, these lengths are approximately the same. As you study the table, notice that

$$\sin \theta \leq \theta \leq \tan \theta,$$

as you would expect from Fig. 4–49. Of course you know that

$$\sin \theta < \theta < \tan \theta,$$

for $0 < \theta \leq .1047$. It is the approximations of the table that lead to the apparent equality of $\sin \theta$, θ, and $\tan \theta$, for a small angle.

Fig. 4–50.

The following examples illustrate the ways in which practical people use these ideas to simplify calculations with measured numbers.

(3) When you look at the sun, the angle that its diameter *subtends* at your eye is about $\frac{1}{2}$ degree. If the distance to the sun is 9.3×10^7 mi, what is its diameter? (Fig. 4–50).

You think of the diameter d of the sun as the arc of a circle of radius $r = 9.3 \times 10^7$ mi, and $\frac{1}{2}$ degree as θ radians, where $.5/\theta = 180/\pi$. Then

$$\theta = \frac{.5\pi}{180} = \frac{d}{9.3 \times 10^7} \text{ yields } d \doteq \frac{4.6 \times 10^7\pi}{180} \doteq 8.1 \times 10^5 \text{ mi.}$$

(4) A gunner fires at a point 3600 yd away (at a range of 3600 yd). He sees the shell burst .007 radian (often called 7 *milliradians*, or 7 *mils*) to the left

Fig. 4–51.

of the target. By how many yards did he miss the target? (Fig. 4–51).

Here
$$\theta = .007 = \frac{d}{3600} \text{ yields } d \doteq 25 \text{ yd.}$$

(5) A gunner knows that the wingspan of an attacking plane is 60 ft. He uses his ringsight to measure the angle that the wingspan subtends at his eye and gets 10 mils ($= .010$ radian). How far away is the attacking plane? (Fig. 4–52).

Here $a = 60$ ft and $\theta = .01$ radian.

$$.01 = \frac{60}{r} \text{ yields } r = 6000 \text{ ft.}$$

Gun   ↑10 mils

Fig. 4–52.

EXERCISES §410

1. The following angles are measured in revolutions. Determine the number of degrees and the number of radians in the measure of each angle.

(a) 0.4 rev.   (b) $\frac{3}{4}$ rev.   (c) $\frac{2}{3}$ rev.

(d) 1.62 rev.   (e) $-\frac{5}{6}$ rev.   (f) $-2\frac{1}{4}$ rev.

Answers: (a) 144°, 2.513; (d) 583.2°, 10.179; (f) −810°, −14.137.

2. The following angles are measured in degrees. Determine the number of revolutions and the number of radians in the measure of each angle.

(a) 90°   (b) 225°   (c) 540°

(d) −45°   (e) −162°   (f) 1000°.

Answers: (a) $1/4, \pi/2 \doteq 1.571$; (e) $-9/20, -9\pi/10 \doteq -2.827$.

3. The following angles are measured in radians. Determine the number of degrees and the number of revolutions in the measure of each angle.

(a) $\pi/2$ radians   (b) $-\pi/6$ radian   (c) $3\pi/4$ radians

(d) −2.3   (e) 7 radians   (f) −5.4 radians.

Answers: (b) $-30°, -1/12$; (d) $-131.78°, -.366$.

4. Make a drawing of each of the following angles in standard position:

(a) 225°   (b) −36°   (c) 0.4 rev.

(d) $-2\frac{1}{4}$ rev.   (e) $\pi/2$ radians   (f) 2 radians

(g) 540°   (h) −2.3 radians   (i) $3\pi/4$ radians

(j) 1000°   (k) 3/4 rev.   (l) −162°

(m) −400°   (n) 7 radians   (o) −5.4 radians.

5. Use $\pi \doteq 3.14159$ to determine (accurate to six decimal places):

$$1° = \underline{\hspace{3cm}} \text{ radians}$$

$$1' = \underline{\hspace{3cm}} \text{ radians}$$

$$1'' = \underline{\hspace{3cm}} \text{ radians}$$

Locate the conversion table for degrees, minutes, and seconds to radians in your book of mathematical tables and compare results.

6. Use the results of Exercise 5 or a conversion table to express each of the following angles in radians (accurate to four decimal places):

(a) 10°   (b) 32°   (c) 200°   (d) 40′
(e) 52′   (f) 32°40′   (g) 65°52′   (h) 126°10′.

Answers: (a) .1745; (c) 3.4907; (g) 1.1496.

7. Determine the number of degrees in 1 radian. Give the result in two ways: (a) degrees, minutes, and seconds; (b) degrees and decimal parts of a degree. Compare with conversion tables for radians to degrees.

8. The following angles are measured in radians. Use the results of Exercise 7 or a conversion table to express each angle in the degree system of measurement.

(a) 3   (b) 0.6   (c) 3.6   (d) −1.7
(e) 5.4   (f) 0.84   (g) 3.84   (h)   7.31.

Answers: (a) 171.887° or 171°53′14″; (d) −97.403° or −97°24′10″.

9. Find the length of the arc cut off by a central angle whose measure is 1.42 radians in a circle of radius 6 ft.

Answer: 8.52 ft.

10. A pendulum bob is hanging on a string 30 in. long. How many radians does the string rotate as the bob swings along an arc 24 in. long? How many degrees?

Answers: 0.8, 45.84°.

11. An automobile travels at a speed of 35 mph. Show that this is equivalent to a speed of 616 in. per second. If the radius of a wheel on the automobile is 14 in., how many radians is the wheel turning in each second? How many revolutions in each second?

Answers: 44 radians per second;   7.00 revolutions per second.

12. A teacher wants to make a wooden blackboard protractor. It is to be in the shape of a semi-circle of radius 10 in. with markers every 5°. How many radians are there in 5°? What should be the distance along the arc between successive markers?

Answers: 0.0873, 0.873 in.

13. A fan blade 18 in. in diameter rotates at 500 revolutions per minute. How many radians per minute does the blade rotate? How far does the tip of one of the blades move in 1 min?

14. The latitude of Cedar Falls, Iowa is 42°30′. If the radius of the earth is approximately 4000 mi, how far is Cedar Falls from the equator?

15. How many radians per minute is the minute hand of a clock turning? If a large clock on a tower has a minute hand 4 ft long, how many inches per minute does the tip of the hand move?

Answers: 0.105 radians/min;   5.04 in./min.

16. At 30 mph, an automobile engine is making 1200 revolutions per minute. How many radians per minute is this? The pulley that drives the fan belt is 6 in. in diameter. How fast is the fan belt moving?

17. As seen from the earth, the moon subtends an angle of about .009 radian. (How large is this angle in the degree system of measurement?) If the moon is about 239,000 miles distant, what is its approximate diameter?

18. A football field, 100 yd long as seen from an airplane overhead, appears to subtend an angle of 24 mils. Approximately how high is the airplane?

Answer: 4200 ft.

19. A gunner, firing on a target at a range of 6000 yd, observes that the burst is about 35 yd to the right of the target. By how many mils should he correct the direction of fire of his gun?

Answer: 6 mils.

20. Some field glasses are calibrated in mils so that small angles may be easily estimated. If a 6-ft man subtends an angle of 3 mils, how far away is he?

21. A tree $1\frac{1}{2}$ mi away subtends an angle of 9 mils. How tall is the tree?

Now that you know how to measure angles, we proceed to a second definition of sin x, cos x, and tan x. You met these expressions as names for certain vectors in the unit circle.

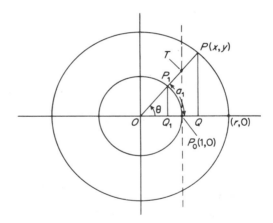

Fig. 4–53.

In Fig. 4–53, we drew a unit circle and a circle of radius r. By definition,

$$\sin a_1 = \sin \theta = Q_1 P_1.$$

By proportion, $\dfrac{QP}{OP} = \dfrac{Q_1 P_1}{OP_1}$,   that is, $\dfrac{y}{r} = \dfrac{\sin \theta}{1}$.

This condition is often used to define the *trigonometric ratio* sin θ. We say that

$$\sin \theta = \frac{y}{r}$$

is the ratio of the y-coordinate of a point $P(x,y)$ on the terminal side of angle θ (placed in standard position, $\theta = P_0OP$) to the distance of this point from the origin ($OP = r$).

Similarly, $\qquad \cos a_1 = \cos \theta = \dfrac{OQ_1}{1} = \dfrac{OQ}{OP} = \dfrac{x}{r}$

and $\qquad \tan a_1 = \tan \theta = \dfrac{P_0T}{1} = \dfrac{QP}{OQ} = \dfrac{y}{x}.$

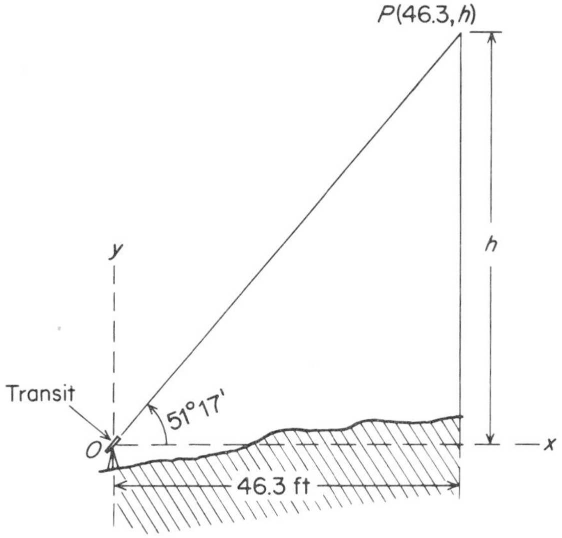

Fig. 4–54.

We shall return to further study of the trigonometric ratios in Chapter 9. So far you know four important ratios:

$$\theta = \frac{a}{r} \quad \text{(the radian measure of angle } \theta\text{)},$$

$$\sin \theta = \frac{y}{r},$$

$$\cos \theta = \frac{x}{r},$$

and $\qquad \tan \theta = \dfrac{y}{x}.$

We close this section with an application of the tangent function that is drawn from the field of surveying. A surveyor sets up his transit 46.3 ft from the center of a flagpole, the distance being measured horizontally. He measures the *angle of elevation* of the top of the pole (the angle from the level line to the line of sight toward the top of the pole) as 51°17′. Find the height (above the telescope of the transit) of the flagpole (see Fig. 4–54).

Think of the transit as placed at the origin. The coordinates of the point P (the top of the pole) are $(46.3, h)$. We know that

$$\tan 51°17' = \frac{h}{46.3}.$$

Tables yield $\tan 51°17' = 1.2475$. Hence

$$\frac{h}{46.3} = 1.2475 \quad \text{and} \quad h = 57.8 \text{ ft.}$$

This example illustrates the use of trigonometric ratios in surveying. You will meet other examples in the exercises, and in Chapter 9.

EXERCISES §410 (cont.)

22. Decide whether each of the following is positive, negative, or zero.

(a) $\cos 31°$
(b) $\sin 99°$
(c) $\sin 214°$

(d) $\tan 78°$
(e) $\cos 315°$
(f) $\cos \dfrac{\pi}{2}$

(g) $\tan \dfrac{\pi}{6}$
(h) $\tan \dfrac{8\pi}{7}$
(i) $\sin \dfrac{-5\pi}{2}$

(j) $\sin 3\pi$
(k) $\cos 2$
(l) $\tan \dfrac{\pi}{2}$

23. Make a careful scale drawing on graph paper, similar to Fig. 4–35 (page 150), to find approximations to the values of the sine and cosine of various angles by measurement. Choose the unit on the graph paper fairly large so as to cover most of the page. On the same circle, use a protractor to draw triangles QOP with $\alpha = $ angle $QOP = 15°, 30°, 45°, 75°, 130°, 200°,$ and $321°$.

(a) By measuring the lengths of QP for these different triangles, make up a table of the approximate values of $\sin \alpha$ for these five angles.
(b) Repeat with the measurements of OQ for a table of approximate values of $\cos \alpha$.
(c) Compare these approximations with the values found in your book of mathematical tables.

24. You probably noticed in Exercise 23 that the measured value of $\sin 15°$ is approximately the same as that for $\cos 75°$. Use the idea of congruent triangles in geometry to prove that $\sin 15° = \cos 75°$. Suggest a generalization of this equality to other angles.

25. Make a careful scale drawing on graph paper, similar to Fig. 4–42 (page 157). Use angles $\alpha = $ angle $P_0OP = 15°, 30°, 45°, 75°, 105°, 120°, 135°, 150°,$ and $165°$

(a) Measure P_0T for each angle, and make a table of values of $\tan \alpha$ for these nine angles.
(b) Compare these approximations to the values of $\tan \alpha$ found in your book of mathematical tables.

(c) On the graph of $y = \tan x$ (Section 409, page 159), locate points on the horizontal axis to correspond to 15°, 30°, 45°, 75°, 105°, etc. Measure the corresponding values of y and compare these values with those found in part (a).

26. Graph $y = \sin \alpha$ and $y = \cos \alpha$ with α measured in degrees. Notice that the units along the α-axis are degrees. When you compare the graph of $y = \sin \alpha$ (α in degrees) to the graph of $y = \sin x$ (x in radians, or in arc-length along the unit circle), notice that the difference is merely a scale-change on the horizontal axis.

27. Recall how we used the graph of $y = x^2$ to suggest the appearance of the graph of $y = ax^2$. Use similar ideas to sketch $y = \sin x$ and $y = 2 \sin x$ on the same coordinate system. (*Hint:* for each value of x, $2 \sin x$ is twice $\sin x$.)

28. Use your knowledge of the shape of $y = \sin x$, $y = \cos x$, and $y = \tan x$ to draw sketches for

(a) $y = 4 \sin x$ (b) $y = -3 \sin x$ (c) $y = 2 \cos x$
(d) $y = \frac{1}{2} \sin x$ (e) $y = \frac{1}{4} \tan x$ (f) $y = -2.5 \cos x$
(g) $y \geq 2 \sin x$ (h) $y < -2 \cos x$ (i) $y > \frac{1}{2} \tan x$.

29. The voltage E at the meter box in a home is related to time T by the equation $E = 155 \sin 2\pi T$, where T is measured in units of sixtieths of a second. Sketch the graph of this condition for $0 \leq T \leq 1$. (Convenient values to use are $T = 0$, 1/8, 2/8, 3/8, etc.)

30. A boy scout wants to find the height of a cliff. At a distance of 57 ft from the base of the cliff, the angle of elevation to the top of the cliff is 72°. How high is the cliff above the level of his eye?

Answer: 175 ft.

31. The shadow of a 6-ft man is 8.25 ft long. What is the angle of elevation of the sun? (*Hint:* Compare with the illustration in this section (page 169). This is the *inverse* problem.)

32. For a stretch of several miles, the gradient of a highway is constant and equal to 3°37′. (The gradient is the angle the highway makes with the horizontal.) How many feet does the elevation of a traveler change as his car moves 1 mi horizontally?

5

Powers and Roots of Real Numbers

In previous chapters you learned to add and multiply real numbers. You learned to interpret subtraction as the inverse of addition, and division as the inverse of multiplication. Thus, except for the forbidden operation of division by zero, you know how to add, subtract, multiply, and divide real numbers.

Perhaps without realizing it, you began to explore another operation, *raising to powers*. This operation looks harmless enough when you meet it first. Expressions like $a^2 (= a \cdot a)$, $a^3 (= a \cdot a \cdot a)$, etc., are merely convenient ways to express special multiplications.

When you begin to explore this operation of raising to powers, it leads you to new complications. For example, the inverse of raising to powers is *finding roots*. You know how to find the fourth *power* of 5:

$$5^4 = 5 \cdot 5 \cdot 5 \cdot 5 = 625$$

What about the inverse operation of finding the number whose fourth power is 625? Like division, this operation of finding roots is basically a try-and-check process. To do the division $24 \div 8$, you say the answer is 3 *because* $3 \times 8 = 24$. To do the operation of finding a fourth root of 625, you say an answer is 5 *because* $5^4 = 625$. This try-and-check process can become very tedious. You can find an approximate value of the fourth root of 600 by guessing and checking; but, before long, you will want a calculating machine.

We use the symbol $\sqrt[n]{b}$ to represent a certain number x such that $x^n = b$. We call $\sqrt[n]{b}$ a *radical*, b the *radicand*, and n the *index*. When the index is 2, we omit it. For example, $\sqrt[4]{600}$ is the fourth root of 600, $\sqrt{3}$ is the square root of 3, and $\sqrt[11]{12}$ is the eleventh root of 12.

The symbolism for roots involves new complications. If you ask for a number whose square is 16, you may see at once that 4 works ($4^2 = 16$);

but -4 also works because $(-4)^2 = 16$. This is something new. Division problems have *unique* answers. There is just one number that you can multiply by -7 to get 35; the quotient, $35 \div (-7) = -5$, is unique. But there is more than one number whose square is 81; both 9 and -9 work.

To avoid using the same symbol, $\sqrt{16}$, to represent two different numbers, we agree that $\sqrt{16}$ represents only the positive number whose square is 16; to represent the other square root of 16 we use $-\sqrt{16}$. While the solution set of the condition $x^2 = 16$ is $\{4, -4\}$, and hence both 4 and -4 are square roots of 16, we write $\sqrt{16} = 4$ and $-\sqrt{16} = -4$. As further examples: $\sqrt{49} = 7$; $\sqrt{49} \neq -7$; $-\sqrt{\frac{1}{4}} = -\frac{1}{2}$; $-\sqrt{\frac{1}{4}} \neq \frac{1}{2}$.

One more difficulty: Except for divisions by zero, division problems are always possible within the set L. When you ask for a replacement of x such that $a/b = x$, $b \neq 0$, you are sure that you can find one. But when you ask for a replacement of x such that $\sqrt[n]{b} = x$, you may or may not be able to find one. For example, take $b = -4$ and $n = 2$. Then you seek a value of x such that

$$\sqrt{-4} = x.$$

This implies, by definition, that the square of x is to be -4; that is,

$$x^2 = -4.$$

Recall that $x \in L \Rightarrow (x > 0 \text{ or } x = 0 \text{ or } x < 0)$. In each case $x^2 = x \cdot x \geq 0$. Hence there is no replacement of x such that $x^2 = -4$; that is, the symbol $\sqrt{-4}$ does not stand for a real number.

This last difficulty may remind you of the corresponding difficulty with division of natural numbers. When you limit yourself to the set of natural numbers, a condition like $7 \div 4 = x$ has no solution. There is no value of x such that $x \in N$ and $7 = 4x$. You need to enlarge the set of numbers you permit yourself to use. You need the fractions of arithmetic to do divisions like $7 \div 4$. Later, we shall find it convenient to enlarge the set of real numbers to build a set of numbers that contains the roots of all real numbers.

These introductory comments point to the need for a careful exploration of the structure of the set L with respect to the inverse operations of raising to powers and finding roots. As we proceed, you will discover practical applications of this further exploration of the structure of the set L.

500. Intuitive approach to finding roots

At first we shall avoid roots of negative numbers. We consider only roots of the form

$$\sqrt[n]{b}, \quad b \geq 0 \quad \text{and} \quad n \in N.$$

Moreover we agree that then

$$\sqrt[n]{b} \geq 0.$$

Consider, for example, the expression $\sqrt{x}$, $x \geq 0$ and $\sqrt{x} \geq 0$. The following table pairs values of x with values of y that satisfy the condition $y = \sqrt{x}$.

x	0	1	4	9	16	...
y	0	1	2	3	4	...

Notice that we selected values of x that are perfect squares. This makes it easy to calculate values of $y = \sqrt{x}$.

Now examine the graph (Fig. 5–1). Notice how we limited ourselves to

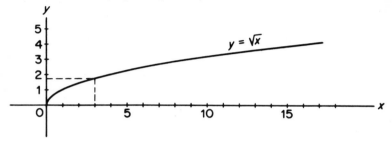

Fig. 5–1.

the first quadrant ($x \geq 0$ and $y = \sqrt{x} \geq 0$), and to values of x that are perfect squares. Then we took the bold step of drawing a smooth curve through the plotted points.

It seems reasonable to read square roots from the graph ($\sqrt{3}$ is approximately 1.7 in the figure); but, of course, the precision of your readings will depend upon precision of your graph.

There are many ways to improve the approximation, $\sqrt{3} \doteq 1.7$. We describe a method that emphasizes the meaning of square roots:

You are looking for a value of y such that $y^2 = yy = 3$. As a first approximation, take $y_1 = 1.7$. Now perform the division,

$$
\begin{array}{r}
1.7647 \\
1.7)\overline{3.00000} \\
\underline{1\ 7} \\
1\ 30 \\
\underline{1\ 19} \\
110 \\
\underline{102} \\
80 \\
\underline{68} \\
120 \\
\underline{119} \\
1
\end{array}
$$

and neglect the remainder, 1. From this,

$$(1.7)(1.7647) \doteq 3$$

But you seek a value of y, such that $y \cdot y = 3$. Take $y_2 = \frac{1}{2}(1.7 + 1.7647) \doteq$ 1.7323 as a second approximation. This y_2 is the *arithmetic mean* of the divisor, 1.7, and the quotient, 1.7647. It seems reasonable that y_2 will be a better approximation to y than y_1 was. To check this, perform the division

$$3 \div 1.7323 \doteq 1.7318$$

From this $$(1.7323)(1.7318) \doteq 3.$$

Notice that $$1.7323 \doteq 1.732 \text{ (nearest .001)}$$

and $$1.7318 \doteq 1.732 \text{ (nearest .001)}.$$

Hence $$y \doteq 1.732 \text{ (nearest .001)}.$$

If you need a still better approximation, take $y_3 = \frac{1}{2}(1.7323 + 1.7318) = $ 1.73205 and proceed as before.

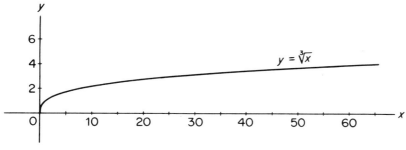

Fig. 5–2.

Notice that you can adapt this method to find the positive square root of any positive, decimally expressed, number. You should try to round off your results at each successive step to save work without sacrificing useful figures. But, at the moment, efficiency of calculation is of lesser concern. The important thing is to see that you can calculate square roots to any desired precision.

Next, consider the expression $\sqrt[3]{x}$, where $x \geq 0$ and $\sqrt[3]{x} \geq 0$. We make a table for the condition $y = \sqrt[3]{x}$, using values of x that are perfect cubes:

x	0	1	8	27	64	...
y	0	1	2	3	4	...

The corresponding graph is shown in Fig. 5–2. Notice that we enlarged the units on the y-axis to make it easier to read the graph.

From the graph, $y_1 = \sqrt[3]{6} \doteq 1.9$. To improve this approximation, calculate

$$(1.9)^3 = 6.859.$$

Since this is too large, calculate

$$(1.8)^3 = 5.832.$$

Hence $$1.8 < \sqrt[3]{6} < 1.9.$$

Now we select a second approximation, say $y_2 = 1.82$ (closer to 1.8 than to 1.9, since 1.8^3 is closer to 6 than 1.9^3 is). In this way, continue to squeeze the number $\sqrt[3]{6}$ between closer and closer limits. Of course you may discover a more orderly way to proceed (as we did for square roots). But, even if you do not discover such a short cut, you can proceed to better and better approximations for $\sqrt[3]{6}$.

You can discuss, in this same way, the expression $\sqrt[n]{x}$, where $n \in N$, $x \geq 0$, and $\sqrt[n]{x} \geq 0$. For some values of n you may discover short cuts. For example, you will learn in Section 505 that $\sqrt[4]{x} = \sqrt{\sqrt{x}}$. But, with or without short cuts, the try-and-check process will work.

From now on we shall avoid the rather messy details of calculating roots of real numbers. We shall concentrate on the structure of the set L with respect to the operation of raising to powers, and the inverse operation of taking roots. Eventually, this exploration of structure will lead us to the idea of *logarithms*, and to practical methods for calculating roots of real numbers.

EXERCISES §500

1. From the graph of $y = \sqrt{x}$, estimate $\sqrt{2}$; $\sqrt{5}$; $\sqrt{11}$.

2. Estimate $\sqrt{11}$ to three decimal places. Use the method of dividing and averaging.

3. Estimate $\sqrt[3]{13}$ to three decimal places.

Partial answer: Since $2^3 < 13 < 3^3$, $2 < \sqrt[3]{13} < 3$; 13 is closer to 8 than it is to 27, so take 2.3 as your first estimate. By calculating $(2.3)^3 = 12.167$ and $(2.4)^3 = 13.824$, you conclude: $2.3 < \sqrt[3]{13} < 2.4$ (apparently about half-way between, perhaps a little closer to 2.4). Next, calculate $(2.35)^3$, etc.

4. Sketch the graph of $y = \sqrt[4]{x}$. Choose your units along the x- and y-axes to make the graph easy to read.

5. From the graph in Exercise 4, estimate $\sqrt[4]{21}$; $\sqrt[4]{41}$; and $\sqrt[4]{50}$.

6. Calculate $\sqrt{\sqrt{21}}$ by the method of dividing and averaging. Carry your answer to the nearest .001. Is $\sqrt[4]{21} = \sqrt{\sqrt{21}}$?

7. Estimate $\sqrt{2}$, $\sqrt{5}$, and $\sqrt{10}$ to three decimal places. Multiply the estimates for $\sqrt{2}$ and $\sqrt{5}$ and compare the product with the estimate for $\sqrt{10}$.

501. Graphs of inverse functions

You have learned to think of certain pairs of operations as inverses of one another. For example, addition and subtraction, multiplication and division, and raising to powers and extracting roots, are pairs of inverse operations.

We introduce you now to the idea of pairs of inverse functions. Like the corresponding idea of inverse operations, this new idea of inverse functions simplifies the presentation of mathematical ideas. It cuts the things you need to remember almost in half.

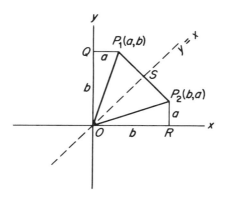

Fig. 5–3.

Consider the two relations $\{(x,y) \mid y = p(x)\}$ and $\{(x,y) \mid x = p(y)\}$. That is, consider two relations for which the roles that the variables x and y play are interchanged. We call such a pair of relations *inverses* of one another. For example:

$$\{(x,y) \mid y = x + 2\} \quad \text{and} \quad \{(x,y) \mid x = y + 2\}$$
$$\{(x,y) \mid y = 3x\} \quad \text{and} \quad \{(x,y) \mid x = 3y\}$$
$$\{(x,y) \mid y = 5x - 4\} \quad \text{and} \quad \{(x,y) \mid x = 5y - 4\}$$
$$\{(x,y) \mid y = x^2\} \quad \text{and} \quad \{(x,y) \mid x = y^2\}.$$

When a number-pair (a,b) belongs to a relation, the number-pair (b,a) belongs to the inverse relation. It is convenient to approach this idea graphically and to study the relative positions of the points $P_1(a,b)$ and $P_2(b,a)$ in Fig. 5–3. Triangles OP_1Q and OP_2R are congruent; the line OS $(y = x)$ bisects angle P_1OP_2; $P_1S = SP_2$; angle $OSP_1 =$ angle $OSP_2 = 90°$.

Hence P_2 is the reflection of P_1 in the line $y = x$. When you think of P_1 as a point on the graph of the condition $y = p(x)$, P_2 is a point on the graph of the *inverse condition* $x = p(y)$. The set of points $\{(x,y) \mid x = p(y)\}$ is the reflection in the line $y = x$ of the set of points $\{(x,y) \mid y = p(x)\}$. As examples, study the following graphs of inverse conditions in Fig. 5–4.

To each point $P_1(a,b)$ of the graph of $y = p(x)$, there corresponds a point $P_2(b,a)$ of the graph of $x = p(y)$. Hence the graph of $x = p(y)$ is the reflection in the line $y = x$ of the graph of $y = p(x)$.

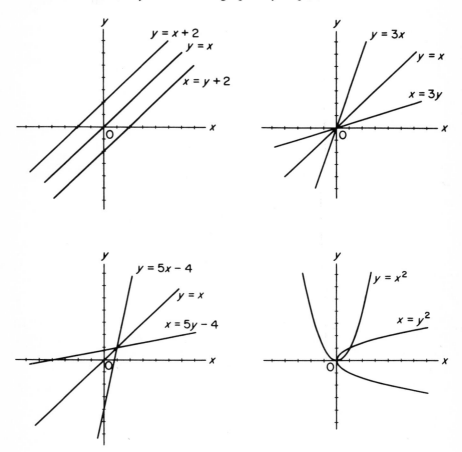

Fig. 5–4.

Notice that points on the line $y = x$ reflect into themselves. The inverse of a one-to-one correspondence is a one-to-one correspondence; but the inverse of a function may or may not be a function. The relation $\{(x,y) \mid y = x^2\}$ is a function; the inverse relation $\{(x,y) \mid x = y^2\}$ is not a function.

As one application of the idea of inverse relations, consider the question of graphing $y = \sqrt[4]{x}$, $x \geq 0$ and $\sqrt[4]{x} \geq 0$. You learned how to graph

$y = x^4$ in Chapter 4. The inverse condition, $x = y^4$, is the reflection of $y = x^4$ in the line $y = x$. By definition,

$$y = \sqrt[4]{x} \Rightarrow x = y^4.$$

Hence each point of the graph of $y = \sqrt[4]{x}$ is a point of the graph of $x = y^4$ (Fig. 5–5). The graph of $y = \sqrt[4]{x}$, $x \geq 0$ and $\sqrt[4]{x} \geq 0$, is the part of the graph of $x = y^4$ that lies in the first quadrant (Fig. 5–6). Notice that $\{(x,y) \mid y = \sqrt[4]{x},\ x \geq 0$ and $\sqrt[4]{x} \geq 0\}$ is a function. It is the subset of $\{(x,y) \mid x = y^4\}$ whose elements correspond to points in the first quadrant.

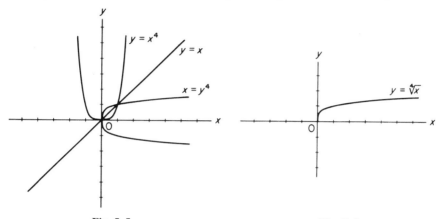

Fig. 5–5.   Fig. 5–6.

We shall give the expression $\sqrt[n]{x}$ somewhat greater freedom in later sections of this chapter. Meanwhile we consider only the case $x \geq 0$ and $\sqrt[n]{x} \geq 0$; that is, we restrict the graph of $y = \sqrt[n]{x}$ to the first quadrant. The exercises provide opportunities to graph instances of $y = \sqrt[n]{x}$, $x \geq 0$ and $\sqrt[n]{x} \geq 0$; you will also gain experience with graphs of inverse conditions.

EXERCISES §501

1. Graph the point $P_1(5,3)$; then graph the inverse point $P_2(3,5)$. Notice that P_1 and P_2 are reflections of one another in the line $y = x$.

2. Repeat Exercise 1 for each pair of points:

(a) $(-5,3)$ and $(3,-5)$ (b) $(2,-3)$ and $(-3,2)$
(c) $(4,4)$ and $(4,4)$ (d) $(0,-3)$ and $(-3,0)$.

3. Graph the relation $\{(1,1),\ (2,3),\ (2,5),\ (3,3),\ (3,-2),\ (4,-5)\}$; then graph the inverse relation. Notice that the two relations are reflections of one another in the line $y = x$.

4. Graph the condition $y = -2x + 5$; then graph the inverse condition $x = -2y + 5$. What is the graphical connection between these inverse conditions?

5. Repeat Exercise 4 for each pair of conditions:

(a) $y = x + 3$ and $x = y + 3$

(b) $y = \frac{1}{3}x$ and $x = \frac{1}{3}y$

(c) $y = \frac{3}{4}x - 5$ and $x = \frac{3}{4}y - 5$

(d) $y = x^3$ and $x = y^3$

(e) $y = 2x^2 - 3$ and $x = 2y^2 - 3$

(f) $y = 3/x$ and $x = 3/y$.

6. Notice that $x = y + 3 \Leftrightarrow y = x - 3$. Hence, in Exercise 5(a), the condition $y = x - 3$ is the inverse of the condition $y = x + 3$. This is the connection between inverse operations and inverse conditions. The inverse of adding 3 is subtracting 3. When you replace x by 7 in the condition $y = x + 3$, you find $y = 7 + 3 = 10$; when you replace x by 10 in the condition $y = x - 3$, you find $y = 10 - 3 = 7$. That is, when you add 3 and then subtract 3, you end up where you started. Try this process again with the replacement $x = 8$.

7. Repeat Exercise 6 with other conditions taken from Exercise 5. For example, $x = \frac{1}{3}y \Leftrightarrow y = 3x$. Hence the conditions $y = \frac{1}{3}x$ and $y = 3x$ are inverses. Interpret this as a question of inverse operations.

8. Consider the condition "y is the social security number of x." The range of x is the set of persons who have social security numbers; the range of y is the set of social security numbers. Write the inverse condition. What is the new range of x? What is the new range of y? What about the question: "What is the social security number of a person whose social security number is 479-30-1895?"

9. Graph the function $\{(x,y) \mid y = x^3\}$. Graph the inverse relation $\{(x,y) \mid x = y^3\}$. Is the inverse relation a function? Now graph the relation $\{(x,y) \mid y = \sqrt[3]{x}, x \geq 0$ and $\sqrt[3]{x} \geq 0\}$. Notice that this relation is a subset of $\{(x,y) \mid x = y^3\}$. Is it a function?

10. Repeat Exercise 9 for the functions:

(a) $\{(x,y) \mid y = x^5\}$

(b) $\{(x,y) \mid y = 4x^2\}$ [Inverse relation $\{(x,y) \mid x = 4y^2\}$; subset $\{(x,y) \mid y = \frac{1}{2}\sqrt{x}\}$]

(c) $\{(x,y) \mid y = \frac{1}{8}x^3\}$ [Inverse relation $\{(x,y) \mid x = \frac{1}{8}y^3\}$; subset $\{(x,y) \mid y = 2\sqrt[3]{x}\}$].

11. Compare the graphs of $y = \sqrt{x}$ and $y = 3\sqrt{x}$. As usual, restrict these graphs to the first quadrant.

12. Use the idea of alias with $Y = y - 2$ and $X = x - 1$ to sketch the graph of $y - 2 = \sqrt{x - 1}$.

13. Make sketches of:

(a) $y = 2\sqrt{x}$ (b) $y = -3\sqrt{x}$

(c) $y - 4 = \sqrt{x + 2}$ (d) $y = 3 + \sqrt{x - 2}$

(e) $y = \sqrt{-x}$ and $x \leq 0$ (f) $y = 2\sqrt{x} - 3$

(g) $y \leq 5\sqrt{x}$ (h) $y - 5 > 2\sqrt[3]{x - 1}$

(i) $y + 2 < 6\sqrt[4]{x - 3}$.

502. Rational powers of positive real numbers

Since the operation of raising to powers appears to be simpler than the inverse operation of finding roots, we shall examine it first. The strategy is to learn more about powers of real numbers. This may shed new light upon the inverse operation of finding roots of real numbers.

At first we limit ourselves to powers of positive, real numbers. Actually, powers of 0 are trivial: $0^n = 0$, $n \in N$. Hence we study the properties of symbols of the form a^n, $a > 0$, and $n \in N$.

We make the definition,

D 1 $$a^n = a \cdot a \cdot a \cdot \ldots \cdot a \ (n \text{ factors}).$$

Hence a^n symbolizes the product of n factors each equal to a. For example, $3^5 = 3 \cdot 3 \cdot 3 \cdot 3 \cdot 3$.

Notice that $a^n + a^n = (1 + 1)a^n = 2a^n$, and $sa^n + ta^n = (s + t)a^n$. This is nothing more than applying the distributive law to combine terms. But the expression $a^m + a^n$ involves unlike powers of a when $m \neq n$. For example, adding a^2 and a^5 is somewhat like adding x and y; of course you can say that $a^2 + a^5 = a^2(1 + a^3)$, but the addition of unlike powers of a does not yield convenient identities.

Contrast this with the situation for multiplication. The basic property is

P 1 $$a^m \cdot a^n = (a \cdot a \cdot a \cdot \ldots \cdot a)(a \cdot a \cdot a \cdot \ldots \cdot a) = a^{m+n}$$
$$(m \text{ factors}) \qquad (n \text{ factors})$$

It seems evident that m factors each equal to a, multiplied by n factors each equal to a, yield $m + n$ factors each equal to a. Mathematicians prove this by generalizing the associative law for multiplication of real numbers, namely, $a(bc) = (ab)c$.

The property, $a^m \cdot a^n = a^{m+n}$ (P 1), provides important insights into the structure of the set L with respect to the operation of raising to powers. To illustrate this, we shall experiment with symbols like a^{-5}, a^{-2}, a^0, $a^{1/5}$, $a^{3/4}$, and the like.

So far, the symbol a^n $(a > 0)$ is meaningful only when $n \in N$. This presents an opportunity and a challenge. On the one hand we have an opportunity to give meaning to expressions like $a^{2/3}$, a^{-5}, a^0, etc. On the other hand, we have the challenge to fit them into a consistent system. Can we make these new symbols convenient and useful generalizations of the old ones? We use P 1 as a guide. We try to define the new symbols to *preserve* P 1.

Look first at the (so far, undefined) symbol a^0. Applying P 1,

$$a^0 \cdot a^n = a^{0+n} = a^n.$$

Notice that a^0 acts like the identity for multiplication. Previously we have used the symbol 1 for this number. We have said $1 \cdot a^n = a^n$. To preserve P 1 and our previous ideas about the number 1, we make the definition,

D 2 $$a^0 = 1.$$

This means that $5^0 = 1$, $146^0 = 1$, $(3/4)^0 = 1$, etc. But recall that $a > 0$. Now study the symbol a^{-n}, where $n \in N$. Applying P 1,

$$a^{-n} \cdot a^n = a^{-n+n} = a^0.$$

We use D 2, and conclude that $a^0 = 1$. Hence

$$a^{-n} \cdot a^n = 1.$$

Notice that a^{-n} acts like the inverse of a^n with respect to multiplication. We have said $\dfrac{1}{a^n} \cdot a^n = 1$. To preserve the structure that we have built previously, we make

D 3 $$a^{-n} = \frac{1}{a^n}.$$

This means that $3^{-5} = \dfrac{1}{3^5}$, $1.08^{-6} = \dfrac{1}{(1.08)^6}$, $(2/3)^{-4} = \dfrac{1}{(2/3)^4}$, etc. But recall that $a > 0$.

To interpret fractional exponents it is convenient to have the property

P 2 $$(a^m)^n = a^{nm}.$$

For example, $(a^2)^3 = a^2 \cdot a^2 \cdot a^2 = a^{3 \cdot 2} = a^6$, and $(a^5)^4 = a^{4 \cdot 5} = a^{20}$.
P 2 holds for exponents that are natural numbers. Thus,

$$(a^m)^n = a^m \cdot a^m \cdot a^m \dots \cdot a^m \quad (n \text{ factors}) \qquad \qquad \text{(D 1)}$$
$$= a^{m+m+\dots+m} \quad (n \text{ addends}) \qquad \qquad \text{(Extension of P 1)}$$
$$= a^{nm} \quad (nm = m + m + \dots + m) \quad (n \text{ addends})$$

Now we define the symbol $a^{1/n}$, $n \in N$, to preserve P 2. By P 2,

$$(a^{1/n})^n = a^{n \cdot (1/n)} = a^1.$$

We use D 1, and conclude that $a^1 = a$. Hence

$$(a^{1/n})^n = a.$$

Notice that $a^{1/n}$ acts like an nth root of a. In Section 500, we used the symbol $\sqrt[n]{a}$ to stand for a number whose nth power is a; that is, $(\sqrt[n]{a})^n = a$. Now we identify the new symbol, $a^{1/n}$, with the familiar symbol $\sqrt[n]{a}$. We make

D 4 $$a^{1/n} = \sqrt[n]{a}.$$

This means that $4^{1/2} = \sqrt{4} = 2$, $\sqrt[3]{7} = 7^{1/3}$, etc. But recall that $a > 0$, and that we have restricted ourselves to positive, real numbers when we use symbols like $\sqrt[n]{a}$ and $a^{1/n}$. We shall return, in Section 504, to cases where $a < 0$. For example, we shall say $(-8)^{1/3} = \sqrt[3]{-8} = -2$ [because $(-2)^3 = -8$]; but we shall always give a unique meaning to the symbols $\sqrt[n]{a}$ and $a^{1/n}$, for each replacement of the variables a and n. For the time being, the symbol $\sqrt[n]{a}$ stands for a number that you can compute approximately, by the methods of Section 500.

Now study the symbol $a^{m/n}$ where $m \in N$ and $n \in N$. Again we preserve P 2, and notice that

$$a^{m/n} = (a^{1/n})^m = (\sqrt[n]{a})^m;$$

also, $$a^{m/n} = (a^m)^{1/n} = \sqrt[n]{a^m}.$$

It turns out that the symbols $(\sqrt[n]{a})^m$ and $\sqrt[n]{a^m}$ (for each value of a, and $a > 0$) represent the same real number. (See Exercise 14, page 203 for a proof.) So we may make

D 5 $$a^{m/n} = (\sqrt[n]{a})^m = \sqrt[n]{a^m}.$$

This means that $8^{2/3} = (\sqrt[3]{8})^2 = 2^2 = 4$; also $8^{2/3} = \sqrt[3]{8^2} = \sqrt[3]{64} = 4$. But recall that $a > 0$.

Notice that D 5 permits you to interpret the symbol a^x, where $a > 0$ and the range of x is the positive rational numbers. You can broaden D 3, and say $a^{-m/n} = 1/(a^{m/n})$. Also, by D 2, $a^0 = 1$. Hence you can interpret the symbol a^x, $a > 0$, where the range of x is the set R of rational numbers (positive, negative, and zero). For example,

$$7^{2/3} = (\sqrt[3]{7})^2, \quad \text{and} \quad 8^{-1/3} = \frac{1}{8^{1/3}} = \frac{1}{\sqrt[3]{8}} = \frac{1}{2}.$$

This still leaves symbols like $a^{\sqrt{2}}$ undefined. We might say $a^{\sqrt{2}} \doteq a^{1.4} = a^{7/5} = \sqrt[5]{a^7}$. An even better approximation is $a^{\sqrt{2}} \doteq a^{1.414} = a^{707/500} = \sqrt[500]{a^{707}}$. For the time being, we set aside the question of exponents that are real but not rational. Rigorous definitions of symbols like $a^{\sqrt{2}}$ would lead us too far from our present theme.

We mention just two more properties of powers of positive real numbers. We state these properties first when the exponents are restricted to the set of natural numbers:

P 3 $$a^n \cdot b^n = (ab)^n.$$

Notice that $a^n \cdot b^n = (a \cdot a \cdot a \cdot \ldots \cdot a) \cdot (b \cdot b \cdot b \cdot \ldots \cdot b)$

$$(n \text{ factors}) \qquad\qquad (n \text{ factors})$$

By applying the associative and the commutative laws of multiplication of real numbers,

$$(a \cdot a \cdot a \cdot \ldots \cdot a) \cdot (b \cdot b \cdot b \cdot \ldots \cdot b) = (ab) \cdot (ab) \cdot \ldots \cdot (ab)$$

$$= (ab)^n \qquad\qquad\qquad (\text{D } 1)$$

P 4
$$\frac{a^m}{a^n} = a^{m-n}$$

$$\frac{a^m}{a^n} = a^m \cdot \frac{1}{a^n} \qquad (\text{Properties of real numbers})$$

$$= a^m \cdot a^{-n} \qquad\qquad\qquad (\text{D } 3)$$

$$= a^{m+(-n)} \qquad\qquad (\text{Preserving P } 1)$$

$$= a^{m-n} \qquad (\text{Properties of real numbers})$$

We shall apply Properties 1, 2, 3, and 4 to symbols a^x, $a > 0$, where the range of x is the set L of real numbers. This really amounts to *postulating* these properties for real powers of positive real numbers. Actually it is possible to prove that these properties are consequences of the structure of the set L (Chapter 2), and of the definitions that we have made. Some of these proofs are not easy.

We shall apply Definitions 1, 2, 3, 4, and 5 to assign meanings to rational powers of positive, real numbers. To assign meanings to symbols like $5^{\sqrt{3}}$, $(\sqrt{3})^\pi$, etc., that involve real exponents that are not rational, we shall use rational approximations. For example, $5^{\sqrt{3}} \doteq 5^{1.73}$, $(\sqrt{3})^\pi \doteq (1.73)^{3.14}$, etc.

We repeat the definitions and properties of this section in convenient form below. Then we provide exercises for practicing the manipulation of these new symbols. In the next section we shall apply the new symbols to gain further insights into the exponential function, $\{(x, y) \mid y = b^x\}$.

DEFINITIONS

D 1　$a > 0, n \in N, a^n = a \cdot a \cdot \ldots \cdot a$　(n factors)

D 2　$a > 0 \Rightarrow a^0 = 1$

D 3　$a > 0, x \in L \Rightarrow a^{-x} = 1/a^x$

D 4　$a > 0, n \in N \Rightarrow a^{1/n} = \sqrt[n]{a}$

D 5　$a > 0, m \in N, n \in N \Rightarrow a^{m/n} = (\sqrt[n]{a})^m = \sqrt[n]{a^m}$.

PROPERTIES

P 1　$a > 0, x \in L, y \in L \Rightarrow a^x \cdot a^y = a^{x+y}$

P 2　$a > 0, x \in L, y \in L \Rightarrow (a^x)^y = a^{xy}$

P 3　$a > 0, b > 0, x \in L \Rightarrow a^x \cdot b^x = (ab)^x$

P 4　$a > 0, x \in L, y \in L \Rightarrow a^x/a^y = a^{x-y}$.

EXERCISES §502

1. Evaluate each of the following as a number free of exponents.

(a) 8^3

(b) 2^{10}

(c) $3^2 \cdot 3^3$

(d) $3^2 + 3^3$

(e) $\left(\dfrac{2}{7}\right)^3$

(f) $16^{1/2}$

(g) $16^{1/4}$

(h) $\left(\dfrac{9}{25}\right)^{1/2}$

(i) 7^{-2}

(j) $(2.3)^2$

(k) $\left(\dfrac{4}{5}\right)^{-2}$

(l) 21^0

(m) $4(10)^0$

(n) $7.4(10^3)$

(o) $12^{1/2}$

(p) $25^{-1/2}$

(q) $(4^2)^3$

(r) $125^{4/3}$

(s) $16^{-3/4}$

(t) $5^{3/2} \cdot 5^{1/2}$.

Answers: (i) $\frac{1}{49}$; (m) 4; (o) $\sqrt{12}$; (s) $\frac{1}{8}$.

2. Rewrite with positive exponents.

(a) 5^{-3}

(b) 8^{-1}

(c) $\left(\dfrac{2}{3}\right)^{-4}$

(d) $\dfrac{1}{4^{-2}}$

(e) $2^2 \cdot 2^{-5}$

(f) $7^{-1/2}$

(g) $4^2 \div 4^{-2}$

(h) $\dfrac{1}{12^{-1/2}}$

(i) y^{-3}

(j) $(2y)^{-3}$

(k) $2y^{-3}$

(l) $7a^{-1/2}b^2$.

Answers: (c) $\left(\dfrac{3}{2}\right)^4$; (j) $\dfrac{1}{(2y)^3}$; (k) $\dfrac{2}{y^3}$.

3. Rewrite in exponential form.

(a) $\sqrt{3}$

(b) $\sqrt[3]{7}$

(c) $\sqrt[4]{m}$

(d) $\sqrt[4]{m^3}$

(e) $\sqrt{2t}$

(f) $2\sqrt{t}$

(g) $\sqrt[3]{(3x)^2}$

(h) $\sqrt[5]{2b^3}$

(i) $\sqrt[4]{3^6}$

(j) $\sqrt{\sqrt{5}}$

(k) $\sqrt[6]{81x^4}$

(l) $\sqrt{\sqrt[3]{4y^2}}$.

Answers: (b) $7^{1/3}$; (g) $(3x)^{2/3}$; (h) $(2b^3)^{1/5}$; (k) $(3x)^{2/3}$.

4. Rewrite in radical form.

(a) $9^{1/3}$

(b) $22^{2/5}$

(c) $(7x)^{3/4}$

(d) $12^{0.5}$

(e) $6^{1.3}$

(f) $(2y^2)^{3.2}$

(g) $(ab)^{-1/2}$

(h) $(3b)^{-0.4}$

Answers: (b) $\sqrt[5]{22^2}$; (e) $\sqrt[10]{6^{13}}$; (g) $1/\sqrt{ab}$.

5. Use the properties of exponents to carry out the indicated operations. Simplify where possible.

(a) $2^8 \div 2^5$

(b) $4^3 \cdot 4^{-2}$

(c) $(r^2s^2)(r^3s)$

(d) $(5^2)^3$

(e) $(5^2)^{1/2}$

(f) $x^{1/2} \cdot x^{-1/2}$

(g) $y^{3/2}y^{1/2}$

(h) $4w^2/8w^5$

(i) $(2a^2b)^3$

(j) $r^{4/3} \div r^{2/3}$

(k) $(16x^6y^2)^{1/2}$

(l) $(25a^{-2})^{-1/2}$

(m) $(81a^{-4}b^8c^{12})^{1/4}$

(n) $\dfrac{(3x^2y)^3}{(9xy^4)^2}$

(o) $y^{1/2}(2y^{3/2} + 5y^{-1/2})$.

Answers: (c) r^5s^3; (f) 1; (i) $8a^6b^3$; (l) $a/5$.

6. Prove that the property of exponents $(a^n)^x = a^{nx}$ is valid when $n = 0$ and $x \in L$. (Suggestion: Evaluate $(a^0)^x$ with the help of D 2. Similarly, find the value of the right hand side.)

7. Write P 3 in terms of roots when the exponent, x, is $1/3$.

8. Show that the statement "The square root of the square root of a number is equal to the fourth root of that number" is equivalent to P 2 when the exponents are replaced by the appropriate rational numbers.

9. Write an approximation for $7^{\sqrt{2}}$ as a root of a positive real number.

10. Expand:

(a) $(x^{1/2} + y^{1/2})(x^{1/2} - y^{1/2})$ (b) $(x^{1/2} - 3)^2$
(c) $(x^{-1} + y^{-1})^2$ (d) $(a^{-1} + a)^2$
(e) $(a^{-2} + a^2)^2$ (f) $x^{1/2}(1 - x^{1/2} + x^{-3/2})$
(g) $(x - 2^{1/2})(x + 2^{1/2})$ (h) $(3y + 2^{1/2})(y - 3^{-1/2})$
(i) $(a^{1/2} + 2^{1/2})^2$.

Answers: (a) $x - y$;   (d) $a^{-2} + 2 + a^2$;   (f) $x^{1/2} - x + x^{-1}$.

11. Prove that the following are conditions and *not* identities. That is, find a replacement instance of each sentence that is a false statement.

(a) $(x + y)^{-1} = x^{-1} + y^{-1}$ (b) $(x^{1/2} + y^{1/2})^2 = x + y$
(c) $\sqrt[3]{x}\sqrt[2]{x} = \sqrt[5]{x}$ (d) $(a^2 + b^2)^{1/2} = a + b$
(e) $(a^{-1/2} + b^{-1/2})^2 = a^{-1} + b^{-1}$.

12. After zero and negative integral exponents have been defined, the decimal notation for numbers can be conveniently interpreted in exponential form using powers of 10. For example:

$$478.652 = 4(10^2) + 7(10^1) + 8(10^0) + 6(10^{-1}) + 5(10^{-2}) + 2(10^{-3}).$$

Write each of the following in this *expanded* form.

(a) 7,213.54   (b) 36.264
(c) .00354   (d) 420.003.

503. More about exponential functions

When you met exponential functions in Section 407, you were severely limited as you worked with the expression b^x. Recall the restrictions $b \in L$, $b > 0$, $b \neq 1$, and $x \in N$.

Now we can remove some of these restrictions. We shall continue to insist that $b \in L$ and $b > 0$. Since powers of 1 are trivial ($1^x = 1$), you may think of $b \neq 1$ in what follows. (This is a restriction that is convenient rather than mathematically essential.) But now you may think of the range of x as the set L of real numbers, that is, $x \in L$.

To illustrate this gain in generality, compare the graphs in Fig. 5–7. In the graph of the function $\{(x,y) \mid y = 2^x \text{ and } x \in N\}$, the plotted points correspond to the number-pairs (1,2), (2,4), (3,8), (4,16), (5,32). Of course the complete graph contains other points that correspond to the number-pairs (6,64), (7,128), etc. The graph of $\{(x,y) \mid y = 2^x \text{ and } x \in L\}$ is continuous. It contains all of the points shown in the figure and many more. For example, the number-pairs (0,1), $(\frac{1}{2}, 2^{1/2})$ [or $(\frac{1}{2}, \sqrt{2})$ or $(.5, \sqrt{2})$], $(-\frac{1}{2}, 2^{-1/2})$ [or $(-.5, 1/\sqrt{2})$] are also elements of the function.

Notice that $x < 0 \Rightarrow 0 < y < 1$; for small values of x (far to the left in the graph) the corresponding values of y are positive but very close to 0 (when $x = -100$, $y = 2^{-100} = 1/2^{100}$, for example); $x = 0 \Rightarrow y = 1$; for large values of x (far to the right in the graph), the corresponding values of y are even larger numbers (when $x = 100$, $y = 2^{100}$, for example).

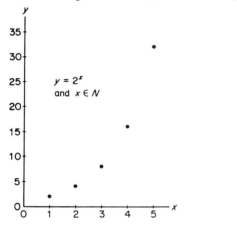

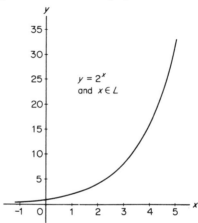

Fig. 5–7.

If we were to stop at this point, you might or might not feel a sense of achievement. Some people feel satisfied when they learn to fill in the gaps and extend the graph of an exponential function. A graph that consists of isolated points seems to make them tense. They cannot relax until they replace (what seems to them) the ugliness of such a figure by the beautiful smoothness of a continuous curve.

But there is another kind of satisfaction that you may find by going a step further. The function $\{(x,y) \mid y = 10^x\}$ has been tabulated for convenient use. Actually, this is usually done by tabulating the inverse function $\{(x,y) \mid x = 10^y\}$, usually expressed as $\{(x,y) \mid y = \log_{10} x\}$. Its graph is the reflection, in the line $y = x$, of the graph of $y = 10^x$ (see Fig. 5–8). We shall continue, for the time being, to think of the exponential function, but we shall use a table of logarithms to find corresponding values of x and y.

First you must learn to read a table of logarithms. In the form that we shall use it, this table fills 18 pages of a standard book of tables. At first you may ignore the fact that the table headings speak of logarithms. We shall use the table to find corresponding values of x and y in the equation $y = 10^x$.

In the N column of your table find 145; then in the row opposite 145, and in the column below 4, find the number *16256*. (Only the digits *256* appear; you get the *16* from the first column on the left side of the table. This saves a great deal of printing in the table.) You interpret this to mean $1.454 \doteq 10^{.16256}$.

You can use the table in this way to find values of y from 1.000 to 9.999, reading the first three figures in the N column and the fourth figure at the head of the appropriate column of the table. The corresponding values of x are the entries in the table; these are the exponents on 10 that correspond to each value of y from 1.000 (in steps of .001) to 9.999.

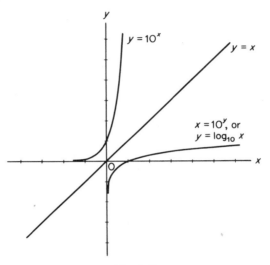

Fig. 5–8.

Use your table of logarithms to check the following statements: $1.258 \doteq 10^{.09968}$; $1.386 \doteq 10^{.14176}$ (notice the * in the table to warn you that this is .14176 rather than .13176); $2.430 \doteq 10^{.38561}$; $9.129 \doteq 10^{.96042}$.

Of course these values of x and y are rounded numbers; but the precision of the table is adequate for many practical calculations. The table certainly gives more accurate number-pairs, $\{(x,y)\}$, than you can read from a graph of the equation $y = 10^x$. We call it a *five-place* table, since it provides values of x, like .92174, expressed to five-figure accuracy. You can get six- or seven-place tables if you need them.

Now notice that $76.51 = 7.651 \times 10^1$. From the table of logarithms, $7.651 \doteq 10^{.88372}$; hence $76.51 \doteq 10^{.88372} \times 10^1 = 10^{1.88372}$, P 1 (page 184). Similarly $765.1 = 7.651 \times 10^2 \doteq 10^{2.88372}$; $7651 = 7.651 \times 10^3 \doteq 10^{3.88372}$; $76510 \doteq 10^{4.88372}$; etc. Also, $.7651 = 7.651 \times 1/10 = 7.651 \times 10^{-1} \doteq 10^{.88372} \times 10^{-1} = 10^{-1+.88372}$; $.07651 \doteq 10^{-2+.88372}$, etc. We shall not rewrite $-1 + .88372$ as $-.11628$ or $-2 + .88372$ as -1.11628. It is more convenient to use the same decimal, .88372, throughout, rather than introduce the new decimal, —.11628.

The convenient property of the base 10 of our number system, that we used in the preceding paragraph, enables you to use the same table for all values of y. First you rewrite y as a four-figure number between 1 and 10, multiplied by the appropriate power of 10. Thus

$$784,500 = 7.845 \times 10^5$$

$$612.865 \doteq 612.9 = 6.129 \times 10^2$$

$$.000586 = 5.860 \times (1/10^4) = 5.860 \times 10^{-4}$$

$$.0031284 \doteq .003128 = 3.128 \times 10^{-3}, \text{ etc.}$$

Then you use the table of logarithms and P 1 to get the corresponding value of x. For example, $.0031284 \doteq 3.128 \times 10^{-3} \doteq 10^{.49527} \cdot 10^{-3} = 10^{-3+.49527}$.

Now that you know how to read a table of logarithms, you can perform certain arithmetic calculations in new, and sometimes easier, ways. You can perform other arithmetic calculations that were practically impossible for you before. Study the following calculations to get the idea:

(1) 2.861×846.7

$2.861 \doteq 10^{.45652}$

$846.7 = 8.467 \times 10^2 \doteq 10^{.92773} \cdot 10^2 = 10^{2.92773}$

$2.861 \times 846.7 \doteq 10^{.45652+2.92773}$

$$= 10^{3.38425}$$

$$= 10^{.38425} \cdot 10^3$$

Now you use the table of logarithms backwards. You look for 38425 in the body of the table. You look for the value of y (in the N column) that corresponds to $x = .38425$ (in the body of the table). You find

$$10^{.38417} \doteq 2.422$$

$$10^{.38435} \doteq 2.423$$

Hence $2.422 < 10^{.38425} < 2.423.$

Notice that $.38425 - .38417 = .00008$ and $.38435 - .38425 = .00010$. Since .38417 is the closest entry of the table to the value .38425, which we are seeking, we say

$$10^{.38425} \doteq 2.422.$$

Hence $2.861 \times 846.7 \doteq 2.422 \times 10^3$

$$= 2422.$$

The product 2.861×846.7 is 2422, accurate to 4 figures.

(2) $35.68 \div .0042817$

$35.68 = 3.568 \times 10^1 \doteq 10^{1.55242}$

$.0042817 \doteq 4.282 \times 10^{-3} \doteq 10^{-3+.63165}$

$$\frac{35.68}{.004282} \doteq 10^{1.55242-(-3+.63165)}$$

$$= 10^{4.55242-.63165}$$

$$= 10^{3.92077}$$

$10^{3.92077} = 10^{.92077} \cdot 10^3$

$\qquad = 8.332 \times 10^3$ (using the table backwards and choosing the closest table-entry)

$\qquad = 8332.$

The quotient $35.68 \div .0042817$ is 8332, accurate to 4 figures.

(3) $(4.165)^{12}$

$4.165 \doteq 10^{.61962}$

$(4.165)^{12} \doteq (10^{.61962})^{12}$

$\qquad = 10^{7.43544}$

$\qquad = 10^{.43544} \cdot 10^7$

$\qquad \doteq 2.725 \times 10^7$ (using the table backwards and choosing the closest table-entry)

$\qquad = 27,250,000$

Notice carefully that only the first four figures of the number 27,250,000 are dependable. We say the number 27,250,000 has 4 *significant figures*. Students of science prefer to express this number as 2.725×10^7, to emphasize that it contains just 4 significant figures.

You may be surprised that $4.165^{12} > 25,000,000$. Powers of numbers greater than 1 may fool you if you fail to realize how large they can be. Recall from Section 407 (page 138) our discussion of quantities that "increase exponentially."

(4) $\sqrt[7]{126.8}$

$126.8 = 1.268 \times 10^2$

$\qquad \doteq 10^{2.10312}$

$\sqrt[7]{126.8} = 126.8^{1/7}$ (D 4)

$\qquad \doteq (10^{2.10312})^{1/7}$

$\qquad \doteq 10^{.30045}$ (P 2; also notice that 2.10312/7 is closer to .30045 than to .30044)

$\qquad \doteq 1.997.$ (using the table backwards and choosing the closest table-entry)

Notice that this example could be solved by the try-and-check method of Section 500; but think how tedious the solution would be!

(5) $\dfrac{(38.42)\sqrt[5]{.04861}}{288.5}$

$38.42 \doteq 10^{1.58456}$

$(.04861)^{1/5} \doteq (10^{-2+.68673})^{1/5}$

$\qquad = (10^{-5+3.68673})^{1/5}$ (a step to gain the convenience of an easy whole number to divide by 5)

$\qquad \doteq 10^{-1+.73735}$

$(38.42)\sqrt[5]{.04861} \doteq 10^{1.58456+(-1+.73735)}$

$\qquad = 10^{.58456+.73735}$

$\qquad = 10^{1.32191}$

$288.5 \doteq 10^{2.46015}$

$\dfrac{(38.42)\sqrt[5]{.04861}}{288.5} \doteq 10^{1.32191-2.46015}$

$\qquad = 10^{-2+3.32191-2.46015}$ (a step to avoid negative decimal fractions)

$\qquad = 10^{-2+.86176}$

$\qquad = 10^{.86176} \cdot 10^{-2}$

$\qquad \doteq 7.274 \times 10^{-2}$

$\qquad \doteq .07274$

Notice that in a continued calculation of this sort you may be able to work through the steps, one at a time, using powers of 10.

We have taken rather a long detour into the topic of calculations with powers of 10. Our purpose has been to illustrate the importance of extending the range of the exponential function. We have shown, for the function $\{(x,10^x)\}$, how to use a tabulation of an exponential function to perform otherwise difficult calculations of arithmetic.

We shall return to the exponential and logarithmic functions in Chapter 8. At that time we shall extend both the theory and the technical aspects of exponential calculations. Meanwhile, you should use Exercises 503 to help you assimilate the ideas of this section.

EXERCISES §503

1. With the help of a table of logarithms, express each number approximately as a power of 10.

(a) 3.824	(b) 1.72	(c) 4
(d) 7.913	(e) 791.3	(f) .07913
(g) .6378	(h) 81.32	(i) 521,000.

Answers: (a) $10^{.58252}$;   (g) $10^{-1+.80468}$;   (i) $10^{5.71684}$.

2. Determine the approximate value of each power of 10.

(a) $10^{0.84726}$ (b) $10^{0.57054}$ (c) $10^{2.65137}$

(d) $10^{4.09272}$ (e) $10^{-3+.72444}$ (f) $10^{0.21552}$

(g) $10^{-1+.35261}$ (h) $10^{7.32984}$ (i) $10^{-2+.57834}$.

Answers: (a) 7.035; (c) 448.1; (e) .005302.

3. Carry out the following calculations (approximately) with the help of a table of logarithms.

(a) $(2.314)(4.197)$ (b) $(1.562)^3$

(c) $(9.321) - (5.64)$ (d) $\sqrt{236.7}$

(e) $\dfrac{(423.7)(6.463)}{391.5}$ (f) $\dfrac{3651\sqrt[3]{7294}}{\sqrt{865}}$

(g) $(2187)^{2/7}$ (h) $(1.07)^{50}$.

Answers: (a) 9.712; (d) 15.38; (e) 6.994.

4. If negative decimals appear in the exponents, a slight change of form permits you to use the table of logarithms. For example:

$$10^{-.17875} = 10^{-1+(1-.17875)} = 10^{-1+.82125} = .6626$$

Evaluate:

(a) $10^{-.33686}$ (b) $10^{-2.65502}$ (c) $10^{-1.18740}$

(d) $\dfrac{2.431}{\sqrt{3354}}$ (e) $(4.31)^{-2/3}$ (f) $7^{-.32}$.

Answers: (a) .4604; (c) .06495; (e) .3776.

5. Notice that $\log_{10} 4 \doteq .60206$ and $\log_{10} \frac{1}{4} = \log_{10} .25 \doteq -1 + .39794 = -.60206$. Explain why you would expect $\log_{10} y = -\log_{10}(1/y)$ for $y \in L$ and $y > 0$. (*Hint:* Let $y = 10^x$, then $1/y = 1/10^x = 10^{-x}$.)

6. From tables verify that $10^{\log_{10} 3} \doteq 10^{.47712} \doteq 3$. Explain why you would expect $10^{\log_{10} y} = y$ for $y \in L$ and $y > 0$.

7. A table of logarithms can be used as an aid to approximating symbols that involve irrational exponents. For example, we find that $\sqrt{3} \doteq 1.7321$ in a table of square roots. Hence, $5^{\sqrt{3}} \doteq 5^{1.7321} \doteq [10^{(.69897)}]^{(1.7321)} \doteq$, etc. Complete these calculations to estimate $5^{\sqrt{3}}$. (You may wish to carry out the multiplication of the exponents with the help of logarithms.) In a similar fashion, estimate $(\sqrt{3})^\pi$.

8. Plot the graph of $y = 10^x$ for $0 \le x \le 1$ on a large sheet of graph paper. Use 0, 0.1, 0.2, 0.3, ... , 1.0 as replacements for x. Determine y in each case from a table of logarithms.

9. Find how much \$234 will amount to at the end of 25 yr if invested at the rate of 5%, compounded yearly. (See Exercise 5 of Section 407.)

10. Often, you can simplify the calculations arising out of the formulas for the kth term, and the sum of k terms, of a geometric progression by using a table of logarithms. Return to Exercises 408, page 147. Calculate answers to:

  (a) Exercise 3(b) and 3(c).
  (b) Exercise 6 for $n = 20$.
  (c) Exercise 8 for the distance traveled on the 30th swing, and in the first 30 swings.

504. Real roots of real numbers

In previous sections, when we used the symbol $\sqrt[n]{b}$, we imposed the restrictions: $n \in N$, $b \geq 0$, and $\sqrt[n]{b} \geq 0$. This was convenient when our object was to study the function $\{(x,y) \mid y = b^x\}$. We identified b^0 with 1, $b^{1/2}$ with $\sqrt{b}$, $b^{1/3}$ with $\sqrt[3]{b}$, etc. We assumed $b \in L$, $b > 0$, $b \neq 1$, and $b^x > 0$ when $x \in L$.

Now we examine the symbol $\sqrt[n]{a}$, $n \in N$ and $a \in L$. As before, we give the symbol $\sqrt[n]{a}$ the property:

$$x = \sqrt[n]{a} \Rightarrow x^n = a.$$

For example, if $x = \sqrt[4]{16}$ then $x^4 = 16$.

What about the *converse* proposition, $x^n = a \Rightarrow x = \sqrt[n]{a}$? You know that $(-4)^2 = 16$. Does this imply $-4 = \sqrt{16}$? We agreed (page 173) that $4 = \sqrt{16}$ ($\sqrt{16}$ is the positive square root of 16); we wish to avoid the contradiction:

$$(-4 = \sqrt{16} \text{ and } 4 = \sqrt{16}) \Rightarrow (-4 = 4).$$

Here is a formal definition of $\sqrt[n]{a}$: For $n \in N$, we define $x = \sqrt[n]{a}$ to be the *principal root* of the equation $x^n = a$; that is,

  (a) when $a \geq 0$: $x = \sqrt[n]{a} \Leftrightarrow x^n = a$ and $x \geq 0$.
  (b) when $a < 0$ and n is odd: $x = \sqrt[n]{a} \Leftrightarrow x^n = a$ and $x < 0$.

When $a < 0$ and n is even, $\sqrt[n]{a}$ is not defined. We *shall not use the symbol $\sqrt[n]{a}$ when $a < 0$ and n is even.*

The agreement that $\sqrt[n]{a}$ is the principal root of $x^n = a$ makes the symbol $\sqrt[n]{a}$ stand for a unique real number in all cases for which it is defined. When n is even and a is positive, $x^n = a$ has two real nth roots; but, according to (a), the principal root is the positive real number. From your table, $\sqrt{126} \doteq 11.22497$. This is the principal root of $x^2 = 126$. To represent the other root of $x^2 = 126$ ($\doteq -11.22497$) you use the symbol $-\sqrt{126}$. When n is odd, there is no ambiguity because there is only one real number such that $x^n = a$; $\sqrt[n]{a}$ is positive when a is positive, and negative when a is negative. Hence $\sqrt[3]{64} = 4$, and $\sqrt[3]{-64} = -4$. Notice that when $a < 0$ and n is even, there is no real number x such that $x^n = a$. For example:

(1) $\sqrt[3]{44}$ is a positive, real number. From your table, $\sqrt[3]{44} \doteq 3.530348$.

(2) $\sqrt[4]{16} = 2$. Notice that $\sqrt[4]{16} \neq -2$, because the symbol $\sqrt[4]{16}$ is to stand for the principal root. [The fact that $(-2)^4 = 16$ and $-2 \neq \sqrt[4]{16}$ is enough to *disprove* the proposition $x^n = a \Rightarrow x = \sqrt[n]{a}$; that is, to *prove* the proposition $x^n = a \not\Rightarrow x = \sqrt[n]{a}$.]

(3) $\sqrt[7]{0} = 0$.

(4) $\sqrt[3]{-8}$ is a negative, real number. Since $(-2)^3 = -8$, then $\sqrt[3]{-8} = -\sqrt[3]{8} = -2$.

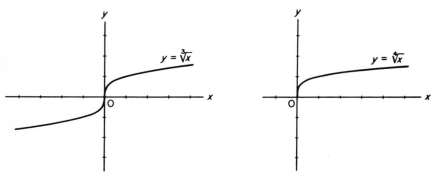

Fig. 5–9.

(5) $\sqrt[3]{-36}$ is a negative, real number. From your table, $\sqrt[3]{36} \doteq 3.301927$. From this you may conclude that $\sqrt[3]{-36} \doteq -3.301927$.

(6) $\sqrt{-2}$ is not a real number because there is no replacement of x, $x \in L$, such that $x^2 = -2$. We shall not use symbols like $\sqrt{-2}$, $\sqrt[4]{-8}$, $\sqrt[6]{-5}$, etc. Such symbols are not defined.

Now that we have defined the symbol $\sqrt[n]{a}$ as the principal root of the equation $x^n = a$, you can perform calculations with expressions like $\sqrt[n]{a}$; but you must avoid symbols like $\sqrt[4]{-2}$ (even roots of negative real numbers).

We shall return, in Section 505, to the algebra of roots of real numbers; that is, you will study identities for operations with these roots. Meanwhile you should study the graphs of the family of conditions $y = \sqrt[n]{x}$, $n \in N$.

You know that $x \geq 0 \Rightarrow \sqrt[n]{x} \geq 0$

$$x < 0 \text{ and } n \text{ odd} \Rightarrow \sqrt[n]{x} < 0$$

$$x < 0 \text{ and } n \text{ even} \Rightarrow \sqrt[n]{x} \notin L.$$

This means that the condition $y = \sqrt[n]{x}$ gives a unique value of y for each value of x, $x \in L$, when n is odd; and gives a unique value of y for each value of x, $x \in L$, and $x \geq 0$, when n is even. The two graphs of Fig. 5–9 illustrate these statements.

Notice, in the graph of $y = \sqrt[3]{x}$, that the range of x is the set L. Notice, in the graph of $y = \sqrt[4]{x}$, that the range of x is the subset of L defined by the condition $x \geq 0$. When n is even, the symbol $\sqrt[n]{x}$ represents a real number only when $x \geq 0$.

EXERCISES §504

1. Classify each instance of the symbol $\sqrt[n]{a}$ as (1) a non-negative real number ($x \in L$ and $x \geq 0$), (2) a negative real number ($x \in L$ and $x < 0$), or (3) not a real number ($x \notin L$).

(a) $\sqrt[3]{-18}$ (b) $\sqrt{47}$ (c) $\sqrt{-32}$ (d) $\sqrt[4]{-16}$

(e) $\sqrt[8]{0}$ (f) $\sqrt[10]{37}$ (g) $\sqrt[10]{-37}$ (h) $\sqrt[15]{-54}$.

2. Use tables of roots, or a table of logarithms, to evaluate the symbols in Exercise 1 that are symbols for real numbers. Of course you cannot evaluate a symbol like $\sqrt[4]{-16} \notin L$; $\sqrt[5]{-32} = -2$ is exact; $\sqrt{47} \doteq 6.856$ is approximate.

3. Graph each condition:

(a) $y = 2\sqrt{x}$ (b) $y = 5\sqrt[3]{x}$

(c) $y = 10\sqrt[5]{x}$ (d) $y = 5\sqrt[4]{x}$

(e) $y - 5 = -3\sqrt{x - 1}$ (f) $y + 2 = \sqrt[3]{x + 3}$

(g) $y \geq 3\sqrt{x}$ (h) $y + 4 < 2\sqrt[3]{x - 5}$.

4. Consider the expression $\sqrt{x^2}$. Evaluate when $x = 4$; $x = 7$; $x = -5$; $x = -\frac{1}{2}$. Is $\sqrt{x^2} = x$ an identity?

5. Is $(\sqrt{x})^2 = x$ an identity when the range of x is $\{x \mid x \geq 0\}$? Why or why not? Compare with Exercise 4.

505. Calculations with radicals

When a calculation with real numbers involves radicals (root symbols like $\sqrt{x}$, $\sqrt[3]{x}$, and the like), you can make the number under the radical sign positive. Radicals like $\sqrt[4]{-3}$ do not concern you, because even roots of negative numbers are not defined; you can replace the radical $\sqrt[5]{-3}$ by $-\sqrt[5]{3}$, $\sqrt[3]{-7}$ by $-\sqrt[3]{7}$, etc. In general, you can replace an odd root of a negative number by the negative of the corresponding root of a positive number. Hence we assume, without loss of generality, that replacements of phrases under radical signs are positive real numbers.

We seek useful identities for operations with radicals like $\sqrt[n]{a}$, $a \in L$ and $a > 0$. (If $a = 0$, $\sqrt[n]{a} = 0$; you already know the properties of the real number zero. If $a < 0$ and n is odd, $\sqrt[n]{a} = -\sqrt[n]{-a}$, where $-a > 0$.)

Addition and subtraction of radicals, like addition and subtraction of powers, do not yield convenient identities.

For multiplication and division of radicals, $a > 0$ and $b > 0$:

P 5 $$\sqrt[n]{a} \cdot \sqrt[n]{b} = \sqrt[n]{ab}$$

P 6 $$\sqrt[m]{a} \cdot \sqrt[n]{b} = \sqrt[mn]{a^n b^m}$$

P 7 $$\sqrt[n]{a}/\sqrt[n]{b} = \sqrt[n]{a/b}$$

P 8 $$\sqrt[m]{a}/\sqrt[n]{b} = \sqrt[mn]{a^n/b^m}$$

P 9 $$\sqrt[m]{\sqrt[n]{a}} = \sqrt[mn]{a}.$$

Notice that **P 5** is an instance of **P 3** (page 184):

$$(a > 0, b > 0, \text{ and } x \in L) \Rightarrow a^x b^x = (ab)^x.$$

The replacement $x = 1/n$ yields $a^{1/n} b^{1/n} = (ab)^{1/n}$; that is,

$$\sqrt[n]{a}\sqrt[n]{b} = \sqrt[n]{ab} \qquad \text{(D 4, page 184)}$$

To relate **P 6** to fractional exponents, write

$$\sqrt[m]{a}\sqrt[n]{b} = a^{1/m} b^{1/n} \qquad \text{(D 4)}$$

$$= a^{n/mn} b^{m/mn} \qquad \text{(Properties of real numbers)}$$

$$= (a^n b^m)^{1/mn} \qquad \text{(P 3)}$$

$$= \sqrt[mn]{a^n b^m} \qquad \text{(D 4)}$$

Notice that **P 7** is an instance of **P 4** (page 184):

$$(a > 0, b > 0 \quad \text{and} \quad x \in L) \Rightarrow a^x/b^x = (a/b)^x.$$

The replacement $x = 1/n$ yields $\dfrac{a^{1/n}}{b^{1/n}} = \left(\dfrac{a}{b}\right)^{1/n}$; that is,

$$\frac{\sqrt[n]{a}}{\sqrt[n]{b}} = \sqrt[n]{\frac{a}{b}}. \qquad \text{(D 4)}$$

You should relate **P 8** to fractional exponents, following the pattern for **P 6**.

For **P 9**, write $$\sqrt[m]{\sqrt[n]{a}} = (a^{1/n})^{1/m} \qquad \text{(D 4)}$$

$$= a^{1/mn} \qquad \text{(P 2 page 184)}$$

$$= \sqrt[mn]{a}. \qquad \text{(D 4)}$$

The following examples will help you learn to apply Properties 5 through 9 to perform calculations with radicals:

(1) Perform the addition $\sqrt{9} + \sqrt{4}$.

$$\sqrt{9} + \sqrt{4} = 3 + 2 = 5.$$

Some people find it tempting to suppose that $\sqrt[n]{a} + \sqrt[n]{b} = \sqrt[n]{a + b}$.

Notice that $\sqrt{9} + \sqrt{4} \neq \sqrt{13}$. Hence the equation $\sqrt[n]{a} + \sqrt[n]{b} = \sqrt[n]{a+b}$ is *not* an identity. It is a condition that imposes restrictions upon the values of n, a, and b. For example, the replacement instance $n = 2, a = 0$, and $b = 5$ yields the *true* statement $\sqrt{0} + \sqrt{5} = \sqrt{0+5}$. But most choices of n, a, and b yield false statements. For example $n = 3, a = 8$, and $b = 27$ yields the *false* statement $\sqrt[3]{8} + \sqrt[3]{27} = \sqrt[3]{35}$.

(2) Perform the addition $\sqrt{5} + \sqrt{7}$. The simplest answer to this question is $(\sqrt{5}) + (\sqrt{7}) = (\sqrt{5} + \sqrt{7})$. Of course you can express the answer approximately, using decimals: $\sqrt{5} + \sqrt{7} \doteq 2.236 + 2.646 = 4.882$; but the simplest exact answer is $(\sqrt{5} + \sqrt{7})$.

(3) Perform the addition $5\sqrt{12} + 6\sqrt{3}$. Notice that $5\sqrt{12} = 5\sqrt{4 \cdot 3} = 10\sqrt{3}$ (P 5). Hence

$$5\sqrt{12} + 6\sqrt{3} = 10\sqrt{3} + 6\sqrt{3} = 16\sqrt{3} \quad \text{(Distributive law)}$$

(4) Perform the addition $2\sqrt{-18} + 3\sqrt{45}$. Since $\sqrt{-18}$ is not defined in L, you must reject this question as meaningless.

(5) Perform the addition $2\sqrt[3]{-54} + 5\sqrt[3]{48}$.

Since $2\sqrt[3]{-54} = -2\sqrt[3]{54} = -2\sqrt[3]{27 \cdot 2} = -2\sqrt[3]{27}\sqrt[3]{2} = -6\sqrt[3]{2},$

and $5\sqrt[3]{48} = 5\sqrt[3]{8 \cdot 6} = 5\sqrt[3]{8}\sqrt[3]{6} = 10\sqrt[3]{6},$

then $2\sqrt[3]{-54} + 5\sqrt[3]{48} = -6\sqrt[3]{2} + 10\sqrt[3]{6}.$

This answer is exact and appropriate. It is, of course, possible to express the answer in other ways. For example, $10\sqrt[3]{6} = 10\sqrt[3]{3}\sqrt[3]{2}$; hence

$$-6\sqrt[3]{2} + 10\sqrt[3]{6} = -6\sqrt[3]{2} + 10\sqrt[3]{3}\sqrt[3]{2} = (-6 + 10\sqrt[3]{3})\sqrt[3]{2}.$$

It is impossible to decide which expression is simplest until you know how you want to use it. The expression $-6\sqrt[3]{2} + 10\sqrt[3]{6}$ lends itself well to approximate calculation with tables; of course the expression $-2\sqrt[3]{54} + 5\sqrt[3]{48}$ is equally convenient for use with tables. But, in the calculation

$$\frac{2\sqrt[3]{-54} + 5\sqrt[3]{48}}{\sqrt[3]{2}},$$

it is convenient to write

$$\frac{(-6 + 10\sqrt[3]{3})\sqrt[3]{2}}{\sqrt[3]{2}} = -6 + 10\sqrt[3]{3}.$$

(6) Perform the multiplication $\sqrt[3]{-4} \cdot \sqrt[3]{2}$. You have

$$\sqrt[3]{-4} \cdot \sqrt[3]{2} = -\sqrt[3]{4} \cdot \sqrt[3]{2} = -\sqrt[3]{8} = -2.$$

(7) Perform the multiplication $\sqrt[5]{-7} \cdot \sqrt[5]{-3}$. You have

$$\sqrt[5]{-7}\sqrt[5]{-3} = (-\sqrt[5]{7})(-\sqrt[5]{3}) = \sqrt[5]{21}.$$

(8) To illustrate the pitfalls of careless calculations with roots of real numbers, consider the following *misapplication* of P 5:

$$\sqrt{-1}\sqrt{-1} = \sqrt{(-1)(-1)} = \sqrt{1} = 1.$$

But $(-1)^{1/2} \cdot (-1)^{1/2} = (-1)^1 = -1$. This seems to say $1 = -1$; but notice that P 5 does *not* apply; $\sqrt{-1} \notin L$.

(9) Perform the multiplication $\sqrt[3]{4}\sqrt[6]{2}$. Using P 6,

$$\sqrt[3]{4}\sqrt[6]{2} = \sqrt[18]{4^6 \cdot 2^3} = \sqrt[18]{(2^2)^6 \cdot 2^3} = \sqrt[18]{2^{12} \cdot 2^3}$$
$$= \sqrt[18]{2^{15}} = \sqrt[6]{\sqrt[3]{2^{15}}} \qquad\qquad \text{(P 9)}$$
$$= \sqrt[6]{\sqrt[3]{(2^5)^3}} = \sqrt[6]{2^5}$$
$$= \sqrt[6]{32}.$$

Most people prefer to work with fractional exponents, rather than with radicals, in a calculation of this sort. Thus

$$\sqrt[3]{4}\sqrt[6]{2} = (2^2)^{1/3} \cdot 2^{1/6} = 2^{2/3+1/6} = 2^{5/6} = (2^5)^{1/6} = \sqrt[6]{32}.$$

(10) Perform the multiplication $\sqrt{5} \cdot \sqrt[3]{7}$. Again you could use P 6. We prefer to use fractional exponents and proceed as follows:

$$\sqrt{5} \cdot \sqrt[3]{7} = 5^{1/2} \cdot 7^{1/3} = 5^{3/6} \cdot 7^{2/6} = (5^3)^{1/6} \cdot (7^2)^{1/6}$$
$$= (5^3 \cdot 7^2)^{1/6} = \sqrt[6]{5^3 \cdot 7^2}.$$

(11) Rewrite the symbol $1/\sqrt{2}$ in a form better-suited to calculation with tables.

From your tables, $\sqrt{2} \doteq 1.414214$. The division $1 \div 1.414214$ involves tedious arithmetical calculation. It is much easier to proceed as follows:

$$\frac{1}{\sqrt{2}} \doteq \frac{1 \cdot \sqrt{2}}{\sqrt{2} \cdot \sqrt{2}} = \frac{\sqrt{2}}{2}.$$

This yields $\dfrac{1}{\sqrt{2}} \doteq \dfrac{1.414}{2} = .707.$

Root symbols characteristically lead to clumsy decimals, like 1.414. Such numbers are awkward as divisors, and hence as denominators of fractions. Thus it is common, in algebra, to *rationalize the denominator* of a fraction. The following examples will illustrate the process of rationalizing denominators, that is, of making the denominators rational expressions, free of radicals:

(12) $\dfrac{3\sqrt{2}}{\sqrt{7}} = \dfrac{3\sqrt{2} \cdot \sqrt{7}}{\sqrt{7} \cdot \sqrt{7}} = \dfrac{3\sqrt{14}}{7}.$

(To calculate the value of $3\sqrt{2}/\sqrt{7}$ you can find $\sqrt{2}$ in your table; you round off the value given in the table to the number of significant figures that you need for the problem in hand; you multiply this number by 3; you find $\sqrt{7}$ in your table and round off the table value; then you do a long division. It is much easier to calculate the value of $3\sqrt{14}/7$. Try it!)

$$(13) \qquad \frac{5}{\sqrt[3]{4}} = \frac{5 \cdot (\sqrt[3]{4})^2}{\sqrt[3]{4} \cdot (\sqrt[3]{4})^2} = \frac{5\sqrt[3]{4^2}}{(\sqrt[3]{4})^3} = \frac{5\sqrt[3]{16}}{4}.$$

The fraction $5\sqrt[3]{16}/4$ lends itself well to calculations with tables. However, you can proceed in a still more efficient way. Thus:

$$\frac{5}{\sqrt[3]{4}} = \frac{5}{\sqrt[3]{2^2}} = \frac{5\sqrt[3]{2}}{\sqrt[3]{2^2} \cdot \sqrt[3]{2}} = \frac{5\sqrt[3]{2}}{\sqrt[3]{2^3}} = \frac{5\sqrt[3]{2}}{2}.$$

The advantages of smaller numbers, in the fraction $5\sqrt[3]{2}/2$, are obvious. But, of course, $5\sqrt[3]{16}/4 = 5\sqrt[3]{2}/2$.

$$(14) \qquad \frac{3}{1 - \sqrt{2}} = \frac{3(1 + \sqrt{2})}{(1 - \sqrt{2})(1 + \sqrt{2})} = \frac{3 + 3\sqrt{2}}{1 - (\sqrt{2})^2} = \frac{3 + 3\sqrt{2}}{1 - 2} =$$

$$\frac{3 + 3\sqrt{2}}{-1} = -3 - 3\sqrt{2}.$$

Notice how we used the identities of Chapter 2 to rationalize the denominator of the fraction $3/(1 - \sqrt{2})$. Recall that $(a - b)(a + b) = a^2 - b^2$. Hence

$$(1 - \sqrt{2})(1 + \sqrt{2}) = 1 - (\sqrt{2})^2 = 1 - 2 = -1.$$

$$(15) \qquad \frac{a - 1}{\sqrt{b} - \sqrt{c}} = \frac{(a - 1)(\sqrt{b} + \sqrt{c})}{(\sqrt{b} - \sqrt{c})(\sqrt{b} + \sqrt{c})} = \frac{(a - 1)(\sqrt{b} + \sqrt{c})}{b - c}.$$

This example of rationalizing a denominator has much the same form as the previous one. But it is by no means foolproof. Recall the restrictions $b > 0$ and $c > 0$ upon such a calculation with radicals; recall also that the division is possible only when $b \neq c$.

The preceding examples will help you as you begin to perform calculations with real roots of real numbers. Exercises §505 provide practice materials.

Now that you know how to interpret the symbol $\sqrt[n]{a}$, provided it represents a real number, we can remove many of the restrictions upon the properties and definitions of Section 502. Some of these restrictions had the effect of avoiding divisions by zero; others had the effect of avoiding even roots of negative numbers, and ambiguities in expressions that involve radicals. We repeat the properties and definitions of Sections 502, 504, and 505 with the minimum of restrictions that we need at this stage.

In each case we suppose only that a and b are such that real numbers are defined.

D 1 $n \in N \Rightarrow a^n = a \cdot a \cdot a \cdot \ldots \cdot a$ (n factors)

D 2 $a \neq 0 \Rightarrow a^0 = 1$

D 3 $a \neq 0 \Rightarrow a^{-x} = \dfrac{1}{a^x}$

D 4 $n \in N \Rightarrow a^{1/n} = \sqrt[n]{a}$

D 5 $m \in N, n \in N \Rightarrow a^{m/n} = \sqrt[n]{a^m} = (\sqrt[n]{a})^m$

D 6 $x = \sqrt[n]{a} \Leftrightarrow x^n = a$, and $x \geq 0$, if n is even

P 1 $x \in L \Rightarrow a^x a^y = a^{x+y}$

P 2 $x \in L, y \in L \Rightarrow (a^x)^y = a^{xy}$

P 3 $x \in L \Rightarrow a^x b^x = (ab)^x$

P 4 $x \in L, y \in L, a \neq 0 \Rightarrow \dfrac{a^x}{a^y} = a^{x-y}$

P 5 $n \in N, a > 0, b > 0 \Rightarrow \sqrt[n]{a}\sqrt[n]{b} = \sqrt[n]{ab}$

P 6 $m \in N, n \in N, a > 0, b > 0 \Rightarrow \sqrt[m]{a}\sqrt[n]{b} = \sqrt[mn]{a^n b^m}$

P 7 $n \in N, a > 0, b > 0 \Rightarrow \dfrac{\sqrt[n]{a}}{\sqrt[n]{b}} = \sqrt[n]{\dfrac{a}{b}}$

P 8 $m \in N, n \in N, a > 0, b > 0 \Rightarrow \dfrac{\sqrt[m]{a}}{\sqrt[n]{b}} = \sqrt[mn]{\dfrac{a^n}{b^m}}$

P 9 $m \in N, n \in N, a \geq 0 \Rightarrow \sqrt[m]{\sqrt[n]{a}} = \sqrt[mn]{a}$.

It is often convenient to work with fractional exponents, rather than with radicals, and thus to dispense with Properties 5 through 9. Properties 6, 8, and 9 are usually less convenient to apply than the corresponding properties of fractional exponents.

EXERCISES §505

1. Apply the definitions and properties of this section to find simpler-looking symbols for each of the following numbers:

(a) $(\sqrt[4]{5})^4$ (b) $\sqrt{2}\sqrt{18}$ (c) $\sqrt[3]{12}\sqrt[3]{18}$ (d) $\sqrt{\dfrac{3}{4}}$

(e) $\sqrt{\dfrac{7}{12}}$ (f) $\dfrac{\sqrt[3]{24}}{\sqrt[3]{3}}$ (g) $\sqrt[3]{\dfrac{5}{4}}$ (h) $\sqrt[4]{9}$

(i) $\sqrt[6]{8}$ (j) $\sqrt[5]{-32}$ (k) $\sqrt{4^3}$ (l) $\sqrt{\sqrt[3]{16}}$

(m) $\dfrac{\sqrt{2} \cdot \sqrt[3]{9}}{\sqrt{6}}$.

Answers: (b) 6;   (e) $\frac{1}{6}\sqrt{21}$;   (g) $\frac{1}{2}\sqrt[3]{10}$;   (h) $\sqrt{3}$;   (l) $\sqrt[3]{4}$.

2. Sometimes you can simplify a radical by factoring the number under the radical sign and applying P 5. For example, $\sqrt[3]{54} = \sqrt[3]{27 \cdot 2} = \sqrt[3]{27} \cdot \sqrt[3]{2} = 3\sqrt[3]{2}$. In each of the following, remove all perfect nth powers from under the radical signs.

(a) $\sqrt{48}$ (b) $\sqrt[3]{108}$ (c) $\sqrt[4]{405}$ (d) $\sqrt{50}$

(e) $\sqrt{75}$ (f) $\sqrt[3]{-250}$ (g) $\sqrt[5]{-96}$ (h) $\sqrt[3]{-48}$.

(Notice that $\sqrt[4]{-48}$ is not defined. You must reject this question as meaningless.)

Answers: (a) $4\sqrt{3}$;   (c) $3\sqrt[4]{5}$;   (f) $-5\sqrt[3]{2}$.

3. Change the form of each expression to eliminate radicals in the denominator and denominators under radical signs.

(a) $\dfrac{\sqrt{5}}{\sqrt{2}}$ (b) $\sqrt{\dfrac{8}{3}}$ (c) $\dfrac{\sqrt[3]{14}}{\sqrt[3]{4}}$ (d) $\dfrac{2}{\sqrt{3}}$

(e) $\dfrac{1}{\sqrt{2}}$ (f) $\dfrac{\sqrt{2}}{\sqrt[3]{5}}$ (g) $\dfrac{\sqrt[5]{-3}}{\sqrt{2}}$ (h) $\dfrac{\sqrt{2}}{\sqrt{3}}$

(i) $\dfrac{\sqrt{5}}{\sqrt{5} - \sqrt{2}}$ (j) $\dfrac{1}{\sqrt{7} + \sqrt{3}}$ (k) $\dfrac{\sqrt{3}}{2\sqrt{2} - \sqrt{5}}$

(l) $\dfrac{2\sqrt{7} + 3\sqrt{6}}{\sqrt{7} + \sqrt{6}}$ (m) $\dfrac{1}{\sqrt{x} + \sqrt{y}}$.

Answers: (a) $\frac{1}{2}\sqrt{10}$;   (c) $\frac{1}{2}\sqrt[3]{28}$;   (d) $\frac{2}{3}\sqrt{3}$;   (f) $\frac{1}{5}\sqrt[6]{5000}$;   (i) $\dfrac{5 + \sqrt{10}}{3}$.

4. What restrictions must you place upon the ranges of x and y in Exercise 3(m)?

5. Write each term of an expression in simplest form; then collect terms.

(a) $3\sqrt{2} + \sqrt{8}$ (b) $\sqrt{27} - \sqrt{12} + \sqrt{48}$

(c) $\sqrt{75} - \sqrt{\frac{1}{3}}$ (d) $2\sqrt{2} - 3\sqrt{32} + 6\sqrt{\frac{1}{2}} + \sqrt[4]{64}$

(e) $\sqrt[3]{27a} - \sqrt[3]{8a}$.

Answers: (b) $5\sqrt{3}$;   (c) $\dfrac{14}{3}\sqrt{3}$.

6. What restrictions must you place upon the range of a in Exercise 5(e)? Notice that the radicals are negative when a is negative, and positive when a is positive. Hence the range of a is $a \in L$. Contrast this with the expression: $\sqrt{12a} - \sqrt{75a} = -3\sqrt{3a}$.

7. Carry out the indicated multiplications.

(a) $\sqrt{7}\sqrt{3}$ (b) $(2\sqrt{2})^2$ (c) $(2\sqrt{15})\sqrt{3}$

(d) $\sqrt[3]{14}\sqrt[3]{4}$ (e) $\sqrt{2}\sqrt[3]{2}$ (f) $\sqrt{6}\sqrt[3]{4}$

(g) $\sqrt{12a}\sqrt{3ab}$ (h) $\sqrt{x}\sqrt[3]{x}$.

Answers: (b) 8;   (d) $2\sqrt[3]{7}$;   (e) $\sqrt[6]{32}$.

8. What restrictions must you place upon the variables in Exercise 7 (g) and (h)?

9. (a) If $p(x) = x^2 - 4x + 3$, determine $p(2 + \sqrt{7})$.

    (b) If $p(x) = x^2 - 4x - 3$, determine $p(2 - \sqrt{7})$.

    (c) If $p(x) = x^2 + 2\sqrt{5}x - 1$, determine $p(\sqrt{6} - \sqrt{5})$.

Answers: (a) 6;   (c) 0.

10. Rewrite the formula $F = \dfrac{5}{\sqrt{T} - 2}$ to rationalize the denominator. What is the permissible range of T?

11. In Section 502 we defined rational powers of positive real numbers in terms of radicals. In this section we related P 5 through P 9 to the corresponding properties from Section 502. If you wish to prove that rational powers of positive real numbers obey the laws of exponents (rather than to assume that they do, as in Section 502), you should begin by proving certain properties of radicals. For example,

To prove: $n \in N$, $a \geq 0$, and $b \geq 0 \Rightarrow \sqrt[n]{ab} = \sqrt[n]{a}\sqrt[n]{b}$.

(a) Fill in the missing reasons for each step in the proof. Let $z = \sqrt[n]{a}$ and $w = \sqrt[n]{b}$; then:

Proof	*Reason*
1. $z \geq 0$ and $w \geq 0$	
2. $z^n = a$ and $w^n = b$	
3. $z^n w^n = ab$	
4. $z^n w^n = (zw)^n$	P 1 for exponents that are natural numbers
5. $(zw)^n = ab$	
6. $zw \geq 0$	
7. $zw = \sqrt[n]{ab}$	
8. $\sqrt[n]{a}\sqrt[n]{b} = \sqrt[n]{ab}$	

(b) Modify the proof of part (a) when n is odd, $a < 0$ and $b > 0$.

(c) Modify the proof of part (a) when n is odd, $a < 0$ and $b < 0$.

12. Serious difficulties with rational exponents may arise when the base is negative. Consider the expression $N = (-64)^{2/6}$.

(a) If you say $(-64)^{2/6} = [(-64)^2]^{1/6}$, then $N = 4$.

(b) If you say $(-64)^{2/6} = [(-64)^{1/6}]^2$, then N is undefined.

(c) If you say $(-64)^{2/6} = (-64)^{1/3}$, then $N = -4$.

Hence the symbol $(-64)^{2/6}$ is ambiguous. We shall not use such symbols.

13. Show that the following conditions are *not* identities. That is, find a replacement instance of each sentence that is a false statement.

(a) $(\sqrt{a} + \sqrt{b})^2 = a + b$

(b) $\sqrt[3]{a + b} = \sqrt[3]{a} + \sqrt[3]{b}$

(c) $\sqrt{\sqrt[3]{a}} = \sqrt[5]{a}$

(d) $\sqrt{(a^2 + b^2)} = a + b$.

14. (a) Show that the condition $\sqrt[n]{a^m} = (\sqrt[n]{a})^m$ is equivalent to the condition $(a^m)^{1/n} = (a^{1/n})^m$ provided $a \geq 0$.

(b) Complete the following proof, based upon the definition of a radical, that $n \in N$, $m \in N$, and $a \geq 0 \Rightarrow \sqrt[n]{a^m} = (\sqrt[n]{a})^m$. Let $w = (\sqrt[n]{a})^m$; then:

	Proof	*Reason*
1.	$w^n = [(\sqrt[n]{a})^m]^n$	
2.	$w^n = (\sqrt[n]{a})^{mn}$	
3.	$w^n = [(\sqrt[n]{a})^n]^m$	P 2 for exponents that are natural numbers
4.	$w^n = a^m$	
5.	$w \geq 0$	
6.	$w = \sqrt[n]{a^m}$	

15. Use P 9 to write each of the following with a single radical:

(a) $\sqrt[3]{\sqrt{10}}$ (b) $\sqrt{\sqrt{29}}$ (c) $\sqrt[3]{\sqrt{8}}$ (d) $\sqrt[3]{\sqrt[3]{35}}$.

Answers: (a) $\sqrt[6]{10}$; (c) $\sqrt{2}$.

16. (a) Show that $\sqrt[6]{36} = \sqrt[3]{6}$. (b) Approximate $\sqrt[6]{42}$ and $\sqrt[4]{40}$ with the help of the table of square roots and cube roots. Check your work by evaluating these roots with logarithms.

506. Absolute value of a real number

When you work with radicals that involve one or more variables, you must restrict the range of each variable in accordance with the definition of $\sqrt[n]{a}$ (Section 504) (page 193). This complicates the discussion of an expression like

$$\sqrt{18x^3y^6z}.$$

If you apply the identities of Section 505 mechanically, you say

$$\sqrt{18x^3y^6z} = \sqrt{(9x^2y^6)(2xz)} = 3xy^3\sqrt{2xz}.$$

But recall the restriction $18x^3y^6z \geq 0$. This condition is satisfied when

$$y \in L, \ x \geq 0, \quad \text{and} \quad z \geq 0 \quad \text{or} \quad y \in L, \ x \leq 0, \quad \text{and} \quad z \leq 0.$$

There is also the restriction $3xy^3\sqrt{2xz} \geq 0$. This condition is satisfied when

$$y \geq 0, \ x \geq 0, \text{ and } z \geq 0 \quad \text{or} \quad y \leq 0, \ x \leq 0, \text{ and } z \leq 0.$$

Hence the identities of Section 505 apply only when the replacements of x, y, and z are all positive or all negative.

As an example of failing to observe these restrictions, consider the instance $x = z = 1$, $y = -1$:

$$\sqrt{18x^3y^6z} = \sqrt{18} = 3\sqrt{2}.$$

The replacements of x and z are positive. The replacement of y is negative. Yet the expression $\sqrt{18x^3y^6z}$ represents a real number. Of course the expression

$$3xy^3\sqrt{2xz} = -3\sqrt{2}.$$

represents a different real number.

We introduce you to a new symbol that simplifies the discussion of radicals that involve variables. When $x \in L$, we call $|x|$ the *absolute value* of x. We define $|x|$ as follows:

(a) $x < 0 \Rightarrow |x| = -x$

(b) $x = 0 \Rightarrow |x| = 0$

(c) $x > 0 \Rightarrow |x| = x$.

The effect of this definition is to make the values of $|x|$ non-negative real numbers. Graphically, $|x|$ is a magnitude; that is, it is a distance measured without regard to sign. It is like a number of elementary arithmetic as contrasted with a signed number of algebra.

Now consider the equation

$$\sqrt{18x^3y^6z} = |3xy^3\sqrt{2xz}|.$$

The absolute value bars make the right hand side non-negative. The condition is an identity provided the symbols represent real numbers. The necessary restriction is

$$x \geq 0 \text{ and } z \geq 0 \quad \text{or} \quad x \leq 0 \text{ and } z \leq 0.$$

The range of y is the set L.

The following examples will guide you in your use of absolute values to simplify the discussion of radicals that involve variables:

(1) $\sqrt{x^3} = x\sqrt{x}$. Notice that the condition $x \geq 0$ is necessary to be sure that both $\sqrt{x^3}$ and $x\sqrt{x}$ are defined; hence $x\sqrt{x} \geq 0$. There is no need here for the symbol $|x\sqrt{x}|$.

(2) $\sqrt{x^2y} = |x|\sqrt{y}$. The condition $y \geq 0$ is necessary; but the range of x is $x \in L$. Notice that $|x\sqrt{y}| = |x|\sqrt{y}$, because $\sqrt{y} \geq 0$.

(3) $\sqrt{9a^2 - 9} = \sqrt{9(a^2 - 1)} = 3\sqrt{a^2 - 1}$. The condition $a^2 \geq 1$ is necessary.

(4) $\sqrt{a^2b^2 - b^2} = \sqrt{b^2(a^2 - 1)} = |b|\sqrt{a^2 - 1}$. The condition $a^2 \geq 1$ is necessary; but the range of b is $b \in L$.

(5) $\sqrt{ax^2 + 2ax + a} = \sqrt{a(x^2 + 2x + 1)} = |x + 1|\sqrt{a}$. The condition $a \geq 0$ is necessary; but the range of x is $x \in L$.

(6) $\sqrt[4]{64a^{10}y^6x^5} = \sqrt[4]{(16a^8y^4x^4)4a^2y^2x} = 2a^2x|y|\sqrt[4]{4a^2y^2x}$. The condition $x \geq 0$ is necessary; but the ranges of a and y are $a \in L$ and $y \in L$. Notice that $x \geq 0 \Rightarrow |2a^2xy\sqrt[4]{4a^2y^2x}| = 2a^2x|y|\sqrt[4]{4a^2y^2x}$.

(7) $\sqrt[3]{x^3y^2z^6} = xz^2\sqrt[3]{y^2}$. Notice that $x < 0 \Rightarrow x^3y^2z^6 < 0$ and $\sqrt[3]{x^3y^2z^6} < 0$. The symbol $|xz^2\sqrt[3]{y^2}|$ has no place here!

(8) $\quad \dfrac{\sqrt{8y^3a^2}}{\sqrt{2y}} = \sqrt{\dfrac{8y^3a^2}{2y}} = \sqrt{4y^2a^2} = 2y|a|.$

The condition $y > 0$ is necessary ($y \neq 0$ to avoid division by 0); but the range of a is $a \in L$.

(9) $\sqrt{\dfrac{2x^3}{3y}} = \sqrt{\dfrac{2x^3 \cdot 3y}{9y^2}} = \dfrac{x}{3y}\sqrt{6xy}.$

The condition $x \geq 0$ and $y > 0$ or $x \leq 0$ and $y < 0$ is necessary. This condition makes $(x/3y)\sqrt{6xy} \geq 0$; hence there is no need for absolute value symbols.

(10) $\sqrt{8x^2b} - \sqrt{18y^2b} = 2|x|\sqrt{2b} - 3|y|\sqrt{2b}$

$$= \sqrt{2b}(2|x| - 3|y|).$$

The condition $b \geq 0$ is necessary; but the ranges of x and y are $x \in L$ and $y \in L$.

EXERCISES §506

1. Rewrite each expression to eliminate the absolute value bars:

(a) $|-5|$ (b) $|1/2|$ (c) $|0|$ (d) $|-62|$

(e) $|\pm 47|$ (f) $|7 - 15|$ (g) $|33 - 6|$ (h) $|4\sqrt{3} - 7|$

(i) $\left|\pi - \dfrac{22}{7}\right|$ (j) $|a^2|$ (k) $|x - a|$ (l) $|x + a|$

(m) $|x^2 - a^2|$ (n) $|x^2 + a^2|$ (o) $|(-a)^2|$ (p) $||-3| - 2|.$

Answers: (a) 5;   (e) 47;   (h) $7 - 4\sqrt{3}$;   (k) $x - a$ when $x \geq a$, $a - x$ when $x < a$.

2. Supply absolute-value bars where needed in the following. Indicate any necessary restrictions on the range of other variables to make the radicals defined in L.

(a) $\sqrt{4x^2} = 2x$ (b) $\sqrt{\frac{1}{4}y^2(x - 4)} = \frac{1}{2}y\sqrt{x - 4}$

(c) $\sqrt{6a^3} = a\sqrt{6a}$ (d) $\sqrt[3]{24x^6y^4z^2} = 2x^2y\sqrt{3yz^2}$

(e) $\sqrt{a^4} = a^2$ (f) $(\sqrt{a})^4 = a^2$

(g) $\sqrt{t^2x^2 + t^2y^2} = t\sqrt{x^2 + y^2}$ (h) $\sqrt{x^2 - 6x + 9} = x - 3$

(i) $\sqrt[4]{y^3z^8u^6} = z^2u\sqrt[4]{y^3u^2}$ (j) $\sqrt{(2 - x)^2} = 2 - x$

(k) $\sqrt{xy^2}\sqrt{x^2y} = xy\sqrt{xy}$ (l) $\dfrac{\sqrt{4xy^4}}{\sqrt{xy^2}} = 2y.$

Answers: (a) $2|x|$;   (b) $\frac{1}{2}|y|\sqrt{x - 4}$, $x \geq 4$;   (c) $a \geq 0$;   (h) $|x - 3|$.

3. Simplify the following radicals by removing factors, rationalizing denominators, and carrying out indicated operations.

(a) $\sqrt{9y^2}$

(b) $\sqrt{3a^2(b-2)}$

(c) $\sqrt{48x^3y^2z^5}$

(d) $\sqrt{x^2 + 14x + 49}$

(e) $\sqrt[3]{120a^5x^2}$

(f) $\dfrac{\sqrt{8a^4}}{\sqrt{4ax^3}}$

(g) $\sqrt{2xa^2}\,\sqrt{6x}$

(h) $\sqrt{x^3y^2}$

(i) $\sqrt{9 - 6x + x^2}$

(j) $\sqrt[3]{9x^6y^2}$

(k) $x\sqrt{x-1} - \sqrt{x-1}$

(l) $\sqrt[3]{32a^5b^2c}.$

Answers: (b) $|a|\sqrt{3(b-2)}$, $b \geq 2$; (e) $2a\sqrt[3]{15a^2x^2}$; (f) $\dfrac{|a|}{x^2}\sqrt{2ax}$, $a > 0$ and $x > 0$ or $a < 0$ and $x < 0$.

4. The condition $x^2 = 9$ can be written as $|x| = 3$, using absolute value symbols. Rewrite each of the following conditions in a form that uses the absolute value bars.

(a) $x^2 = 25$

(b) $x = 8$ or $x = -8$

(c) $(x - b)^2 = 4$

(d) $x = \pm\frac{1}{2}$

(e) $x - y = 3$ when $x \geq y$, $x - y = -3$ when $x < y$.

Answers: (b) $|x| = 8$; (c) $|x - b| = 2$; (e) $|x - y| = 3$.

5. Which of the following are identities for $a \in L$ and $b \in L$?

(a) $|a| = |-a|$

(b) $|a + b| = |a| + |b|$

(c) $|a + b| \leq |a| + |b|$

(d) $|ab| = |a||b|.$

Answer: All are identities except (b).

6. Does the first sentence in each of the following imply the second?

(a) $|a| = 2 \Rightarrow a = 2$

(b) $|a| = 0 \Rightarrow a = 0$

(c) $|a| = 5 \Rightarrow a = 5$ or $a = -5$

(d) $|a| = |b| \Rightarrow a = b$

(e) $|a| = |b| \Rightarrow a^2 = b^2$

(f) $a^2 = b^2 \Rightarrow |a| = |b|.$

Answers: (a) No; (b) yes; (e) yes; (f) yes.

As you study more advanced mathematics, you will often find it convenient to use absolute value symbols to express conditions upon variables. We illustrate such conditions now.

Notice that when $b > 0$,

$$|a| = b \Leftrightarrow a = b \text{ or } a = -b, \qquad \text{(See Exercise 9)}$$
$$|a| < b \Leftrightarrow -b < a < b,$$
$$|a| > b \Leftrightarrow a > b \text{ or } a < -b.$$

Thus, you can write the condition $|x - 5| = 3$ as

$$x - 5 = 3 \quad \text{or} \quad x - 5 = -3;$$

that is,

$$x = 8 \quad \text{or} \quad x = 2.$$

You may find it convenient to think in terms of vectors. The vector $x - 5$ is the directed distance from the point 5 to the point x on the line of numbers.

Its length, $|x - 5|$, is to be 3 (see Fig. 5–10). Hence $x = 8$ or $x = 2$, since 8 and 2 are the only two points to which you can draw vectors 3 units long from the point 5.

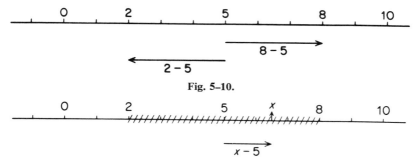

Fig. 5–10.

Fig. 5–11.

You can write the condition $|x - 5| < 3$ as

$$-3 < x - 5 < 3,$$
$$2 < x < 8.$$

Again, in the vector interpretation, if the length of the vector from the point 5 to the point x is to be less than 3, then you must choose replacements of x between 2 and 8 (see Fig. 5–11). Thus the set $\{x \mid |x - 5| < 3\}$ is the same as the set $\{x \mid 2 < x < 8\}$.

You can graph a condition like $y = |x - 4|$, in $L \times L$, most easily by writing an equivalent condition without the absolute value symbols. Notice that

$$|x - 4| = x - 4 \qquad\qquad \text{for } x \geq 4,$$
$$|x - 4| = -(x - 4) = -x + 4 \qquad\qquad \text{for } x < 4;$$

then

$$y = |x - 4| \Leftrightarrow \begin{cases} y = x - 4 & \text{if } x \geq 4 \\ y = -x + 4 & \text{if } x < 4. \end{cases}$$

Figure 5–12 shows the graph of the function $\{(x,y) \mid y = |x - 4|\}$ in $L \times L$.

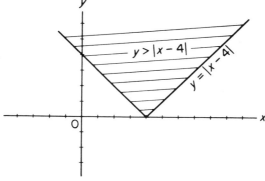

Fig. 5–12.

The graph of $\{(x,y) \mid y > |x - 4|\}$ is, of course, the set of points above the intersecting *half lines*.

EXERCISES §506 (cont.)

7. Rewrite each condition to eliminate absolute value symbols:

(a) $|x - 2| = 6$ (b) $|x - 5| = 2$
(c) $|x + 4| = 10$ (d) $|x + 7| = 3$
(e) $|x - 2| < 6$ (f) $|x + 4| < 10$
(g) $|x + 7| \leq 3$ (h) $|x - 4| > 13$
(i) $|2x - 1| = 15$ (j) $|2x - 1| < 15$
(k) $|7 - x| < 11$ (l) $|4x - 7| > 12$
(m) $|7 - 4x| > 12$ (n) $|x - 1| + |x - 3| = 8.$

Answers: (a) $x = 8$ or $x = -4$; (d) $x = -10$ or $x = -4$; (f) $-14 < x < 6$; (h) $x < -9$ or $x > 17$; (l) $x < -1\frac{1}{4}$ or $x > 4\frac{3}{4}.$

8. Graph each of the following conditions in the plane:

(a) $y = |x|$ (b) $x = |y|$
(c) $y = |x^3|$ (d) $|x - 3| = 5$
(e) $|3 - x| = 5$ (f) $|y - 3| \leq 2$
(g) $|y - 1| \geq 2$ (h) $y \leq |x|$
(i) $|y| \leq |2 - x|$ (j) $y = 2 - |x|$
(k) $y = |4 - x^2|$ (l) $y = x|x - 1|$
(m) $y = |x - 2| + |x - 5|$ (n) $|x - y| = 3$
(o) $(x + y) + |x - y| = 4.$

9. Prove that, when $b > 0$,

(a) $|a| = b \Leftrightarrow a = b$ or $a = -b$
(b) $|a| < b \Leftrightarrow -b < a < b$
(c) $|a| > b \Leftrightarrow a > b$ or $a < -b.$

Proof for part (b): If $a \geq 0$, then

$$|a| = a. \qquad \text{(by definition)}$$

In this case, $|a| < b \Leftrightarrow a < b.$

If $a < b$, and $a \geq 0$, then $0 \leq a < b$; since $-b < 0$, $-b < a < b$. Conversely, if $-b < a < b$ and $a \geq 0$, then $|a| < b$.

If $a < 0$, then

$$|a| = -a. \qquad \text{(by definition)}$$

In this case, $|a| < b \Leftrightarrow -a < b.$

The condition $-a < b$ is equivalent to $a > -b$; that is, $-b < a$. If $-b < a$ and $a < 0$, then $-b < a < 0$; since $0 < b$,

$$-b < a < b.$$

Conversely, if $-b < a < b$ and $a < 0$, then $-b < a$, $b > -a$, $-a < b$, and $|a| < b$.

10. Show that $|x - a| < 8 \Leftrightarrow a - 8 < x < a + 8$.

11. Many elementary algebra texts use absolute value symbols to state the rules for addition, subtraction, multiplication and division of signed numbers. For example: to find ab, $a \in L$ and $b \in L$, first find $|a| \cdot |b|$; if a and b have the same sign, $ab = |a| \cdot |b|$; if a and b have opposite signs, $ab = -|a| \cdot |b|$.

Explore, in this way, the rules for adding, subtracting, multiplying, and dividing signed numbers.

As you look back over this discussion of the absolute value of a real number, notice how convenient this idea is. It enables you to express certain ideas more briefly and more precisely.

507. The set of complex numbers—a structure

In Section 106 (page 34) you worked with integers as ordered pairs of natural numbers; then you worked with rational numbers as ordered pairs of integers. You studied operations with ordered pairs of natural numbers as a basis for operations with integers; you studied operations with ordered pairs of integers as a basis for operations with rational numbers.

Now we use a similar technique to define the algebra of the set of *complex numbers*. As before, we use the symbol C for this set of ordered pairs of real numbers.

As in Chapter 1, we define equality, addition, and multiplication of ordered pairs. Subtraction is inverse to addition, and division is inverse to multiplication.

Consider, then, the set $C = \{(a,b) \mid a \in L \text{ and } b \in L\}$:

For *equality*, we use the definition
D 1: $(a,b) = (c,d) \Leftrightarrow a = c$ and $b = d$.

For *addition*,
D 2: $(a,b) + (c,d) = (a + c, b + d)$.

For *multiplication*,
D 3: $(a,b) \cdot (c,d) = (ac - bd, ad + bc)$.

For *subtraction*,
D 4: $(a,b) - (c,d) = (e,f) \Leftrightarrow (c,d) + (e,f) = (a,b)$.

For *division*,
D 5: $[(c,d) \neq (0,0)]$:

$(a,b) \div (c,d) = (e,f) \Leftrightarrow (c,d) \cdot (e,f) = (a,b)$.

These definitions enable you to perform operations with complex numbers by performing familiar operations with real numbers.

Before proceeding to an exploration of the algebraic structure of the set C, you should look critically at the first three definitions:

Consider, first, the subset of C: $\{(a,b) \mid b = 0\} = \{(a,0)\}$:

$$(a,0) = (c,0) \Leftrightarrow a = c \qquad \text{(D 1)}$$

$$(a,0) + (c,0) = (a + c,0) \qquad \text{(D 2)}$$

$$(a,0) \cdot (c,0) = (ac,0) \qquad \text{(D 3)}$$

Notice that the elements of $\{(a,0)\}$ behave exactly like real numbers. If $(a,0)$ corresponds to the real number a, and $(c,0)$ corresponds to the real number c, then

$$(a,0) + (c,0) = (a + c,0)$$

corresponds to the real number $a + c$, and

$$(a,0) \cdot (c,0) = (ac,0)$$

corresponds to the real number ac. Mathematicians call such a one-to-one correspondence between two sets of numbers, which is *preserved* under addition and multiplication, an *isomorphism*. They say the subset $\{(a,0)\}$ of C is *isomorphic* to L under the correspondence of $(a,0)$ to a.

Do not be frightened by a new, and very convenient, word. It tells you that the elements of $\{(a,0)\}$ behave exactly like the elements of L so far as addition and multiplication (and hence the inverse operations of subtraction and division) are concerned. From another point of view, you can think of the symbols $(a,0)$ and a as symbols for the same thing.

You used the idea of isomorphism repeatedly in Chapter 1. The set I contains a subset isomorphic to the set N; R contains subsets isomorphic to N and I; L contains subsets isomorphic to N, I, and R. Now you find that C contains a subset isomorphic to L.

As in Chapter 1, we shall not distinguish between the sets $\{(a,0)\}$ and $\{a\} = L$. It is convenient to use the symbol a for an element of L and for an element of C.

The fact that C contains a subset $\{(a,0)\}$ isomorphic to L means that the set C is an *extension* of the set L. As we proceed to study the algebraic structure of C, you will find interpretations for the Definitions D 1 through D 5. In particular, you will find that these definitions lead to a useful algebra for vectors in the plane. This algebra follows up the preliminary studies of Section 105 (page 22).

Now consider the product

$$(0,1) \cdot (0,1) = (-1,0) = -1. \qquad \text{(D 3)}$$

This means that the product of the complex number $(0,1)$ with itself corresponds to the real number -1; that is,

$$(0,1)^2 = -1.$$

Hence the set C contains an element, $(0,1)$, whose square is -1.

You should work the following exercises to get the feel of the new definitions you have met so far. Then we shall return to the study of the algebraic structure of C.

EXERCISES §507

1. Decide whether each statement about complex numbers is true or false:

(a) $(5, -3) = (\sqrt{25}, -\sqrt{9})$

(b) $(2\sqrt{6}, 1) = (\sqrt{24}, -1)$

(c) $(\frac{3}{4}, 0) = \frac{3}{4}$

(d) $(1,1) + (-2,3) = (-1,4)$

(e) $(4, -3) + (3,3) = (7,0) = 7$

(f) $(2, -1) + (-2,1) = 0$

(g) $(2,2) \cdot (1,1) = (2,2)$

(h) $(2,2) \cdot (1,0) = (2,2)$

(i) $(3,0) \cdot (5,1) = (15,3)$

(j) $(3,0)^2 = (9,0) = 9$

(k) $(0,3)^2 = (-9,0) = -9$

(l) $(0, -3)^2 = (-9,0) = -9$

(m) $(1,1)^2 = (0,2)$.

2. Recall, from Section 104, the geometric representation of the vector from the origin to the point (a,b) of the plane. You placed the point (a,b) at a directed distance a along the axis of reals, and a directed distance b parallel to the axis of imaginaries, from the origin. There are one-to-one correspondences among the sets of complex numbers, of points in the cartesian plane, and of vectors.

(a) Graph the complex numbers $(1,5)$ and $(4,1)$. Label the points $(1,5)$ and $(4,1)$; label the corresponding vectors v_1 and v_2. Now graph the complex number $v = (1,5) + (4,1) = (5,6)$. Complete a parallelogram to show the vector $v_1 + v_2 = v$.

(b) Repeat part (a) for the complex numbers: $(3,2)$ and $(-2,5)$; $(-1,5)$ and $(-3,2)$; $(0,5)$ and $(2, -3)$; $(5,0)$ and $(3,0)$; $(-5,0)$ and $(3,0)$; $(0, -2)$ and $(0, -1)$; $(0,2)$ and $(0,3)$.

Notice how the definition D 2 is equivalent to the rules for adding vectors as given in Section 105, page 22. We shall return, in Chapter 9, to the graphical interpretation of multiplication of vectors.

3. In Chapter 1, we said that $\sqrt{2}$ is not a rational number. Then we invented the set L to include every number that corresponds to a point on the line of numbers. This step from the rational numbers to the real numbers is a big step, which we took boldly, without inquiring much into the underlying assumptions. In this exercise we guide you through a smaller step, which resembles the extension of the set L to the set C:

Suppose you wish to extend the set R, to build a set of ordered pairs of rational numbers that includes a number whose square is 2. We construct the set:

$$R_{\sqrt{2}}: \quad \{(a,b)\}, \ a \in R \text{ and } b \in R.$$

We define

$$(a,b) = (c,d) \Longleftrightarrow a = c \text{ and } b = d$$

$$(a,b) + (c,d) = (a + c, b + d)$$

$$(a,b) \cdot (c,d) = (ac + 2bd, ad + bc).$$

(a) Show that the set $R_{\sqrt{2}}$ contains a subset $\{(a,0)\}$ isomorphic to the set R.

(b) Show that $(0,1) \cdot (0,1) = (2,0) = 2$; that is,

$$(0,1)^2 = 2.$$

Notice that the definitions for equality and addition are the same for the set $R_{\sqrt{2}}$ as for the set C (except of course that the ranges of a and b are R, rather than L). Notice the new definition of multiplication. Perhaps you will see the motivation for this definition if you examine the identity

$$(a + b\sqrt{2})(c + d\sqrt{2}) = (ac + 2bd) + (ad + bc)\sqrt{2}.$$

4. Following the pattern of Exercise 3, extend the set R to build a set

$$R_{\sqrt{3}}:\quad \{(a,b)\},\ a \in R \text{ and } b \in R$$

that includes a number whose square is 3. *Hint:* Try

$$(a,b) \cdot (c,d) = (ac + 3bd, ad + bc).$$

We list the properties of addition and multiplication of complex numbers, as we previously listed the corresponding properties of real numbers in Chapter 2 (page 63). Then we prove several of these properties of complex numbers as consequences of the definitions above, and the properties of real numbers.

PROPERTIES OF ADDITION   PROPERTIES OF MULTIPLICATION

Closure

AC 1:   For each (a,b) and (c,d) there is a complex number (e,f) such that

$$(a,b) + (c,d) = (e,f)$$

MC 1:   For each (a,b) and (c,d) there is a complex number (e,f) such that

$$(a,b) \cdot (c,d) = (e,f)$$

Uniqueness

AC 2: $[(a,b) = (c,d) \text{ and } (e,f) = (g,h)]$ $\Rightarrow [(a,b) + (e,f) = (c,d) + (g,h)]$

MC 2: $[(a,b) = (c,d) \text{ and } (e,f) = (g,h)]$ $\Rightarrow [(a,b) \cdot (e,f) = (c,d) \cdot (g,h)]$

Commutative

AC 3: $(a,b) + (c,d) = (c,d) + (a,b)$

MC 3: $(a,b) \cdot (c,d) = (c,d) \cdot (a,b)$

Associative

AC 4: $[(a,b) + (c,d)] + (e,f)$ $= (a,b) + [(c,d) + (e,f)]$

MC 4: $[(a,b) \cdot (c,d)] \cdot (e,f)$ $= (a,b) \cdot [(c,d) \cdot (e,f)]$

Identity Element

AC 5:   There is a unique identity for addition, $(0,0) = 0$, such that

$$(a,b) + 0 = (a,b)$$

for each complex number (a,b)

MC 5:   There is a unique identity for multiplication, $(1,0) = 1$, such that

$$(a,b) \cdot 1 = (a,b)$$

for each complex number (a,b)

Inverse Element

AC 6:   For each complex number (a,b), there is a unique inverse for addition, $(-a, -b)$, such that

$$(a,b) + (-a, -b) = 0$$

MC 6:   For each complex number (a,b), $(a,b) \neq 0$, there is a unique inverse for multiplication, $1/(a,b)$, such that

$$(a,b) \cdot \frac{1}{(a,b)} = 1$$

Inverse Operation

AC 7: $(a,b) - (c,d) = (a,b) + (-c,-d)$ MC 7: $(c,d) \neq 0 \Rightarrow (a,b) \div (c,d)$

$$= \frac{(a,b)}{(c,d)} = (a,b) \cdot \frac{1}{(c,d)}$$

Order

We shall not use the connective phrases, "$<$" and "$>$," for complex numbers. Hence there are no properties AC 8 and MC 8 corresponding to properties A 8 and M 8 (page 63) for real numbers.

PROPERTIES FOR COMBINING ADDITION AND MULTIPLICATION

DC 1: $(a,b) \cdot [(c,d) + (e,f)] = (a,b) \cdot (c,d) + (a,b) \cdot (e,f)$

We shall not list properties DC 2 through DC 10 corresponding to properties D 2 through D 10 (page 64) for real numbers. You may wish to state these properties, and prove them from the preceding properties of complex numbers.

You can prove each of the properties of complex numbers as a consequence of D 1 through D 5 and the properties of real numbers. The following examples illustrate the technique:

(1) To prove MC 3: $(a,b) \cdot (c,d) = (c,d) \cdot (a,b)$.

Proof: $(a,b) \cdot (c,d) = (ac - bd, ad + bc)$ (D 3, page 209)

$$= (ca - db, cb + da) \quad \text{(Properties of real numbers)}$$

$$= (c,d) \cdot (a,b). \qquad\qquad\qquad\qquad\qquad\qquad \text{(D 3)}$$

(2) To prove MC 6: For each $(a,b) \in C$, $(a,b) \neq 0$, there is a unique inverse for multiplication, that we call $1/(a,b)$, such that $(a,b) \cdot 1/(a,b) = 1$. *Proof*: We wish to find a complex number $(c,d) = 1/(a,b)$ such that

$$(a,b) \cdot (c,d) = (1,0)$$

$$(a,b) \cdot (c,d) = (ac - bd, ad + bc) \qquad \text{(D 3, page 209)}$$

This requires $ac - bd = 1$ and $ad + bc = 0$. In Chapter 7 you will learn to solve such a pair of conditions for c and d in terms of a and b, provided $a^2 + b^2 \neq 0$. Since $(a,b) \neq (0,0)$, a and b are not both 0; hence $a^2 + b^2 \neq 0$. The unique solution is

$$(c,d) = \left(\frac{a}{a^2 + b^2}, \frac{-b}{a^2 + b^2} \right).$$

To prove that this value of (c,d) is an inverse for multiplication of (a,b),

$$(a,b) \cdot (c,d) = (a,b) \cdot \left(\frac{a}{a^2 + b^2}, \frac{-b}{a^2 + b^2} \right)$$

$$= \left(\frac{a^2}{a^2 + b^2} + \frac{b^2}{a^2 + b^2}, \frac{-ab}{a^2 + b^2} + \frac{ba}{a^2 + b^2} \right) \qquad \text{(D 3)}$$

$$= (1,0) \qquad\qquad\qquad\qquad\qquad \text{(Properties of real numbers)}$$

$$= 1.$$

To prove that you may write $(c,d) = 1/(a,b) = (1,0) \div (a,b)$, recall that

$$(1,0) \div (a,b) = (c,d) \Leftrightarrow (a,b) \cdot (c,d) = (1,0) \qquad \text{(D 5)}$$

We have already shown that

$$(a,b) \cdot (c,d) = (a,b)\left(\frac{a}{a^2 + b^2}, \frac{-b}{a^2 + b^2}\right) = (1,0).$$

(3) To prove AC 7: $(a,b) - (c,d) = (a,b) + (-c,-d)$.

Proof:
$$[(a,b) + (-c,-d)] + (c,d) = (a - c, b - d) + (c,d) \quad \text{(D 2, p. 209)}$$
$$= (a - c + c, b - d + d)$$
$$= (a,b) \quad \text{(Properties of real numbers)}$$

Hence $\qquad\qquad (a,b) - (c,d) = (a,b) + (-c,-d) \qquad\qquad$ (D 4, p. 209)

You may wish to prove others of the properties of complex numbers right away; or you may wish to use the hints given in the following exercises.

EXERCISES §507 (cont.)

5. Apply D 1 through D 5 (page 209), to prove the following identities:

(a) $(a,b) + (0,0) = (a,b)$ (This is AC 5)

(b) $[(a,b) + (c,d)] + (e,f) = (a,b) + [(c,d) + (e,f)]$ (This is AC 4)

(c) $(a,b) \cdot (1,0) = (a,b)$ (This is MC 5)

(d) $(a,b)[(c,d) + (e,f)] = (a,b) \cdot (c,d) + (a,b) \cdot (e,f)$ (This is DC 1)

Hint: Use D 2 and D 3 to reduce each side of an equation to a single complex number. Then apply D1.

6. Prove the following properties:

(a) $(-1,0)(a,b) = (-a, -b)$

(b) $(-1,0)[(a,b) + (c,d)] = (-a, -b) + (-c, -d)$

(c) $(a,b) \div (c,d) = \left(\dfrac{ac + bc}{c^2 + d^2}, \dfrac{bc - ad}{c^2 + d^2}\right)$

(d) $(a,b)^2 - (c,d)^2 = [(a,b) + (c,d)][(a,b) - (c,d)]$

(e) $(0,0)(a,b) = (0,0)$

(f) $(a,b)[(c,d) - (e,f)] = (a,b)(c,d) - (a,b)(e,f)$.

As you look back over Section 507 to ask questions like "What have I learned?" and "Why is this important?" notice the following:

Except for the order properties, the algebra of set C is identical to the algebra of set L. This is an excellent reason for calling the elements of C numbers. You call them complex numbers to remind yourself that they are really pairs of real numbers.

With the exception of order properties, all that you have learned about the algebra of real numbers applies equally well to complex numbers. You apply D 1 through D 5 (page 209), and proceed with confidence because complex numbers have the same properties of addition and multiplication as real numbers do. The only exceptions are properties of order that involve the connective phrases "$<$" and "$>$." The use of these connectives is not defined for the set C.

508. A special notation for complex numbers

When you use the number-pair notation for complex numbers (Section 507) you realize that you can treat complex numbers as ordered pairs of real numbers. Once you have accomplished this, it is natural to seek a convenient notation for the arithmetic of complex numbers. This is exactly what we did in Section 106 for integers, page 34, and for rational numbers, page 37 For integers, we replaced an ordered pair of natural numbers, (a,b), by the symbol $a - b$; for rational numbers, we replaced an ordered pair of integers, (a,b), by the symbol a/b.

Notice, then, that you can write the complex number, (a,b), as follows:

$$(a,b) = (a,0)(1,0) + (b,0)(0,1).$$

Using the definitions of addition and multiplication of complex numbers,

$$(a,0)(1,0) = (a,0),$$
$$(b,0)(0,1) = (0,b),$$

and
$$(a,0) + (0,b) = (a,b).$$

Recall that, in the sense of isomorphism,

$$(a,0) = a, \quad (b,0) = b, \quad \text{and} \quad (1,0) = 1.$$

Also, $(0,1)$ has the special property

$$(0,1)^2 = (0,1)(0,1) = (-1,0) = -1.$$

Hence $(0,1)$ is not a real number. For historical reasons we call it an *imaginary* number. You should not suppose that imaginary numbers are any more "imaginary" than real numbers. This is a technical use of the term.

Mathematicians use the symbol i to represent the complex number $(0,1)$. They write

$$(a,b) = (a,0)(1,0) + (b,0)(0,1)$$
$$= a \cdot 1 + b \cdot i$$
$$= a + bi.$$

They speak of the complex number $a + bi$ with *real* part a and *imaginary* part bi. The symbol i represents an imaginary number; it has the property

$$i^2 = -1.$$

Notice the convenience of this special notation for complex numbers.

To perform the addition

$$(a + bi) + (c + di) = (a + c) + (b + d)i,$$

you treat $a + bi$ and $c + di$ as polynomials in i. You use the same algebraic techniques you learned previously for polynomials. You do not need to remember the definition

$$(a,b) + (c,d) = (a + c, b + d)$$

of Section 507 (page 209). Similarly, for the multiplication

$$(a + bi)(c + di) = ac + (ad + bc)i + bdi^2$$
$$= (ac - bd) + (ad + bc)i,$$

you replace the definition

$$(a,b)(c,d) = (ac - bd, ad + bc)$$

by the familiar definition for multiplying polynomials in i; then you impose the condition $i^2 = -1$.

The sets of symbols $\{(a,b)\}$ and $\{a + bi\}$ are clearly isomorphic. For, if

(a,b) corresponds to $a + bi$,

and (c,d) corresponds to $c + di$,

then $(a,b) + (c,d)$ corresponds to $(a + bi) + (c + di)$,

and $(a,b)(c,d)$ corresponds to $(a + bi)(c + di)$.

We drop the notation (a,b) for a complex number; we shall use, instead, the more convenient notation $a + bi$. When $b = 0$, we write $a + 0i = a$; the complex number $a + bi$ reduces to the real number a. When $a = 0$, we write $0 + bi = bi$; the complex number $a + bi$ reduces to the *pure imaginary number* bi. The following exercises will familiarize you with the notation $a + bi$.

EXERCISES §508

1. Determine the real and imaginary part of each complex number.

(a) $2 + 5i$ (b) $-7 + 3i$ (c) $2\sqrt{2} - 2i$

(d) $4\sqrt{6}$ (e) $4i$ (f) $-\frac{1}{2} + \pi i$

(g) 0 (h) -1.

2. Perform each of the following additions of complex numbers. First think of adding the corresponding ordered pairs of real numbers; then think of each complex number as a polynomial in i. Compare the ease and convenience of these two ways of thinking.

(a) $(5 + 5i) + (4 + i)$ (b) $(3 + 2i) + (-1 + 2i)$

(c) $(-4 - 4i) + (-2 + 3i)$ (d) $(5 + 3i) + (-4)$

(e) $(6 - 2i) + (-4 - 2i)$ (f) $(2 - 3i) + (-2 - 3i)$

(g) $(2 - 3i) + (-2 + 3i)$ (h) $(-1 + 2i) + (-1 + 2i)$.

Answers: (a) $9 + 6i$; (c) $-6 - i$; (f) $-6i$.

3. Perform each subtraction of complex numbers. Think of the complex numbers as polynomials in i, and as ordered pairs of real numbers.

(a) $(2 + 4i) - (5 + 2i)$ (b) $(-1 + 3i) - (4 + i)$

(c) $(3 - 2i) - (-1 - 5i)$ (d) $(3 - 2i) - (1 + 5i)$.

Answers: (a) $-3 + 2i$;   (c) $4 + 3i$.

4. Evaluate the powers of i by successive multiplication:

$$i^2 = -1$$
$$i^3 = (i)(-1) = -i$$
$$i^4 = (-i)i = -i^2 = 1$$
$$i^5 = i, \text{ etc.}$$

5. Carry out the indicated multiplications of complex numbers. Think of the complex numbers as polynomials in i, with $i^2 = -1$.

(a) $(5 + 3i)(1 + 4i)$ (b) $(-5 + i)(2 + i)$

(c) $(2 + \sqrt{3}i)(2 - \sqrt{3}i)$ (d) $(6i)(2i)$

(e) $(-2i)(4 + 3i)$ (f) $(1 + i)^2$

(g) $(5 - 4i)^2$ (h) $(\sqrt{2} - 3i)(\sqrt{2} + 3i)$.

Answers: (a) $-7 + 23i$;   (b) $-11 - 3i$;   (f) $2i$.

6. Given $p(x) = x^2 - 6x + 1$, find

(a) $p(3 + 2i)$ (b) $p(1 - 2i)$ (c) $p(1 + 2i)$.

Answer: (c) $-8 - 8i$.

7. Given $q(x) = x^2 + (1 - i)x - (2 + 2i)$, find

(a) $q(1 + i)$ (b) $q(1 - i)$.

For each complex number, $a + bi$, there is a second complex number, $a - bi$, called the *conjugate* of $a + bi$. Note that

$$(a + bi) + (a - bi) = 2a.$$

That is, the sum of a complex number and its conjugate is a real number; it is twice the real part of the given complex number. Also,

$$(a + bi)(a - bi) = a^2 + b^2.$$

That is, the product of a complex number and its conjugate is a real number. This real number has a useful interpretation in the geometry of vectors that you will study in Section 907.

Recall, for the division $(a,b)/(c,d)$, $(c,d) \neq (0,0)$, the formula

$$\frac{(a,b)}{(c,d)} = \left(\frac{ac + bd}{c^2 + d^2}, \frac{-ad + bc}{c^2 + d^2} \right).$$ (Exercise 6(c), page 214)

In the special notation for complex numbers, you can use the technique

$$\frac{a + bi}{c + di} = \frac{(a + bi)(c - di)}{(c + di)(c - di)} = \frac{ac + bd}{c^2 + d^2} + \frac{-ad + bc}{c^2 + d^2}i.$$

This makes a division of complex numbers like rationalizing the denominator of a fraction (page 199). To divide two complex numbers, you can write the division as a fraction; then multiply numerator and denominator by the conjugate of the denominator. You do not need a special formula for division of complex numbers.

EXERCISES §508 (cont.)

8. Carry out the indicated divisions of complex numbers. In parts (a) to (g) show that your answer satisfies the definition of division.

(a) $\dfrac{6 + 4i}{1 + i}$

(b) $\dfrac{2 + i}{3 - 2i}$

(c) $\dfrac{3 + 4i}{2i}$

(d) $\dfrac{3}{1 + 2i}$

(e) $\dfrac{1}{i}$

(f) $5 \div (1 - 3i)$

(g) $(2 + i)^{-1} = \dfrac{1}{2 + i}$

(h) $(1 + i)^{-2}$

(i) $\dfrac{(2 + 3i)^3}{1 + i}$

(j) $\left(\dfrac{1 - 2i}{i}\right)^4$.

Answers: (a) $5 - i$; (b) $\frac{4}{13} + \frac{7}{13}i$; (c) $2 - \frac{3}{2}i$; (h) $-\frac{1}{2}i$; (j) $-7 + 24i$.

9. Show that the sentence $(x - 2) + \dfrac{17}{(x - 2)} = 2$ becomes a true statement when x is replaced by a member of the set $\{3 + 4i, 3 - 4i\}$.

509. Powers and roots of complex numbers

Integral powers of real numbers are real numbers; but you have found that roots of real numbers may or may not be real numbers. The set L is not closed under the operation of root extraction. In Chapter 9, you will find that the set C is closed under the operations of forming powers and extracting roots. This is an important advantage of the set C over the set L.

Recall from Section 105 (page 22) operations with vectors in the plane. In particular, the sum of two vectors is obtained by laying the vectors end to end. The product of two vectors is the vector whose magnitude is the product of the magnitudes, and whose amplitude is the sum of the amplitudes, of the two vectors. We shall prove, in Chapter 9, that the set of vectors in the plane behaves like the set of complex numbers. Once you assume this result, it is graphically apparent that the set C is closed under the operations of forming powers and extracting roots.

6

Conditions in One Unknown

In Chapter 4 you met the elementary functions. When you used an equation to find the second element of a number-pair, the equation was a formula for calculating the values of y that correspond to the values you assign to x. For example, the equation $y = 2x + 5$ is a convenient formula for finding the values of y that correspond to different values of x; when $x = -3$, you calculate $y = 2(-3) + 5 = -1$.

It is less convenient to assign a value to y and proceed to calculate the corresponding values of x. For example, when $y = 2x + 5$, and $y = 9$, you get $9 = 2x + 5$; to find the values of x, you must *solve* the equation $9 = 2x + 5$ for x. This is a problem that arises so frequently in algebra that we make it the topic of this chapter.

In Chapter 2 you called an equation like $9 = 2x + 5$ a condition. You thought of x as a variable with a certain range. Each replacement of x yields a statement. For example, the replacement 3 yields the false statement $9 = 2(3) + 5$; the replacement 2 yields the true statement $9 = 2(2) + 5$. To solve an equation in the variable x means to find the set of values of x that yield true statements. People call the variable x, when used in this way, the *unknown*. They think of solving a condition as finding the value, or values of the unknown that *satisfy* the condition.

Other examples of conditions in one unknown are:

(1) $t^2 - 3t = 7$

(2) $s^3 - 12s^2 = 0$

(3) $\sin x = .84792$

(4) $3^v = 32.8$

(5) $16t^2 > 21.8$

(6) $3^n < 17.2$

The first two equations are associated with algebraic functions. For example, equation (1) may arise from the function $\{(t,u) \mid u = t^2 - 3t\}$. If you ask what values of t correspond to $u = 7$, you encounter the equation $7 = t^2 - 3t$. Equation (2) may arise when you ask what values of s correspond to $t = 0$ in the algebraic condition $t = s^3 - 12s^2$.

The third equation is associated with the trigonometric function

$\{(x,y) \mid y = \sin x\}$. When $y = .84792$, you get the equation $.84792 = \sin x$ as a condition on the variable x.

The fourth equation is associated with the exponential function $\{(v,w) \mid w = 3^v\}$. When $w = 32.8$, v must satisfy the condition $32.8 = 3^v$.

The fifth and sixth conditions are inequalities. We shall use the equality $y = 16t^2$ to help you visualize the inequality $16t^2 > 21.8$; we shall associate condition (6) with the exponential function $\{(n,y) \mid y = 3^n\}$.

We proceed with the solution of conditions in one unknown. Although the meaning of the problem is always the same, namely, to find the set of values of the unknown that satisfy the condition, the difficulty of solving the problem varies widely. We begin with the simpler problems, and continue our discussions as far as is feasible and useful at this stage of your study of algebra. We could not finish the problem even if we wanted to. Mathematicians are still doing research to find efficient ways to solve knotty conditions in one unknown.

600. First-degree conditions

A first-degree equation in x is an algebraic equation that involves the unknown x, and no higher powers of x. You can use the properties of real numbers to reduce any first-degree equation to an equivalent equation of the form $ax + b = 0$, $a \neq 0$; then $x = -b/a$.

Consider, for example, the equation, $3x - 2 = x - (2x - 7)$. First you rewrite the equation as $3x - 2 = x - 2x + 7$, or $3x - 2 = -x + 7$. Notice how you use properties of real numbers, like the distributive law, to simplify the right *member* of the equation. Then you collect terms that involve x on one side of the equation, and terms that do not involve x on the opposite side of the equation. To eliminate a term from one member of the equation you use its inverse for addition. Thus $3x - 2 = -x + 7$ becomes

$$(3x - 2) + (2) + (x) = (-x + 7) + (2) + (x);$$

2 is the inverse of -2, and x is the inverse of $-x$. You get $4x + 0 = 9 + 0$, or $4x = 9$. Finally you use the inverse for multiplication. Thus $4x = 9$ becomes $\frac{1}{4} \cdot 4x = \frac{1}{4} \cdot 9$, or $1 \cdot x = 9/4$, or $x = 9/4$. Notice how you use the inverses for addition and multiplication, and the uniqueness properties of addition and multiplication, to proceed from the equation $3x - 2 = -x + 7$ to the equation $x = 9/4$.

When you manipulate the equation $3x - 2 = x - (2x - 7)$ to get the equation $x = 9/4$, you really prove

$$[3x - 2 = x - (2x - 7)] \Rightarrow [x = 9/4].$$

Recall, from Chapter 2, that all of these steps are reversible. That is, you can prove

$$[x = 9/4] \Rightarrow [3x - 2 = x - (2x - 7)].$$

Hence the conditions $3x - 2 = x - (2x - 7)$ and $x = 9/4$ are *equivalent* conditions, that is,

$$[3x - 2 = x - (2x - 7)] \Leftrightarrow [x = 9/4].$$

We call $9/4$ a solution of the equation $3x - 2 = x - (2x - 7)$; the solution set, $\{x \mid 3x - 2 = x - (2x - 7)\} = \{9/4\}$, has just one element; hence $9/4$ is *the* solution of $3x - 2 = x - (2x - 7)$.

Sometimes a problem leads to what appears to be a first-degree equation but really is not. For example:

(1) Find a number such that two more than three times the number is five less than three times the number.

The algebraic condition is

$$3x + 2 = 3x - 5.$$

This condition looks like a first-degree equation, but

$$(3x + 2) + (-2) + (-3x) = (3x - 5) + (-2) + (-3x)$$
$$3x - 3x = -7$$
$$0x = -7.$$

For each replacement of x, $0x = 0$. The condition $0x = -7$ is equivalent to the condition $0 = -7$. This is not a first-degree equation in x because it does not involve the variable x.

The condition $0 = -7$ is a false statement. No replacement of x yields a true statement. That is, the condition $3x + 2 = 3x - 5$ defines the null set; $\{x \mid 3x + 2 = 3x - 5\} = \{\ \}$.

(2) Solve the equation $2 - (3 - 2x) = (2x + 5) + (-6)$. This condition looks like a first-degree condition, but

$$2 - 3 + 2x = 2x + 5 - 6$$
$$2x - 1 = 2x - 1.$$

The condition is an identity. It defines a subset of L equal to the set L. Notice that

$$(2x - 1) + (1) + (-2x) = (2x - 1) + (1) + (-2x)$$
$$0x = 0.$$

The condition $0x = 0$ becomes a true statement for each replacement of x. No replacement of x yields a false statement. That is, the condition $2 - (3 - 2x) = (2x + 5) + (-6)$ defines the set L; $\{x \mid 2 - (3 - 2x) = (2x + 5) + (-6)\} = L$.

We rule out these trivial cases by specifying that a first-degree equation in x is an equation that can be reduced to an equivalent equation of the form $ax + b = 0$, where $a \neq 0$. Then every first-degree equation has exactly one solution.

When an equation involves one or more parameters, you must be alert to watch for trivial cases. For example, the equation we associated with the general linear function is $y = mx + b$. The graph is a two-parameter family of straight lines; the slope m is any element of the set L; the y-intercept b is any element of the set L. Suppose you ask what value of x corresponds to $y = 0$? That is, what is the *x-intercept* of the graph of $y = mx + b$?

It is tempting to proceed mechanically, as follows: When $y = 0$, $0 = mx + b$. Hence $mx + b = 0$, $mx = -b$, $x = -b/m$; but you must restrict the values that the parameter m may take and specify $m \neq 0$. When $m = 0$, you get the one-parameter family of straight lines, $y = b$. There are two possibilities: When $b \neq 0$, you get lines, like $y = 4$, that are parallel to the x-axis. These lines do not intersect the x-axis, and hence they *do not have x-intercepts*. When $b = 0$, you get the line $y = 0$ which is the x-axis. This line intersects the x-axis at every one of its points, and hence has *as many x-intercepts as there are points on the line of numbers.*

A similar situation arises when you try to rewrite a formula, like $A = P(1 + rt)$, to make it convenient for calculating values of one of the other variables (like r). Thus $P(1 + rt) = A$, $P + Prt = A$, $Pt \cdot r = A - P$, $r = (A - P)/Pt$. You must restrict yourself, in this instance, to values of P and t such that $Pt \neq 0$. Of course, $Pt \neq 0 \Leftrightarrow P \neq 0$ and $t \neq 0$.

The formula $A = P(1 + rt)$ gives you the amount (A) of a principal (P) invested at a simple interest rate of r per year for t years. People call A the *dependent* variable. The value of A depends upon the values you assign to the *independent* variables P, r, and t.

The formula $r = (A - P)/Pt$ gives you the rate of simple interest (r) if a principal (P) yields an amount (A) when invested for t years. In this formula r is the dependent variable, and A, P, and t are the independent variables. When $P = 0$, or when $t = 0$, r is not defined. For example, at what rate of interest does 0 dollars amount to 10 dollars when invested at simple interest for 20 yr? You should invent other questions to assure yourself that the mathematical restrictions, $P \neq 0$ and $t \neq 0$, are also sensible restrictions.

So far we have dealt with first-degree equations. First-degree conditions also include first-degree inequalities. For example, $2x + 7 > x - 1$ is a first-degree condition upon the variable x.

Recall, from Chapter 2, that the properties of inequalities are similar to the properties of equations, with two important exceptions. If $a = b$, then $b = a$; but if $a > b$, then $b < a$. If $a = b$, and c is any real number, then $ac = bc$; but if $a > b$, and $c < 0$, then $ac < bc$. Notice how much the treatment of Example (3), below, resembles the treatment of a first-degree equation; notice how the special properties of inequalities enter into the treatment of Example (4).

(3) $3x + 7 > x - 1$
  $(3x + 7) + (-7) + (-x) > (x - 1) + (-7) + (-x)$
  $2x > -8$
  $x > -4.$

(4) $x + 5 > 4x - 2$

$(x + 5) + (-5) + (-4x) > (4x - 2) + (-5) + (-4x)$

$-3x > -7$

$x < -7/-3$

$x < 7/3.$

You could also solve the inequality $x + 5 > 4x - 2$ as follows:

$(x + 5) + (-x) + (2) > (4x - 2) + (-x) + (2)$

$7 > 3x$

$7/3 > x$

$x < 7/3.$

We specify that a first-degree inequality in x is one that can be reduced to an equivalent inequality of the form $ax + b > 0$, where $a \neq 0$. That is, we rule out inequalities that lead to sentences like $0x - 5 > 0$ (that define the null set), or $0x + 5 > 0$ (that define a subset of L equal to the set L). With this understanding, every linear inequality defines a subset of L that is not the set L or the null set.

If $ax + b > 0$ and $a > 0$, then $x > -b/a$, and, conversely, if $x > -b/a$ then $ax + b > 0$. Hence

$$a > 0 \Rightarrow \{x \mid ax + b > 0\} = \{x \mid x > -b/a\}.$$

If $ax + b > 0$ and $a < 0$, then $x < -b/a$, and conversely. Hence

$$a < 0 \Rightarrow \{x \mid ax + b > 0\} = \{x \mid x < -b/a\}.$$

You should study the examples below to further compare and contrast first-degree equations and first-degree inequalities:

(5) $3x - 2 < x - (2x + 5)$

$3x - 2 < x - 2x - 5$

$3x - 2 < -x - 5$

$(3x - 2) + (2) + (x) < (-x - 5) + (2) + (x)$

$4x < -3$

$x < -3/4.$

Notice that the inequality $x < -3/4$, defines a subset of L with infinitely many elements. The graph of Fig. 6–1 may help you to visualize this subset of L. Every point to the left of $-3/4$ corresponds to a number in this subset of L.

Contrast this inequality with the equation $3x - 2 = x - (2x + 5)$. You get the equivalent equation, $x = -3/4$, by exactly the same steps we used above; but $x = -3/4$ defines a subset of L with just one member, namely, $\{-3/4\}$.

The easiest way to check the solution of an equation is by substitution. Thus

$$x = -3/4 \Rightarrow 3x - 2 = 3(-3/4) - 2 = -17/4$$
$$x = -3/4 \Rightarrow x - (2x + 5) = (-3/4) - [2(-3/4) + 5] = -\frac{17}{4}.$$

Hence $x = -3/4 \Rightarrow 3x - 2 = x - (2x + 5)$.

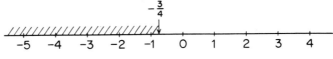

Fig. 6–1.

It is impossible to substitute each element of a set that contains infinitely many elements. Hence you cannot check the solution set, $\{x \mid x < -\frac{3}{4}\}$, of the inequality $3x - 2 < x - (2x + 5)$ by substitution. You can, however, reverse the steps of the solution. Thus

$$x < -3/4$$
$$4x < -3$$
$$4x + (-2) + (-x) < -3 + (-2) + (-x)$$
$$3x - 2 < -x - 5$$
$$3x - 2 < x - (2x + 5).$$

The steps of the solution of a first-degree inequality are always reversible. Hence the simplified inequality (like $x < -3/4$) is always equivalent to the given inequality [like $3x - 2 < x - (2x + 5)$], unless you make errors in applying the properties of real numbers. To detect such errors in calculation you may want to try one or two elements of your solution set to see whether they satisfy the given inequality. For example, the condition $x < -3/4$ is satisfied by $x = -1$ (that is, $-1 < -3/4$ is a true statement). Now

$$x = -1 \Rightarrow 3x - 2 = 3(-1) - 2 = -5$$
$$x = -1 \Rightarrow x - (2x + 5) = -1 - (-2 + 5) = -4$$
$$-5 < -4.$$

Hence $x = -1 \Rightarrow 3x - 2 < x - (2x + 5)$.

You can try other replacements of x, like $x = -2$, $x = -3$, etc., that satisfy the condition $x < -3/4$; but you can not try every element of a set that contains infinitely many elements; hence you cannot perform a *complete* check by substitution.

(6) Solve for r the inequality $t > 5 - ar/b$, $b \neq 0$.

$$t + (ar/b) + (-t) > (5 - ar/b) + (ar/b) + (-t)$$
$$(a/b)r > 5 - t.$$

If $a/b = 0$, this is not a first-degree inequality in the variable r. It reduces to the sentence $0 > 5 - t$; this sentence is true or false depending upon the value you assign to t; the value you assign to r does not affect its truth or falsity.

If $a/b > 0$, $\qquad [1/(a/b)] \cdot (a/b)r > [1/(a/b)] \cdot (5 - t)$

$$r > (b/a) \cdot (5 - t).$$

If $a/b < 0$, $\qquad [1/(a/b)] \cdot (a/b)r < [1/(a/b)] \cdot (5 - t),$

$$r < (b/a) \cdot (5 - t).$$

The following exercises provide practice in reducing linear conditions to equivalent linear conditions that are simpler; that is, in solving linear conditions; that is, in finding the solution set for a given linear condition.

EXERCISES §600

1. Solve each equation for x. Check your solutions. (See hint, below.)

(a) $2x - 14 = 0$ $\qquad\qquad$ (b) $0 = 5x + 9$

(c) $3x = 4x + 2$ $\qquad\qquad$ (d) $6x + 7 = 3(-x + 1) + x$

(e) $5(x - 3) = x + 3(x + 1)$ $\qquad$ (f) $2(x + 2) - 4(x - 1) = 3(x + 3)$

(g) $-3x - 2 = -(x - 1) - 1$ $\qquad$ (h) $x/3 - x/4 = 2$

(i) $3(x + \frac{1}{2}) = \frac{1}{2}(x - 4)$ $\qquad$ (j) $(x + 2)/2 - (x - 5)/5 = 4$

(k) $3.2x - 7.6 = 1.2(x + 1)$ $\qquad$ (l) $4.16 - x = 1.6(x - 1)$

(m) $2/x = 3/x - 5$ $\qquad\qquad$ (n) $4/(x - 5) = 5/(x - 4)$.

Hint: For practice in using the language of this section, you should express your results as follows. We use part (a) as a sample:

$$2x - 14 = 0 \Leftrightarrow x = 7;$$

hence $\qquad\qquad \{x \mid 2x - 14 = 0\} = \{x \mid x = 7\} = \{7\}.$

The solution of $2x - 14 = 0$ is 7.

2. Solve each equation for x. Check your solutions. Indicate the restrictions on the other variables that are necessary to avoid division by zero.

(a) $sx - t = 0$ $\qquad\qquad$ (b) $3x + b = rx - 7$

(c) $3(px - c) = p(x - c)$ $\qquad$ (d) $2a - 3x = 6x + 7b$

(e) $2ax + b = 2bx + a$ $\qquad$ (f) $mx + n^2 = nx + m^2$

(g) $Ax + By + C = 0$ $\qquad$ (h) $x/a + y/b = 1$

(i) $2tx - 6t^2 = 4t(t + x)$ $\qquad$ (j) $1/x - 1/m = 1/n - 1/x$.

Answers: (b) $x = \dfrac{b + 7}{r - 3}, r \neq 3;$ (e) $x = \frac{1}{2}, a \neq b;$ (j) $x = \dfrac{2mn}{m + n}, m \neq -n.$

3. Solve each formula for the variable that is specified. Indicate the restrictions, if any, on the other variables.

(a) $PV = K$ for V (b) $C = \pi d$ for d

(c) $C = \frac{5}{9}(F - 32)$ for F (d) $u = (x - x_0)/k$ for x

(e) $A = \frac{1}{2}h(b_1 + b_2)$ for b_1 (f) $V = \pi h r^2$ for h

(g) $1/R = 1/R_1 + 1/R_2$ for R (h) $S = (a - rL)/(1 - r)$ for r

(i) $r = de/(1 - eC)$ for C (j) $r = de/(1 - eC)$ for e.

Answers: (a) $V = \dfrac{K}{P}, P \neq 0$; (d) $x = ku + x_0$; (h) $r = \dfrac{a - S}{L - S}, L \neq S$.

4. Solve the inequalities for the variable involved. (See hint, below.)

(a) $3x > 12$ (b) $-3x > 12$

(c) $2x + 5 > 0$ (d) $-2x - 5 < 0$

(e) $3z - 7 < 5z + 9$ (f) $\frac{1}{2}z < \frac{1}{4}(z + 2)$

(g) $4(W - 2) - 7(W - 2) > 3(W - 2)$ (h) $3(a - 5) < \frac{1}{2}a$

(i) $2 - 5r > 3(1 - r)$ (j) $1/x > 2$ and $x > 0$

(k) $1/x < 2$ and $x < 0$ (l) $1/(2x - 3) > 3$ and $x > 3/2$.

Hint: For practice in using the language of this section, you should express your results as follows. We use part (d) as a sample:

$$-2x - 5 < 0 \Leftrightarrow x > -\tfrac{5}{2};$$

hence $\{x \mid -2x - 5 < 0\} = \{x \mid x > -\tfrac{5}{2}\}.$

The solutions of $-2x - 5 < 0$ are the real numbers that correspond to points to the right of $-2\frac{1}{2}$ on the line of numbers.

5. Label each of the following as: (1) linear condition; (2) sentence that defines the null set; (3) sentence that defines the entire set L.

(a) $2x - 3 = 0$ (b) $4x + 5 = 4x$

(c) $4x + 5 > 4x$ (d) $4x + 5 < 4x$

(e) $2x + 5 = 3x - 2$ (f) $6(x - 1) = 2x + 5$

(g) $2(4 - x) + 3(x - 3) = x$ (h) $2(x - 3) = 2x - 6$

(i) $\frac{1}{2}(x - 1) + \frac{1}{4}(x + 1) = \frac{1}{4}(3x + 4)$ (j) $\frac{1}{2}(x - 1) + \frac{1}{4}(x + 1) < \frac{1}{4}(3x + 4)$

(k) $4(x - 1) - 7 = 2x - 3(x + 2)$ (l) $2(3x + 4) = 7(x + 1) - (x - 1)$

(m) $1/x = 4$ (n) $1/x = 0$.

You can now solve any first-degree condition by algebraic methods. However, there is much to be gained by taking a look at the graphical solutions of these conditions. The graphical approach will help you to visualize the algebraic approach, and hence will make it mean more to you.

Recall that first-degree equations can be reduced to equivalent equations of the form $ax + b = 0$, $a \neq 0$. Consider the graph of $y = ax + b$, $a \neq 0$. This is a straight line of slope a and y-intercept b (Fig. 6–2). To solve the equation $ax + b = 0$ is to find the value of x that corresponds to $y = 0$ on the graph of $y = ax + b$. This is the x-intercept, $-b/a$, of the straight line in the figure.

The following examples illustrate the way in which questions about

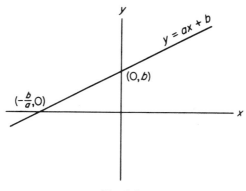

Fig. 6–2.

first-degree equations can be interpreted as questions about graphs of straight lines and vice-versa:

(7) Solve for x, the equation $-\frac{1}{2}x + 2 = 0$. Algebraically, $-\frac{1}{2}x + 2 = 0$, $-\frac{1}{2}x = -2$, $x = -2/(-\frac{1}{2}) = 4$. Graphically (Fig. 6–3), the x-intercept of the graph of $y = -\frac{1}{2}x + 2$ is 4.

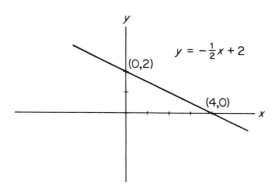

Fig. 6–3.

(8) Find the value of x that corresponds to $y = 5$ on the graph of $3x - 2y - 7 = 0$. Algebraically, $y = 5$ yields $3x - 10 - 7 = 0$, $3x - 17 = 0$, $x = 5\frac{2}{3}$. Graphically (Fig. 6–4), $3x - 2y - 7 = 0$ is equivalent to $-2y = -3x + 7$, or $y = (3/2)x - 7/2$. The graph is the line of slope $3/2$ and y-intercept $-7/2$.

When $y = 5$, $x = 5\frac{2}{3}$. Notice that you can read from the graph the value of x that corresponds to any desired value of y (until the graph runs off the page); also you can read the value of y that corresponds to any desired value of x. However, these values of x or y that you read from the graph depend upon measurement. Their accuracy depends upon the accuracy of the graph.

The algebraic solutions are, by contrast, exact solutions. They depend only upon the properties of real numbers.

Recall that first-degree inequalities can be reduced to equivalent inequalities of the form $ax + b > 0$, $a \neq 0$. Again, consider the graph of $y = ax + b$; the solution set of $ax + b > 0$ is the set of the values of x that make $y = ax + b > 0$ (Fig. 6–5).

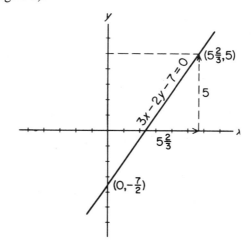

Fig. 6–4.

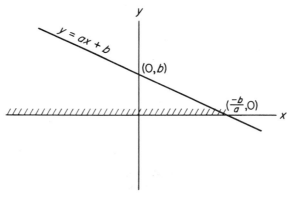

Fig. 6–5.

Each point on the graph to the left of $(-b/a, 0)$ has an x-coordinate that makes y positive. Hence, for this line of negative slope, a, the condition $x < -b/a$ describes the subset of L for which $y = ax + b > 0$. You should draw a second straight line for which the slope a is positive. You will find, for this line, that the condition $x > -b/a$ describes the subset of L for which $y = ax + b > 0$.

EXERCISES §600 (cont.)

6. Draw the graph of $y = 2x - 5$. From the graph, determine the solution set of:

(a) $2x - 5 = 0$ (b) $2x - 5 = 3$
(c) $2x - 5 = 4.5$ (d) $2x - 5 < 0$
(e) $2x - 5 > 0$ (f) $2x - 5 > 7$.

7. Draw the graph of $y = -\frac{3}{4}x + 6$. From the graph, determine the solution set of:

(a) $-\frac{3}{4}x + 6 = 0$ (b) $-\frac{3}{4}x + 6 = 2$
(c) $-\frac{3}{4}x + 6 < 0$ (d) $-\frac{3}{4}x + 6 > 0$
(e) $-\frac{3}{4}x + 6 > 6$ (f) $-\frac{3}{4}x + 6 < 3$.

8. Draw the graphs of $y = 2x - 5$ and $y = -\frac{3}{4}x + 6$ on the same coordinate system. Show how to determine graphically the solution set of the linear equation $2x - 5 = -\frac{3}{4}x + 6$.

9. Solve the inequality $mx + 6 < 2x + 3m$ for x. Show that the solution depends on the parameter, m.

Partial answer: If $m > 2$, then $x < 3$. If $m < 2$, then $x > 3$. What about $m = 2$?

10. Solve $mx - 4 < x(1 - m) - 3$ for x. (*Hint:* The solution depends on whether $m > \frac{1}{2}$, $m = \frac{1}{2}$, or $m < \frac{1}{2}$.)

11. Twice the sum of a number and 3 is equal to 7 more than one half the number. Find the number.

Answer: $\frac{2}{3}$.

12. A boy is now two thirds as old as he will be six years from now. What is his present age?

Answer: 12.

13. A solution contains 6% salt. If the solution weighs 50 grams, how many grams of salt must be added to make the solution 10% salt?

Answer: $2\frac{2}{9}$.

14. Two freight trains start at the same time from two towns 297 miles apart. One train travels 15 mph faster than the other. The trains meet in 3 hr. Find the rate of the faster train.

15. A line has a slope of 3 and passes through the point $(-2,4)$. Since $m = 3$, then $y = mx + b$ becomes $y = 3x + b$. Determine the value of b. (Compare Section 402, page 109.)

601. Second-degree conditions

A second-degree, or quadratic, equation in x is one that can be reduced to an equivalent equation of the form $ax^2 + bx + c = 0$, where $a \neq 0$.

A second-degree inequality in x is one that can be reduced to an equivalent inequality of the form $ax^2 + bx + c > 0$ where $a \neq 0$. The letters a, b, and c are parameters whose range is the set L.

Notice that $a = 0$ makes $ax^2 + bx + c = bx + c$. Hence the expression $ax^2 + bx + c$ reduces to $bx + c$. If $b \neq 0$, the expression $bx + c$ is of degree 1 in x; if $b = 0$, $bx + c = c$ is an expression that is independent of x. In either event the condition is like the ones you studied in Section 600.

We shall discuss equations of degree 2 first; then we shall apply our findings to inequalities of degree 2.

Recall, from Section 404 (page 121), the parabola whose equation is $y = ax^2 + c$. In Fig. 6–6 we have pictured $y = ax^2 + c$ with $a > 0$ and $c < 0$. Notice that this parabola crosses the x-axis at two points that are symmetrically placed to the left and right of the y-axis. These are the points whose y-coordinates are zero. Their x-coordinates satisfy the equation $0 = ax^2 + c$, or $ax^2 + c = 0$.

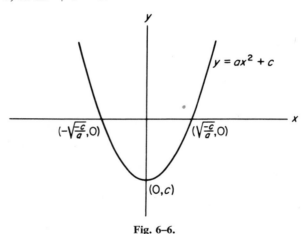

Fig. 6–6.

If $ax^2 + c = 0$, then $ax^2 = -c$, and $x^2 = -c/a$. There are three possibilities:

(a) If $-c/a > 0$, then $x^2 = -c/a \Leftrightarrow x = \sqrt{-c/a}$ or $x = -\sqrt{-c/a}$
(b) If $-c/a = 0$, then $x^2 = -c/a \Leftrightarrow x = 0$
(c) If $-c/a < 0$, then $x^2 = -c/a \Leftrightarrow x = i\sqrt{c/a}$ or $x = -i\sqrt{c/a}$.

Figure 6–6 illustrates case (a):

$$a > 0 \quad \text{and} \quad c < 0 \Rightarrow c/a < 0 \Rightarrow -c/a > 0.$$

You should prepare a second graph with $a < 0$ and $c > 0$; again $-c/a > 0$, and the graph crosses the x-axis at $(\sqrt{-c/a},0)$ and $(-\sqrt{-c/a},0)$. Notice that

$$[-c/a > 0] \Leftrightarrow [(a > 0 \text{ and } c < 0) \text{ or } (a < 0 \text{ and } c > 0)].$$

Figure 6–7 illustrates case (b). We pictured $y = ax^2 + c$ with $a < 0$ and $c = 0$;

$$a < 0 \quad \text{and} \quad c = 0 \Rightarrow -c/a = 0;$$

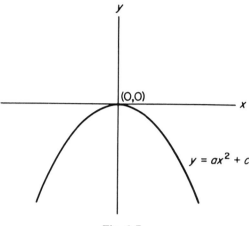

Fig. 6–7.

the graph *touches* the x-axis at $(0,0)$. You should prepare a second graph with $a > 0$ and $c = 0$; again $-c/a = 0$, and the graph touches the x-axis at $(0,0)$. Notice that

$$[-c/a = 0] \Leftrightarrow [(a > 0 \text{ and } c = 0) \text{ or } (a < 0 \text{ and } c = 0)].$$

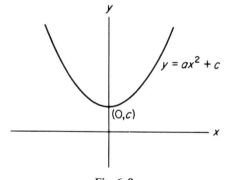

Fig. 6–8.

Figure 6–8 illustrates case (c). We pictured $y = ax^2 + c$ with $a > 0$ and $c > 0$;

$$a > 0 \quad \text{and} \quad c > 0 \Rightarrow -c/a < 0.$$

The graph does not *intersect* (cross or touch) the x-axis; there is no replacement of x, from the set L, that corresponds to $y = ax^2 + c = 0$. You should prepare a second graph with $a < 0$ and $c < 0$; again $-c/a < 0$, and the graph does not intersect the x-axis; there is no replacement of x, from the set L, that corresponds to $y = ax^2 + c = 0$. Notice that

$$[-c/a < 0] \Leftrightarrow [(a > 0 \text{ and } c > 0) \text{ or } (a < 0 \text{ and } c < 0)].$$

In summary:

When the range of x is L, the solution set of the second-degree equation $ax^2 + c = 0$ is:

    (a)   for $-c/a > 0$, $\{\pm\sqrt{-c/a}\}$ (read $+\sqrt{-c/a}$ or $-\sqrt{-c/a}$)

    (b)   for $-c/a = 0$, $\{0\}$

    (c)   for $-c/a < 0$, $\{\ \ \}$.

When the range of x is C, the solution set of the second-degree equation $ax^2 + c = 0$ is:

    (a)   for $-c/a > 0$, $\{\pm\sqrt{-c/a} + 0i\}$

    (b)   for $-c/a = 0$, $\{0 + 0i\}$

    (c)   for $-c/a < 0$, $\{0 \pm \sqrt{c/a} \cdot i\}$.

In cases (a) and (b) the solutions are real numbers; in case (c) the solutions are imaginary numbers.

Notice that the graph of $y = ax^2 + c$ crosses the x-axis in two points, or touches the x-axis at one point, or does not intersect the x-axis; the second-degree condition $ax^2 + c = 0$ has two real solutions, or one real solution, or two imaginary solutions.

When the graph of $y = ax^2 + c$ crosses the x-axis at two points we shall speak of the x-axis as a *secant* to the parabola. When $c = 0$ the two points of intersection coincide, and we call the x-axis a *tangent* to the parabola.

It is sometimes convenient to think of the tangent as crossing the parabola at two coincident points. To be consistent, you think of the solution set of $ax^2 = 0$ as $\{x \mid ax^2 = 0\} = \{\pm 0\}$. With this agreement about the solutions, or *roots*, of $ax^2 = 0$, we may say that every second-degree equation of the form $ax^2 + c = 0$ has exactly two roots. These two roots may be either real and unequal, or real and equal, or imaginary and unequal.

Here are some examples to help you interpret questions about second-degree equations of the form $ax^2 + c = 0$ as questions about the graphs of parabolas whose equations take the form $y = ax^2 + c$. The examples also call for interpreting questions about parabolas as questions about second-degree equations in one unknown.

(1) Solve the equation $3x^2 + 2 = x^2 + 20$. Algebraically, $3x^2 + 2 = x^2 + 20$, $2x^2 = 18$, $x^2 = 9$, $x = \pm 3$. The equation $3x^2 + 2 = x^2 + 20$ is equivalent to the equation $x^2 - 9 = 0$. Examine the graph of $y = x^2 - 9$ (Fig. 6–9). The parabola whose equation is $y = x^2 - 9$ has its *vertex* at $(0, -9)$; it has x-intercepts 3 and -3. Apart from the difficulty of accuracy

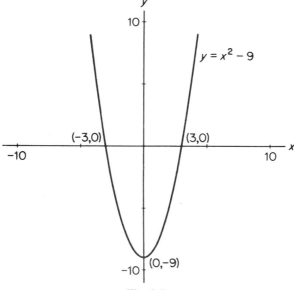

Fig. 6–9.

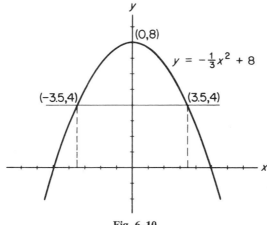

Fig. 6–10.

in measurements, you could solve the equation $3x^2 + 2 = x^2 + 20$ by reading the x-intercepts of the graph of $y = x^2 - 9$.

(2) What values of x correspond to $y = 4$ in the graph of $y = -\frac{1}{3}x^2 + 8$? To answer this question directly, you can draw a graph (Fig. 6–10). Then you can read the x-coordinates of the two points on the graph where $y = 4$; that is, you can read the x-coordinates of the two points of intersection of the graphs of $y = -\frac{1}{3}x^2 + 8$ and $y = 4$. They appear to be about ± 3.5. Of

course the accuracy of this solution depends upon the accuracy of your measurements.

You can also interpret this question as the algebraic question, "What are the roots of the equation $4 = -\frac{1}{3}x^2 + 8$?" This equation is equivalent to $\frac{1}{3}x^2 = 4$, $x^2 = 12$, $x = \pm 2\sqrt{3}$. The exact coordinates of the two points of intersection are $(2\sqrt{3}, 4)$ and $(-2\sqrt{3}, 4)$. The exact values of x that correspond to $y = 4$ are $x = \pm 2\sqrt{3}$.

(3) What values of x correspond to $y = -2$ in the graph of $y = 3x^2 + 1$? The algebraic interpretation of this question is, "What are the roots of the equation $-2 = 3x^2 + 1$?" This equation is equivalent to $3x^2 = -3$, $x^2 = -1$, $x = \pm i$. Since the equation has imaginary roots, we conclude that no real values of x correspond to $y = -2$ in the graph of $y = 3x^2 + 1$. Now study Fig. 6–11. The line $y = -2$ does not intersect the parabola $y = 3x^2 + 1$.

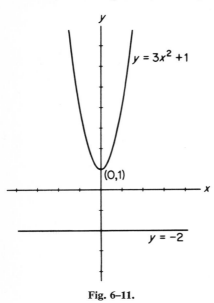

Fig. 6–11.

$y = 3x^2 + 1$

$(0,1)$

$y = -2$

EXERCISES §601

1. For each equation of the form $ax^2 + c = 0$, determine the real roots graphically by drawing the graph of the associated second-degree condition, $y = ax^2 + c$.

(a) $x^2 - 8 = 0$ (b) $\frac{1}{2}x^2 - 6 = 0$

(c) $x^2 + 4 = 0$ (d) $-\frac{1}{4}x^2 + 9 = 0$

(e) $-2x^2 + 7 = 0$ (f) $-x^2 - 1 = 0$.

2. Solve each equation in Exercise 1 algebraically.

3. Solve the quadratic equation $-\frac{1}{2}x^2 + 8 = \frac{1}{4}x^2 + 1$ in three different ways, as follows:

(a) Reduce to the form $ax^2 + c = 0$; then determine the solution from the graph of $y = ax^2 + c$.

(b) Graph $y = -\frac{1}{2}x^2 + 8$ and $y = \frac{1}{4}x^2 + 1$ on the same coordinate system. The solutions of the given equation will be the x-coordinates of the points of intersection. (Why?)

(c) Solve algebraically and compare with the approximate results obtained by the first two methods.

4. Recall, from Section 404, the language of direct variation as the square. The area (A) of a screen lighted by a movie projector varies as the square of the distance (d) from the projector to the screen. Given that $A = 6$ when $d = 10$, find the value of d that corresponds to $A = 15$.

Hint: $A = kd^2$ and the number-pair (10,6) yield the condition $10 = 36k$; hence $k = \frac{10}{36}$. $A = \frac{10}{36}d^2$ and $A = 15$ yield $d = 3\sqrt{6}$. Notice that the range of d is the set of non-negative real numbers. This excludes the solution $-3\sqrt{6}$.

5. When you throw a ball into the air with an initial velocity upward of 96 ft per second, it rises to a height of approximately 144 ft in 3 sec, then falls back to the ground. The formula

$$s = 144 - 16t^2$$

gives the height above the ground where the range of t (sec) is $-3 \le t \le 3$. The ball is thrown at time $t = -3$, reaches its highest point at time $t = 0$, and strikes the ground at time $t = 3$.

(a) Find the value of s that corresponds to each value of t: $t = -2.5$, -1.5, -0.5, 0.5, 1.5, 2.5.

(b) Find the values of t that correspond to each value of s: $s = 20$, 40, 60, 80, 100, 120, 140. What do facts like $s = 20 \Rightarrow t = \sqrt{31}/2$ or $t = -\sqrt{31}/2$ mean in this problem?

So far we have worked with equations of the form $ax^2 + c = 0$, and with the corresponding parabolas whose equations take the form $y = ax^2 + c$. To solve the *general quadratic* equation $ax^2 + bx + c = 0$, $a \ne 0$, we reduce it to an equivalent equation of the form $X^2 = C$; then we use what we already know about this equation.

Recall that $(x + h)^2 = x^2 + 2hx + h^2$. A *perfect-square trinomial* [like $x^2 + 2hx + h^2$] is one that can be rewritten as the *square of a binomial* [like $(x + h)^2$]. For example,

$$x^2 + 10x + 25 = (x + 5)^2$$

and

$$x^2 + 7x + \frac{49}{4} = \left(x + \frac{7}{2}\right)^2.$$

Notice the form of the perfect-square trinomial, $x^2 + 2hx + h^2$; the coefficient of x is $2h$; the term that is independent of x is h^2.

You can use your knowledge of the form of the perfect-square trinomial to construct perfect-square trinomials. For example:

If $x^2 + 10x = 0$, then $(x^2 + 10x + 25) = 25$, or $(x + 5)^2 = 25$.
If $x^2 + 6x + 2 = 0$, then $(x^2 + 6x + 9) - 7 = 0$, or $(x + 3)^2 = 7$.
If $5x^2 + 15x + 8 = 0$, then $(x^2 + 3x) = -\frac{8}{5}$,
$x^2 + 3x + (\frac{3}{2})^2 = \frac{9}{4} - \frac{8}{5}$, or $(x + \frac{3}{2})^2 = \frac{13}{20}$.

Notice what you can do by constructing a perfect-square trinomial! You begin with an equation like $x^2 + 10x = 0$; you reduce it to an equivalent equation like $(x + 5)^2 = 25$. The equation now has the form $X^2 = C$, where

$X = x + 5$ and $C = 25$; now you solve the equation $X^2 = C$ by methods you have already learned. In this instance,

$$X^2 = 25 \Leftrightarrow X = 5 \quad \text{or} \quad X = -5;$$

that is, $(x + 5)^2 = 25 \Leftrightarrow x + 5 = 5 \quad \text{or} \quad x + 5 = -5;$

that is, $x^2 + 10x = 0 \Leftrightarrow x = 0 \quad \text{or} \quad x = -10.$

Similarly, you rewrite the equation

$$5x^2 + 15x + 8 = 0 \quad \text{as} \quad (x + \tfrac{3}{2})^2 = \tfrac{13}{20}.$$

Its roots are the roots of

$$x + \frac{3}{2} = \pm \sqrt{\frac{13}{20}} = \pm \sqrt{\frac{65}{100}} = \pm \frac{\sqrt{65}}{10};$$

hence $x = -\dfrac{3}{2} + \dfrac{\sqrt{65}}{10} \quad \text{or} \quad x = -\dfrac{3}{2} - \dfrac{\sqrt{65}}{10}.$

You are now ready to solve the general quadratic equation: If $ax^2 + bx + c = 0$, and $a \neq 0$, then

$$\left(x^2 + \frac{b}{a} \cdot x\right) = -\frac{c}{a}$$

$$x^2 + \frac{b}{a} \cdot x + \left(\frac{b}{2a}\right)^2 = \frac{b^2}{4a^2} - \frac{c}{a}$$

$$\left(x + \frac{b}{2a}\right)^2 = \frac{b^2}{4a^2} - \frac{4ac}{4a^2}$$

$$= \frac{(b^2 - 4ac)}{4a^2}.$$

This last equation has the form $X^2 = C$, where $X = x + b/2a$, and $C = (b^2 - 4ac)/4a^2$.

It is convenient to introduce the symbol $\Delta = b^2 - 4ac$; mathematicians call Δ the *discriminant* of the quadratic equation $ax^2 + bx + c = 0$.

There are three possibilities:

     (a)   If $\Delta > 0$, then $ax^2 + bx + c = 0 \Leftrightarrow x + \dfrac{b}{2a} = \pm \dfrac{\sqrt{\Delta}}{2a}.$

     (b)   If $\Delta = 0$, then $ax^2 + bx + c = 0 \Leftrightarrow x + \dfrac{b}{2a} = \pm 0.$

     (c)   If $\Delta < 0$, then $ax^2 + bx + c = 0 \Leftrightarrow x + \dfrac{b}{2a} = \pm \dfrac{\sqrt{-\Delta}}{2a} \cdot i.$

Thus the discriminant Δ tells you whether the quadratic has roots that are

     (a)   real and unequal ($\Delta > 0$)
     (b)   real and equal ($\Delta = 0$)
     (c)   imaginary and unequal ($\Delta < 0$).

We summarize these important results: The general quadratic equation is $ax^2 + bx + c = 0$, $a \neq 0$; for particular values of the parameters a, b, and c, you can calculate the discriminant

I $$\Delta = b^2 - 4ac;$$

then

II $$\{x \mid ax^2 + bx + c = 0 \text{ and } \Delta \geq 0\} = \left\{ \frac{-b}{2a} \pm \frac{\sqrt{\Delta}}{2a} \right\}$$

III $$\{x \mid ax^2 + bx + c = 0 \text{ and } \Delta < 0\} = \left\{ \frac{-b}{2a} \pm \frac{\sqrt{-\Delta}}{2a} \cdot i \right\}.$$

We shall return to the graphical interpretation of these results. But first, you should study some examples of their application to solve second-degree equations in one unknown:

(4) Solve the equation $3x^2 - 4x + 5 = 0$. This equation is an instance of the general quadratic equation, $ax^2 + bx + c = 0$. Since this equation is $3x^2 + (-4)x + 5 = 0$, $a = 3$, $b = (-4)$, and $c = 5$. Hence, by I,

$$\Delta = b^2 - 4ac = 16 - 4(3)(5) = -44.$$

Since $\Delta < 0$, we use III and conclude

$$\{x \mid 3x^2 - 4x + 5 = 0\} = \left\{ \frac{-(-4)}{6} \pm \frac{\sqrt{44}}{6} \cdot i \right\}$$

$$= \left\{ \frac{2}{3} \pm \frac{\sqrt{11}}{3} \cdot i \right\}.$$

Notice that the equation $3x^2 - 4x + 5 = 0$ has two unequal imaginary roots.

(5) Solve the equation $5x^2 - 3x - 2 = 0$. Here $a = 5$, $b = -3$, and $c = -2$. Hence

$$\Delta = 9 - 4(5)(-2) = 49.$$

Since $\Delta \geq 0$, we use II and conclude

$$\{x \mid 5x^2 - 3x - 2 = 0\} = \left\{ \frac{-(-3)}{10} \pm \frac{\sqrt{49}}{10} \right\}$$

$$= \left\{ 1, \frac{-2}{5} \right\}.$$

Notice that the equation $5x^2 - 3x - 2 = 0$ has two roots that are real and unequal.

The following exercises provide practice in constructing perfect-square trinomials and in applying the formulas for the solution set of the general quadratic equation. Although you can use the formulas to find the solution set of each instance of the general quadratic equation, the technique of "completing the square" is often useful for other purposes. Hence it is worthwhile in itself.

EXERCISES §601 (cont.)

6. Solve each quadratic equation by constructing a perfect-square trinomial. (See hint, below, for form of presentation.)

(a) $x^2 + 6x + 5 = 0$ (b) $x^2 - 4x + 1 = 0$

(c) $x^2 - x - 6 = 0$ (d) $3x^2 + 5x - 2 = 0$

(e) $x^2 + x + \frac{1}{4} = 0$ (f) $5x^2 - 11x + 3 = 0$

(g) $x^2 - 2x + 5 = 0$ (h) $3x^2 + 5x + 3 = 0.$

Hint for part (a):   If $x^2 + 6x + 5 = 0$, then

$$x^2 + 6x + \left(\frac{6}{2}\right)^2 = \left(\frac{6}{2}\right)^2 - 5$$

$$(x + 3)^2 = 4$$

$$x + 3 = 2 \quad \text{or} \quad x + 3 = -2$$

$$x = -1 \quad \text{or} \quad x = -5.$$

Hence $x^2 + 6x + 5 = 0 \Rightarrow (x = -1 \quad \text{or} \quad x = -5).$

The steps are clearly reversible. Thus if $(x = -1$ or $x = -5)$, then

$$x + 3 = 2 \quad \text{or} \quad x + 3 = -2.$$

In either event, $(x + 3)^2 = 4$

and $x^2 + 6x + 5 = 0.$

Hence $x^2 + 6x + 5 = 0 \Leftrightarrow (x = -1$ or $x = -5)$; that is,

$$\{x \mid x^2 + 6x + 5 = 0\} = \{-1, -5\}.$$

Solution sets: (b) $\{2 + \sqrt{3}, 2 - \sqrt{3}\}$;   (e) $\{-\frac{1}{2}\}$;   (g) $\{1 + 2i, 1 - 2i\}$.

7. Apply the appropriate formula to find the solution set of each equation below. Check some of your solutions to verify your calculations. (See hint, below.)

(a) to (h) The equations of Exercise 6.

(i) $8x^2 - 14x + 9 = 0$ (j) $3x^2 + 6x + 4 = 0$

(k) $4 - 3x - x^2 = 0$ (l) $5x - 2x^2 = 3$

(m) $3x^2 = 3x + 7$ (n) $\frac{1}{2}x^2 - 6x - 9 = 0$

(o) $\frac{1}{2} - \frac{1}{4}x = 2x^2$ (p) $x^2 - \sqrt{5}x - 3 = 0$

(q) $\sqrt{2}x^2 - 3x + \sqrt{2} = 0$ (r) $x^2 - 2mx - 4 = 0$

(s) $x^2 + 2x + h = 0$ (t) $x^2 - 4tx + (4t^2 - r) = 0.$

Hint for part (q): If $\sqrt{2}x^2 - 3x + \sqrt{2} = 0$, then

$$\Delta = (-3)^2 - 4(\sqrt{2})(\sqrt{2}) = 1.$$

Since $\Delta \geq 0$, we use II and conclude

$$\{x \mid \sqrt{2}x^2 - 3x + \sqrt{2} = 0\} = \left\{\frac{3}{2\sqrt{2}} \pm \frac{\sqrt{1}}{2\sqrt{2}}\right\} = \{\sqrt{2}, \tfrac{1}{2}\sqrt{2}\}.$$

To check the solution $\frac{1}{2}\sqrt{2}$:

$$x = \frac{1}{2}\sqrt{2} \Rightarrow \sqrt{2}x^2 - 3x + \sqrt{2} = \sqrt{2}(\frac{1}{4} \cdot 2) - \frac{3}{2}\sqrt{2} + \sqrt{2} = 0.$$

Solution sets: (i) $\left\{\frac{7}{8} \pm \frac{\sqrt{23}}{8}i\right\}$; (l) $\left\{1, \frac{3}{2}\right\}$; (m) $\left\{\frac{1}{2} \pm \frac{1}{6}\sqrt{93}\right\}$;

(r) $\{m \pm \sqrt{m^2 + 4} \mid m \in L\}$.

8. If $ax^2 + bx + c$ is easy to factor into two linear expressions, the roots of the corresponding quadratic equation can be found quickly by equating each factor to zero. As an illustration, consider the equation $x^2 - 2x - 15 = 0$. Since $x^2 - 2x - 15 = (x + 3)(x - 5)$ is an identity, $(x + 3)(x - 5) = 0$ is equivalent to the given equation. But $(x + 3)(x - 5) = 0 \Leftrightarrow x + 3 = 0$ or $x - 5 = 0$, by theorem T 1 (page 70). Hence $x = -3$ or $x = 5$. The solution set is $\{-3,5\}$. Solve the following equations by factoring.

(a) $x^2 + 3x - 4 = 0$ (b) $x^2 - 5x - 14 = 0$
(c) $x^2 + 7x + 12 = 0$ (d) $x^2 + 5x = 0$
(e) $x^2 = 8x$ (f) $3x^2 + 2x - 1 = 0$
(g) $4x^2 - 4x - 3 = 0$ (h) $x^2 - mx - 2x + 2m = 0$.

9. Without solving the equation, decide whether the roots are: (1) real and unequal; (2) real and equal; (3) unequal imaginary numbers.

(a) $x^2 - 4x + 4 = 0$ (b) $2x^2 + 5x - 1 = 0$
(c) $7x^2 + x = 0$ (d) $3x^2 + 2x + 1/3 = 0$
(e) $x^2 = 5x - 7$ (f) $x^2 + x + 1 = 0$
(g) $5x^2 - 5x + 6 = 0$ (h) $4x^2 - 5x - 4 = 0$
(i) $nx^2 - mx - n = 0$ (m and n are real numbers).

Hint for part (e): $x^2 = 5x - 7 \Leftrightarrow x^2 - 5x + 7 = 0$.

Hence $\Delta = (-5)^2 - 4(1)(7) < 0$. The roots are unequal imaginary numbers.

10. The product of two consecutive integers is 272. Find the numbers.

11. The area of a rectangle is 12 sq ft and its perimeter is 19 ft. Find the length and width.

12. If an object is thrown straight up from the ground with an initial velocity of 112 ft per second, its distance in feet, h, above the ground after t seconds (neglecting air resistance) is given by the formula $h = -16t^2 + 112t$.

(a) At what times will the object be 160 ft above the ground?
(b) At what time will the object reach its highest point? How high will it go?
(c) How many seconds will have elapsed when the object returns to the ground?

Answers: (a) 2 sec, 5 sec; (b) 3.5 sec, 196 ft; (c) 7 sec.

13. Find the coordinates of the points of intersection of the parabola $y = \frac{1}{2}x^2 - 3x + 5$ and the line $y = \frac{1}{2}x + 2$.

Answer: (6,5) and (1,2½).

14. The sum of two numbers is 4 and their product is -1. What are the numbers?

(6) Solve the equation $5x^2 - 3x - 2 = 0$. To solve example (5), above, by graphical methods, you need to graph the equation $y = 5x^2 - 3x - 2$. We do this now, by constructing a perfect-square trinomial in x:

$$y + 2 = 5(x^2 - \tfrac{3}{5}x \qquad)$$
$$y + 2 + 5(\tfrac{3}{10})^2 = 5[x^2 - \tfrac{3}{5}x + (\tfrac{3}{10})^2]$$
$$y + \tfrac{49}{20} = 5(x - \tfrac{3}{10})^2.$$

Recall, from Section 404 (page 122), that the equation $y + \tfrac{49}{20} = 5(x - \tfrac{3}{10})^2$ represents a parabola with its vertex at $(\tfrac{3}{10}, -\tfrac{49}{20})$ (see Fig. 6–12). Notice that the x-intercepts of the graph are 1 and $-2/5$. These are the roots of the equation $5x^2 - 3x - 2 = 0$, as found in Example (5) above.

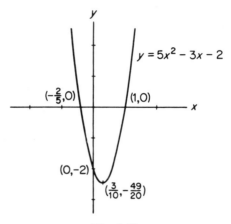

Fig. 6–12.

To solve the equation $ax^2 + bx + c = 0$ by graphical methods, you can graph the equation $y = ax^2 + bx + c$. Of course you can not do this until you assign definite values to the parameters a, b, and c. Still, you can construct a perfect-square trinomial in x and solve the problem up to a point:

$$y - c = a\left(x^2 + \frac{b}{a} \cdot x \qquad \right)$$
$$y - c + a\left(\frac{b^2}{4a^2}\right) = a\left[x^2 + \frac{b}{a} \cdot x + \left(\frac{b}{2a}\right)^2\right]$$
$$y - \frac{4ac}{4a} + \frac{b^2}{4a} = a\left(x + \frac{b}{2a}\right)^2$$
$$y - \frac{4ac - b^2}{4a} = a\left(x + \frac{b}{2a}\right)^2$$

This is a parabola with its vertex at $\left(\dfrac{-b}{2a}, \dfrac{4ac - b^2}{4a}\right)$.

This formula for finding the vertex of the parabola $y = ax^2 + bx + c$ may look discouragingly complicated. It really is not, as the following examples will show.

(7) Graph the parabola $y = 5x^2 - 3x - 2$. (This is the same parabola we graphed before; but now we can do the job more efficiently.) Compare the equations $y = ax^2 + bx + c$ and $y = 5x^2 - 3x - 2$. Notice that $a = 5$, $b = -3$, and $c = -2$. The x-coordinate of the vertex is $-b/2a = -(-3)/10 = 3/10$. You can find the y-coordinate of the vertex by the formula $(4ac - b^2)/4a = (-40 - 9)/20 = -49/20$. However, it is usually easier to substitute in the equation of the parabola as follows: Every point on the parabola has coordinates that satisfy the equation $y = 5x^2 - 3x - 2$; at the vertex, $x = 3/10$; hence the y-coordinate of the vertex is $y = 5(3/10)^2 - 3(3/10) - 2 = -49/20$. Hence the vertex is $(3/10, -49/20)$.

In the equation $y = 5x^2 - 3x - 2$, when $x = 0$, $y = -2$. Hence the y-intercept of the parabola is -2.

Usually the coordinates of the vertex, together with the y-intercept are enough to enable you to sketch the graph of the parabola (see Fig. 6–12). If not, you can calculate the coordinates of a few more points.

(8) Graph the parabola $y = 3x^2 - 4x + 5$. Here $a = 3$, $b = -4$, and $c = 5$. The x-coordinate of the vertex is $-b/2a = 4/6 = 2/3$. To find the y-coordinate of the vertex by substitution, $y = 3(2/3)^2 - 4(2/3) + 5 = 11/3$. Hence the vertex of the parabola is $(2/3, 11/3)$.

When $x = 0$, $y = 5$. Hence the y-intercept of the parabola is 5 (see Fig. 6–13). The x-intercepts of the graph are clearly imaginary. Hence the equation $3x^2 - 4x + 5 = 0$ has imaginary roots. Refer to Example (4), page 237, for the algebraic way to establish this same fact.

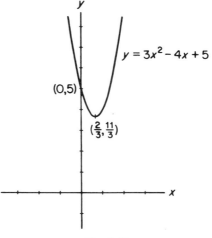

$y = 3x^2 - 4x + 5$

$(0,5)$

$(\frac{2}{3}, \frac{11}{3})$

Fig. 6–13.

Notice, once again, how you can translate questions about graphs into algebraic equations and vice versa. The following example illustrates this further.

(9) For what values of x does $y = 3$ in the graph of $y = -3x^2 + 2x + 7$? In the graphical solution (Fig. 6–14) we find the x-coordinate of the vertex first: $-b/2a = -2/-6 = 1/3$. When $x = 1/3$, $y = -3(1/9) + 2/3 + 7 = 7\frac{1}{3}$. Hence the vertex is $(\frac{1}{3}, 7\frac{1}{3})$; the y-intercept is 7; also $x = 2$ yields $y = -1$. It is not easy to read the x-coordinates of the two points where $y = 3$.

In the algebraic solution, we let $y = 3$ and solve the equation $3 = -3x^2 + 2x + 7$ for x. For the equation $3x^2 - 2x - 4 = 0$,

$$\Delta = 4 + 48 = 52.$$

We use II, and conclude

$$\{x \mid 3x^2 - 2x - 4 = 0\} = \left\{\frac{2}{6} \pm \frac{\sqrt{52}}{6}\right\} = \left\{\frac{1}{3} \pm \frac{\sqrt{13}}{3}\right\}.$$

The required values of x are $1/3 + \sqrt{13}/3$ and $1/3 - \sqrt{13}/3$.

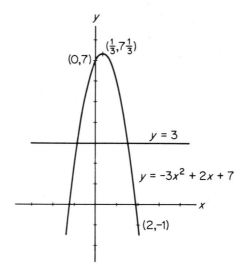

Fig. 6–14.

Graphs are especially convenient when you solve second-degree inequalities. Consider, for example, the inequality $2x^2 - 3x + 4 > 0$. We begin with the graph of $y = 2x^2 - 3x + 4$. This is the parabola, with vertex $(\frac{3}{4}, 2\frac{7}{8})$ and y-intercept 4. Notice in Fig. 6–15 that $y = 2x^2 - 3x + 4 > 0$ for all real values of x. The graph shows the result clearly and saves you some careful algebraic reasoning. The solution set, $\{x \mid 2x^2 - 3x + 4 > 0\} = L$.

Now consider some further examples of solutions of second-degree inequalities.

(10) Solve for x the inequality $2x^2 - 3x + 4 \leq 0$. Figure 6–15 shows that no real value of x makes $y = 2x^2 - 3x + 4 \leq 0$. Hence this sentence defines the null set; $\{x \mid 2x^2 - 3x + 4 \leq 0\} = \{\ \}$.

(11) Solve the inequality $2x^2 - 3x - 4 < 0$ for x. Figure 6–16 shows the parabola $y = 2x^2 - 3x - 4$ with vertex $(\frac{3}{4}, -5\frac{1}{8})$ and y-intercept -4. It is not easy to read the x-coordinates of the two points where the parabola crosses the x-axis. To find these two points exactly, you reduce the equation

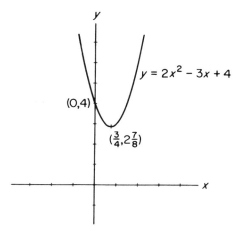

$y = 2x^2 - 3x + 4$

$(0,4)$

$(\frac{3}{4}, 2\frac{7}{8})$

Fig. 6–15.

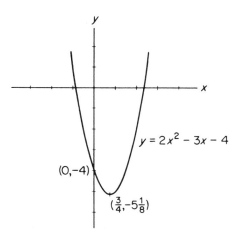

$y = 2x^2 - 3x - 4$

$(0,-4)$

$(\frac{3}{4}, -5\frac{1}{8})$

Fig. 6–16.

$2x^2 - 3x - 4 = 0$ to the equivalent condition $x = 3/4 \pm \sqrt{41}/4$. Then you use the graph to conclude that

$$\{x \mid 2x^2 - 3x - 4 < 0\} = \left\{x \;\middle|\; \frac{3}{4} - \frac{\sqrt{41}}{4} < x < \frac{3}{4} + \frac{\sqrt{41}}{4}\right\}.$$

Notice how the graph helps you to visualize the solution of this inequality. (12) Solve the inequality $2x^2 - 3x - 4 > 0$ for x. Figure 6–16 shows that

$$\{x \mid 2x^2 - 3x - 4 > 0\} = \left\{x \;\middle|\; x < \frac{3}{4} - \frac{\sqrt{41}}{4} \quad \text{or} \quad x > \frac{3}{4} + \frac{\sqrt{41}}{4}\right\}.$$

EXERCISES §601 (cont.)

15. (a) From the graph of $y = x^2 - 3x - 3$, estimate the roots of

$$x^2 - 3x - 3 = 0.$$

(b) Determine the roots algebraically and compare results.

16. Without graphing, determine the coordinates of the vertex of each parabola. State whether the parabola opens up or down.

(a) $y = x^2 + 6x + 2$ (b) $y = 2x^2 - 4x + 1$
(c) $y = -5x^2 + x - 2$ (d) $y = -\frac{1}{4}x^2 - 3x + 7$
(e) $y = x^2 + x + 1$ (f) $y = -4x^2 + 4x - 1$.

Answers: (a) $(-3, -7)$, up;   (d) $(-6, 16)$, down.

17. Use the coordinates of the vertex, the y-intercept, and other points if necessary, to sketch each parabola of Exercise 16. Estimate the roots of the corresponding equation (obtained by replacing y by zero) from the graph; then check your results by finding the exact roots algebraically.

Answers: (a) $\{-5.5, -.5\}$;   (d) $\{2, -14\}$;   (e) no real roots.

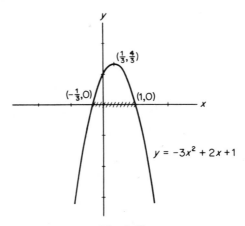

Fig. 6–17.

18. Solve each inequality. Combine graphic and algebraic methods to find the solution set for each condition. (See hint, below.)

(a) $x^2 - x - 6 < 0$ (b) $x^2 - x - 6 > 0$
(c) $x^2 + 3x - 5 < 0$ (d) $x^2 - x + \frac{1}{4} \leq 0$
(e) $2x^2 + 5x - 3 > 0$ (f) $-3x^2 + 2x + 1 > 0$
(g) $2x^2 - x - 2 < 0$ (h) $x^2 - x + 1 > 0$.

Hint for part (f): The graph of $y = -3x^2 + 2x + 1$ is shown in Fig. 6–17. The roots of $-3x^2 + 2x + 1 = 0$ are 1 and $-\frac{1}{3}$. From the graph,

$$\{x \mid y = -3x^2 + 2x + 1 > 0\} = \{x \mid -\tfrac{1}{3} < x < 1\}$$

Answers: (b) $\{x \mid x > 3 \text{ or } x < -2\}$;   (d) $\{\frac{1}{2}\}$;   (h) $\{ \ \}$.

19. Find the coordinates of the points where the line $y = -2$ intersects the parabola $y = -3x^2 + 2x + 1$.

20. Find the coordinates of the points where the line $y = -2$ intersects the parabola $y = 3x^2 + 2x + 1$.

We close this discussion of second-degree conditions in one unknown with a further look at the roots of the general quadratic equation $ax^2 + bx + c = 0$, $a \neq 0$. We symbolize these two roots by x_1 and x_2:

$$\text{When } \Delta \geq 0, \quad x_1 = -\frac{b}{2a} + \frac{\sqrt{\Delta}}{2a}, \quad x_2 = -\frac{b}{2a} - \frac{\sqrt{\Delta}}{2a}$$

$$\text{When } \Delta < 0, \quad x_1 = -\frac{b}{2a} + \frac{\sqrt{-\Delta}}{2a} \cdot i, \quad x_2 = -\frac{b}{2a} - \frac{\sqrt{-\Delta}}{2a} \cdot i$$

x_1 and x_2 are real and unequal if and only if $\Delta > 0$; then the parabola $y = ax^2 + bx + c$ crosses the x-axis at two distinct points.

x_1 and x_2 are real and equal if and only if $\Delta = 0$; then the parabola $y = ax^2 + bx + c$ is tangent to (touches) the x-axis at two coincident points.

x_1 and x_2 are imaginary and unequal if and only if $\Delta < 0$; then the parabola $y = ax^2 + bx + c$ does not intersect the x-axis.

Notice that
$$x_1 + x_2 = 2\left(-\frac{b}{2a}\right) = -\frac{b}{a},$$

and
$$x_1 x_2 = \frac{b^2}{4a^2} - \frac{\Delta}{4a^2}$$

$$= \frac{b^2}{4a^2} - \frac{b^2 - 4ac}{4a^2}$$

$$= \frac{c}{a}.$$

You should check these formulas for the cases $\Delta \geq 0$ and $\Delta < 0$. They give the sum of the roots $(-b/a)$, and the product of the roots (c/a) of the general quadratic. For example, for the equation

$$2x^2 - 5x + 17 = 0$$

$$x_1 + x_2 = -\frac{(-5)}{2} = 2\tfrac{1}{2}$$

$$x_1 x_2 = \frac{17}{2} = 8\tfrac{1}{2}.$$

You can check these facts by solving $2x^2 - 5x + 17 = 0$ to find its roots x_1 and x_2.

The following exercises suggest ways to use the discriminant, and the formulas for $x_1 + x_2$ and $x_1 x_2$, to save calculation.

EXERCISES §601 (cont.)

21. Without graphing, determine whether each parabola: (1) is tangent to the *x*-axis; (2) crosses the *x*-axis at two distinct points; (3) does not touch the *x*-axis.

(a) $y = 2x^2 + 2x + 1$ (b) $y = 2x^2 + 2x - 1$

(c) $y = 2x^2 + 2x + \frac{1}{2}$ (d) $y = 5x^2 - 7x + 2$

(e) $y = -x^2 - 3x - 1$ (f) $y = -2x^2 + 5x - 4.$

22. What condition must k satisfy in order that the roots have the character indicated?

(a) $x^2 + kx + 9 = 0$, equal   (b) $2x^2 + 3x + k = 0$, equal

(c) $2x^2 + 3x + k = 0$, real   (d) $2x^2 + 3x + k = 0$, imaginary

(e) $2x^2 - kx + k = 0$, real   (f) $2x^2 - kx + k = 0$, imaginary.

Hint for part (d): $(x_1$ and x_2 imaginary$) \Leftrightarrow \Delta = 9 - 8k < 0$. Hence $k > 9/8$.

Hint for part (e): $(x_1$ and x_2 real$) \Leftrightarrow \Delta = k^2 - 8k \geq 0$

$$\{k \mid k^2 - 8k \geq 0\} = \{k \mid k \leq 0 \quad \text{or} \quad k \geq 8\}.$$

23. If x_1 and x_2 are numbers such that $x_1 + x_2 = -b/a$ and $x_1 x_2 = c/a$, show that $a(x - x_1)(x - x_2) = ax^2 + bx + c$ is an identity. (*Hint:* Expand the product on the left side, then replace the sum and product of x_1 and x_2 with $-b/a$ and c/a.)

24. The identity of Exercise 23 implies that every quadratic expression can be factored into linear factors (if you are willing to use imaginary numbers in the factors when they occur). For example, suppose you wish to factor $8x^2 - 8x - 3$. Form the quadratic equation $8x^2 - 8x - 3 = 0$ for the purpose of determining x_1 and x_2: $x_1 = \frac{1}{2} + \frac{1}{4}\sqrt{10}$ and $x_2 = \frac{1}{2} - \frac{1}{4}\sqrt{10}$. Since the roots of the quadratic equation $ax^2 + bx + c = 0$ satisfy the conditions $x_1 + x_2 = -b/a$ and $x_1 x_2 = c/a$, you may use the identity of Exercise 23 and write $8x^2 - 8x - 3 = 8(x - \frac{1}{2} - \frac{1}{4}\sqrt{10})(x - \frac{1}{2} + \frac{1}{4}\sqrt{10})$. Factor each of the following expressions.

(a) $2x^2 - 5x + 2$ (b) $3x^2 - 7x + 3$

(c) $12x^2 + x - 6$ (d) $x^2 - 4x + 13$

(e) $2x^2 + 2x + \frac{1}{2}$ (f) $x^2 + x + 1.$

Answers: (b) $3\left(x - \dfrac{7}{6} - \dfrac{\sqrt{13}}{6}\right)\left(x - \dfrac{7}{6} + \dfrac{\sqrt{13}}{6}\right)$; (d) $(x - 2 - 3i)(x - 2 + 3i)$.

25. Solve the condition $y = ax^2 + bx + c$ for x in terms of y. (Hint: Solve the quadratic equation $ax^2 + bx + (c - y) = 0$ for x.) From your solution, determine what value of y will result in just one value of x. What is this value of x? How is this related to the formulas for the vertex of the parabola derived in this section?

Partial answer: $x = \dfrac{-b \pm \sqrt{b^2 - 4ac + 4ay}}{2a}$

26. Show by direct substitution that $\dfrac{-b + \sqrt{b^2 - 4ac}}{2a}$ satisfies the equation $ax^2 + bx + c = 0$.

27. Show that the *x*-coordinate of the vertex of any parabola $y = ax^2 + bx + c$ that crosses the *x*-axis is the mid-point of the line segment joining the *x*-intercepts.

602. Polynomial conditions and approximation by secant lines

When you look over what we did with first-degree equations ($ax + b = 0$, $a \neq 0$) and second-degree equations ($ax^2 + bx + c = 0$, $a \neq 0$) in Sections 600 and 601, you may expect to study the equation $ax^3 + bx^2 + cx + d = 0$, $a \neq 0$ next. This is the general equation of degree 3 in x, often called the *general cubic*. Then you would expect to study the general equation of degree 4 in x, ($ax^4 + bx^3 + cx^2 + dx + e = 0$, $a \neq 0$) called the *general quartic*. And so on.

As you recall the complexity of the general quadratic equation, as contrasted with the simplicity of the general linear equation, you may not have much enthusiasm for tackling cubics and quartics. If you have these feelings, your mathematical insights are working well. Actually, it is possible to solve cubic and quartic equations in somewhat the same way we solved quadratics. Practically speaking, the formulas become more complicated, and hence less useful. Then, when you come to fifth-degree equations (*quintics*) you encounter new difficulties. Some quintic equations cannot be solved in terms of expressions that involve roots of the coefficients of these equations. The *impossibility proof* was given by a Norwegian mathematician named Abel in 1824.

Mathematicians have developed efficient ways to locate the real roots of equations of degree five and higher, and to evaluate these roots to any desired decimal accuracy. But the methods do not yield formulas like the ones for the solution set of the general quadratic.

Rather than expose you to special methods for solving cubic and quartic equations, we shall proceed at once to more general methods for solving polynomial equations of degree n. These equations take the form $a_n x^n + a_{n-1} x^{n-1} + \ldots + a_2 x^2 + a_1 x + a_0 = 0$, $a_n \neq 0$; n represents an element of the set N of natural numbers; the coefficients $a_n, a_{n-1}, \ldots, a_1, a_0$, are elements of the set L of real numbers.

Notice that $n = 1$ yields the first-degree equation $a_1 x + a_0 = 0$; $n = 2$ yields the second-degree equation $a_2 x^2 + a_1 x + a_0 = 0$; etc. In Sections 603 and 604 we shall explore approximate methods for working with polynomial conditions and the corresponding polynomial functions. In particular, we shall develop methods for evaluating the real roots of polynomial equations to any desired decimal accuracy.

First recall, from Section 402 (page 112), the formula for an equation of a straight line through two given points. In Fig. 6–18, $P_1(x_1, y_1)$ and $P_2(x_2, y_2)$ are the given points. An equation of the line through P_1 and P_2 is

$$y - y_1 = \frac{y_2 - y_1}{x_2 - x_1}(x - x_1).$$

It is convenient to use the symbol Δx for the directed distance $x_2 - x_1$; the Greek letter Δ (delta) suggests the word *difference*, and Δx is a difference

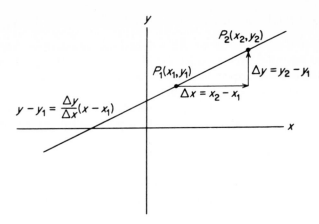

Fig. 6–18.

between two values of x. Similarly $\Delta y = y_2 - y_1$. If $\Delta x \neq 0$, the slope of the line joining P_1 and P_2 is

$$\frac{\Delta y}{\Delta x} = \frac{y_2 - y_1}{x_2 - x_1},$$

and an equation of this line is

$$y - y_1 = \frac{\Delta y}{\Delta x}(x - x_1).$$

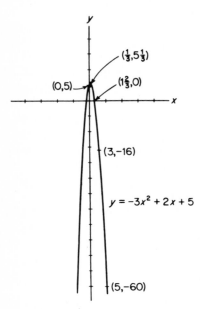

Fig. 6–19.

Since you know how to write the equation of a straight line through two points, you can write the equation of the straight line that joins two points on the graph of a polynomial function. We call such a straight line a *secant* of the curve. For example, you can write the equation of the secant joining the two points on the parabola $y = -3x^2 + 2x + 5$ where $x = 3$ and $x = 5$.

First examine the graph of the parabola (Fig. 6–19). The vertex is $(\frac{1}{3}, 5\frac{1}{3})$; the y-intercept is 5; when $x = 3$, $y = -16$; when $x = 5$, $y = -60$. Notice that there was no need to give you the y-coordinates of the points where $x = 3$ and $x = 5$. You can calculate these y-coordinates by substituting the values $x = 3$ and $x = 5$ in the equation of the parabola.

To get the equation of the secant of the parabola that joins $P_1(3,-16)$ and $P_2(5,-60)$, we calculate Δy and Δx for these two points:

$$\Delta y = (-60) - (-16) = -44$$

$$\Delta x = 5 - 3 = 2.$$

The slope is $\qquad \dfrac{\Delta y}{\Delta x} = \dfrac{-44}{2} = -22.$

An equation of the secant is

$$y + 16 = -22(x - 3), \quad \text{or} \quad y = -22x + 50.$$

Often the secant is a good approximation to the curve itself. Lay a ruler on the two points, $(3,-16)$ and $(5,-60)$, of the graph. Notice that the ruler edge is scarcely distinguishable from the *arc* of the parabola joining $(3,-16)$ and $(5,-60)$.

Suppose you want to find the value of y that corresponds to $x = 3.6$ on the parabola $y = -3x^2 + 2x + 5$. Of course the direct way to do this is to substitute $x = 3.6$ in the equation of the parabola. Thus $y = -3(3.6)^2 + 2(3.6) + 5 = -26.68$. This substitution requires tiresome arithmetic calculations, even when you use a table of squares to find $(3.6)^2 = 12.96$. You can avoid some of the calculation if you are willing to use an approximate value of y. The value of y that corresponds to $x = 3.6$ on the secant is $y = -22(3.6) + 50 = -29.2$. This value of y (using the secant) is a crude approximation to the desired value of y (using the parabola itself). It has the advantage of being easier to calculate.

To find what values of x make $y = 0$, you find the roots of the equation $-3x^2 + 2x + 5 = 0$. These are $5/3$ and -1. You can get a crude approximation to the root $x = 1\frac{2}{3}$ (see Fig. 6–19) by finding out where the secant, $y = -22x + 50$, crosses the x-axis. The x-intercept of the secant satisfies the equation $0 = -22x + 50$; it is $x = 50/22 = 25/11 = 2\frac{3}{11}$. You will learn to improve such approximations as you read further.

The following example will help you to generalize the method for finding the equation of a secant of the graph of a polynomial, and learn to use secants as approximations to the graphs themselves.

Write the equation of the secant that joins the points where $x = -2$ and $x = -1$ on the graph of $y = 3x^5 - 2x^3 + 3x - 4$. The algebraic solution of this problem is straightforward: When $x = -2$, $y = 3(-2)^5 - 2(-2)^3 + 3(-2) - 4 = -90$; when $x = -1$, $y = -8$. Hence the slope of the secant joining $P_1(-2,-90)$ and $P_2(-1,-8)$ is $\dfrac{\Delta y}{\Delta x} = \dfrac{(-8) - (-90)}{(-1) - (-2)} = 82.$

We shall think of the secant as a line through $(-1,-8)$ with slope 82. We use the point $(-1,-8)$ because the numbers are easier to handle. This is the straight line $y + 8 = 82(x + 1)$, or $y = 82x + 74$, of slope 82 and y-intercept 74.

Until you draw a rather accurate graph of the quintic $y = 3x^5 - 2x^3 + 3x - 4$, you have no right to use the secant as an approximation to the graph. As an experiment, however, we calculate the values of y that correspond to $x = -1.5$ on the quintic and on its secant. Thus

$$y \text{ (on the quintic)} = 3(-1.5)^5 - 2(-1.5)^3 + 3(-1.5) - 4$$

$$= -24.53125$$

$$y \text{ (on the secant)} = 82(-1.5) + 74$$

$$= -49.$$

Notice that the y of the secant is *not* a close approximation to the y of the quintic. Notice, however, that the y of the secant is much easier to calculate. Whenever you can safely use the y of the secant as an approximation to the y of a curve, the saving in calculation may make this approximation worth while.

EXERCISES §602

1. For each pair of points, calculate Δx, Δy, and the slope $\Delta y/\Delta x$ ($\Delta x \neq 0$) of the line joining the two points; then write an equation of the line, and reduce your equation to the form $y = mx + b$; then graph the line.

(a) (1,5); (4,4)　　　　　　　　　　(b) (3,−3); (5,2)

(c) (−2,5); (3,7)　　　　　　　　　(d) (−3, −2); (4,−3)

(e) (4,4); (7,4) [$\Delta y = 0$ and $\Delta x \neq 0 \Rightarrow \Delta y/\Delta x = 0$]

(f) (−2,5); (−2,7) [$\Delta y \neq 0$ and $\Delta x = 0 \Rightarrow \Delta y/\Delta x$ is undefined; the line is $x = -2$.]

(g) (3,−2); (3,−2) [$\Delta y = 0$ and $\Delta x = 0 \Rightarrow \Delta y/\Delta x$ is undefined; no line is determined.]

(h) (s,t); (p,q) [restrictions?]　　　　　(i) (p − q,q); (p,p + q) [restrictions?].

2. Given $y = \frac{1}{4}x^2 - 2x + 5$. Determine the coordinates of the points on the curve where $x_1 = 6$ and $x_2 = 10$. What is the slope of the secant through these points? What is the equation of this secant? Draw the graph of the parabola and the secant to check your work.

Answers: (6,2) and (10,10);　2;　$y = 2x - 10$.

3. For each of the algebraic conditions listed below, determine the slope of the secant through the points of the graph whose x coordinates are given. Draw the graph to check your work.

(a) $y = 2x^2$; $x_1 = 1$, $x_2 = 2$　　　　(b) $y = -x^2$; $x_1 = 1$, $x_2 = 4$

(c) $y = -\frac{1}{2}x^2$; $x_1 = \frac{1}{4}$, $x_2 = 2$　　　(d) $y = x^3$; $x_1 = 1$, $x_2 = 2$

(e) $y = \frac{1}{2}x^4 + 3$; $x_1 = 3$, $x_2 = 4$　　(f) $y = \sqrt{x}$; $x_1 = 4$, $x_2 = 9$.

Answers: (a) 6;　(e) 87.5;　(f) .2.

4. Using the same parabola as in Exercise 2, $y = \frac{1}{4}x^2 - 2x + 5$, and $x_1 = 6$, replace x_2 by $8; 4; 2; 1; -1$. For each pair of points, determine the slope and draw the secant to see whether your results look reasonable.

5. Use the equation of the secant of Exercise 2 to estimate y when $x = 9$. Compare with the actual value found from the equation of the parabola.

To continue the discussion of polynomials, it is convenient to use the notation of Section 406 (page 135); we shall use the symbol $p(x)$ to represent a value of a polynomial in x. Thus

$$p(x) = a_n x^n + a_{n-1} x^{n-1} + \ldots + a_1 x + a_0, \quad a_n \neq 0,$$

represents the value of a polynomial, of degree n, that corresponds to a value of x. If, in a particular problem, $p(x) = 3x^3 - 2x + 1$, then

$$p(2) = 3(2)^3 - 2(2) + 1 = 21$$
$$p(a) = 3a^3 - 2a + 1$$

and
$$p(x_1) = 3x_1^3 - 2x_1 + 1.$$

The corresponding function is the set of ordered number-pairs $\{(x, p(x))\}$.

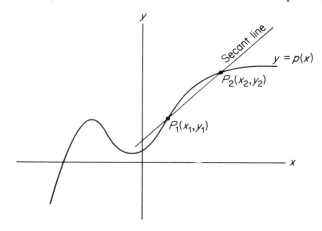

Fig. 6–20.

We return now to the question of how closely the secant approximates the arc of the curve. The closer you choose the point $P_2(x_2, y_2)$ to the point $P_1(x_1, y_1)$ the better the approximation. What happens in the graph when you choose a point P_2 close to the point P_1? It seems evident that the *chord* P_1P_2 is a close approximation to the *arc* P_1P_2 of the graph (Fig. 6–20).

To illustrate this we use the instance $p(x) = x^3$ of the polynomial $p(x)$. From your book of tables, you find:

x	523	524	525
$p(x) = x^3$	143,055,667	143,877,824	144,703,125

The slope of the secant joining $P_1(523,143055667)$ and $P_2(525,144703125)$ is

$$\frac{\Delta y}{\Delta x} = \frac{144,703,125 - 143,055,667}{525 - 523}$$

$$= \frac{1,647,458}{2}$$

$$= 823,729.$$

An equation of the secant is

$$y - 143,055,667 = 823,729(x - 523).$$

When $x = 524$,

$$y = 143,055,667 + 823,729(524 - 523) = 143,879,396.$$

The point $(524,143879396)$ on the secant is an approximation to the point $(524,143877824)$ on the curve. The error in using the y of the secant to estimate the y of the curve is

$$143,879,396 - 143,877,824 = 1572.$$

This is a *relative* error of $1572/143,877,824$, or about $1/100,000$. Such accuracy is sufficient for many practical problems.

This technique of using the secant as an approximation to a curve is exactly the one people use when they *interpolate* values between the entries in a table. We illustrate this by returning to the equation, $y = x^3$. A common way to organize the calculations is to place the values of the variables in columns as follows:

$$
\begin{array}{ccc}
x & & y = p(x) = x^3 \\
\left.\begin{array}{c}\text{-}523.0\text{-} \\ 523.4 \\ \text{-}524.0\text{-}\end{array}\right] \begin{array}{c}0.4 \\ \\ \end{array} \quad 1.0 & \qquad 822,157 & \left[\begin{array}{c}143,055,667 \\ ? \\ 143,877,824\end{array}\right] (822,157)(.4)
\end{array}
$$

You think: As x changes 1 unit, y changes 822,157 units; thus, on the average, y is changing $822,157/1$ times as fast as x in this interval. Then, when x changes .4, a good estimate for the change in y is $(822,157)(.4) = 328,862.8$. Hence, you estimate, when x is .4 more than 523, y is approximately 328,862.8 more than 143,055,667, or

$$p(523.4) = 523.4^3 \doteq 143,055,667 + (822,157)(.4)$$

$$\doteq 143,384,530.$$

Using the language of secants, for $P_1(523,143055667)$ and $P_2(524,143877824)$,

$$\frac{\Delta y}{\Delta x} = \frac{822,157}{1};$$

the equation of the secant is

$$y - 143,055,667 = 822,157(x - 523);$$

for $x = 523.4$,

$$y = 143,055,667 + 822,157(.4) = 143,384,530,$$

as before.

The general pattern for *linear interpolation* follows the form

$$x \qquad\qquad\qquad\qquad y = p(x)$$

$$\Delta x \begin{bmatrix} x_1 \\ x \\ x_2 \end{bmatrix} x - x_1 \qquad\qquad \Delta y \begin{bmatrix} y_1 \\ y_e \\ y_2 \end{bmatrix} y_e - y_1$$

As x changes Δx units, y changes Δy units. On the average, y changes $\Delta y / \Delta x$ times as fast as x in this interval. When x changes from x_1 to x, you may estimate the change in y as $y_e - y_1$, and

$$y_e - y_1 = \frac{\Delta y}{\Delta x}(x - x_1)$$

or

$$y_e = y_1 + \frac{\Delta y}{\Delta x}(x - x_1).$$

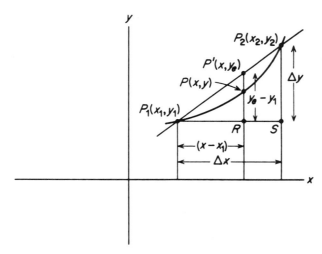

Fig. 6–21.

You can picture this in a graph (Fig. 6–21). If $P'(x, y_e)$ is a point on the secant, in the similar triangles $P_1 R P'$ and $P_1 S P_2$,

$$\frac{y_e - y_1}{x - x_1} = \frac{\Delta y}{\Delta x}.$$

Solving for y_e,

$$y_e = y_1 + \frac{\Delta y}{\Delta x}(x - x_1).$$

Notice that y_e is the y-coordinate of the point P' on the secant; y_e is an estimate of the y-coordinate of the point P on the curve. Mathematicians call this process linear interpolation, because a straight line is used to approximate the curve.

EXERCISES §602 (cont.)

6. Let $p(x) = x^2 - 5x + 10$. Find

(a) $p(1)$ (b) $p(0)$
(c) $p(-2)$ (d) $p(6)$
(e) $p(4)$ (f) $p(6) - p(4)$
(g) $p(x_2)$ (h) $p(t)$
(i) $p(t + h)$ (j) $p(r^2)$.

Answers: (a) 6; (f) 10; (h) $t^2 - 5t + 10$; (i) $(t + h)^2 - 5(t + h) + 10$.

7. Let $p(x) = -\frac{1}{2}x^3 + 3x^2 - 4$. Give the elements of the function $\{(x, p(x))\}$, for $x = 1; 0; -2; 6; 4; t; r^2$.

8. Look up the cubes of 275 and 276 in a book of tables. Estimate the cube of 275.8 by linear interpolation. Compute the exact value of $(275.8)^3$ to check the accuracy of the approximation.

9. Find $\sqrt{842}$ and $\sqrt{843}$ in a book of tables. Estimate $\sqrt{842.3}$ by linear interpolation.

10. Estimate $\sqrt[3]{227.4}$ by linear interpolation.

11. The logarithms of 8.51 and 8.52 can be found in a book of tables. Use these values to estimate the logarithm of 8.517.

12. If an object falls from rest, the number of feet that it falls in t seconds is given by the formula $d = 16t^2$. How far will it fall in 2 sec? How far in 4 sec? What is the *average* speed of the object over the interval from $t_1 = 2$ to $t_2 = 4$? Show that this average speed is, geometrically, the slope of the secant line of the graph of $d = 16t^2$ through the points where $t_1 = 2$ and $t_2 = 4$.

In Section 604 we shall discuss efficient procedures for evaluating real roots of polynomial equations to any desired degree of accuracy. As a preliminary to this discussion, you should apply what you already know about linear interpolation.

Suppose you wish to find the real roots of the polynomial equation $p(x) = 0$; that is, you wish to find the values of x that make $y = 0$ in the graph of $y = p(x)$; that is, you wish to find the *zeros of the function* $\{(x,p(x))\}$, the values of x in the set $\{x \mid p(x) = 0\}$.

Suppose you locate two replacements, x_1 and x_2, of x such that $p(x_1)$ and $p(x_2)$ are of opposite sign. Figure 6–22 will help you to visualize this situation. In this figure, $y_1 = p(x_1) > 0$ and $y_2 = p(x_2) < 0$; in another figure you might have $p(x_1) < 0$ and $p(x_2) > 0$; the important thing is to have $p(x_1)$ and $p(x_2)$ of opposite sign.

Since the graph of $y = p(x)$ is continuous, it must cross the x-axis between P_1 and P_2; that is, there is at least one point $(r,0)$ on the graph, and $x_1 < r < x_2$. Of course the graph may cross the x-axis several times between P_1 and P_2; you can be sure that it crosses the x-axis at least once.

Suppose the secant P_1P_2 crosses the x-axis at $(r_e,0)$; then you may use r_e as an estimate of r. Of course r_e may be a crude approximation for r; but you will learn to improve this approximation by a sequence of repetitions of the process of interpolation.

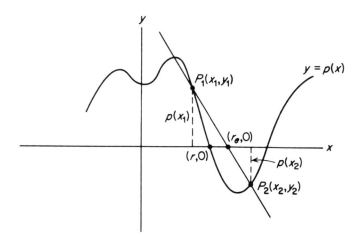

Fig. 6–22.

To calculate r_e we use the secant

$$y - y_1 = \frac{\Delta y}{\Delta x}(x - x_1)$$

and calculate the value $x = r_e$ that corresponds to the replacement $y = 0$; then

$$0 - y_1 = \frac{\Delta y}{\Delta x}(r_e - x_1)$$

and

$$r_e = x_1 - \frac{1}{\Delta y/\Delta x} \cdot y_1.$$

Since $y_1 = p(x_1)$,

I

$$r_e = x_1 - \frac{1}{\Delta y/\Delta x} p(x_1).$$

Formula I expresses r_e in terms of $x_1, p(x_1)$, and the slope of the secant P_1P_2.
We illustrate this procedure for the polynomial $p(x) = -5x^3 - 17x^2 + 24$. The table lists five elements of the function $\{(x,p(x))\}$:

x	-2	-1	0	1	2
$p(x)$	-4	12	24	2	-84

Notice that $p(-2)$ and $p(-1)$ are of opposite sign; also, $p(1)$ and $p(2)$ are of opposite sign. Hence there is at least one real root of $p(x) = 0$ in the range $-2 < x < -1$, and at least one real root of $p(x) = 0$ in the range $1 < x < 2$.

We proceed to find successive approximations for the real root of $p(x) = 0$ in the range $1 < x < 2$. We leave it for you (Exercise 13) to find successive approximations for the real root of $p(x) = 0$ in the range $-2 < x < -1$.

For $P_1(1,2)$ and $P_2(2,-84)$, $x_1 = 1$, $p(x_1) = 2$, $\Delta y/\Delta x = -86/1$. Hence

$$r_e = 1 - \frac{1}{-86}(2) = 1 + \frac{1}{43} \doteq 1.02.$$

Take $r_e \doteq 1.02$ as a first approximation for the real root r of $p(x) = 0$ in the range $1 < r < 2$. To continue the process, calculate

$$p(1.02) = -5(1.02)^3 - 17(1.02)^2 + 24 = 1.007160$$

$$p(1.03) = 0.501065 \quad \text{and} \quad p(1.04) = -0.011520.$$

Notice that $p(x)$ changes sign in the range $1.03 < x < 1.04$. Hence $1.03 < r < 1.04$.

Now begin again with new points P_1 and P_2, selecting $P_1(1.03, 0.501065)$ and $P_2(1.04, -0.011520)$ with y-coordinates of opposite sign. For these new points, $x_1 = 1.03$, $p(x_1) = 0.501065$, and $\Delta y/\Delta x = -0.51317/.01 = -51.317$. Hence

$$r_e = 1.03 - \frac{1}{-51.317}(.501065) \doteq 1.0398.$$

Take this value of r_e as a second approximation for the real root r of $p(x) = 0$ in the range $1.03 < r < 1.04$.

You can now continue the process by calculating $p(1.0397)$, $p(1.0398)$, etc., and selecting new points P_1 and P_2 whose y-coordinates are of opposite sign. The successive values of r_e *converge* upon the real root r of $p(x) = 0$ in the range $1 < r < 2$.

EXERCISES §602 (cont.)

13. Estimate the real root r of $p(x) = 0$ in the range $-2 < x < -1$, when $p(x) = -5x^3 - 17x^2 + 24$. Calculate at least the first and second approximations, r_e.

14. Locate the positive real roots of each of the following equations between two successive integers, then calculate the first approximation, r_e, to r.

(a) $-2x^3 + 6x + 13 = 0$ (b) $x^3 - 14 = 0$
(c) $x^4 - 3x^3 - 6x - 4 = 0$ (d) $x^5 + x - 24 = 0$.

Answers: (a) $r_e = 2.3$;   (c) $r_e = 3.4$.

15. (a) Show that $r_e = x_2 - \dfrac{1}{\Delta y/\Delta x} \cdot p(x_2)$ will give exactly the same results as formula I.

(b) Verify part (a) for the example at the top of this page.

603. Slopes of tangent lines as limits of slopes of secant lines

In Section 602 you learned to find the slope of the secant that joins $P_1(x_1,y_1)$ and $P_2(x_2,y_2)$ on the graph of a polynomial. Calculating the slope of a secant often involved extensive arithmetical calculations.

In this section we develop some special formulas for slopes of secants. Then we show that it is easier to calculate the slope of a *tangent* than to calculate the slope of a secant to the graph of a polynomial.

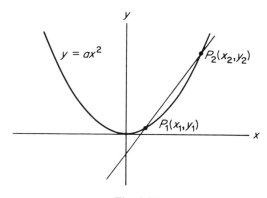

Fig. 6–23.

We begin with the parabola $y = ax^2$ (Fig. 6–23). Consider the secant that joins the points $P_1(x_1,ax_1^2)$ and $P_2(x_2,ax_2^2)$, $x_2 \neq x_1$, on the parabola; its slope is

$$\frac{\Delta y}{\Delta x} = \frac{ax_2^2 - ax_1^2}{x_2 - x_1} = \frac{a(x_2 - x_1)(x_2 + x_1)}{x_2 - x_1} = a(x_2 + x_1).$$

For two points on the parabola $y = ax^2$, $x_2 \neq x_1$, the slope of the secant is

I
$$\frac{\Delta y}{\Delta x} = a(x_2 + x_1).$$

For example, the slope of the secant that joins the points where $x = -2$ and $x = 3$ on the parabola $y = \frac{1}{5}x^2$ is

$$\frac{\Delta y}{\Delta x} = \frac{1}{5}[3 + (-2)] = \frac{1}{5}.$$

Next consider the cubical parabola $y = ax^3$. As before, the secant that joins $P_1(x_1,ax_1^3)$ and $P_2(x_2,ax_2^3)$, $x_2 \neq x_1$, has slope

$$\frac{\Delta y}{\Delta x} = \frac{ax_2^3 - ax_1^3}{x_2 - x_1} = \frac{a(x_2^3 - x_1^3)}{x_2 - x_1}.$$

You may know the identity

$$x_2{}^3 - x_1{}^3 = (x_2 - x_1)(x_2{}^2 + x_2 x_1 + x_1{}^2).$$

If not, you can prove it by repeated applications of the distributive law:

$$(x_2 - x_1)(x_2{}^2 + x_2 x_1 + x_1{}^2) = (x_2 - x_1)x_2{}^2 + (x_2 - x_1)x_2 x_1 + (x_2 - x_1)x_1{}^2$$
$$= x_2{}^3 - x_1 x_2{}^2 + x_2{}^2 x_1 - x_2 x_1{}^2 + x_2 x_1{}^2 - x_1{}^3$$
$$= x_2{}^3 - x_1{}^3.$$

Hence, for two points on the cubical parabola $y = ax^3$, $x_2 \neq x_1$, the slope of the secant is

II $\qquad \dfrac{\Delta y}{\Delta x} = \dfrac{a(x_2 - x_1)(x_2{}^2 + x_2 x_1 + x_1{}^2)}{x_2 - x_1} = a(x_2{}^2 + x_2 x_1 + x_1{}^2).$

For example, the slope of the secant that joins the points where $x = -1$ and $x = 2$ on the graph of $y = \frac{1}{7}x^3$ is

$$\frac{\Delta y}{\Delta x} = \frac{1}{7}[2^2 + 2(-1) + (-1)^2] = \frac{3}{7}.$$

Next consider the parabolic-type curve $y = ax^n$, $n \in N$. As before, the secant that joins $P_1(x_1, ax_1{}^n)$ and $P_2(x_2, ax_2{}^n)$, $x_2 \neq x_1$, has slope

$$\frac{\Delta y}{\Delta x} = \frac{ax_2{}^n - ax_1{}^n}{x_2 - x_1} = \frac{a(x_2{}^n - x_1{}^n)}{x_2 - x_1}.$$

You can prove the identity

$$x_2{}^n - x_1{}^n = (x_2 - x_1)(x_2{}^{n-1} + x_2{}^{n-2}x_1 + \ldots + x_2 x_1{}^{n-2} + x_1{}^{n-1})$$

for particular replacements of $n \in N$, by repeated applications of the distributive law. Hence, for two points on the parabolic-type curve $y = ax^n$, $n \in N$, $x_2 \neq x_1$, the slope of the secant is

III $\qquad \dfrac{\Delta y}{\Delta x} = a(x_2{}^{n-1} + x_2{}^{n-2}x_1 + \ldots + x_2 x_1{}^{n-2} + x_1{}^{n-1}).$

For example, the slope of the secant that joins the points where $x = -2$ and $x = 1$ on the graph of $y = \frac{2}{3}x^5$ is

$$\frac{\Delta y}{\Delta x} = \frac{2}{3}[1^4 + 1^3(-2) + 1^2(-2)^2 + 1(-2)^3 + (-2)^4] = \frac{22}{3}.$$

You can now proceed to build a formula for the slope of the secant line that joins two points on the graph of any polynomial. Take, for example,

$y = p(x) = a_3x^3 + a_2x^2 + a_1x + a_0$. The slope of the secant line that joins $P_1(x_1, p(x_1))$ and $P_2(x_2, p(x_2))$, $x_2 \neq x_1$, is

$$\frac{\Delta y}{\Delta x} = \frac{p(x_2) - p(x_1)}{x_2 - x_1}$$

$$= \frac{(a_3x_2^3 + a_2x_2^2 + a_1x_2 + a_0) - (a_3x_1^3 + a_2x_1^3 + a_1x_1 + a_0)}{x_2 - x_1}$$

$$= \frac{a_3(x_2^3 - x_1^3)}{x_2 - x_1} + \frac{a_2(x_2^2 - x_1^2)}{x_2 - x_1} + \frac{a_1(x_2 - x_1)}{x_2 - x_1}.$$

Hence

IV $\qquad \dfrac{\Delta y}{\Delta x} = a_3(x_2^2 + x_2x_1 + x_1^2) + a_2(x_2 + x_1) + a_1.$

For example, the slope of the secant line that joins the points where $x = 1$ and $x = 3$ on the graph of the cubic $y = 2x^3 + 3x - 1$ is

$$\frac{\Delta y}{\Delta x} = 2(3^2 + 3 \cdot 1 + 1^2) + 0(3 + 1) + 3 = 29.$$

EXERCISES §603

1. For each of the following equations, determine y_1 and y_2, then find the slope of the secant through $P_1(x_1, y_1)$ and $P_2(x_2, y_2)$, using $m = \dfrac{\Delta y}{\Delta x} = \dfrac{y_2 - y_1}{x_2 - x_1}$.
Compare with the illustrative examples in the text.
   (a) $y = \frac{1}{5}x^2$; $x_1 = -2$, $x_2 = 3$
   (b) $y = \frac{1}{7}x^3$; $x_1 = -1$, $x_2 = 2$
   (c) $y = \frac{2}{3}x^5$; $x_1 = -2$, $x_2 = 1$
   (d) $y = 2x^3 + 3x - 1$; $x_1 = 1$, $x_2 = 3$.

2. Graph the parabola $y = \frac{1}{4}x^2$. Let the x-coordinate of P_1 on the parabola be $x_1 = 2$. Use Formula I to find the slope of the secant through P_1 and a second point P_2 on the parabola for each of the following values of x_2: $-6, -4, -2, 0, 1, 4, 6$. Draw each secant, label its slope, and check the results graphically.

3. Find the slope of the secant that joins the points where $x = -4$ and $x = 1$ on the graph of the quartic $y = 3x^4$.

4. Find the slope of the secant that joins the points where $x = 2$ and $x = 3$ on the graph of the cubic $y = 2x^3 - 3x^2 - 4x + 5$.

We are now ready to develop some ideas that will lead to a definition of the tangent to a continuous curve at a given point on the curve. In elementary geometry you may have learned to think of the tangent to a circle as a line that intersects the circle only at the point of tangency. You can readily see that this definition is not adequate for curves in general. If a curve has several bend-points, like those pictured in Section 602 (e.g., on page 255), there may be points on the curve where it is impossible to draw a line that intersects the curve only at that point. We now look at the graph of a continuous curve to find a more general way to proceed.

In Fig. 6–24, $P_1(x_1,y_1)$ is a given point on the curve. $P_2(x_2,y_2)$ is a point on the curve in the *neighborhood* of P_1. We do not say how far it is from P_1 to P_2 because we plan to consider several different placements of P_2. For each position of P_2 there is a secant, P_1P_2. You can think of P_2 as taking a sequence of positions on the curve, closer and closer to P_1. As x_2 approaches x_1, the secant P_1P_2 appears to turn about the point P_1. Intuitively, it seems reasonable to call the line in the *limiting position* of the secant the tangent to the curve at $P_1(x_1,y_1)$.

Notice that it is inappropriate to make P_2 coincide with P_1, for then no secant is determined; you can draw a line in any direction through a single point. However, you may place P_2 arbitrarily close to P_1, and thus place the secant as close as you like to its limiting position. The "limiting position of a line" is an intuitive concept that we now define analytically.

Consider the point $P_1(3,1.8)$ on the graph of $y = \frac{1}{5}x^2$. Let $P_2(x_2,y_2)$ have the following sequence of x-coordinates: $\{5, 4, 3.5, 3.1, 3.01, 3.001, \ldots\}$. For each position of P_2, the table below shows the values of x_2, y_2, $\Delta x = x_2 - x_1$, $\Delta y = y_2 - y_1$, and $\Delta y/\Delta x$.

$$x_1 = 3, \quad y_1 = 1.8$$

x_2	5	4	3.5	3.1	3.01	3.001
y_2	5	3.2	2.45	1.922	1.81202	1.8012002
Δx	2	1	.5	.1	.01	.001
Δy	3.2	1.4	.65	.122	.01202	.0012002
$\Delta y/\Delta x$	1.6	1.4	1.3	1.22	1.202	1.2002

Notice that (as x_2 approaches 3), Δx approaches zero, and Δy approaches zero; but the slope of the secant $\Delta y/\Delta x$ appears to approach 1.2. The closer x_2 is to 3, the closer $\Delta y/\Delta x$ will be to 1.2. (Calculate $\Delta y/\Delta x$ when $x_2 = 3.00001$.)

We now show that $\Delta y/\Delta x$ can be held within any given *tolerance* to 1.2 for all values of x_2 that are sufficiently close, but not equal, to $x_1 = 3$.

For each value of $x_2 \neq 3$, consider the absolute value of the difference

$$\left| \frac{\Delta y}{\Delta x} - 1.2 \right| = \left| \frac{\frac{1}{5}x_2^2 - 1.8}{x_2 - 3} - 1.2 \right|$$

$$= \left| \frac{\frac{1}{5}(x_2^2 - 9)}{(x_2 - 3)} - 1.2 \right|$$

$$= \left| \frac{1}{5}(x_2 + 3) - 1.2 \right| \qquad (x_2 \neq 3)$$

$$= \frac{1}{5}\left| x_2 - 3 \right|.$$

If someone challenges you to choose x_2 so that $\Delta y/\Delta x$ is within .01 unit of 1.2, you can choose any value of x_2 such that $|x_2 - 3| < .05$ and $x_2 \neq 3$; for then

$$\left|\frac{\Delta y}{\Delta x} - 1.2\right| = \tfrac{1}{5}|x_2 - 3| < \tfrac{1}{5}(.05) = .01.$$

Notice the restriction $x_2 \neq 3$. This is necessary because if $x_2 = 3$, then $\Delta x = 0$ and $\Delta y/\Delta x$ is not defined. (Geometrically, there is no secant line.)

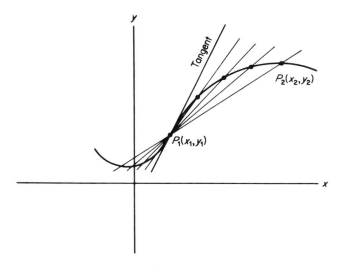

Fig. 6–24.

If he requests a tolerance of .000001, you can select any member of the set $\{x_2 \mid x_2 \neq 3 \text{ and } |x_2 - 3| < .000005\}$.

In general, if he requests a tolerance e,

$$\left|\frac{\Delta y}{\Delta x} - 1.2\right| < e,$$

you can select any member of the set

$$\{x_2 \mid x_2 \neq 3 \quad \text{and} \quad |x_2 - 3| < d\},$$

where $d = 5e$. We express the fact that you can meet each specified tolerance by writing

$$\lim_{x_2 \to 3} \frac{\Delta y}{\Delta x} = 1.2.$$

Recall, for polynomial functions, that $\Delta y/\Delta x$ is a polynomial in x_2. When

we say, for a polynomial $p(x)$, that the limit of $p(x)$, as x approaches a, is b
we mean

$$\left(\lim_{x \to a} p(x) = b\right) \Leftrightarrow \text{(for each positive number } e, \text{ no matter how}$$
small, a number d can be found such that
$|p(x) - b| < e$ for each member of the set
$\{x \mid x \neq a \text{ and } |x - a| < d\}).$

It was this definition that we applied to $\Delta y/\Delta x$ above when we stated
that the limit of $\Delta y/\Delta x$ as x_2 approaches 3 is 1.2. You can also apply this
definition to limits of functions other than polynomial functions; but we
shall restrict our discussion to polynomial functions.

The limit of $p(x)$ as x approaches a does not give you any information
about $p(a)$. We strictly avoid $x = a$. Rather it tells you about the values of
$p(x)$ in the neighborhood of $x = a$.

We now define the tangent to a curve at $P_1(x_1, y_1)$ to be a line passing
through P_1 with slope

$$\lim_{x_2 \to x_1} \frac{\Delta y}{\Delta x} = \lim_{\Delta x \to 0} \frac{\Delta y}{\Delta x}.$$

For our example, the equation of the tangent is

$$y - 1.8 = 1.2(x - 3) \quad \text{or} \quad y = 1.2x - 1.8.$$

For any parabola of the form $y = ax^2$, we know, from Formula I, that the
slope of the secant through $P_1(x_1, y_1)$ and $P_2(x_2, y_2)$ is

$$\frac{\Delta y}{\Delta x} = a(x_2 + x_1) \quad x_2 \neq x_1.$$

It seems evident that, by taking the range of x_2 as a set of numbers close
enough, but not equal, to x_1, we should be able to make $\Delta y/\Delta x$ as close as
we like to $a(x_1 + x_1) = 2ax_1$. Hence we anticipate that

$$\lim_{x_2 \to x_1} \frac{\Delta y}{\Delta x} = 2ax_1.$$

To show that this is the case we apply the definition. We have

$$\left| \frac{\Delta y}{\Delta x} - 2ax_1 \right| = |a(x_2 + x_1) - 2ax_1| = |a(x_2 - x_1)| = |a| \cdot |x_2 - x_1|.$$

Then, for any positive e, no matter how small,

$$\left| \frac{\Delta y}{\Delta x} - 2ax_1 \right| < e$$

for every member of the set $\{x_2 \mid x_2 \neq x_1 \text{ and } |x_2 - x_1| < d\}$, where $d = \dfrac{e}{|a|}$;

this follows from the fact that

$$|x_2 - x_1| < \frac{e}{|a|} \Rightarrow |a| \cdot |x_2 - x_1| < e.$$

Thus we have used the definition to show that, for the parabola $y = ax^2$, the slope of the tangent at $P_1(x_1, y_1)$ is

$$\lim_{x_2 \to x_1} \frac{\Delta y}{\Delta x} = 2ax_1.$$

Compare this result with the previous example where $a = \frac{1}{5}$ and $x_1 = 3$.

The idea of limits is a fundamental notion in mathematical analysis. In fact, the branch of mathematics known as the calculus is devoted entirely to the study of limits and their consequences. In the remaining part of this section we shall evaluate several rather easy limits. In each case the limit will be evident, as it was in the case above; hence we shall not return each time to the definition. But you should remember that the idea of limit of a function rests upon this definition and the properties of real numbers. When you study calculus you will investigate these problems much more thoroughly.

Before continuing, we return briefly to the idea of *continuity* mentioned in Section 303 (page 85). We can define continuity of a function in terms of the idea of limit. Let $\{(x, f(x))\}$ be any function with the range of x some interval of L. Notice that we use $f(x)$ to represent the number that is paired with x. We define this function to be continuous at the point where $x = a$ if and only if $\lim_{x \to a} f(x) = f(a)$. If a given function is continuous at every point in a given interval, this fact has important consequences that you will study in more advanced mathematics. We content ourselves with stating here, without any proof, that polynomial functions are continuous over each interval of the set L.

We now apply these ideas to study the limiting value of the set of slopes of secants through the point where $x_1 = -2$ on the cubic

$$y = 2x^3 - 3x^2 + 2x + 7.$$

Using Formula IV (page 259),

$$\frac{\Delta y}{\Delta x} = 2[x_2^2 + x_2(-2) + (-2)^2] + (-3)[x_2 + (-2)] + 2$$

$$= 2x_2^2 - 7x_2 + 16.$$

For each replacement of x_2 there is a definite secant through the point on the cubic where $x = -2$; this secant has a slope that you can calculate from the formula. As $x_2 \to -2$ (or $\Delta x \to 0$), it appears that $\Delta y/\Delta x$ approaches a limit, namely,

$$\lim_{\Delta x \to 0} \frac{\Delta y}{\Delta x} = \lim_{x_2 \to -2} (2x_2^2 - 7x_2 + 16)$$

$$= 2(-2)^2 - 7(-2) + 16 = 38.$$

This amounts to assuming that $\Delta y/\Delta x$ can be made as close as you please to 38 for all values of x_2 that are sufficiently close, but not equal, to -2. Hence the slope of the tangent to the curve at the point where $x = -2$ is 38.

Corresponding to $x_1 = -2$, you have $y_1 = -25$. The equation of the tangent to the cubic at $(-2, -25)$ is

$$y + 25 = 38(x + 2),$$

or

$$y = 38x + 51.$$

EXERCISES §603 (cont.)

5. On the graph of the quadratic $y = 3x^2$, take $x_1 = 2$. Consider the following sequence of values of x_2: 4, 3, 2.5, 2.1, 2.01, 2.001, 2.0001. For each value of x_2, compute y_2, Δx, Δy, and $\Delta y/\Delta x$. What appears to be the limit of $\Delta y/\Delta x$ as x_2 approaches x_1 ($\Delta x \to 0$)?

6. Repeat Exercise 5 with $y = x^2$ and $x_1 = 1.5$. Use the sequence 2, 1.8, 1.6, 1.51, 1.501, 1.5001, 1.50001 of values of x_2.

7. Repeat Exercise 5 with $y = -\frac{1}{4}x^2$ and $x_1 = 1$. Use 2, 1.5, 1.2, 1.1, 1.01, 1.001, 1.0001 as the sequence for x_2.

8. Now use the procedure of the example on page 261 to find $\lim\limits_{\Delta x \to 0} \dfrac{\Delta y}{\Delta x}$ for the quadratics of Exercises 5, 6, and 7. Compare your results with the intuitive conclusions you reached above.

In Exercises 9 and 10, find a formula for $\Delta y/\Delta x$, the slope of a secant through the fixed point on the graph of the given polynomial condition; then find $\lim\limits_{\Delta x \to 0} \dfrac{\Delta y}{\Delta x}$; then write an equation of the tangent to the graph at the given point; then write this equation in the form $y = mx + b$.

9. The point where $x_1 = -1$ on the graph of the polynomial $y = \frac{1}{2}x^3$.
Hint: Formula II (page 258) gives

$$\frac{\Delta y}{\Delta x} = \tfrac{1}{2}[x_2{}^2 + x_2(-1) + (-1)^2] = \tfrac{1}{2}[x_2{}^2 - x_2 + 1]$$

Intuitively, $\lim\limits_{\Delta x \to 0} \dfrac{\Delta y}{\Delta x} = \lim\limits_{x_2 \to -1} \tfrac{1}{2}[x_2{}^2 - x_2 + 1]$

$$= \tfrac{1}{2}[(-1)^2 - (-1) + 1] = \tfrac{3}{2}.$$

Corresponding to $x_1 = -1$, $p(-1) = \frac{1}{2}(-1)^3 = -\frac{1}{2}$. An equation of the tangent to the cubic at $(-1, -\frac{1}{2})$ is

$$y + \tfrac{1}{2} = \tfrac{3}{2}(x + 1) \quad \text{or} \quad y = \tfrac{3}{2}x + 1.$$

10. The point where $x_1 = 2$ on the graph of $y = \frac{1}{5}x^6$. *Hint:* Use Formula III (page 258).

11. Use the formula for the slope of the tangent to $y = ax^2$ at $P(x_1,y_1)$, developed on page 263, to write the equation of the tangent to:

(a) $y = \frac{1}{2}x^2$ at $(2,2)$ (b) $y = \frac{1}{2}x^2$ at $(-2,2)$

(c) $y = 7x^2$ at $(3,63)$ (d) $y = -4x^2$ at $(-1,-4)$

(e) $y = -\frac{3}{4}x^2$ at $(-2,-3)$ (f) $y = 0.1x^2$ at $(4,1.6)$

(g) $y = 10x^2$ at $(-5,250)$ (h) $y = \frac{1}{4}x^2$ at $(-8,16)$.

Answers: (a) slope 2, $y = 2x - 2$; (d) slope 8, $y = 8x + 4$; (g) slope -100, $y = -100x - 250$.

12. Show that the equation of the tangent to the parabola $y = ax^2$ at the point (x_1,y_1) on the parabola is $y = (2ax_1)x - y_1$. *Hint:* Remember that $y_1 = ax_1^2$ since (x_1,y_1) is a point on the parabola.

Now we develop a formula for the slope of the tangent to the graph of $y = p(x)$. Once you have this formula, you do not need to remember the special formulas for slopes of secant lines to graphs of polynomial conditions; you remember one simple formula rather than many comparatively complicated ones, and you simplify your calculations too.

First consider $y = ax^n$, $n \in N$. Formula III (page 258) yields

$$\frac{\Delta y}{\Delta x} = a(x_2^{n-1} + x_2^{n-2}x_1 + \dots + x_2x_1^{n-2} + x_1^{n-1}).$$

As $x_2 \to x_1$ (or $\Delta x \to 0$), you have:

$$\lim_{\Delta x \to 0} \frac{\Delta y}{\Delta x} = \lim_{x_2 \to x_1} a(x_2^{n-1} + x_2^{n-2}x_1 + \dots + x_2x_1^{n-2} + x_1^{n-1})$$

$$= a(x_1^{n-1} + x_1^{n-2}x_1 + \dots + x_1x_1^{n-2} + x_1^{n-1})$$

$$= a(x_1^{n-1} + x_1^{n-1} + \dots + x_1^{n-1} + x_1^{n-1}) \quad (n \text{ addends})$$

$$= a(nx_1^{n-1})$$

$$= nax_1^{n-1}.$$

Hence the tangent to the graph of $y = ax^n$ at the point where $x = x_1$ has slope nax_1^{n-1}. We shall use the symbol $y' = nax^{n-1}$ for the slope of the tangent to the graph of $y = ax^n$ at the point $P(x,y)$.

Hence we obtain:

V $y = ax^n \Rightarrow y' = nax^{n-1}.$

For example, the slope of the tangent to the graph of $y = \frac{1}{5}x^8$ at the point $P(x,y)$ is $y' = 8(\frac{1}{5})x^{8-1} = \frac{8}{5}x^7$.

Now consider $y = ax^n + bx^m$: It is easy to prove that

$$\frac{\Delta y}{\Delta x} = a(x_2^{n-1} + x_2^{n-2}x_1 + \dots + x_2x_1^{n-2} + x_1^{n-1})$$

$$+ b(x_2^{m-1} + x_2^{m-2}x_1 + \dots + x_2x_1^{m-2} + x_1^{m-1})$$

and $\lim_{\Delta x \to 0} \frac{\Delta y}{\Delta x} = nax_1^{n-1} + mbx_1^{m-1}.$

Hence

VI $y = ax^n + bx^m \Rightarrow y' = nax^{n-1} + mbx^{m-1}.$

For example, the slope of the tangent to the graph of $y = \frac{1}{2}x^6 - 2x^3$ at the point $P(x,y)$ is $y' = 3x^5 - 6x^2$.

Finally, if

$$y = p(x) = a_n x^n + a_{n-1}x^{n-1} + \ldots + a_2 x^2 + a_1 x + a_0, \quad a_n \neq 0,$$

VII $y' = p'(x) = na_n x^{n-1} + (n-1)a_{n-1}x^{n-2} + \ldots + 2a_2 x + a_1.$

For example, the slope of the tangent to the graph of $y = 4x^5 - 3x^4 - \frac{1}{2}x^2 + 5$ at the point $P(x,y)$ is $y' = 20x^4 - 12x^3 - x$.

EXERCISES §603 (cont.)

13. Determine y' for each polynomial.

(a) $y = 2x^2$ (b) $y = -3x^2$

(c) $y = x^2 - 4x$ (d) $y = \frac{1}{2}x^2 + 5x$

(e) $y = -\frac{1}{4}x^2 - \frac{1}{4}x$ (f) $y = 1.5x^2 + 4.7x$

(g) $y = 4x^2 - 5x + 7$ (h) $y = 5x^3$

(i) $y = 2x^3 - 4x^2 + x - 6$ (j) $y = -\frac{1}{2}x^3 + 3x^2 + 6x - 5.$

Answers: (a) $y' = 4x$; (c) $y' = 2x - 4$; (i) $y' = 6x^2 - 8x + 1$.

14. Determine the slope of the tangent to the graph of each polynomial at the point whose x coordinate is given.

(a) $y = 2x^2$ at $x = 1$ (b) $y = -3x^2$ at $x = \frac{1}{2}$

(c) $y = x^2 - 4x$ at $x = 0$ (d) $y = \frac{1}{2}x^2 + 5x$ at $x = -2$

(e) $y = -\frac{1}{4}x^2 - \frac{1}{4}x$ at $x = 3$ (f) $y = 1.5x^2 + 4.7x$ at $x = -1$

(g) $y = 4x^2 - 5x + 7$ at $x = -5$ (h) $y = 5x^3$ at $x = 0$

(i) $y = 2x^3 - 4x^2 + x - 6$ at $x = 2$ (j) $y = -\frac{1}{2}x^3 + 3x^2 + 6x - 5$ at $x = 3.$

Answers: (a) 4;   (c) −4;   (i) 9.

In each of the following exercises, use Formula VII (above) to calculate the slope of the tangent to the graph at $P(x,y)$; then replace P by the point suggested; then write an equation of the tangent at this point; then write this equation in the form $y = mx + b$.

15. The graph of $y = 3x^5 - 2x^3$ at the point where $x = 4$. *Hint:* Formula VI, or Formula VII yields

$$y' = 15x^4 - 6x^2.$$

At the point where $x = 4$,

$$y = 3(4^5) - 2(4^3) = 2944$$

and

$$y' = 15(4^4) - 6(4^2) = 3744.$$

The tangent at (4,2944) is

$$y - 2944 = 3744(x - 4)$$

or

$$y = 3744x - 12,032.$$

16. The graph of $y = x^4 - 3x^2 + 2x - 20$ at the point where $x = -2$.

Answer: $y = -18x - 56.$

17. The graph of $y = 5x^3 - 2x^2 + x - 1$ at the point where $x = 5$.

604. Polynomial conditions and approximations by tangent lines

In Section 603 you learned to find the slope of the tangent at $P(x,y)$ to the graph of the polynomial $y = p(x)$; hence you can write the equation of the tangent at $P(x,y)$. In this section you will use these skills to sketch the graph of $y = p(x)$, and to improve the approximations you make when you read the graph. You will learn to use tangent lines to accomplish these results.

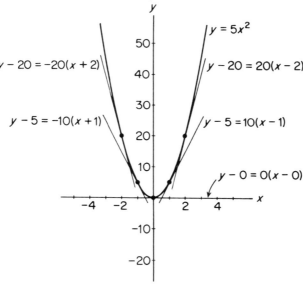

Fig. 6–25.

We begin with parabola $y = ax^2$. The corresponding function is $\{(x,ax^2)\}$. Recall our interpretation of $y' = 2ax$ as the slope of the tangent to the graph of $y = ax^2$ at $P(x,y)$. It is customary to call y' the *derivative of y*. The corresponding function is $\{(x,2ax)\}$. We shall call this function the *first derived function*, or simply the *derived function* of $\{(x,ax^2)\}$.

Consider for example, the parabola $y = 5x^2$. The derivative is $y' = 2 \cdot 5 \cdot x = 10x$. The table gives a few corresponding values of x, $5x^2$, and $10x$. We interpret the table entries according to the pattern: when $x = -3$, $y = 45$ [the point $(-3,45)$ lies on the parabola]; when $x = -3$, $y' = -30$ [the slope of the tangent to the parabola at the point $(-3,45)$ is -30].

x	-3	-2	-1	0	1	2	3
$y = 5x^2$	45	20	5	0	5	20	45
$y' = 10x$	-30	-20	-10	0	10	20	30

Notice how easy it is to write the equation of the tangent to a parabola at a specified point on the parabola. For example, the tangent to the parabola $y = 5x^2$ at the point $(1,5)$ is $y - 5 = 10(x - 1)$. You get the slope, 10, from the table. It is the value of $y' = 10x$ that corresponds to $x = 1$.

Study Fig. 6–25 to see how tangents at selected points reveal the shape of the graph. The tangents at $(-2,20)$, $(-1,5)$, $(0,0)$, $(1,5)$, and $(2,20)$ reveal the shape of the parabola $y = 5x^2$. In other words, the tangents are approximations to the curve for points that are close to the point of tangency. We explore this idea further, using examples.

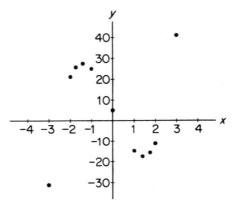

Fig. 6–26.

(1) Find the slope of the tangent to the graph of $y = 4x^3 - 24x + 5$ at the points where $x = -3, -2, -\sqrt{3}, -\sqrt{2}, -1, 0, 1, \sqrt{2}, \sqrt{3}, 2, 3$; then sketch the graph. We have

$$y = 4x^3 - 24x + 5$$
$$y' = 12x^2 - 24.$$

x	-3	-2	$-\sqrt{3}$	$-\sqrt{2}$	-1	0	1	$\sqrt{2}$	$\sqrt{3}$	2	3
y	-31	21	$12\sqrt{3}+5$	$16\sqrt{2}+5$	25	5	-15	$-16\sqrt{2}+5$	$-12\sqrt{3}+5$	-11	41
y'	84	24	12		0	-12	-24	-12	0	12	24	84

The first two rows of the table are familiar. Each number-pair (x,y) gives you the coordinates of a point on the graph of the cubic. The third row of the table gives you the slope of the tangent to the cubic at the corresponding point.

You should check each of the calculations that produce the entries in the table. Then you should think of graphing the equation $y = 4x^3 - 24x + 5$. In Fig. 6–26 we have plotted the 11 tabulated points. It was convenient to use the same length to represent 1 unit in the x-direction as 10 units in the y-direction. Notice that the effect of this choice is to make a line whose slope is 10 appear to have a slope of 1. For the purposes of this rough graph, we used $\sqrt{3} \doteq 1.7$, $\sqrt{2} \doteq 1.4$, $12\sqrt{3} + 5 \doteq 25.8$, etc.

The question arises whether you are justified in joining these 11 points by a smooth curve. The values of y' help you to answer this question. Notice that the slope of the tangent at $(-3,-31)$ is 84; so the curve rises steeply toward the right of this point. Study the slope of the tangent at each plotted

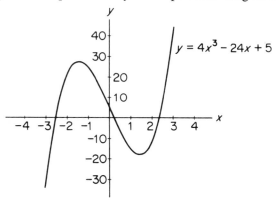

Fig. 6–27.

point, keeping in mind the choice of the units of measurement along the x- and y-axes.

Notice, in particular, that the slopes of the tangents at $(-\sqrt{2},\ 16\sqrt{2} + 5)$ and $(\sqrt{2},\ -16\sqrt{2} + 5)$ are zero; this means that the tangent lines at these two points are horizontal. At the point $(-\sqrt{2}, 16\sqrt{2} + 5)$ the curve ceases to rise and begins to fall; at the point $(\sqrt{2}, -16\sqrt{2} + 5)$ the curve ceases to fall and begins to rise. We say that the function has a *relative maximum*, or simply a *maximum*, at $(-\sqrt{2}, 16\sqrt{2} + 5)$; the function has a *relative minimum*, or simply a *minimum*, at $(\sqrt{2}, -16\sqrt{2} + 5)$. The points where the function has a maximum or minimum value are especially helpful when you are sketching its graph.

A careful study of the values of y' will make you feel more confident about drawing a smooth curve like that of Fig. 6–27.

Recall that the values of x that correspond to $y = 0$ are of special interest. These are the so-called *zeros* of the function. They are the *roots* of the equation $4x^3 - 24x + 5 = 0$. From the table, and the graph, it seems evident that the function has 3 zeroes (that is, that the graph crosses the x-axis at 3 points). One of these zeros is between $x = -3$ and $x = -2$; one is between $x = 0$ and $x = 1$; one is between $x = 2$ and $x = 3$. Recall the technique of Section 602 (page 255) for estimating the zeros of a function to any desired degree of accuracy. Later in this section we shall give you another technique for doing this.

(2) Find the point(s) where the parabola $y = ax^2 + bx + c$ has a maximum or a minimum. Recall, from Section 601 (page 240), that the graph of the parabola $y = ax^2 + bx + c$ has its vertex at the point where $x = -b/a$. To reach this conclusion, we constructed a perfect-square trinomial and wrote

$$y - \frac{(4ac - b^2)}{4a} = a\left(x + \frac{b}{2a}\right)^2.$$

With the new idea of derivative in mind, we have

$$y = ax^2 + bx + c$$
$$y' = 2ax + b.$$

At a point where the function has a maximum or a minimum, the tangent line is horizontal. Hence $y' = 0$ at a maximum or minimum point. The equation

$$y' = 2ax + b = 0$$

is a first-degree equation provided $a \neq 0$ (i.e., provided the original equation represents a parabola). It has exactly one solution, namely $x = -b/2a$. When you substitute $x = -b/2a$ in the equation $y = ax^2 + bx + c$, you can calculate the corresponding value of y, and hence the point (x,y), where the function has a maximum or a minimum.

If you compare this new method of locating the vertex of a parabola with the one we used in Section 601, you will be impressed by two contrasts. The new method is more general, that is, it can be applied to other curves that lack the special properties of parabolas. Also, the new method is easier.

(3) Sketch the graph of

$$y = \tfrac{1}{4}x^4 + \tfrac{11}{3}x^3 + \tfrac{25}{2}x^2 - 25x + 20.$$

We have $y' = x^3 + 11x^2 + 25x - 25$. At a point where the function has a maximum or minimum, the tangent line is horizontal. Hence at these points,

$$y' = x^3 + 11x^2 + 25x - 25 = 0.$$

Recall that we have, as yet, no general method for finding the roots of a cubic equation. We resort to a special method that works in this instance:

$$x^3 + 11x^2 + 25x - 25 = (x + 5)(x^2 + 6x - 5)$$

is an identity that you can check by applying the distributive law to multiply the factors $x + 5$ and $x^2 + 6x - 5$. Hence

$y' = (x + 5)(x^2 + 6x - 5) = 0$ at the points where the function has a maximum or minimum.

$$(x + 5)(x^2 + 6x - 5) = 0 \Rightarrow x + 5 = 0 \quad \text{or} \quad x^2 + 6x - 5 = 0$$
$$x + 5 = 0 \Rightarrow x = -5$$
$$x^2 + 6x - 5 = 0 \Rightarrow x = -3 \pm \sqrt{14}$$
$$\doteq .742 \quad \text{or} \quad -6.742.$$

We conclude that the maximum and minimum values of the function (if any) occur at the points where $x \doteq -6.742$, $x = -5$, and $x \doteq .742$.

We take into consideration these special values of x as we prepare the table:

x	-7	-6.742	-6	-5	0	$.742$	2
y (approx.)	150	149.6	152	155	20	9.9	53
y' (approx.)	-4	0	5	0	-25	0	77

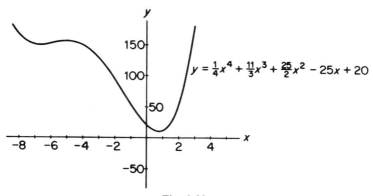

$$y = \tfrac{1}{4}x^4 + \tfrac{11}{3}x^3 + \tfrac{25}{2}x^2 - 25x + 20$$

Fig. 6–28.

Figure 6–28 is a rough sketch of the graph of the function. It was convenient to use the same length to represent 1 unit in the x-direction and 25 units in the y-direction. It would be possible to draw an enlarged picture of any portion of the graph, for instance for the range $-2 \le x \le 2$, to study the corresponding subset of the function in greater detail.

Notice that the graph does not cross the x-axis. (How do we know that the curve does not dip down and cross the x-axis between $x = -5$ and $x = 0$?) This means that the equation $\tfrac{1}{4}x^4 + \tfrac{11}{3}x^3 + \tfrac{25}{2}x^2 - 25x + 20 = 0$ has no real roots. Notice how a graph enables you to *locate* the real roots (if any) of an equation.

This graph is typical of a polynomial of degree 4. The derived function is of degree 3. The solution of the equation $y' = 0$ yields three values of x, not necessarily distinct and not necessarily all real. For each real value of x you may get a maximum, or a minimum, or in special cases you may get a point where the curve looks like one of those in Fig. 6–29.

At P_1 the curve becomes horizontal and then continues to rise (or fall) without giving you either a maximum or a minimum point. We call a point where the tangent crosses the curve a *point of inflection* on the curve. Recall the appearance of the curve $y = x^3$ (Chapter 4, page 125) at the origin.

At P_2 you get a kind of double minimum. Recall the appearance of the curve $y = x^4$ at the origin (Chapter 4, page 126).

The three graphs of Fig. 6–30 show some other possible representations of equations of degree 4. The first graph locates four real roots; the second and third graphs locate just two real roots. The third graph is a limiting case of the second, in which the minimum point, P_2, approaches the maximum point, P_1. Recall the graph of Example (3) as an instance of a polynomial of degree 4 that has no real roots.

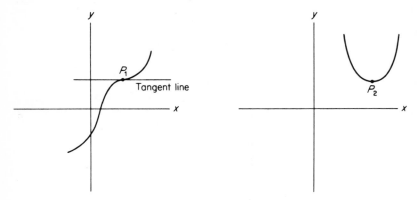

Fig. 6–29.

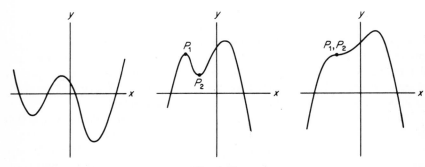

Fig. 6–30.

It is possible to generalize these comments to discuss the roots of the polynomial equation $p(x) = 0$ of degree n. We shall not go into detail. We leave it to you to think about the following theorems in light of our discussion thus far.

(a) $p(x) = 0$ has n roots, not necessarily distinct.

(b) To each complex root $a + bi$ of $p(x) = 0$, there is a corresponding complex root $a - bi$. Hence complex roots of $p(x) = 0$ occur in pairs.

(c) If the degree n of $p(x) = 0$ is odd, $p(x) = 0$ has at least one real root.

(d) The graph of $y = p(x)$ has at most $n - 1$ points at which the function is either a maximum or a minimum.

(e) Maximum points and minimum points alternate as you move from left to right along the graph of $y = p(x)$.

You may be able to formulate still other theorems about the roots of $p(x) = 0$ and the graph of $y = p(x)$. For example:

(f) The y-intercept of the graph of $y = p(x)$ is a_0.

(g) When x is sufficiently large, the sign of $p(x)$ is the same as the sign of a_n.

Watch for instances of these theorems as you work Exercises §604. Try to formulate other generalizations of your own. Mathematicians call the branch of mathematics that considers such generalizations the *theory of equations*.

EXERCISES §604

1. For the cubic polynomial, $y = x^3 - 3x^2 - 6x + 10$, make a table of values of x, y, and y'; use the values of x, $-3, -2, -1, 0, 1, 2, 3, 4$. Plot the corresponding set of points, $\{(x,y)\}$. At each of these points draw the tangent line to the curve (a line through the point with the appropriate slope); then sketch the graph of the cubic.

2. In Exercise 1, for what values of x is $y' = 0$? That is, for what values of x is the tangent line horizontal? Examine your graph to see whether it fits your answers to this question.

3. Find the derivative of $y = x^3 - 3x^2 - 6x + 10$. From the derivative, determine the values of x for which the tangent lines are horizontal. Plot the maximum and minimum points on the graph. Then sketch the graph finding additional information, such as the y-intercept and the like, as needed.

4. Locate the maximum and minimum points on the graphs of:

(a) $y = x^2 + x + 1$ (b) $y = 3x^2 - 5x + 10$

(c) $y = x^3 - 12x$ (d) $y = 2x^3 + 3x^2 - 36x - 12$

(e) $y = x^3 + x^2 - 16x + 32$.

Answers: (a) $(-\frac{1}{2}, \frac{3}{4})$;   (c) $(2, -16)$ and $(-2, 16)$.

5. Show that the equation $x^3 - 12x - 18 = 0$ has only one real root. [*Suggestion:* Draw the graph of $y = x^3 - 12x - 18$. The derivative, y', at selected points may be helpful.]

6. Without graphing, show that there are no places on the graph of $y = x^3 + x^2 + x + 2$ where the tangent is horizontal. (*Hint:* Are there any real numbers that make y' zero?)

7. Determine the equation of the tangent to the graph of $y = x^3 - 3x^2 - 6x + 10$ at the point where $x = 1$. Estimate the root of $x^3 - 3x^2 - 6x + 10 = 0$ that is near $x_1 = 1$ by finding the x-intercept of the tangent.

Answer: $y = -9x + 11$; $1\frac{2}{9}$.

8. Write the equation of the tangent to the graph of $y = 2x^4 - 6x^3 + 2x^2 + 7x + 3$ at the point $(3,42)$. Approximate $p(3.1)$ by finding the point on the tangent where $x = 3.1$. Compute $p(3.1)$ to see how good the approximation is.

9. Show that the graph of $y = x^3 - 6x^2 + 12x + 5$ has a horizontal tangent at only one point. Is this a maximum? a minimum?

10. At what points is the tangent to the graph of $y = \frac{1}{3}x^3 - 2x^2 + 11$ horizontal? For what values of x is the slope of the tangent negative? positive? How many real roots does the equation $\frac{1}{3}x^3 - 2x^2 + 11 = 0$ have?

Answer: Horizontal tangent at $(0,11)$ and $(4,\frac{1}{3})$, slope negative for $0 < x < 4$, positive for $x < 0$ or $x > 4$; one real root.

11. How many real roots does the equation $\frac{1}{3}x^3 - 2x^2 + 10 = 0$ have?

We turn now to the question of estimating the real roots of $p(x) = 0$ to any desired degree of accuracy.

You can locate real roots of an equation without actually drawing a graph. When you find two values of x, say x_1 and x_2, such that $x_1 < x_2$ and $p(x_1)$ and $p(x_2)$ are of opposite sign, there will be a root of $p(x) = 0$ between x_1 and x_2. We have assumed that the graph of $y = p(x)$ is continuous; if $p(x_1) < 0$ and $p(x_2) > 0$, there must be a number x such that $x_1 < x < x_2$ and $p(x) = 0$; also if $p(x_1) > 0$ and $p(x_2) < 0$, there must be a number x such that $x_1 < x < x_2$ and $p(x) = 0$.

A graph like the one on page 269 will help you to see what these statements mean. Look back at this graph and to the table upon which it is based. Recall that the points $(-3,-31)$ and $(-2,21)$ are points on the curve. There must be a point $(x,0)$ on the curve such that $-3 < x < -2$. This is just another way of saying that the graph must cross the x-axis somewhere between $(-3,-31)$ and $(-2,21)$. From other table entries you can conclude that the graph must also cross the x-axis in the intervals $0 < x < 1$, and $2 < x < 3$.

Now examine the graph on page 271 and the table upon which it is based. The values of $y = p(x)$ in Example (3) are all positive. The polynomial $y = p(x)$ does not change sign, either from positive to negative or from negative to positive. Hence, even without drawing the graph, you can tell [from the location of the horizontal tangent lines and the values of $p(x)$] that $p(x) = 0$ has no real roots.

Once you locate a real root of a polynomial equation, $p(x) = 0$, either by drawing the graph of $y = p(x)$, or by finding two values, $x = x_1$ and

$x = x_2$, of x such that $p(x_1)$ and $p(x_2)$ are of opposite sign, you can calculate closer and closer approximations to this root. We return to the polynomial $y = 4x^3 - 24x + 5$ of Example (1) to illustrate the method. Recall that

x	2	3
$y = p(x)$	-11	41
$y' = p'(x)$	24	84

Hence there is a real root r in the interval $2 < r < 3$. To get closer approximations to r means to narrow this interval.

The most obvious way to proceed is by trial and error. If you enjoy calculation, you can calculate $p(2.1)$, $p(2.2)$, ... , $p(2.9)$. When you find that $p(2.3) = -1.532$ and $p(2.4) = 2.696$, you know that $2.3 < r < 2.4$. Then you can calculate $p(2.31)$, $p(2.32)$, ... , $p(2.39)$. When you get a change of sign between two successive values of $p(x)$, you know that r lies between the two corresponding values of x. The only objection to this method is that it takes a great deal of arithmetic to get a value of r correct to, say, five significant figures. Practical problems often require answers to five or more significant figures.

Before you consider more efficient ways to estimate r, you should realize that modern calculating machinery may make the trial-and-error method an excellent one. When you have a great many similar problems to work, it may be practical to set up a *program* for one of the new "giant brain" computors. You "tell" the machine to do the process described in the preceding paragraph. Once the machine has its instructions, it can proceed, on its own, to turn out results with amazing speed. The limitations of this approach are obvious. It is very expensive to prepare and use the machine. Hence it is uneconomical to use the machine unless you have to perform a great many calculations of one particular kind.

The technique of Section 602 (page 255) greatly reduces the calculation required in the trial-and-error process. We proceed, now, to describe a still more efficient technique.

The tangent to $y = 4x^3 - 24x + 5$ at the point $(2, -11)$ is $y + 11 = 24(x - 2)$; this tangent crosses the x-axis at the point where $y = 0$ and $x = 2 + 11/24 \doteq 2.46$. You calculate the y of the point on the graph of the polynomial where $x = 2.46$, and the slope of the tangent at this point. You get $y \doteq 5.51$, $y' \doteq 48.6$. The tangent at $(2.46, 5.51)$ is $y - 5.51 = 48.6(x - 2.46)$; this tangent crosses the x-axis at the point where $y = 0$ and $x = 2.46 - 5.51/48.6 \doteq 2.347$. You can continue this process to get values of x that are closer and closer approximations to the desired root r.

In practice, this method, called Newton's method (after Sir Isaac Newton), usually yields a sequence of values of x that *converges* rapidly upon r. It is also a method that lends itself to machine calculation. We state the method in general terms below. Then we provide, in Exercises 604, opportunities to try it out.

When you locate a root r of the equation $p(x) = 0$, $x_1 < r < x_2$, you may think of x_1 or x_2 as a first approximation, r_1 to the root r. Make sure that there is no maximum or minimum of the function $\{(x, p(x))\}$ between x_1 and x_2; that is, be sure that the graph of $y = p(x)$ either rises or falls from

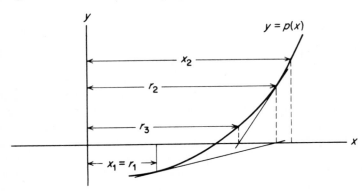

Fig. 6–31.

the point $(x_1, p(x_1))$ to the point $(x_2, p(x_2))$. If there is a maximum or minimum between x_1 and x_2, choose new values of x_1 and x_2 closer together.

The equation of the tangent to $y = p(x)$ at $x = r_1$ is

$$y - p(r_1) = p'(r_1)(x - r_1).$$

Notice the convenience of the symbol $p'(r_1)$. It represents the slope of the graph of $y = p(x)$ at the point $(r_1, p(r_1))$.

This tangent crosses the x-axis at the point where $y = 0$ and

$$x = r_1 - \frac{p(r_1)}{p'(r_1)}.$$

Call this value $x = r_2$; then

I $$r_2 = r_1 - \frac{p(r_1)}{p'(r_1)}$$

and r_2 is a second approximation to r. Now repeat the process with r_2 playing the role that r_1 played previously; this yields a third approximation to r,

II $$r_3 = r_2 - \frac{p(r_2)}{p'(r_2)}.$$

Continue this process until a step produces no change in the approximation to r for the number of decimal places you want in your result. Figure 6–31 may help you to visualize the process.

As you look back over Sections 602, 603, and 604, you will probably guess that the methods of these sections have many applications. The idea of the derivative of a polynomial is especially important. This idea of derivative can be generalized to speak of the derivative of $y = \sin x$, $y = b^x$, etc. This is one of the things that you will do if you take a course in calculus. You have already met some of the principal applications of derivatives: to locate maximum and minimum values of functions, to estimate zeros of functions, to speed up the graphing of functions, etc. There are many other applications of the concept of derivative.

EXERCISES §604 (cont.)

12. For Example (1), page 268, find the root r of $4x^3 - 24x + 5 = 0$ in the interval $0 < r < 1$. Take $r_1 = 0$ and find r_2, r_3, etc. using Formulas I, II, etc., of page 276. Stop the process when you know r to the nearest .0001.

Hint: $r_2 = 0 - \dfrac{p(0)}{p'(0)} = 0 - \dfrac{5}{-24} \doteq .21$;

$r_3 = .21 - \dfrac{p(.21)}{p'(.21)} \doteq .2099$

$r_4 = .2099 - \dfrac{p(.2099)}{p'(.2099)}$.

13. The calculations of $y = p(x)$ and $y' = p'(x)$ for a given value of x are sometimes simplified by a technique known as *synthetic division*. Suppose $y = p(x) = 2x^4 - 5x^3 - 5x^2 + 14$. We illustrate by calculating $p(3)$ and $p'(3)$.

(1) Write down the coefficients in their natural order, as they would appear in $p(x)$. (Notice that the coefficient of x is zero in this example.)

(2) To the right of the row of coefficients, place the number 3 to calculate $p(3)$.

$$
\begin{array}{rrrrr|r}
2 & -5 & -5 & 0 & 14 & \underline{3} \\
  & 6 & 3 & -6 & -18 & \\
\hline
2 & 1 & -2 & -6 & \boxed{-4} & \\
  & 6 & 21 & 57 & & \\
\hline
2 & 7 & 19 & \boxed{51} & &
\end{array}
$$

Skip one row, and draw a line under the row of coefficients.

(3) Write the first coefficient, 2, below this line; multiply it by 3; place this product, 6, under the next coefficient, -5; add and write the sum, 1, below the line.

(4) Repeat this process, from left to right with the entire row of coefficients; the last number in the row, -4, is $p(3)$.

(5) Draw another line. Carry out the same calculations with the row of numbers obtained in Steps (3) and (4), except that this time you stop your calculations one step short. The last number, 51, in this row is $p'(3)$.

Calculate $p(3)$ by substitution in $p(x) = 2x^4 - 5x^3 - 5x^2 + 14$, and verify that -4 is correct. You know that $p'(x) = 8x^3 - 15x^2 - 10x$. Verify by substitution that $p'(3) = 51$. (The process gets its name, synthetic division, from the fact that the numbers in the middle row, except the last one, are the coefficients in the quotient of $p(x)$ and $x - 3$.)

14. You can show that synthetic division works for a polynomial of given degree by carrying it out with general coefficients. For example, if $y = ax^2 + bx + c$, and $x = r$,

$$
\begin{array}{ccc|c}
a & b & c & \underline{}r \\
 & ar & ar^2 + br & \\
\hline
a & ar + b & ar^2 + br + c & \\
 & ar & & \\
\hline
a & 2ar + b & &
\end{array}
$$

Notice that you obtain $ar^2 + br + c$ for $p(r)$, and $2ar + b$ for $p'(r)$. But direct substitution in $p(x) = ax^2 + bx + c$ yields $p(r) = ar^2 + br + c$, and in $p'(x) = 2ax + b$ yields $p'(r) = 2ar + b$. Hence the method will work for any quadratic polynomial. In a similar fashion, prove that the method will work for the general polynomial of degree 3, $y = ax^3 + bx^2 + cx + d$.

15. Repeat Exercise 1 (page 273) of this section, making use of synthetic division to shorten your calculations.

16. Approximate the one positive root of the equation $x^3 - 12x - 18 = 0$ to the nearest hundredth.

Answer: 4.05.

17. Approximate to the nearest hundredth:
(a) The positive root of $x^3 - 3x^2 - 5 = 0$
(b) The positive root of $x^4 + x^3 + x^2 - 3x - 12 = 0$
(c) $\sqrt[3]{17}$ (*Hint:* It is a root of $x^3 - 17 = 0$).

Answer: (b) 1.73.

18. In an example, Section 602 (page 250), we estimated $p(-1.5)$, where $p(x) = 3x^5 - 2x^3 + 3x - 4$; our estimate, using the secant line, was rather poor. Use the tangent line at $(-2, -90)$ to estimate $p(-1.5)$ and compare results.

19. An open-top box is to be made from a rectangular sheet of metal, 18 in. by 12 in. A square will be cut from each corner of the rectangle (see Fig. 6–32) and the edges folded up.
(a) If x is the length of the side of each square, and y is the volume of the box, show that $y = 4x^3 - 60x^2 + 216x$.
(b) What value of x will make the volume of the box 200 cu in.?
(c) What value of x will make the volume a maximum? What is the maximum volume? (*Hint:* Set $y' = 0$. The graph of $y = 4x^3 - 60x^2 + 216x$ may also be helpful.)

20. In Exercise 12, Section 602 (page 254), we related the average speed of a falling object over a given interval, geometrically, to the slope of a secant line. If you hold t_1 fixed and let t_2 take on a sequence of values closer and closer to t_1, you obtain average speeds over smaller and smaller intervals. Physicists call the limit of the average speed, $\dfrac{\Delta d}{\Delta t} = \dfrac{d_2 - d_1}{t_2 - t_1}$, as t_2 approaches t_1, the instantaneous speed, or velocity, at the time t_1. This is the derivative of $d = 16t^2$, namely, $d' = 32t$, for the time $t = t_1$. Perhaps you have met the formula $v = 32t$ in physics. Determine the exact velocity at the time when the object has fallen for 2 sec; 3 sec.

Notice that we have interpreted the derivative in two ways, as the slope of the tangent to the graph at a chosen point, and as the velocity at a particular instant. There are many other interpretations of the derivative.

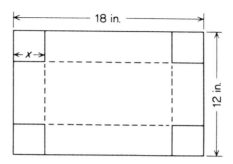

Fig. 6–32.

605. Tabular approximations for the elementary functions

This last section on conditions in one unknown deals partly with speeding up your solutions of equations that you already know how to solve. Then it deals with solving equations that you can not yet solve. When you have a table of sines, or table of logarithms, you can often obtain a practically useful solution of an equation; but, thus far you have no way to improve upon the approximations in the table.

Suppose you want to find the diameter of a circle whose area is 21.357 sq ft. Perhaps you recall the formula $A = \pi r^2$, which gives the area of a circle (A) in terms of its radius (r). You can solve the equation $\pi r^2 = 21.357$ for r; then you can calculate the diameter (D) from the formula $D = 2r$.

A better way to proceed is to combine the formulas $D = 2r$ and $A = \pi r^2$ to obtain the formula $A = \pi D^2/4$. Your book of tables gives you $\pi/4 \doteq 0.78539816$. Hence $21.357 \doteq 0.785398 D^2$, and $D \doteq \sqrt{21.357/0.785398}$. Even when you round off $\pi/4$ to six significant figures (appropriate in a problem where the area A is given to five significant figures) the calculation becomes laborious. Although the answer will be practically useful, it is not exact. The exact solution of $21.357 = \pi D^2/4$ is, of course $D = \sqrt{21.357 \times 4/\pi}$; but as soon as you use a decimal approximation for π your answer will be an approximation.

A still better way to proceed is to use your book of tables to obtain $4/\pi = 1.27323954$; then $D \doteq \sqrt{21.357 \times 1.27324}$. This is better than the previous method because multiplication is easier than division.

Notice that the advantages of one method over another are, so far, a question of convenience of calculation. By looking up more and more precise values of π, you can get more and more precise values of D. But, practically speaking, the value $A = 21.357$ sq ft is a measurement to five significant figures. The precision of the measurement is what limits the precision of the value of D that you calculate.

In your book of tables you find

n	521	522
$A = \pi n^2/4$	213189.3	214008.4

Recall that multiplying n by 10 multiplies n^2 (and hence A) by 100. Hence you can read the table as

n	5.21	5.22
$A = \pi n^2/4$	21.31893	21.40084

The problem becomes a problem in interpolation, to find the value of n that corresponds to $A = 21.357$. When you use the approximate process of replacing an arc of a curve by its secant, you may as well round off the figures in the table as follows:

$$.01 \begin{bmatrix} d \begin{bmatrix} 5.21 \\[4pt] 5.22 \end{bmatrix} \end{bmatrix} \qquad \begin{matrix} A \\ \begin{bmatrix} \left.\begin{matrix} 21.319 \\[2pt] 21.357 \end{matrix}\right] .038 \\[2pt] 21.401 \end{bmatrix} .082 \end{matrix}$$

Interpolation yields $d/.01 = .038/.082$; hence $d \doteq .0046$, and $n = 5.2146$. You should recall that this is the value of n that corresponds to $A = 21.357$ on the secant line. It is approximately the value of n that corresponds to $A = 21.357$ on the curve.

This last method of finding D saves calculation, and hence reduces errors of calculation and speeds up the work. Its disadvantage is that you never feel sure about how good your approximation is. Might the correct answer be 5.2147 instead of 5.2146? In this problem you can go back to one of the other methods of solution to check your result. In other problems it is impractical or even impossible for you to do this. You use interpolation and keep your fingers crossed. One of the reasons for studying more advanced mathematics becomes clear. Someone needs to know how the tables are computed; someone needs to know how to calculate a value of π to more significant figures than the table provides; someone needs to know how to calculate a value of sin (.76872) to more significant figures than the table provides; etc.

We give you two more examples of tabular approximations for elementary functions. Then we provide a variety of examples in Exercises §605. One of the major purposes of this section is to learn to use your book of tables to reduce the calculations you must perform. A saving of this sort represents a saving of time. In practice it also reduces errors of calculation to a minimum. The entries in the tables have been checked and rechecked to eliminate such errors.

(1) Solve for x the equation $\cos x = .84646$. From the tables:

$$
1' \left[d \left[\begin{array}{c} x \\ 32°10' \\ \\ 32°11' \end{array} \right. \right. \qquad \left. \left. \begin{array}{c} \cos x \\ .84650 \\ .84646 \\ .84635 \end{array} \right] 4 \right] 15
$$

Notice that $\cos x$ decreases as x increases in this portion of the table. Notice that we used 4 and 15 instead of .00004 and .00015. This saves time and no confusion results when you keep in mind what you are doing. By interpolation, $d/1 = 4/15$. Hence $d \doteq .27$, and $x \doteq 32°10' + .3' = 32°10.3'$.

This solution yields a value x as a measure of an angle in degrees and minutes. Recall, from Chapter 4 that x may also represent the arc of a unit circle (page 152), or the radian measure of an angle (page 162). Using the table called "Trigonometric Functions in Radian Measure," you find:

$$
.01 \left[d \left[\begin{array}{c} x \\ .56 \\ \\ .57 \end{array} \right. \right. \qquad \left. \left. \begin{array}{c} \cos x \\ .8473 \\ .8465 \\ .8419 \end{array} \right] 8 \right] 54
$$

Notice that this is a four-place table; hence we rounded off the value $\cos x = .84646$ to the four-figure value $\cos x = .8465$. Interpolation yields $d/.01 = 8/54$. Hence $d \doteq .0015$, and $x \doteq .56 + .0015 = .5615$. You may be suspicious of the last figure (5) in this answer. But you have no way, for the time being, to check it. The only check available to you is to look for a more complete table. Meanwhile it is obviously foolish to say $d \doteq .00148$ and $x \doteq .56 + .00148 = .56148$. This would be stretching the accuracy of the table beyond its limits.

You now have two answers, $x = 32°10.3'$ and $x = .5615$. Recall that they are really two ways of saying the same thing. The arc of a circle of radius 1 ft, that subtends an angle of $32°10.3'$ at the center of the circle is approximately .5615 ft long.

In Chapter 9 you will find other solutions of the equation $\cos x = .84646$. Look back to the graph of $y = \cos x$ in Section 409 (page 153). Recall that just one value of y corresponds to each value of x; but each value of y yields either infinitely many values of x, or else no value of x. Our solution, $x = .5616$, is the smallest positive value of x that satisfies the condition $\cos x = .84646$. In Chapter 9 we shall discuss inverse trigonometric functions and learn to find the whole set of values of x.

(2) Solve the equation $e^{-x} = .11091$ for x. We have not mentioned the number e previously. It is an irrational number, like the number π, which enters into many mathematical discussions. From some points of view it is

the simplest base to use when you work with the equation $y = b^x$. Thus the function $\{(x,e^x)\}$ is often called *the* exponential function.

For the time being we need not concern ourselves with the significance of e. You should find in your book of tables:

$$
.01 \begin{bmatrix} d & \begin{bmatrix} \overset{\displaystyle x}{2.19} \\[1em] 2.20 \end{bmatrix} \end{bmatrix} \qquad \begin{bmatrix} \overset{\displaystyle e^{-x}}{} \\ \begin{bmatrix} .11192 \\ .11091 \end{bmatrix} 101 \\ .11080 \end{bmatrix} 112
$$

By interpolation, $d/.01 = 101/112$. Hence $d \doteq .00902$, and $x \doteq 2.1990$. We express the value of x to five significant figures, although the last figure may be in error.

This method of solving equations by interpolation in tables has much practical usefulness. A great variety of tables is available to fit special purposes. The construction of such tables pays for itself in time-saving and in avoidance of errors of calculation. Exercises §605 provide a few further illustrations of tabular approximations.

EXERCISES §605

1. From a table of areas of circles, estimate the diameter n when A is:

(a) 3600   (b) 524.31   (c) 17.22.

2. If division by π occurs in a calculation, a table of circumferences of circles may be helpful. The condition $C = \pi n$ (where n is the diameter and C is the circumference of a circle) is equivalent to $n = C/\pi$. Given C, you can find n (interpolating if necessary) from the table. Estimate:

(a) $1420/\pi$ (b) $23.77/\pi$ (c) $1.6342/\pi$.

3. From a table of trigonometric functions in degrees, estimate a value of x for each of the following:

(a) $\cos x = .72829$ (b) $\sin x = .43377$
(c) $\tan x = .27000$ (d) $\tan x = 11.265$
(e) $\sin x = .94000$ (f) $\sin x = .66667$.

4. From a table of trigonometric functions in radian measure, estimate a value of x for each of the following:

(a) $\cos x = .7283$ (b) $\sin x = .4338$
(c) $\tan x = .2700$ (d) $\tan x = 11.26$
(e) $\sin x = .9400$ (f) $\sin x = .6667$.

5. Estimate each of the following with interpolation. Notice that some are in degrees, and others in radians.

(a) $\sin 24°13.5'$ (b) $\tan 19°57.7'$
(c) $\tan 54°26.9'$ (d) $\cos 41°50.3'$
(e) $\sin 0.883$ (f) $\cos 1.127$
(g) $\tan 1.512$ (h) $\cos 1.598$.

6. Estimate to five significant digits:

(a) $10^{0.32039}$ (b) $10^{0.58155}$

(c) $10^{1.22430}$ (d) $10^{2.50000}$

(e) $10^{-2+.72720}$ (f) $10^{-0.86517}$.

7. Estimate:

(a) $\log_{10}(4.7921)$ (b) $\log_{10}(8.9473)$

(c) $\log_{10}(53.757)$ (d) $\log_{10}(.17225)$

(e) $\log_{10}(.067484)$ (f) $\log_{10}(229.63)$.

8. In situations involving compound interest (see Exercise 5, page 144), it is important to be able to estimate $S = (1 + i)^n$. Many tables give i only to the nearest 1%. Using such a table (look for a table headed Amount of 1 at Compound Interest), estimate:

(a) $(1 + .0275)^8$ (b) $(1 + .022)^8$

(c) $(1 + .0425)^{12}$ (d) $(1 + .018)^{20}$.

9. From the table of the exponential function, estimate:

(a) $e^{1.425}$ (b) $e^{0.333}$

(c) $e^{-2.226}$ (d) $e^{5.28}$.

10. When using interpolation with the ratio symbolized by $y = \sin x$, would you expect better results near $x = 10°$, or near $x = 80°$? Why? (See Fig. 4-37, the graph of $y = \sin x$, page 153.)

11. The following table gives the populations of Brazil and Canada in millions of persons from 1915 to 1955 at 5-yr intervals.

Year	Brazil (millions)	Canada (millions)
1915	24.7	8.0
1920	27.4	8.6
1925	30.3	9.3
1930	33.6	10.2
1935	37.2	10.8
1940	41.1	11.4
1945	46.2	12.1
1950	52.0	13.7
1955	58.5	15.6

(a) Estimate the population of Brazil in 1921; 1924; 1952.

(b) Estimate the population of Canada in 1927; 1939; 1953.

12. (a) From the data of Exercise 11, estimate the population of Brazil in 1945 by interpolating with the populations given for 1940 and 1950. Compare with the population in 1945 given in the table.

(b) Estimate the population of Brazil in 1960 from the data of Exercise 11. Is one likely to have less confidence in an estimate of this type? Why?

7

Conditions in Several Unknowns

Problems commonly involve more than one unknown. A problem may deal with the ages of three persons, the values of the parameters a, b, c, and d in the cubic, $y = ax^3 + bx^2 + cx + d$, and so forth.

You use the things you know about the problem to set up conditions that the unknowns in the problem must satisfy. For example, suppose that the cubic, $y = ax^3 + bx^2 + cx + d$, passes through the points $(-2,5)$, $(0,-3)$, $(1,4)$, and $(3,-2)$; then the coordinates of each of these points must satisfy the equation $y = ax^3 + bx^2 + cx + d$. Hence the parameters a, b, c, and d must satisfy the four conditions:

$$5 = a(-8) + b(4) + c(-2) + d$$
$$-3 = a(0) + b(0) + c(0) + d$$
$$4 = a(1) + b(1) + c(1) + d$$
$$-2 = a(27) + b(9) + c(3) + d.$$

Notice that the second condition reduces to $d = -3$. This is equivalent to saying that the y-intercept of the graph of $y = ax^3 + bx^2 + cx + d$ is -3; that is, the graph passes through the point $(0,-3)$. When you impose the condition $d = -3$, you have the three conditions

$$-8a + 4b - 2c = 8$$
$$a + b + c = 7$$
$$27a + 9b + 3c = 1$$

on the parameters a, b, and c.

In this chapter you will learn to find the *solution set* of such a system of conditions. In the example, this is the set, $\{(a,b,c)\}$, of *ordered number-triples* that satisfy all three conditions. The replacements $a = -7/5$, $b = 34/15$, and $c = 92/15$ yield an ordered triple $(-\frac{7}{5}, \frac{34}{15}, \frac{92}{15})$ that satisfies the three

284

conditions; try them! It turns out that $(-\frac{7}{5},\frac{34}{15},\frac{92}{15})$ is the only *solution*; hence the solution set of the three conditions is $\{(-\frac{7}{5},\frac{34}{15},\frac{92}{15})\}$.

This means there is exactly one cubic, $y = ax^3 + bx^2 + cx + d$, whose graph passes through the points $(-2,5)$, $(0,-3)$, $(1,4)$ and $(3,-2)$; it is $y = -\frac{7}{5}x^3 + \frac{34}{15}x^2 + \frac{92}{15}x - 3$.

700. Equivalent systems of algebraic conditions

You should recall the idea of equivalent conditions that you met in Chapter 2. We call the conditions $x + y = 7$ and $2x + 2y = 14$ equivalent because $(x + y = 7) \Leftrightarrow (2x + 2y = 14)$. When you work with a system of conditions in several unknowns, you try to derive a new system of conditions that is equivalent to the given system. Usually you seek equivalent systems that are simpler to interpret than the given system. To *solve* a system of conditions means to derive an equivalent system of conditions whose solution set is obvious.

We devote the remainder of this section to illustrating the solution of systems of algebraic conditions.

(1) Solve the system

$$2x - y = 5$$
$$x^2 - xy + 2x = 6.$$

Notice that $\qquad\qquad 2x - y = 5 \Rightarrow y = 2x - 5$

and

$$[y = 2x - 5 \text{ } and \text{ } x^2 - xy + 2x = 6] \Rightarrow [x^2 - x(2x - 5) + 2x = 6].$$

Notice the effect of these two steps. We used the linear equation $(2x - y = 5)$ to express y in terms of x; then we substituted this value of y in the other equation to get a new equation in the one unknown, x. These two steps yield an equation in one unknown, like the ones you solved in Chapter 6. We proceed, as in Chapter 6:

$$x^2 - x(2x - 5) + 2x = 6$$
$$x^2 - 2x^2 + 5x + 2x = 6$$
$$x^2 - 7x + 6 = 0$$
$$(x - 6)(x - 1) = 0$$
$$x = 6 \quad or \quad x = 1.$$

To continue,

$$[x = 6 \text{ and } y = 2x - 5] \Rightarrow [x = 6 \text{ and } y = 7]$$

and $\qquad\quad [x = 1 \text{ and } y = 2x - 5] \Rightarrow [x = 1 \text{ and } y = -3].$

Hence

$$[2x - y = 5 \text{ } and \text{ } x^2 - xy + 2x = 6] \Rightarrow$$
$$[(x = 6 \text{ and } y = 7) \text{ } or \text{ } (x = 1 \text{ and } y = -3)]$$

That is, *if* the system of conditions,

$$2x - y = 5$$
$$x^2 - xy + 2x = 6$$

has a solution, this solution is (6,7) or (1,−3).

The easiest way to prove that (6,7) is a solution is to substitute: Thus

$$[x = 6 \text{ and } y = 7] \Rightarrow [2x - y = 2(6) - 7 = 5 \text{ and }$$
$$x^2 - xy + 2x = 36 - 42 + 12 = 6].$$

Also,

$$[x = 1 \text{ and } y = -3] \Rightarrow [2x - y = 2 + 3 = 5 \text{ and }$$
$$x^2 - xy + 2x = 1 + 3 + 2 = 6].$$

Hence

$$[2x - y = 5 \text{ and } x^2 - xy + 2x = 6] \Leftrightarrow$$
$$[(x = 6 \text{ and } y = 7) \text{ or } (x = 1 \text{ and } y = -3)].$$

This means that the system of conditions $(2x - y = 5$ and $x^2 - xy + 2x = 6)$ has exactly two solutions. These solutions are (6,7) and (1,−3); the solution set is $\{(6,7), (1,-3)\}$.

(2) Solve the system

$$x - 3y = 5$$
$$2x + y = 3.$$

First we use a procedure much like that of Example (1):

$$[x - 3y = 5] \Rightarrow [x = 3y + 5]$$
$$[x = 3y + 5 \text{ and } 2x + y = 3] \Rightarrow [2(3y + 5) + y = 3].$$
$$2(3y + 5) + y = 3$$
$$7y = -7; \quad y = -1$$
$$[x = 3y + 5 \text{ and } y = -1] \Rightarrow [x = 2 \text{ and } y = -1].$$

Hence $[x - 3y = 5 \text{ and } 2x + y = 3] \Rightarrow [x = 2 \text{ and } y = -1].$
Conversely,

$$[x = 2 \text{ and } y = -1] \Rightarrow [x - 3y = 2 + 3 = 5 \text{ and } 2x + y = 4 - 1 = 3].$$

Hence $[x - 3y = 5 \text{ and } 2x + y = 3] \Leftrightarrow [x = 2 \text{ and } y = -1].$

The system of conditions

$$x - 3y = 5$$
$$2x + y = 3$$

has exactly one solution, namely, (2,−1); the solution set is $\{(2,-1)\}$.

There may be several efficient ways to solve a system of conditions.

When, as in this example, both conditions are linear equations, it is often convenient to proceed as follows:

$$[x - 3y = 5 \text{ and } 2x + y = 3] \Rightarrow [x - 3y = 5 \text{ and } 6x + 3y = 9].$$

This new system of conditions is convenient because you can add them to get an equation free of y. Thus

$$[x - 3y = 5 \text{ and } 6x + 3y = 9] \Rightarrow [(x - 3y) + (6x + 3y) = 5 + 9]$$
$$(x - 3y) + (6x + 3y) = 14,$$
$$7x = 14; \qquad x = 2$$
$$[x = 2 \text{ and } (x - 3y = 5)] \Rightarrow [x = 2 \text{ and } y = -1].$$

As before, you can show that

$$[x - 3y = 5 \text{ and } 2x + y = 3] \Leftrightarrow [x = 2 \text{ and } y = -1].$$

We shall make frequent use of this so-called *method of addition or subtraction* to solve systems of equations. It involves eliminating one of the unknowns by suitable multiplication followed by addition or subtraction of the resulting equations.

(3) Solve the system

$$x - 3y = 7$$
$$5x - 16 = 15y.$$

We abbreviate the solution by addition or subtraction as follows:

$$x - 3y = 7 \qquad 5x - 15y = 35$$
$$5x - 15y = 16 \qquad 5x - 15y = 16.$$

Subtraction yields $0x - 0y = 19$; that is, $0 = 19$. Notice that the conditions $5x - 15y = 35$ and $5x - 15y = 16$ are *inconsistent*. There are no values of x and y that will make $5x - 15y$ equal to *both* 35 and 16. Hence the solution set of $x - 3y = 7$ and $5x - 16 = 15y$ is the null set, { }.

(4) Solve the system

$$x = 3y - 5z + 2$$
$$x + 2y - z = 7$$
$$2x + yz - 3z^2 = 52/5.$$

$$[x = 3y - 5z + 2 \text{ and } x + 2y - z = 7] \Rightarrow [(3y - 5z + 2) + 2y - z = 7]$$
$$[x = 3y - 5z + 2 \text{ and } 2x + yz - 3z^2 = 52/5] \Rightarrow$$
$$[2(3y - 5z + 2) + yz - 3z^2 = 52/5].$$

This yields a system of conditions in the unknowns y and z (free of the unknown x). Thus $(3y - 5z + 2) + 2y - z = 7$ reduces to $5y - 6z = 5$, and $2(3y - 5z + 2) + yz - 3z^2 = 52/5$ reduces to $6y - 10z + yz - 3z^2 = 32/5$. We solve the system

$$5y - 6z = 5$$
$$6y - 10z + yz - 3z^2 = 32/5$$

by the methods of Example (1). Thus

$$5y - 6z = 5 \Rightarrow y = \tfrac{6}{5}z + 1$$

$[y = \tfrac{6}{5}z + 1$ and $6y - 10z + yz - 3z^2 = \tfrac{32}{5}] \Rightarrow$

$$[6(\tfrac{6}{5}z + 1) - 10z + (\tfrac{6}{5}z + 1)z - 3z^2 = \tfrac{32}{5}]$$

$$\tfrac{36}{5}z + 6 - 10z + \tfrac{6}{5}z^2 + z - 3z^2 = \tfrac{32}{5}$$

$$36z + 30 - 50z + 6z^2 + 5z - 15z^2 = 32$$

$$9z^2 + 9z + 2 = 0$$

$$(3z + 2)(3z + 1) = 0$$

$$z = -\tfrac{2}{3} \text{ or } z = -\tfrac{1}{3}$$

$[z = -\tfrac{2}{3}$ and $y = \tfrac{6}{5}z + 1$ and $x = 3y - 5z + 2] \Rightarrow$

$$[x = \tfrac{89}{15}, \, y = \tfrac{1}{5}, \, z = -\tfrac{2}{3}],$$

$[z = -\tfrac{1}{3}$ and $y = \tfrac{6}{5}z + 1$ and $x = 3y - 5z + 2] \Rightarrow$

$$[x = \tfrac{82}{15}, \, y = \tfrac{3}{5}, \, z = -\tfrac{1}{3}].$$

You should substitute the number-triples $(\tfrac{89}{15}, \tfrac{1}{5}, -\tfrac{2}{3})$ and $(\tfrac{82}{15}, \tfrac{3}{5}, -\tfrac{1}{3})$ in the three equations of the original system. You will find that each of the triples is a solution of the given system. Hence the solution set is

$$\{(\tfrac{89}{15}, \tfrac{1}{5}, -\tfrac{2}{3}), \, (\tfrac{82}{15}, \tfrac{3}{5}, -\tfrac{1}{3})\}.$$

(5) Solve the system

$$y = 6x - 7$$
$$\sqrt{y - x^2} = 1.$$

$[y = 6x - 7$ and $\sqrt{y - x^2} = 1] \Rightarrow [\sqrt{6x - 7 - x^2} = 1].$

$$\sqrt{6x - 7 - x^2} = 1$$

$$6x - 7 - x^2 = 1 \quad \text{(squaring both sides)}$$

$$x^2 - 6x + 8 = 0$$

$$(x - 4)(x - 2) = 0$$

$$x = 4 \quad \text{or} \quad x = 2$$

$[x = 4$ and $y = 6x - 7] \Rightarrow [x = 4$ and $y = 17]$
$[x = 2$ and $y = 6x - 7] \Rightarrow [x = 2$ and $y = 5].$

Hence

$[y = 6x - 7$ and $\sqrt{y - x^2} = 1] \Rightarrow [(x = 4$ and $y = 17)$ or $(x = 2$ and $y = 5)].$

But

$$[x = 4 \text{ and } y = 17] \Rightarrow [y = 6x - 7 \text{ and } \sqrt{y - x^2} = \sqrt{17 - 16} = 1],$$

and

$$[x = 2 \text{ and } y = 5] \Rightarrow [y = 6x - 7 \text{ and } \sqrt{y - x^2} = \sqrt{5 - 4} = 1].$$

So

$$[y = 6x - 7 \text{ and } \sqrt{y - x^2} = 1] \Leftrightarrow$$

$$[(x = 4 \text{ and } y = 17) \text{ or } (x = 2 \text{ and } y = 5)].$$

The system $y = 6x - 7$ and $\sqrt{y - x^2} = 1$ has exactly two solutions, namely, (4,17) and (2,5); the solution set is $\{(4,17), (2,5)\}$.

(6) Solve the system

$$y = 6x - 7$$
$$\sqrt{y - x^2} = -1.$$

By the steps used in Example (5), you find

$$[y = 6x - 7 \text{ and } \sqrt{y - x^2} = -1] \Rightarrow$$

$$[(x = 4 \text{ and } y = 17) \text{ or } (x = 2 \text{ and } y = 5)].$$

But $[x = 4 \text{ and } y = 17] \Rightarrow [\sqrt{y - x^2} = \sqrt{17 - 16} = 1 \neq -1]$

and $[x = 2 \text{ and } y = 5] \Rightarrow [\sqrt{y - x^2} = \sqrt{5 - 4} = 1 \neq -1].$

Hence this system of equations has no solution; the solution set of this system of equations is the null set, $\{ \ \}$.

Notice the importance, in this example, of being sure that number-pairs are really solutions of the given system of conditions. You might have foreseen the difficulty by examining the equation $\sqrt{y - x^2} = -1$. Recall, from Chapter 5, that $\sqrt{y - x^2}$ represents a positive real number. Hence $\sqrt{y - x^2} \neq -1$ for each replacement of x and y.

In this section we have illustrated ways to solve systems of algebraic conditions. You should notice that the method of solution involves seeking equivalent systems of conditions whose solution sets are obvious. Sometimes you solve one of the conditions to express one unknown in terms of the other unknowns; then you eliminate this unknown by substitution. Sometimes you use the method of addition or subtraction to eliminate one or more of the unknowns. Sometimes you will find still other methods to eliminate one or more unknowns. Solving a system of conditions often calls for ingenuity and considerable mathematical insight; but the underlying idea is always the same. You want to find all of the sets of values of the unknowns that satisfy the given conditions.

In the remaining sections of Chapter 7 we shall discuss some of the simpler systems of conditions in several unknowns. You will experiment with several ways to think about systems of conditions in search of deeper insights into the problem of solving these systems.

EXERCISES §700

1. Determine the equation of the parabola (i.e., the equation of the form $y = ax^2 + bx + c$) that passes through the points $(2,1)$, $(-2,13)$, and $(0,5)$.
Answer: $y = \frac{1}{2}x^2 - 3x + 5$.

2. Determine the equation of the line that passes through the points $(\frac{1}{2},5)$ and $(2,2)$ by using the equation $y = mx + b$ to set up conditions that m and b must satisfy. Then determine the equation of the line by the methods of Section 402 (page 112) and compare results.

3. Solve the following systems of conditions.

(a) $2x - 4y = -6$
    $x + 2y = 5$

(b) $3x + 5y = 7$
    $2x - 9y = 14$

(c) $x + y = 10$
    $xy = 8$

(d) $y = x^2 + x$
    $y = x^2 - 2x + 9$

(e) $x^2 + y^2 = 10$
    $2x^2 - 3y^2 = 15$

(f) $y = 2x + 1$
    $x^2 - 2xy + y^2 = 9$

(g) $2x - 4y = -6$
    $x - 2y = 5$

(h) $2x - 4y = -6$
    $-3x + 6y = 9$

(i) $x^2 + x + y = 6$
    $y = 8$

(j) $x^2 + y^2 - 2y + 7x = 14$
    $x = 0$.

Answers: (a) $\{(1,2)\}$; (b) $\{(\frac{133}{37}, -\frac{28}{37})\}$; (c) $\{(5 + \sqrt{17}, 5 - \sqrt{17}), (5 - \sqrt{17}, 5 + \sqrt{17})\}$; (i) $\{ \quad \}$ in L.

4. Carry out the steps of Example (6) of this section. Indicate the step in the chain of reasoning that is not reversible. Explain why. (*Hint:* $a = b \Rightarrow a^2 = b^2$; but $a^2 = b^2 \not\Rightarrow a = b$.)

5. To solve the system

$$y = x + 1$$
$$y = 3 + \sqrt{x},$$

one proceeds as follows:

$$x + 1 = 3 + \sqrt{x}$$
$$x - 2 = \sqrt{x}$$
$$x^2 - 4x + 4 = x$$
$$x^2 - 5x + 4 = 0$$
$$x = 1 \quad \text{or} \quad x = 4.$$

But when $x = 1$, $y = 3 + \sqrt{1} = 4$; and when $x = 4$, $y = 3 + \sqrt{4} = 5$. Hence the solutions are $(1,4)$ and $(4,5)$. Are these number-pairs solutions? How do you know? Explain how this could happen.

6. Find all the solutions of the system

$$x = y^2 + 2$$
$$y = \sqrt{x} + 2.$$

7. Find the coordinates of the points of intersection of the parabola $y = x^2 + x + 1$ and the line $y = 2x + 3$.
Answer: $\{(-1,1), (2,7)\}$.

8. Show that the line $y = x - 2$ is tangent to the parabola $y = \frac{1}{2}x^2 - 3x + 6$. (*Hint:* Show that they have one and only one point in common.)

9. Show algebraically that the line $y = 2x + 5$ does not meet the parabola $y = -x^2 + 5x + 2$. (*Hint:* Are there any real values of x and y that satisfy both conditions?)

10. A rectangle has a perimeter of 56 ft and an area of 192 sq ft. Find the length and width.

11. The diagonal of a rectangle is 13 in., and the perimeter is 34 in. Find the length and width of the rectangle.

12. An artillery map is set up as a rectangular coordinate system. An observer is stationed at $(-2,1)$ (meaning 2000 yd west and 1000 yd north of the origin). He sees a flash in the direction of the point $(1,4)$. A second observer station at $(6,1)$ sees this flash in the direction of $(4,4)$.

(a) On graph paper, locate the observers and find the coordinates of the point from which the flash came.
(b) Write the equations of the lines along which: (1) the first observer sees the flash; (2) the second observer sees the flash.
(c) Determine algebraically the coordinates of the point from which the flash came.

13. A radiator filled with water and antifreeze holds 20 qt. The service man at a gas station tests it with a hydrometer and finds that it has enough antifreeze to protect it to $-5°F$. The owner of the car wishes to protect it to $-25°F$. From the chart, he finds that 6 qt of antifreeze are needed for protection to $-5°$ and 8 qt to $-25°F$. How much liquid must be drained out and replaced by antifreeze?

Answer: $2\frac{6}{7}$ qt.

14. In electrical engineering, the conditions $L = 2K/w$, $C = 2/wK$, and $w > 0$ are associated with a certain type of filter section. Show that these conditions imply that the condition $w = 2/\sqrt{LC}$ must hold.

15. Show that the conditions $x + y > 2$ and $y < 3$ imply that $x > -1$.

701. Graphical solutions of systems of conditions

When a system of conditions involves just two unknowns, you can obtain the solution set graphically. Recall that you have already met instances of this technique in Section 601, (page 229).

Consider, for example, the question: For what values of x does $y = 4$ on the graph of the parabola $y = -2x^2 + 5x + 6$? This is really the question: What are the solutions of the system of conditions

$$y = 4$$
$$y = -2x^2 + 5x + 6?$$

Figure 7–1 suggests the graphical solution. The solutions are the circled points. These are approximately (3,4) and (−.4,4). You should solve this system algebraically to find the exact solutions, $\left(\dfrac{5 + \sqrt{41}}{4}, 4\right)$ and $\left(\dfrac{5 - \sqrt{41}}{4}, 4\right)$.

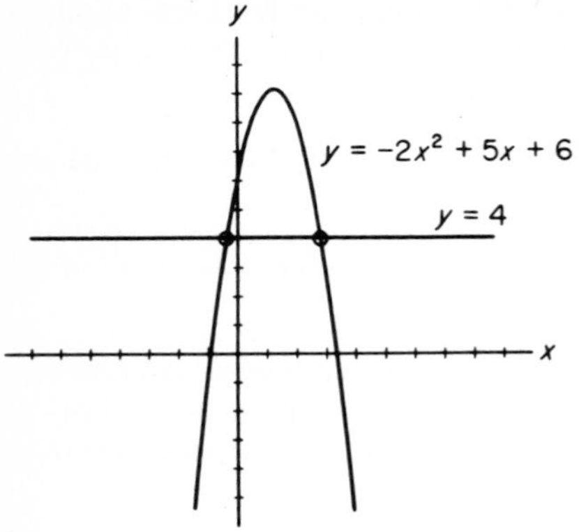

In the remainder of this section we present other examples of graphical solutions:

(1) Use graphical methods to solve the system of conditions:

$$3x - 2y = 7$$
$$x + 3y = 5$$

$$3x - 2y = 7 \Leftrightarrow y = \tfrac{3}{2}x - \tfrac{7}{2}.$$

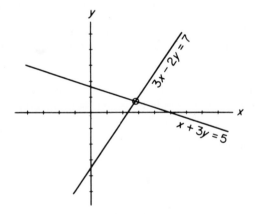

$y = -2x^2 + 5x + 6$

$y = 4$

Fig. 7–1.

Hence the graph of the equation $3x - 2y = 7$ is the straight line of slope $\tfrac{3}{2}$ and y-intercept $-\tfrac{7}{2}$.

$$x + 3y = 5 \Leftrightarrow y = -\tfrac{1}{3}x + \tfrac{5}{3}.$$

The graph is a straight line of slope $-\tfrac{1}{3}$ and y-intercept $\tfrac{5}{3}$. Figure 7–2 displays

$3x - 2y = 7$

$x + 3y = 5$

Fig. 7–2.

the graphs of $3x - 2y = 7$ and $x + 3y = 5$. The graph of $3x - 2y = 7$ *and* $x + 3y = 5$ is the set of points for which both equations hold. There is one and only one point for which $3x - 2y = 7$ *and* $x + 3y = 5$. This is the point where the two straight lines intersect. This point appears, from the graph, to be approximately (3,.8). You should solve this system algebraically to find the exact solution $(\tfrac{31}{11}, \tfrac{8}{11})$.

(2) Use graphical methods to solve the system of conditions:

$$x - 5y = 15$$
$$2x = 10y - 10.$$

As in Example (1):

$$x - 5y = 15 \Leftrightarrow y = \tfrac{1}{5}x - 3$$
$$2x = 10y - 10 \Leftrightarrow y = \tfrac{1}{5}x + 1.$$

Figure 7–3 shows the graphs of two straight lines that are parallel; both lines have slope $\tfrac{1}{5}$. There is no point where the two lines intersect; there is no

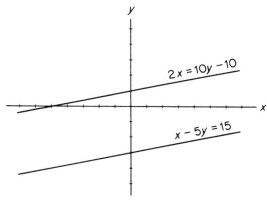

Fig. 7–3.

number-pair (x,y) that satisfies both the equation $x - 5y = 15$ and the equation $2x = 10y - 10$. The solution set of the given system of conditions is the null set. You should solve this system algebraically to see how the algebra tells you that the given system of conditions has no solution.

(3) Use graphical methods to solve the system of conditions:

$$x - 5y = 15$$
$$2x = 10y + 30.$$

As in Example (2):

$$x - 5y = 15 \Leftrightarrow y = \tfrac{1}{5}x - 3$$
$$2x = 10y + 30 \Leftrightarrow y = \tfrac{1}{5}x - 3.$$

Figure 7–4 shows the graphs of two straight lines that are identical; both lines have slope $\tfrac{1}{5}$ and y-intercept -3. Each point on the line $x - 5y = 15$ is also on the line $2x = 10y + 30$; in this sense each point on either line is a point of intersection with the other line. Hence the solution set of the given system is the set of number-pairs, $\{(x, \tfrac{1}{5}x - 3)\}$. This set has infinitely many elements, one for each point on the line $y = \tfrac{1}{5}x - 3$. For example, the points $(0,-3)$, $(5,-2)$, and $(20,1)$ are elements of the solution set.

We summarize Examples (1), (2), and (3) as follows: If $b_1 \neq 0$ and $b_2 \neq 0$, the system of conditions

$$a_1 x + b_1 y = c_1$$
$$a_2 x + b_2 y = c_2$$

represent two non-vertical straight lines. There are three possibilities:

(a) If the slopes $-a_1/b_1$ and $-a_2/b_2$ are unequal, the lines intersect. The system of conditions has one and only one solution. We call the lines *intersecting*. We call the system of conditions *consistent*.

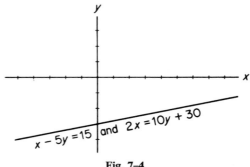

Fig. 7-4.

(b) If the slopes $-a_1/b_1$ and $-a_2/b_2$ are equal and the y-intercepts c_1/b_1 and c_2/b_2 are unequal, the lines are parallel. The system of conditions has no solution. We call the lines *parallel*. We call the system of conditions *inconsistent*. (That is, they contradict one another; no number-pair (x,y) satisfies both conditions.)

(c) If the slopes $-a_1/b_1$ and $-a_2/b_2$ are equal and the y-intercepts c_1/b_1 and c_2/b_2 are equal, the lines coincide. The system of conditions has infinitely many solutions; every point on either of the lines is a solution. We call the lines *coincident*. We call the system of conditions *dependent*. (That is, the second condition is *not* independent of the first one. If a number-pair (x,y) makes one condition true, it makes the other condition true also.)

We shall return to a more formal discussion of this summary in Section 703. Meanwhile, it will be convenient to use the summary as you interpret Exercises 701.

Many of the algebraic conditions of degree greater than 1 that you met in previous chapters were of the form $y = p(x)$. In Examples (4) and (5) you can use your knowledge of the graphs of polynomials.

(4) Use graphical methods to solve the system of conditions:

$$x - 3y - 6 = 0$$
$$y = \tfrac{1}{3}x^3 - \tfrac{1}{2}x^2 - 6x + 4.$$
$$x - 3y - 6 = 0 \Leftrightarrow y = \tfrac{1}{3}x - 2$$
$$y = \tfrac{1}{3}x^3 - \tfrac{1}{2}x^2 - 6x + 4 \Rightarrow y' = x^2 - x - 6 = (x+2)(x-3).$$

The maximum of minimum points (if any) occur where $(x + 2)(x - 3) = 0$; that is, where $x = -2$, or $x = 3$. We construct a table paying attention to these critical values of x.

x	-4	-3	-2	-1	0	1	2	3	4	5
y	$-1\frac{1}{3}$	$8\frac{1}{2}$	$11\frac{1}{3}$	$9\frac{1}{6}$	4	$-2\frac{1}{6}$	$-7\frac{1}{3}$	$-9\frac{1}{2}$	$-6\frac{2}{3}$	$3\frac{1}{6}$
y'	14	6	0	-4	-6	-6	-4	0	6	14

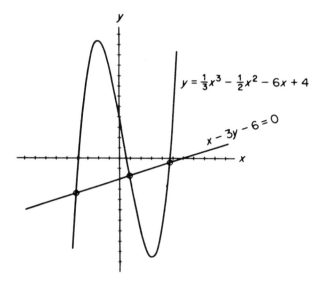

$$y = \tfrac{1}{3}x^3 - \tfrac{1}{2}x^2 - 6x + 4$$

$$x - 3y - 6 = 0$$

Fig. 7–5.

Figure 7–5 displays the graph of the two conditions. The solutions are the three circled points. You may be interested in experimenting with an algebraic solution of the given system. Notice that it involves solving a cubic equation. Thus

$$(y = \tfrac{1}{3}x - 2 \text{ and } y = \tfrac{1}{3}x^3 - \tfrac{1}{2}x^2 - 6x + 4) \Rightarrow$$
$$(\tfrac{1}{3}x - 2 = \tfrac{1}{3}x^3 - \tfrac{1}{2}x^2 - 6x + 4).$$

The x-coordinates of the three points of intersection of the graphs are the solutions of the equation

$$\tfrac{1}{3}x^3 - \tfrac{1}{2}x^2 - \tfrac{19}{3}x + 6 = 0.$$

When you find the three values of x that satisfy this cubic equation you can easily find the three corresponding values of y from the equation $y = \tfrac{1}{3}x - 2$. But solving the cubic is not easy, even when you are willing to round off your answers to three significant figures. Recall Section 604 (page 274).

One advantage, then, of the graphical solution of systems of conditions is that it works even when the conditions get more complicated. Of course it is by no means easy to plot the graphs of some conditions; but you can always plot the graph of a polynomial, point by point, and thus obtain approximate solutions of problems like Example (4).

(5) Use graphical methods to solve the system of conditions:

$$y = x^2 - 2x - 5$$
$$3x^2 + y = 8x + 3.$$
$$3x^2 + y = 8x + 3 \Leftrightarrow y = -3x^2 + 8x + 3.$$

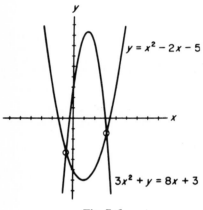

$y = x^2 - 2x - 5$

$3x^2 + y = 8x + 3$

Fig. 7–6.

The graphs of the two conditions are the two parabolas in Fig. 7–6. The solutions are the two circled points. You should perform an algebraic solution to find that these solutions are approximately (3.14, −1.42) and (−.64,−3.31).

Perhaps you are beginning to ask, "Why perform a graphical solution and then perform a more exact, algebraic solution? Why bother with the graph?" There are two good reasons. The graph gives you a picture that helps you to interpret a purely algebraic solution. So you get insights from the graph that you might miss in the algebra. Moreover, you can solve some systems graphically that you would find it difficult or even impossible to solve algebraically. Hence the ideas behind the graphical solution of systems of conditions are important ideas.

The examples that we have given you so far are fairly straightforward. You know how to draw the graphs; what you learned about polynomials in Chapter 6 is a real help on a problem like Example (4). The following exercises provide practice with such graphical solutions.

EXERCISES §701

1. Use graphs to find the solution set of each system of conditions; then compare your results with ones you obtained algebraically in Exercise 3 of Section 700 (page 290).

(a) $2x - 4y = -6$
$x + 2y = 5$

(b) $3x + 5y = 7$
$2x - 9y = 14$

(c) $x + y = 10$
$xy = 8$

(d) $y = x^2 + x$
$y = x^2 - 2x + 9$

(e) $2x - 4y = -6$
$x - 2y = 5$

(f) $2x - 4y = -6$
$-3x + 6y = 9.$

2. Determine whether each system of conditions is consistent, inconsistent, or dependent. Draw the graph.

(a) $x + 2y = 3$
$\quad\ y - 2x = 4$

(b) $4x - 6y = 12$
$\quad\ 2x - 3y = 4$

(c) $y = 3x - 2$
$\quad\ 4x + 7y = 3$

(d) $2x - y = 2$
$\quad\ 2x + y = 2y + x$

(e) $8x = 4y + 3$
$\quad\ y = 2x - 5$

(f) $2x - 3y = -4$
$\quad\ -.5x + .75y = 1$

(g) $x - 4 = 0$
$\quad\ y + 3 = 0$

(h) $y - 4 = 0$
$\quad\ y + 3 = 0$

(i) $6x - 2y = 1$
$\quad\ y = 3x + \frac{1}{2}$

(j) $2x - 8 - 5y = 0$
$\quad\ 2y = x - \frac{1}{2}y - 4.$

Answers: (a) Consistent; (b) inconsistent; (d) consistent; (f) dependent; (h) inconsistent; (j) dependent.

3. Determine graphically the solution set of the system $y = x^2 + x + 1$ and $y = 2x + 3$. Compare with your algebraic solution of Exercise 7, Section 700 (page 290).

4. Determine graphically the solution set of each system of conditions:

(a) $y = \frac{1}{2}x^2 - 3x + 4$
$\quad\ x - 2y = 1$

(b) $y = x^2 + 4x - 1$
$\quad\ y = 2x + 4$

(c) $y = -x^2 - 2x + 7$
$\quad\ y = -3x + 1$

(d) $y = x^2 + 4x - 1$
$\quad\ y = -x^2 - 2x + 7$

(e) $y = x^2 + 4x - 1$
$\quad\ y = x^2 + 4x + 2$

(f) $y = x^2 + 4x - 1$
$\quad\ y = x^2 - 6x + 4.$

5. Solve Exercise 8 of Section 700 (page 291) graphically.

6. Solve Exercise 9 of Section 700 (page 291) graphically.

7. From the graph of Example (4), estimate the solution of the system $y = \frac{1}{3}x^3 - \frac{1}{2}x^2 - 6x + 4$ and $y = \frac{1}{3}x - 2$. Check your estimates by substitution.

8. Show graphically that there is just one real solution of the system $y = \frac{1}{2}x^3 - 6x - 4$ and $y = -\frac{1}{2}x + 4$. Estimate the solution.

Answer: Approximately (3.9,2.1).

9. From the conditions of Exercise 8, write a cubic equation that x must satisfy. Using the technique of Section 604 (page 276), improve the estimate ($x \doteq 3.9$) to the nearest hundredth and thereby improve your answer to Exercise 8.

Answer correct to nearest .001 : (3.888,2.056).

What if you met a condition like $2x^2 + 3y^2 - 2x + 7y = 10$ as one of a system of conditions? Of course, you can plot the graph of this condition. You can find the subset of the cartesian plane whose elements are number-pairs, (x,y), that satisfy the condition. But you would expect the task of plotting the graph to be laborious. You would have to assign values to x

and calculate the corresponding value or values of y. For example, when $x = 3$,

$$2(9) + 3y^2 - 2(3) + 7y = 10$$

$$3y^2 + 7y + 2 = 0$$

$$y = -\frac{7}{6} \pm \frac{\sqrt{25}}{6}$$

$$y = -\frac{1}{3} \quad \text{or} \quad y = -2.$$

Hence the points $(3, -\frac{1}{3})$ and $(3, -2)$ lie on the graph. It would be quite laborious to find enough points in this way to sketch a reasonably accurate graph of the condition $2x^2 + 3y^2 - 2x + 7y = 10$.

People in the field of applied mathematics do plot many graphs point-by-point. They set up their problems in a form that lends itself to machine calculation; then they hire clerks to grind out the results.

In Section 702 we shall discuss the graphs of conditions of degree two in x and y. This discussion will lead to short-cuts in graphing a condition like $2x^2 + 3y^2 - 2x + 7y = 10$. You know already that the points $(3, -\frac{1}{3})$ and $(3, -2)$ lie on this curve. You can pair the same value of x ($x = 3$) with two different values of y ($y = -\frac{1}{3}$ and $y = -2$). Hence you know that the relation

$$\{(x, y) \mid 2x^2 + 3y^2 - 2x + 7y = 10\}$$

is *not* a function. We shall find, however, that its graph is a simple and interesting curve in the cartesian plane.

As conditions become more involved you may have to resort to point-by-point plotting. We give two more examples to show how you can use what you already know to speed up this process. Then we include further examples in the exercises.

(6) Use graphical methods to solve the system of conditions:

$$y = \tfrac{1}{2}x - 1$$

$$y = 2 \sin x.$$

The graph of $y = \frac{1}{2}x - 1$ is the familiar straight line of slope $\frac{1}{2}$ and y-intercept -1. What about the graph of $y = 2 \sin x$? Recall the graph of $y = \sin x$ from Section 409 (page 153). Each y of the graph of $y = 2 \sin x$ is double the corresponding y of the graph of $y = \sin x$. Figure 7–7 displays the graphs of $y = \frac{1}{2}x - 1$ and $y = 2 \sin x$. The solutions of the system of conditions are the three circled points.

Notice how the graph helps you to visualize this problem. Before you draw the graph it is very hard to guess how many solutions you will get. If the straight line rose more slowly it might intersect the graph of $y = 2 \sin x$ several more times. Clearly, the line $y = \frac{1}{10}x - 1$ would do this; and the line $y = -1$ would intersect the graph of $y = 2 \sin x$ in infinitely many points.

Once you have drawn the graph you can use tables to locate the solutions more exactly. Thus

x	2.8	2.9	3.0
$\frac{1}{2}x - 1$	.40	.45	.50
$2 \sin x$	.67	.48	.28

The calculation of $2 \sin x$ involves a rather special use of your book of tables. In the table called Trigonometric Functions in Radian Measure,

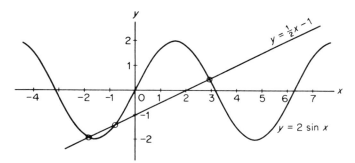

Fig. 7–7.

you find values of x from $x = .00$ to $x = 1.60$. To get $\sin 3.0$, above, recall that x is the arc of a unit circle. The circumference of the unit circle is 2π; one half the circumference is $\pi \doteq 3.14$. Now recall the graph of $y = \sin x$ from page 153; notice that $\sin 3.0 \doteq \sin (3.14 - 3.0) = \sin (.14)$. In general, $\sin x = \sin (\pi - x)$; the graph of $y = \sin x$ goes forward from $x = 0$ in exactly the way that it goes backward from $x = \pi$. Hence $\sin 2.8 \doteq \sin (3.14 - 2.8) = \sin (.34)$; $\sin 2.9 = \sin (3.14 - 2.9) = \sin (.24)$; etc.

The table shows that $x = 2.9$ makes $y = \frac{1}{2}x - 1 \doteq 2 \sin x$. Further study of the table tells you that, for some value of x such that $2.9 < x < 3.0$, you will have $\frac{1}{2}x - 1 = 2 \sin x$. You will learn to refine such approximations in Chapter 9. Meanwhile you may wish to experiment with the other two solutions. Here are some more table entries to check:

x	$-.60$	$-.70$	$-.80$	...	-1.80	-1.90	-2.00
$\frac{1}{2}x - 1$	-1.30	-1.35	-1.40	...	-1.90	-1.95	-2.00
$2 \sin x$	-1.13	-1.29	-1.43	...	-1.95	-1.89	-1.82

The two values of x are such that $-.80 < x < -.70$, and $-1.90 < x < -1.80$.

(7) Use graphical methods to solve the system of conditions:

$$y = \frac{2}{x}$$

$$y - 3 = 5^x.$$

Figure 7–8 shows that there is exactly one solution, namely the circled point.

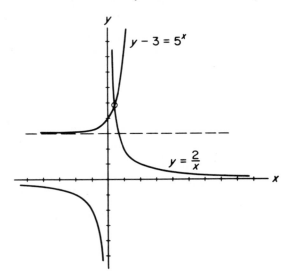

Fig. 7–8.

As you re-read Section 701 you should notice the generality of graphical solutions. If you can graph the conditions of a system, you can solve the system graphically (except, of course, for solutions that are imaginary numbers). Graphical solutions are approximate solutions; hence it is often desirable to improve upon them by methods like those you met in Chapter 6.

In light of these comments, you will recognize the importance of knowing type-graphs. You should be able to sketch straight lines, parabolas, trigonometric and exponential functions quickly. You will meet other important graphs in Section 702 and throughout the remainder of this text.

EXERCISES §701 (cont.)

10. Use graphical methods to show that the system $y = -x + 2$ and $y = 2 \sin x$ has only one solution. (Suggestion: Lay a ruler on the graph in Fig. 7–7, along the line $y = -x + 2$.)

11. Estimate the solution of the system $y = -x + 2$ and $y = 2 \sin x$. Check your estimate by substitution.

Answer: Approximately $(.7, 1.3)$.

12. Explain why you would expect an infinite number of solutions to the system $y = \tan x$ and $y = mx + b$, for each m and b. (Suggestion: See the graph of $y = \tan x$, page 159.)

13. Use graphical methods to solve each system of conditions:

(a) $y = 2^x$ (b) $y = 2^x$ (c) $y = 2^x$

    $y = 2x + 1$ $y = -2x + 1$ $y = 2x - 1$.

14. What are the possible numbers of solutions for a system of conditions of the form $y = b^x$ and $y = mx + b$?

15. Illustrate Exercise 15, Section 700 (page 291) graphically.

16. Graph the set of points that satisfy each system of conditions:

(a) $x + 2y > 3$ (b) $6x - 2y < 1$

    $y - 2x < 4$ $y < 3x + \frac{1}{2}$

(c) $y > x^2 + 4x - 1$ (d) $y < x^2 + 4x - 1$

    $y < 2x + 4$ $y > -x^2 - 2x + 7$

(e) $y > \frac{1}{2}x^3 - 6x - 4$ (f) $y > \frac{1}{2}x - 1$

    $y < -\frac{1}{2}x + 4$ $y < 2 \sin x$.

17. Find the maximum value of A where $A = x + y$, but x and y are restricted by the linear conditions $2x + y \leq 12$ and $2x + 6y \leq 27$. (*Hint:* Draw the graph of the region of the cartesian plane that satisfies the set of inequalities. Treat A as a parameter, drawing a few of the lines $A = x + y$ for $A = 2, 4, 6$, etc. What values of x and y in the restricted region will give the largest value of A?) Problems of this type are of great importance in modern mathematics. See *The Mathematics Teacher*, March 1955, page 130, for an interesting application to industry.

702. Graphs of conditions of degree 2 in x and y

The most general equation of degree 2 in x and y is

$$Ax^2 + Bxy + Cy^2 + Dx + Ey + F = 0, \quad A, B, \text{ or } C \neq 0.$$

The term Bxy is of degree 1 in x and of degree 1 in y; we shall call it a term of degree 2 in x and y. With this understanding, you see that the expression $Ax^2 + Bxy + Cy^2 + Dx + Ey + F$ includes all the possible terms of degree at most 2 in x and y.

We consider some special cases of the general second-degree equation. At first we let $B = 0$ and consider the condition $Ax^2 + Cy^2 + Dx + Ey + F = 0$.

Case 1. If $A = D = 0$, the equation becomes a condition on y alone; if $C = E = 0$, the equation becomes a condition on x alone. These cases are of no interest here. They are conditions in one unknown like the ones you studied in Chapter 6.

Case 2. If $C = 0$ and $E \neq 0$, you get the polynomial in x,

$$y = -\frac{A}{E}x^2 - \frac{D}{E}x - \frac{F}{E},$$

which you studied in Chapter 6.

If $A = 0$ and $D \neq 0$, you get the polynomial in y,

$$x = -\frac{C}{D}y^2 - \frac{E}{D}y - \frac{F}{D}.$$

Notice that you can set up a coordinate system, as in Fig. 7–9, interchanging the x- and y-axes; then you can proceed as in Chapter 6 to graph this polynomial in y. We drew the graph of $x = 3y^2 - 2y - 4$ as an example.

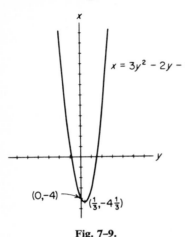

$x = 3y^2 - 2y - 4$

$(0,-4)$

$(\frac{1}{3}, -4\frac{1}{3})$

Fig. 7–9.

Figure 7–10 shows the coordinate axes in the conventional way. The parabola is symmetrical about the line $y = \frac{1}{3}$, parallel to the x-axis.

Notice that the graphs of $y = 3x^2 - 2x - 4$ and $x = 3y^2 - 2y - 4$ are inverse to each other in the sense of Section 501 (page 177). The roles of

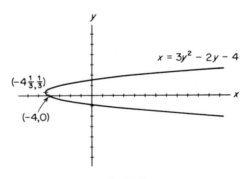

$x = 3y^2 - 2y - 4$

$(-4\frac{1}{3}, \frac{1}{3})$

$(-4,0)$

Fig. 7–10.

x and y are interchanged; hence the graph of $x = 3y^2 - 2y - 4$ is the reflection of the graph of $y = 3x^2 - 2x - 4$ in the line $y = x$ (see Fig. 7–11).

Notice that relation $\{(x,y) \mid y = 3x^2 - 2x - 4\}$ is a function; but the inverse relation, $\{(x,y) \mid x = 3y^2 - 2y - 4\}$ is not a function. Still, the graph of $x = 3y^2 - 2y - 4$ is a parabola. It is easy to draw this graph by using ideas developed in previous chapters. Exercises §702 will provide practice in graphing equations of the form $x = p(y)$.

Case 3. If $A \neq 0$ and $C \neq 0$, it is not possible to express y as a polynomial in x or to express x as a polynomial in y. We shall build up to the

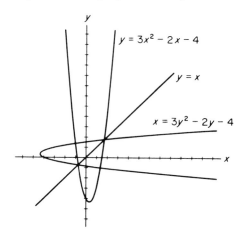

$y = 3x^2 - 2x - 4$

$y = x$

$x = 3y^2 - 2y - 4$

Fig. 7–11.

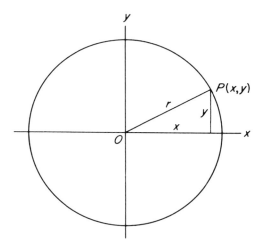

$P(x,y)$

r

y

x

O

Fig. 7–12.

general case by studying special cases, somewhat as we did in Sections 404 and 405.

(1) Graph the equation $x^2 + y^2 = r^2$. Figure 7–12 shows a point $P(x,y)$ that lies on the graph. Since P lies on the graph, $x^2 + y^2 = r^2$. By the theorem of Pythagoras, $x^2 + y^2 = OP^2$; hence $OP = r$, and P lies at a

distance r from the origin. Conversely, suppose that $P(x,y)$ is at a distance r from the origin; hence $x^2 + y^2 = r^2$, and the point P lies on the graph.

The *locus* of P is the subset of the cartesian plane, each point of which lies at a distance r from the origin. We shall call the graph of $x^2 + y^2 = r^2$ a *circle*. It is the set of points, $\{P(x,y)\}$, such that $OP = r$.

The equation $x^2 + y^2 = r^2$ represents a one-parameter family of circles with centers at $(0,0)$; the parameter r represents the radius of a circle.

(2) Graph the equation $(x - h)^2 + (y - k)^2 = r^2$ (see Fig. 7–13). You can use the concept of alias to think of the equation $(x - h)^2 + (y - k)^2 = r^2$ as the equation $X^2 + Y^2 = r^2$, where $X = x - h$ and $Y = y - k$. Then X represents the horizontal distance from (h,k) to (x,y); Y represents the vertical distance from (h,k) to (x,y). The point (h,k) plays the role of the

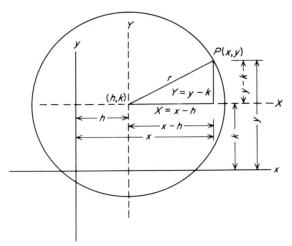

Fig. 7–13.

origin of the XY-coordinate system; hence the graph of $X^2 + Y^2 = r^2$ is a circle with its center at (h,k); or, using its other name, $(x - h)^2 + (y - k)^2 = r^2$ is a circle with its center at (h,k).

You can also look at the equation $(x - h)^2 + (y - k)^2 = r^2$ directly; $(x - h)^2 + (y - k)^2$ represents the square of the distance from (h,k) to (x,y). Hence the condition $(x - h)^2 + (y - k)^2 = r^2$ defines a subset of the cartesian plane, each point of which lies at a distance r from the point (h,k); this is a three-parameter family of circles, with center at (h,k) and radius r.

(3) Graph the equation $Ax^2 + Ay^2 + Dx + Ey + F = 0$. Write the equation as

$$\left(x^2 + \frac{D}{A}x + \quad\right) + \left(y^2 + \frac{E}{A}y + \quad\right) = -\frac{F}{A},$$

recalling that $A \neq 0$. Now construct perfect-square trinomials as in Section 601 (page 235) to get:

$$\left[x^2 + \frac{D}{A}x + \left(\frac{D}{2A}\right)^2\right] + \left[y^2 + \frac{E}{A}y + \left(\frac{E}{2A}\right)^2\right] = \frac{D^2}{4A^2} + \frac{E^2}{4A^2} - \frac{F}{A}$$

$$\left(x + \frac{D}{2A}\right)^2 + \left(y + \frac{E}{2A}\right)^2 = \frac{D^2 + E^2 - 4AF}{4A^2}.$$

The graph is a circle with center at $(-D/2A, -E/2A)$ and radius $r = (1/2A)\sqrt{D^2 + E^2 - 4AF}$. You get a *real circle* if $D^2 + E^2 - 4AF > 0$;

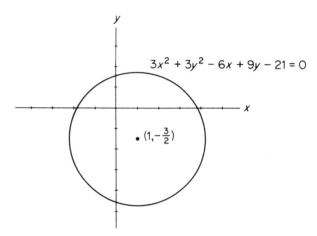

$$3x^2 + 3y^2 - 6x + 9y - 21 = 0$$

$$\left(1, -\tfrac{3}{2}\right)$$

Fig. 7–14.

you get an *imaginary circle* if $D^2 + E^2 - 4AF < 0$. If $D^2 + E^2 - 4AF = 0$, you get a *circle of radius* 0, that is, the point $(-D/2A, -E/2A)$. We shall not ask you to remember this result as a formula. Rather we shall expect you to work out each instance that you meet. An example will illustrate the procedure.

Graph the equation $3x^2 + 3y^2 - 6x + 9y - 21 = 0$. Since $A = C = 3$, this equation has the form, $Ax^2 + Ay^2 + Dx + Ey + F = 0$, of the equation of a circle. Now,

$$(x^2 - 2x \quad) + (y^2 + 3y \quad) = 7$$
$$[x^2 - 2x + 1] + [y^2 + 3y + (\tfrac{3}{2})^2] = 1 + \tfrac{9}{4} + 7$$
$$(x - 1)^2 + (y + \tfrac{3}{2})^2 = \tfrac{41}{4}.$$

The circle has center $(1, -\tfrac{3}{2})$ and radius $\sqrt{41}/2$. Its graph appears in Fig. 7–14. Notice that the graphs of circles are not graphs of functions. The same value of x may yield two distinct values of y.

The equation $3x^2 + 3y^2 - 6x + 9y + 21 = 0$ will reduce to

$(x - 1)^2 + (y + \frac{3}{2})^2 = -\frac{15}{4}$. You may think of the graph as an imaginary circle; as a subset of the cartesian plane, it is the null set.

The equation $3x^2 + 3y^2 - 6x + 9y + \frac{39}{4} = 0$ reduces to $(x - 1)^2 + (y + \frac{3}{2})^2 = 0$. You may think of the graph as a circle of radius 0; as a subset of the cartesian plane, it is the set $\{(1, -\frac{3}{2})\}$ which contains just the point $(1, -\frac{3}{2})$. Before continuing with Case 3, you should pause to work some exercises.

EXERCISES §702

1. Draw the graphs of each of the following pairs of conditions:

(a) $y = x^2$
$\quad x = y^2$

(b) $y = 2x^2 - 3$
$\quad x = 2y^2 - 3$

(c) $y = \frac{1}{2}x^2 - 4x + 7$
$\quad x = \frac{1}{2}y^2 - 4y + 7$

(d) $\frac{1}{4}x^2 + x + y - 3 = 0$
$\quad \frac{1}{4}y^2 + x + y - 3 = 0$.

2. Find the distance between the point $(3,4)$ and the origin. What is the equation of the circle with center at the origin that passes through this point? Which of the following points lie on this circle: $(-3,4)$; $(0,-5)$; $(2,-3)$; $(2\sqrt{6}, -1)$?

3. Write the equation of each circle whose center and radius are given below:

(a) $(0,0); r = 3$

(b) $(0,0); r = \sqrt{7}$

(c) $(1,3); r = 4$

(d) $(-1,5); r = 9$

(e) $(2,-4); r = 4\sqrt{5}$

(f) $(-3,-4); r = 1$.

Answers: (b) $x^2 + y^2 = 7$;   (d) $x^2 + y^2 + 2x - 10y - 55 = 0$.

4. Determine the coordinates of the center and the radius of each circle. Draw the graph.

(a) $x^2 + y^2 = 5$

(b) $x^2 + y^2 - 2x - 4y - 4 = 0$

(c) $x^2 + y^2 - 6x = 0$

(d) $2x^2 + 2y^2 - 8x + 6y + 1 = 0$

(e) $x^2 + y^2 + 3x + 5y - 4 = 0$

(f) $5x^2 + 5y^2 - 5x + 7y + 2 = 0$

(g) $14 + 5y + 2x - 3x^2 - 3y^2 = 0$

(h) $x^2 + y^2 + x + y + \frac{1}{2} = 0$.

Answers: (c) $(3,0), 3$; (d) $(2, -\frac{3}{2}), \frac{1}{2}\sqrt{23}$; (f) $(.5, -.7), \sqrt{.34}$; (h) $(-\frac{1}{2}, -\frac{1}{2}), 0$.

5. Show that there are no pairs of real numbers (x,y) that satisfy the condition $x^2 + y^2 - 7x + 3y + 16 = 0$; that is, show that

$$\{(x,y) \mid x^2 + y^2 - 7x + 3y + 16 = 0\} = \{\ \}.$$

6. For the circle $x^2 + y^2 + 3x + 5y - 4 = 0$, determine the y coordinates of points on the graph for which $x = 2$; $x = 1$; $x = 0$; $x = -2$. Plot these points and compare with the graph of Exercise 4(e).

7. Show that $x^2 + y^2 = 16$ and $y > 0 \Leftrightarrow y = \sqrt{16 - x^2}$. What is the graph of this condition? Does this condition determine a function? What is the range of the variable x?

8. Show on graph paper the set of points

$$\{(x,y) \mid 0 < y < \sqrt{16 - x^2}\}.$$

(See Exercise 7.)

9. Find the equation of thė circle that passes through the points $(0,0)$, $(5,-1)$, and $(-1,-1)$.

10. At what points does the line $2x + y = 9$ intersect the circle $x^2 + y^2 + 2x - 4y - 45 = 0$?

Answer: $\{(0,9), (26/5, -7/5)\}$.

11. At what points does the circle of Exercise 10 intersect the circle $x^2 + y^2 - 4x + 4y - 17 = 0$?

Answer: $\{(6,1), (-2,-5)\}$.

We continue Case 3, that is, graphs of conditions $Ax^2 + Cy^2 + Dx + Ey + F = 0$, with $A \neq 0$ and $C \neq 0$.

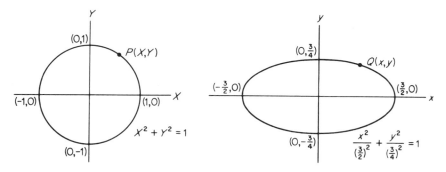

Fig. 7–15.

(4) Graph the equation

$$\frac{x^2}{a^2} + \frac{y^2}{b^2} = 1.$$

Compare this equation to the equation, $X^2 + Y^2 = 1$, of a circle of radius 1. Let $X = x/a$ and $Y = y/b$, where $a > 0$ and $b > 0$; then $x = aX$ and $y = bY$. Study the figure as an instance in which $a = 3/2$ and $b = 3/4$.

In Fig. 7–15, each point $P(X,Y)$ of the left-hand graph is *mapped* into a point $Q(x,y)$ of the right-hand graph by the transformation

$$x = \tfrac{3}{2}X, \qquad y = \tfrac{3}{4}Y.$$

It is convenient to separate the two graphs to study the effect of the transformation; but notice that the effect of the transformation is to stretch the circle horizontally in the ratio 3/2, and shrink it vertically in the ratio 3/4. The result is an oval that mathematicians call an *ellipse*.

Notice that the point $(1,0)$ of the circle maps into the point $(\tfrac{3}{2},0)$ of the ellipse; the point $(-1,0)$ maps into the point $(-\tfrac{3}{2},0)$. Similarly, the points

(0,1) and (0,−1) of the circle map into the points (0,$\frac{3}{4}$) and (0,−$\frac{3}{4}$) of the ellipse.

In general, the transformation

$$x = aX$$
$$a > 0 \text{ and } b > 0$$
$$y = bY$$

maps the circle $X^2 + Y^2 = 1$ into the ellipse $x^2/a^2 + y^2/b^2 = 1$. When you compare the ellipse to the circle you notice that the ellipse has a variable radius; two values of this radius are of special interest, namely, the radius a in the horizontal direction and the radius b in the vertical direction. It is customary to call the longer radius ($\frac{3}{2}$ in Fig. 7–15) the *semi-major axis*, and the shorter radius ($\frac{3}{4}$ in Fig. 7–15) the *semi-minor axis*. The *major axis* is the larger of the numbers 2a and 2b. The *minor axis* is the smaller of the numbers 2a and 2b. It is easy to sketch an ellipse when you know the values of a and b.

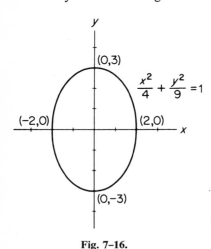

$$\frac{x^2}{4} + \frac{y^2}{9} = 1$$

Fig. 7–16.

For example, to graph $x^2/4 + y^2/9 = 1$, you notice that $a = 2$ (since $a^2 = 4$ and $a > 0$) and $b = 3$. Hence the graph is the ellipse of Fig. 7–16. The major axis is vertical and equal to 6; the minor axis is horizontal and equal to 4.

(5) Graph the equation

$$\frac{(x - h)^2}{a^2} + \frac{(y - k)^2}{b^2} = 1.$$

The graph is clearly an ellipse with center (h,k), horizontal axis 2a, and vertical axis 2b. For example, Fig. 7–17 shows the graph of

$$\frac{(x + 3)^2}{12} + \frac{(y - 2)^2}{9} = 1.$$

Here $a = 2\sqrt{3}$ and $b = 3$. The center of the ellipse is $(-3,2)$. Check the coordinates of the four *vertices* of the ellipse as labeled in the figure.

(6) Graph the equation $Ax^2 + Cy^2 + Dx + Ey + F = 0$, in which A and C have the same algebraic sign (either $A > 0$ and $C > 0$, or $A < 0$ and $C < 0$). Write the equation as

$$A\left[x^2 + \frac{D}{A}x \qquad \right] + C\left[y^2 + \frac{E}{C}y \qquad \right] = -F.$$

Now complete the perfect-square trinomials to get

$$A\left[x^2 + \frac{D}{A}x + \left(\frac{D}{2A}\right)^2\right] + C\left[y^2 + \frac{E}{C}y + \left(\frac{E}{2C}\right)^2\right]$$

$$= A\left(\frac{D}{2A}\right)^2 + C\left(\frac{E}{2C}\right)^2 - F$$

$$A\left(x + \frac{D}{2A}\right)^2 + C\left(y + \frac{E}{2C}\right)^2 = \frac{D^2}{4A} + \frac{E^2}{4C} - F.$$

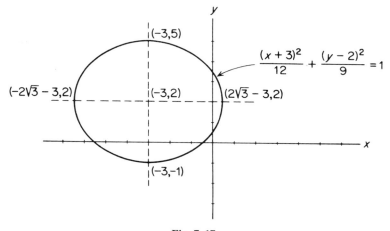

$$\frac{(x+3)^2}{12} + \frac{(y-2)^2}{9} = 1$$

Fig. 7–17.

It is easier to see the form of this condition when you write

$$\frac{D^2}{4A} + \frac{E^2}{4C} - F = G.$$

Then
$$A\left(x + \frac{D}{2A}\right)^2 + C\left(y + \frac{E}{2C}\right)^2 = G.$$

If $G = 0$, the graph is the point $(-D/2A, -E/2C)$. If $G \neq 0$,

$$\frac{(x + D/2A)^2}{G/A} + \frac{(y + E/2C)^2}{G/C} = 1.$$

Since A and C have the same sign, G/A and G/C have the same sign. If G/A and G/C are positive, the graph is an ellipse with center $(-D/2A, -E/2C)$. If G/A and G/C are negative, the graph is imaginary; you may think of it as an imaginary ellipse.

Again, we shall not expect you to learn formulas at this point. Rather, you should work out each instance that you meet. An example will illustrate the procedure.

To graph the equation $5x^2 + 2y^2 - 20x + 6y - 10 = 0$, write

$$5[x^2 - 4x \qquad] + 2[y^2 + 3y \qquad] = 10$$
$$5[x^2 - 4x + 4] + 2[y^2 + 3y + \tfrac{9}{4}] = 20 + \tfrac{9}{2} + 10 = \tfrac{69}{2}$$
$$\frac{(x - 2)^2}{\frac{69}{10}} + \frac{(y + \frac{3}{2})^2}{\frac{69}{4}} = 1.$$

In this example, the numbers $\tfrac{69}{10}$ and $\tfrac{69}{4}$ are positive. The graph (Fig. 7–18) is an ellipse with center $(2, -\tfrac{3}{2})$, horizontal axis $2\sqrt{69/10} = 2\sqrt{6.9}$, and vertical axis $2\sqrt{69/4} = \sqrt{69}$. You should check the approximate coordinates of the four vertices of the ellipse as labeled in the figure.

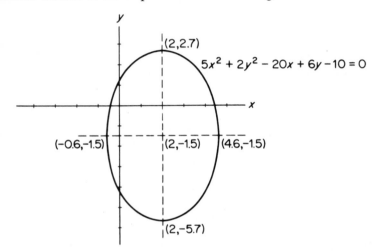

Fig. 7–18.

The equation $5x^2 + 2y^2 - 20x + 6y + \tfrac{49}{2} = 0$ reduces to $5(x - 2)^2 + 2(y + \tfrac{3}{2})^2 = 0$. The graph is the point $(2, -\tfrac{3}{2})$, which you may visualize as a point-ellipse. The equation $5x^2 + 2y^2 - 20x + 6y + 25 = 0$ reduces to $5(x - 2)^2 + 2(y + \tfrac{3}{2})^2 = -\tfrac{1}{2}$. This is an imaginary ellipse. No real point (x, y) lies on the graph; as a subset of the cartesian plane, it is the null set.

EXERCISES §702 (cont.)

12. For each of the following ellipses, determine the coordinates of the center, the semi-major axis, and the semi-minor axis. Sketch the graph.

(a) $\dfrac{x^2}{25} + \dfrac{y^2}{4} = 1$ (b) $\dfrac{x^2}{5} + \dfrac{y^2}{32} = 1$

(c) $9x^2 + 36y^2 = 324$ (d) $7x^2 + y^2 = 49$

(e) $16x^2 + 9y^2 - 64x + 54y + 1 = 0$ (f) $4x^2 + 9y^2 + 20x - 42y + 73 = 0$

(g) $3x^2 + y^2 - 21x + 9y + 57 = 0$ (h) $7x^2 + 2y^2 + 5x - 3y + 7 = 0$.

Answers: (d) (0,0), $a = \sqrt{7}$, $b = 7$; (e) $(2,-3)$, $a = 3$, $b = 4$; (g) $(\frac{7}{2}, -\frac{9}{2})$, $a = 0$, $b = 0$.

13. What is the graph of the relation $y = \frac{1}{2}\sqrt{16 - x^2}$? (*Suggestion:* Rewrite the condition without the radical. Compare with Exercise 7, page 306.)

14. Graph the set of points $\{(x,y) \mid 0 < y < \frac{1}{2}\sqrt{16 - x^2}\}$.

15. Find the set of points at which the line $y = 2x + 10$ and the ellipse $64x^2 + 9y^2 = 576$ intersect.

Answer: $\{(-9/5, 32/5)\}$. How do you interpret finding just one point of intersection?

16. Locate all the points of intersection of the ellipses $2x^2 + 7y^2 = 14$ and $7x^2 + 2y^2 = 14$.

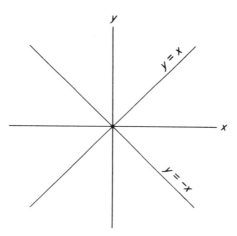

Fig. 7–19.

We continue Case 3, that is, graphs of conditions, $Ax^2 + Cy^2 + Dx + Ey + F = 0$, with $A \neq 0$ and $C \neq 0$.

(7) Graph the equation $x^2 - y^2 = 0$.

$$x^2 - y^2 = (x - y)(x + y)$$

$$(x - y)(x + y) = 0$$

$$x - y = 0 \quad \text{or} \quad x + y = 0.$$

The graph is the pair of straight lines $x - y = 0$ and $x + y = 0$; that is, $y = x$ and $y = -x$ (see Fig. 7–19).

(8) Graph the equation $x^2 - y^2 = 1$.

$$x^2 - y^2 = 1 \iff y^2 = x^2 - 1.$$

Each value of y^2 is 1 less than the corresponding value of x^2. For large values of x,

$$y^2 = x^2 - 1 \doteq x^2.$$

For example, $x = 100$ yields $y^2 = 10{,}000 - 1 = 9{,}999 \doteq 100^2$.

Hence for large values of x, the graph of $y^2 = x^2 - 1$ approximates the graph if $y^2 = x^2$, but $y^2 = x^2 - 1 < x^2$. This means that the graph of $x^2 - y^2 = 1$ *approaches* the graph of $x^2 - y^2 = 0$, as shown in Fig. 7–20.

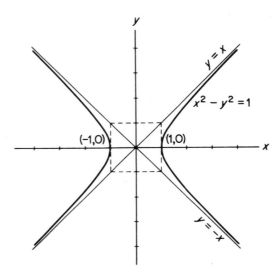

Fig. 7–20.

Notice that $x^2 - y^2 = 1 \Rightarrow |y| < |x|$; that is, each point of the graph of $x^2 - y^2 = 1$ is closer to the x-axis than the corresponding point of the graph of $x^2 - y^2 = 0$. Also,

$$(x^2 - y^2 = 1 \text{ and } x = \pm 1) \Rightarrow (y = 0)$$

$$(x^2 - y^2 = 1 \text{ and } -1 < x < 1) \Rightarrow (y \text{ is imaginary}).$$

Mathematicians call this graph a *rectangular hyperbola*. It is the graph of $y = .5/x$, which you studied in Section 405 (page 128), but it has an alibi. It has been rotated through a 45° angle in the clockwise direction.

Notice that the hyperbola $x^2 - y^2 = 1$, like the circle $x^2 + y^2 = r^2$ and the ellipse $x^2/a^2 + y^2/b^2 = 1$, is symmetrical about the x-axis, the y-axis, and the origin.

For the circle $x^2 + y^2 = r^2$, values of x such that $x < -r$ or $x > r$ yield imaginary values of y; values of y such that $y < -r$ or $y > r$ yield imaginary values of x. For the ellipse, $x^2/a^2 + y^2/b^2 = 1$, values of x such that $x < -a$ or $x > a$ yield imaginary values of y; values of y such that $y < -b$ or $y > b$ yield imaginary values of x. For the hyperbola, $x^2 - y^2 = 1$, values of x such that $-1 < x < 1$ yield imaginary values of y; but each value of y yields two real values of x.

Mathematicians speak of the *extent* of these curves. They mean the range of x (or y) for which you can find one or more real values of y (or x).

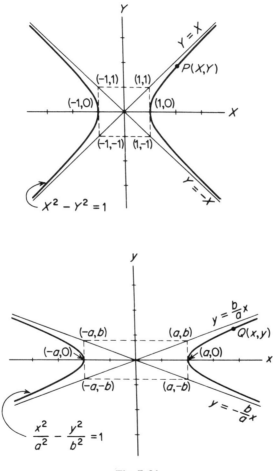

Fig. 7–21.

(9) Graph the equation $x^2/a^2 - y^2/b^2 = 1$. Compare this equation to the equation $X^2 - Y^2 = 1$. Let $X = x/a$ and $Y = y/b$, where $a > 0$ and $b > 0$; then $x = aX$ and $y = bY$. Study Fig. 7–21 as an instance of the

effect of this transformation. For the purpose of drawing the figure, we used $a = 2$ and $b = \frac{3}{4}$.

Each point $P(X, Y)$ of the upper graph is mapped into a point $Q(x,y)$ of the lower graph by the transformation

$$x = 2X, \qquad y = \tfrac{3}{4}Y.$$

Notice that the effect of the transformation is to stretch the rectangular hyperbola horizontally in the ratio 2/1, and shrink it vertically in the ratio 3/4. The result is a "thinner" hyperbola.

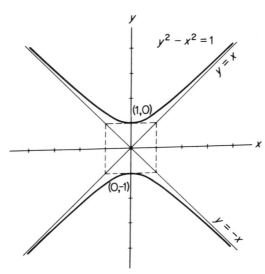

Fig. 7–22.

We call the lines $Y = \pm X$, which the hyperbola $X^2 - Y^2 = 1$ approaches, the *asymptotes* of the curve. Their maps are the lines $y = \pm(b/a)x$; these lines are the asymptotes of the graph of $x^2/a^2 - y^2/b^2 = 1$.

Notice the convenience of the dashed rectangles in the figure. The diagonals of these rectangles are the asymptotes of the hyperbolas. These construction lines help you to place the *vertices* of the hyperbola, $(-1,0)$ and $(1,0)$ in the left-hand graph and $(-a,0)$ and $(a,0)$ in the right-hand graph. You can sketch a hyperbola quickly and accurately when you know its vertices and asymptotes.

(10) Graph the equation $y^2 - x^2 = 1$. The line of reasoning you followed in Example (8) leads you to the graph of Fig. 7–22. You can achieve this same result by noticing that the equations $x^2 - y^2 = 1$ and $y^2 - x^2 = 1$ are the same, except that the roles of x and y are interchanged. This means that the relations, $\{(x,y) \mid x^2 - y^2 = 1\}$ and $\{(x,y) \mid y^2 - x^2 = 1\}$ are inverse

to each other. The graph of $y^2 - x^2 = 1$ is the reflection in the line $y = x$ of the graph of $x^2 - y^2 = 1$.

The graph of $y^2 - x^2 = 1$ is a rectangular hyperbola. It is the same as the graphs of $y = .5/x$ (Section 405, page 130) and $x^2 - y^2 = 1$ but it has an alibi.

(11) Graph the equation $y^2/b^2 - x^2/a^2 = 1$. The line of reasoning that you followed in Example (9) leads you to the graph of Fig. 7–23. Notice that $y^2/b^2 - x^2/a^2 = 1$ is *not* the reflection in the line $y = x$ of $x^2/a^2 - y^2/b^2 = 1$. The reflection of $x^2/a^2 - y^2/b^2 = 1$ in the line $y = x$ is $y^2/a^2 - x^2/b^2 = 1$.

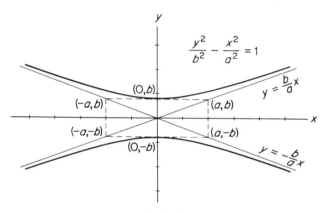

Fig. 7–23.

Notice that the different placement of the parameters of a and b does make a difference.

In the graph of $y^2/b^2 - x^2/a^2 = 1$, values of y such that $-b < y < b$ yield imaginary values of x; but each value of x yields two real values of y. The asymptotes of the curve are the lines $y = \pm(b/a)x$.

(12) The graph of $(x - h)^2/a^2 - (y - k)^2/b^2 = 1$ has its center at (h,k). Its *principal* axis is the line $y = k$, parallel to the x-axis. Its vertices are $(h + a,k)$ and $(h - a,k)$. Its asymptotes are the lines $y - k = \pm(b/a)(x - h)$. Prepare a figure to check these statements.

(13) The graph of $(y - k)^2/b^2 - (x - h)^2/a^2 = 1$ has its center at (h,k). Its principal axis is the line $x = h$, parallel to the y-axis. Its vertices are $(h,k + b)$ and $(h,k - b)$. Its asymptotes are the lines $y - k = \pm(b/a)(x - h)$. Prepare a figure to check these statements.

(14) Graph the equation $Ax^2 + Cy^2 + Dx + Ey + F = 0$ in which A and C have opposite algebraic signs (either $A > 0$ and $C < 0$, or $A < 0$ and $C > 0$).

Rewrite the equation, as in Example (6) in the form

$$A\left(x + \frac{D}{2A}\right)^2 + C\left(y + \frac{E}{2C}\right)^2 = \frac{D^2}{4A} + \frac{E^2}{4C} - F = G.$$

If $G = 0$, the equation becomes

$$\frac{(x - h)^2}{1/A} + \frac{(x - k)^2}{1/C} = 0,$$

where $h = -D/2A$ and $k = -E/2C$. The fact that A and C have opposite signs makes this equation take the form

$$\frac{(x - h)^2}{a^2} - \frac{(y - k)^2}{b^2} = 0.$$

The graph is the pair of straight lines $y - k = \pm(b/a)(x - h)$.

If $G \neq 0$,

$$\frac{(x + D/2A)^2}{G/A} + \frac{(y + E/2C)^2}{G/C} = 1.$$

Since A and C have opposite signs, G/A and G/C have opposite signs. Suppose, first, that $G/A > 0$ and $G/C < 0$. The equation takes the form

$$\frac{(x - h)^2}{a^2} - \frac{(y - k)^2}{b^2} = 1,$$

where $h = -D/2A$ and $k = -E/2C$. This is the hyperbola of Example (12). If, however, $G/A < 0$ and $G/C > 0$, the equation takes the form

$$\frac{(y - k)^2}{b^2} - \frac{(x - h)^2}{a^2} = 1.$$

This is the hyperbola of Example (13).

For your convenience we summarize Case 3. To graph the equation $Ax^2 + Cy^2 + Dx + Ey + F = 0$, $A \neq 0$ and $C \neq 0$:

(a) $A = C$. The graph is a circle that may be real or imaginary. A special case arises when you get a real circle of radius 0, that is, a point (Example 3).

(b) A and C have the same algebraic sign. The graph is an ellipse that may be real or imaginary. A special case arises when the equation reduces to the form

$$\frac{(x - h)^2}{a^2} + \frac{(y - k)^2}{b^2} = 0;$$

then the graph is the single point (h,k) (Example 6).

(c) A and C have opposite algebraic signs. The graph is a real hyperbola with its principal axis parallel to the x-axis or to the y-axis. A special case arises when the equation takes the form

$$\frac{(x - h)^2}{a^2} - \frac{(y - k)^2}{b^2} = 0;$$

then the graph is the pair of straight lines $y - k = \pm(b/a)(x - h)$.

EXERCISES §702 (cont.)

17. For each of the following hyperbolas, determine the coordinates of the center and the vertices, and the equations of the asymptotes. Sketch the graph.

(a) $\dfrac{x^2}{9} - \dfrac{y^2}{4} = 1$

(b) $\dfrac{x^2}{2} - \dfrac{y^2}{16} = 1$

(c) $3x^2 - 25y^2 = 25$

(d) $9y^2 - 4x^2 = 36$

(e) $\dfrac{(x-2)^2}{16} - \dfrac{(y+4)^2}{4} = 1$

(f) $\dfrac{(y+1)^2}{5} - \dfrac{(x+3)^2}{7} = 1$

(g) $9x^2 - 4y^2 + 18x + 12y - 36 = 0$ (h) $3y^2 - 7x^2 + 21x + 15y = 0$.

Answers: (e) center: $(2, -4)$; vertices: $(6, -4)$ and $(-2,4)$; asymptotes: $y = -\frac{1}{2}x - 3$ and $y = \frac{1}{2}x - 5$. (g) center: $(-1,\frac{3}{2})$; vertices: $(1,\frac{3}{2})$ and $(-3,\frac{3}{2})$; asymptotes: $y = \frac{3}{2}x + 3$ and $y = -\frac{3}{2}x$.

18. Show that $4x^2 - 9y^2 = 36$ and $9y^2 - 4x^2 = 36$ have common asymptotes. How do their graphs differ?

19. Do the hyperbolas $\dfrac{(x-h)^2}{a^2} - \dfrac{(y-k)^2}{b^2} = 1$ and $\dfrac{(y-k)^2}{a^2} - \dfrac{(x-h)^2}{b^2} = 1$ have common asymptotes? How do their graphs differ?

20. For each equation of the form $Ax^2 + Cy^2 + Dx + Ey + F = 0$, identify the form of the graph. Be alert for line and point graphs, and for graphs of the null set.

(a) $2x^2 + 5x + 4y - 7 = 0$

(b) $x^2 + y^2 - 12 = 0$

(c) $x^2 + y^2 = 0$

(d) $3x^2 - 2y^2 = 0$

(e) $2x^2 + 2y^2 + 4x - 5y - 10 = 0$

(f) $3x^2 - y^2 + 5 = 0$

(g) $3x^2 + y^2 - 5 = 0$

(h) $4x^2 - y^2 - 4x + 4y - 3 = 0$

(i) $3x^2 + y^2 + x + 4y = 0$

(j) $x^2 + y^2 + 3x - 2y + 4 = 0$

(k) $7x^2 - 12y^2 - 14x + 12y + 18 = 0$ (l) $7x^2 + 12y^2 - 14x + 12y + 18 = 0$.

Answers: (d) Intersecting lines; (e) circle; (i) ellipse; (k) hyperbola; (l) null set.

21. Sketch the graph of each of the following sets of points:

(a) $\{(x,y) \mid y^2 = \frac{1}{4}x^2 - 1\}$

(b) $\{(x,y) \mid y = \sqrt{\frac{1}{4}x^2 - 1}\}$

(c) $\{(x,y) \mid y = -\sqrt{\frac{1}{4}x^2 - 1}\}$

(d) $\{(x,y) \mid y^2 < \frac{1}{4}x^2 - 1\}$

(e) $\{(x,y) \mid 0 < y < \sqrt{\frac{1}{4}x^2 - 1}\}$.

With the completion of Case 3, you have studied all equations of degree 2 in x and y such that $B = 0$. We turn to cases where $B \neq 0$.

Case 4. If $B \neq 0$ and $A = C = D = E = 0$, the equation becomes

$$Bxy + F = 0.$$

This is the equation $y = -F/B \cdot 1/x$, which you studied in Section 405 (page 128). Its graph is a hyperbola with the x and y axes as asymptotes.

Case 5. If $B \neq 0$ and $A = C = 0$, the equation becomes

$$Bxy + Dx + Ey + F = 0.$$

You can write this equation as

$$xy + \frac{D}{B}x + \frac{E}{B}y = -\frac{F}{B},$$

and hence in the form

$$xy - kx - hy = c.$$

Adding hk to each side of the equation, you get

$$xy - kx - hy + hk = c + hk$$

or

$$(x - h)(y - k) = c + hk.$$

This equation has the form

$$y - k = \frac{a}{x - h}.$$

Its graph is a hyperbola with center at (h,k) and the lines $x = h$ and $y = k$ as asymptotes.

Case 6. If $B \neq 0$ and $A \neq 0$ or $C \neq 0$, we shall not discuss the graphs here. What happens is suggested by comparing the graphs of $x^2 - y^2 = 2$ and $xy = 1$. They are the same hyperbola; but the graph of $xy = 1$ must be rotated through an angle of $45°$ in the clockwise direction to get the graph of $x^2 - y^2 = 2$.

We shall prove in Chapter 10 that you can remove the term in xy from the equation

$$Ax^2 + Bxy + Cy^2 + Dx + Ey + F = 0$$

by a proper choice of a new coordinate system. This amounts to picking a new set of axes, to replace the x and y axes by new X and Y axes; you get the new set of axes by a rotation of the old ones through the proper angle.

It turns out that the graphs of second-degree equations in x and y are always parabolas, circles, ellipses, or hyperbolas. Of course, some of the curves reduce to single points, and other curves turn out to be imaginary.

For our present purposes, Case 6 has purely academic interest. The difficulty of working out the proper rotation of axes makes the method impractical for getting a quick sketch of the graph.

We summarize the discussion of the graphs of conditions of degree 2 in x and y:

Equations that reduce to the form	*or the form*
(1) $y = ax^2$	$y - k = a(x - h)^2$

represent parabolas with vertex at $(0,0)$ and the y-axis as principal axis.

represent parabolas with vertex at (h,k) and principal axis the line $x = h$ (parallel to the y-axis).

(2) $\qquad x = ay^2$
$\qquad\qquad\qquad\qquad x - h = a(y - k)^2$

represent parabolas with vertex at (0,0) and the x-axis as principal axis.

represent parabolas with vertex at (h,k) and principal axis the line $y = k$ (parallel to the x-axis).

(3) $\qquad x^2 + y^2 = r^2$
$\qquad\qquad\qquad (x - h)^2 + (y - k)^2 = r^2$

represent circles with center at (0,0) and radius r.

represent circles with center at (h,k) and radius r.

(4) $\qquad \dfrac{x^2}{a^2} + \dfrac{y^2}{b^2} = 1$
$\qquad\qquad\qquad \dfrac{(x - h)^2}{a^2} + \dfrac{(y - k)^2}{b^2} = 1$

represent ellipses with center at (0,0), horizontal axis 2a, and vertical axis 2b.

represent ellipses with center at (h,k), horizontal axis 2a, and vertical axis 2b.

(5) $\qquad \dfrac{x^2}{a^2} - \dfrac{y^2}{b^2} = 1$
$\qquad\qquad\qquad \dfrac{(x - h)^2}{a^2} - \dfrac{(y - k)^2}{b^2} = 1$

represent hyperbolas with center at (0,0), principal axis the x-axis, vertices at (a,0), and (−a,0), asymptotes $y = \pm(b/a)x$.

represent hyperbolas with center at (h,k) principal axis $y = k$ (parallel to the x-axis), vertices (h + a,k) and (h − a,k), and asymptotes $y - k = \pm(b/a)(x - h)$.

(6) $\qquad \dfrac{y^2}{b^2} - \dfrac{x^2}{a^2} = 1$
$\qquad\qquad\qquad \dfrac{(y - k)^2}{b^2} - \dfrac{(x - h)^2}{a^2} = 1$

represent hyperbolas with center at (0,0), principal axis the y-axis, vertices at (0,b) and (0,−b), and asymptotes $y = \pm(b/a)x$.

represent hyperbolas with center at (h,k), principal axis $x = h$ (parallel to the y-axis), vertices (h,k + b) and (h,k − b), and asymptotes $y - k = \pm(b/a)(x - h)$.

These equations and their graphs are important mathematical models. They are more complicated than linear equations and straight lines. Yet they are simple as compared with most equations of higher degree. Parabolas, circles, ellipses, and hyperbolas are convenient models for observations of events in the world of experience. Whether you study art, physics, or philosophy you will soon find yourself using these models to describe your experiences.

We shall return, in Chapter 10, to a further discussion of these curves. Meanwhile we use them to obtain graphical solutions of special systems of conditions in two unknowns.

Graphical methods have great generality. They are a powerful aid to visualizing conditions in two unknowns. Their limitations are worth noting: Unless you recognize a type-graph as you look at an equation, the task of plotting the graph, point by point, may turn out to be a slow process. That is one reason why we have studied various type-graphs. Graphical methods are often restricted to conditions in two unknowns. Although it may sometimes be possible to develop special graphical methods when conditions involve three or more unknowns, each unknown requires a separate *dimension*.

Two unknowns exhaust the east-and-west and north-and-south directions. A third unknown calls for the up-and-down direction. This exhausts the space of three-dimensions in which we move. Further unknowns lead geometers to discuss spaces of four or more dimensions. It is usually impractical to plot a graph in three-space. It is out of the question to plot graphs in four-space, five-space, etc.

EXERCISES §702 (cont.)

22. Sketch the graphs of:

(a) $xy - 3y - 2 = 0$ (b) $xy + x - 1 = 0$

(c) $xy - 3x + 2y - 8 = 0$ (d) $xy - 3x + 2y + 8 = 0$.

23. Solve the system of conditions, $x^2 + y^2 = 10$ and $2x^2 - 3y^2 = 15$, graphically. Compare the results with your algebraic work in Exercise 3(e) of Section 700 (page 290).

24. There were four solutions to Exercise 23. From the graphs of the conditions $x^2 + y^2 = 10$ and $x^2 - 10y^2 = 10$, explain why only two distinct solutions can be expected for this system. Verify this algebraically.

25. Determine whether the line $y = 3x + 4$ meets the hyperbola $xy - 3y - 2 = 0$ in two points, one point, or no points.

26. For the conditions $x^2 + y^2 = r^2$ and $b^2x^2 + a^2y^2 = a^2b^2$, how many solutions can be expected when:

(a) $b^2 < a^2 < r^2$?   (b) $b^2 < a^2 = r^2$?

(c) $b^2 < r^2 < a^2$?   (d) $b^2 = r^2 < a^2$?

(e) $r^2 < b^2 < a^2$?

27. Graph the conditions:

(a) $x^2 + y^2 < 9$ (b) $y < \sqrt{9 - x^2}$ and $y > 0$

(c) $y < \sqrt{9 - x^2}$ and $y > -2$ (d) $(x - 2)^2 + (y - 3)^2 < 4$

(e) $x^2 - y^2 > 4$ (f) $x^2 - y^2 > 4$ and $x^2 + y^2 < 25$

(g) $x^2 + y^2 > 16$ and $x^2 + y^2 < 25$ (h) $x^2 + y^2 + 1 < 0$.

28. Show that if the line $y = mx + b$ is tangent to the circle $x^2 + y^2 = r^2$, then $b = \pm r\sqrt{1 + m^2}$. (*Suggestion:* Solve for the points of intersection by eliminating y; then require that the discriminant of the resulting equation in x be zero in order to produce only one such point.)

29. A line has slope 2 and is tangent to $x^2 + y^2 = 20$. Write the equation of the line (see Exercise 28).

Answer: $y = 2x + 10$ or $y = 2x - 10$.

703. Systems of linear equations and determinants

In previous sections of Chapter 7 you learned to solve systems of conditions in several unknowns. When a system of conditions contains just two unknowns, you found that the graphic method is a slow but sure method.

Many practical problems lead to systems of conditions that involve more than two unknowns. Sometimes the conditions involve trigonometric or exponential functions; sometimes the conditions involve expressions of degree 2 or more. Thus the problem of solving a system of conditions may become complicated.

The simplest systems of conditions are of degree 1 in the several unknowns. Fortunately, many practical problems lead to these, so-called, systems of *linear* conditions. In this section we make an organized study of such systems. We begin with the simplest systems and look for ways to generalize our findings.

We examine, first, a system of two linear equations in two unknowns. To prepare for later generalizations we symbolize this system of conditions as follows:

$$a_{11}x_1 + a_{12}x_2 = c_1$$
$$a_{21}x_1 + a_{22}x_2 = c_2.$$

The unknowns are x_1 and x_2. As we discuss systems that involve more unknowns, we shall call them x_1, x_2, x_3, etc. This is better than using symbols like x, y, z, etc., for the unknowns. Moreover, you soon learn to associate the word unknown with the symbol x. Then you think of x_1 as the *first* unknown, x_2 as the *second* unknown, etc.

Notice how the *subscripts* play the role of adjectives. They tell you which unknown you are talking about; x_1 means the first unknown; x_2 means the second unknown; etc.

Notice, now, the double subscripts that we used with the symbol a: a_{11} appears in the *first* equation as the multiplier of the *first* unknown (x_1); a_{21} appears in the *second* equation as the multiplier of the *first* unknown (x_1); a_{12} appears in the *first* equation as the multiplier of the *second* unknown (x_2); etc. As we generalize, we shall use the symbol a_{ij} in the *i*th equation as the multiplier of the *j*th unknown. Thus the a's are the parameters that multiply the unknowns.

We think of the c's as parameters also; they become numbers in particular problems; c_1 is the *constant term* in the first equation; c_2 is the constant term in the second equation. As we generalize, we shall use the symbol c_i for the constant term in the *i*th equation.

The question of choosing a "good" notation is important. A good notation is one that helps you to discover the basic structure of a problem. As you read the remainder of Chapter 7, you should be alert to notice the ways in which the notation we have chosen helps us to develop general formulas that are easy to remember and convenient to use.

Now we solve the system

(1) $$a_{11}x_1 + a_{12}x_2 = c_1$$

(2) $$a_{21}x_1 + a_{22}x_2 = c_2$$

by the method of addition and subtraction (Section 700, page 287). To eliminate x_2, we multiply in Equation (1) by a_{22}, and multiply in Equation (2) by a_{12}. This yields the equivalent system of equations:

(3) $$a_{11}a_{22}x_1 + a_{12}a_{22}x_2 = c_1 a_{22}$$

(4) $$a_{21}a_{12}x_1 + a_{12}a_{22}x_2 = c_2 a_{12}.$$

Notice that this has the effect of making the multipliers of x_2, in Equations (3) and (4), the same, namely, $a_{12}a_{22}$. The subtraction of (4) from (3) yields:

(5) $$(a_{11}a_{22} - a_{21}a_{12})x_1 = c_1 a_{22} - c_2 a_{12}.$$

This is an equation of the form $Dx_1 = E$, which you can solve for x_1, provided $D \neq 0$.

We begin again with Equations (1) and (2). To eliminate x_1, we multiply in Equation (1) by a_{21}, and multiply in Equation (2) by a_{11}.

(6) $$a_{11}a_{21}x_1 + a_{21}a_{12}x_2 = a_{21}c_1$$

(7) $$a_{11}a_{21}x_1 + a_{11}a_{22}x_2 = a_{11}c_2.$$

Notice that this has the effect of making the multipliers of x_1, in Equations (6) and (7), the same, namely, $a_{11}a_{21}$. The subtraction of (6) from (7) yields:

(8) $$(a_{11}a_{22} - a_{21}a_{12})x_2 = a_{11}c_2 - a_{21}c_1.$$

This is an equation of the form $Dx_2 = F$, which you can solve for x_2, provided $D \neq 0$.

Notice that the multipliers of x_1 in Equation (5) and x_2 in Equation (8) are the same. Hence it was proper to designate these multipliers by the same symbol $D = a_{11}a_{22} - a_{21}a_{12}$.

If $D \neq 0$, we get $x_1 = E/D$, $x_2 = F/D$. These are the coordinates of the point (x_1, x_2), where the graphs of Equations (1) and (2) intersect. If $D = 0$, we shall find that there are two possibilities. Either the lines are parallel and do not intersect; or the lines are coincident and intersect at every point on either one of the lines (Section 701, page 294).

These formulas for x_1 and x_2 look simple; but the letters D, E, and F have no apparent connection with the letters a_{ij} and c_i which appeared in Equations (1) and (2).

We take a closer look at the equation that defines D,

$$D = a_{11}a_{22} - a_{21}a_{12}.$$

Mathematicians rewrite this equation in a form that is easier to remember,

$$D = a_{11}a_{22} - a_{21}a_{12} = \begin{vmatrix} a_{11} & a_{12} \\ a_{21} & a_{22} \end{vmatrix}.$$

The symbol $\begin{vmatrix} a_{11} & a_{12} \\ a_{21} & a_{22} \end{vmatrix}$ is called a *determinant*. We shall use the value of D to determine the nature of the solutions of Equations (1) and (2): if $D \neq 0$, the equations have just one solution; if $D = 0$, the equations have either no solutions, or infinitely many solutions.

By analogy, now,

$$E = c_1 a_{22} - c_2 a_{12} = \begin{vmatrix} c_1 & a_{12} \\ c_2 & a_{22} \end{vmatrix}, \text{ and } F = a_{11} c_2 - a_{21} c_1 = \begin{vmatrix} a_{11} & c_1 \\ a_{21} & c_2 \end{vmatrix}.$$

You can learn to solve two linear equations in two unknowns by an easy-to-remember formula, using determinants. The formula is convenient because the pattern is easy to learn. Moreover, we shall find that the pattern lends itself to generalizations. Here is the pattern:

(1) $$a_{11} x_1 + a_{12} x_2 = c_1$$
(2) $$a_{21} x_1 + a_{22} x_2 = c_2.$$

Calculate

$$D = \begin{vmatrix} a_{11} & a_{12} \\ a_{21} & a_{22} \end{vmatrix} = a_{11} a_{22} - a_{21} a_{12}.$$

If $D \neq 0$,

$$x_1 = \frac{1}{D} \begin{vmatrix} c_1 & a_{12} \\ c_2 & a_{22} \end{vmatrix} \text{ and } x_2 = \frac{1}{D} \begin{vmatrix} a_{11} & c_1 \\ a_{21} & c_2 \end{vmatrix}.$$

Notice that D is expressed by use of a square array of the multipliers of the unknowns as they appear in the system of equations. Mathematicians call D the *determinant of coefficients* of the system of conditions (1) and (2). The *expansion* of D is the difference $a_{11} a_{22} - a_{21} a_{12}$ of the products obtained by following the arrows above.

Notice that you get the determinant $\begin{vmatrix} c_1 & a_{12} \\ c_2 & a_{22} \end{vmatrix}$ by replacing the multipliers of x_1 by the constant terms; notice that you get the determinant $\begin{vmatrix} a_{11} & c_1 \\ a_{21} & c_2 \end{vmatrix}$ by replacing the multipliers of x_2 by the constant terms.

The following examples will help you to assimilate this pattern:
(1) Solve the system:

$$3x + 2y = 5$$
$$x - y = -2.$$

$$D = \begin{vmatrix} 3 & 2 \\ 1 & -1 \end{vmatrix} = 3(-1) - 1(2) = -5.$$

Since $D \neq 0$, there is just one solution, namely,

$$x = \frac{1}{(-5)} \begin{vmatrix} 5 & 2 \\ -2 & -1 \end{vmatrix} \text{ and } y = \frac{1}{(-5)} \begin{vmatrix} 3 & 5 \\ 1 & -2 \end{vmatrix}.$$

Expanding each determinant,

$$x = -\tfrac{1}{5}[5(-1) - (-2)(2)] = \tfrac{1}{5}$$
$$y = -\tfrac{1}{5}[3(-2) - 1(5)] = \tfrac{11}{5}.$$

You should check the solution $(\tfrac{1}{5}, \tfrac{11}{5})$ in the original equations.

(2) Solve the system:

$$x = 3 - 2y$$
$$y = \tfrac{1}{3}x + 5.$$

To apply the pattern, you must rewrite these equations in the form

$$a_{11}x_1 + a_{12}x_2 = c_1$$
$$a_{21}x_1 + a_{22}x_2 = c_2.$$

You get
$$x + 2y = 3$$
$$-\tfrac{1}{3}x + y = 5.$$

To avoid calculations with fractions, it is convenient to multiply in the second equation by 3. This yields the equivalent system:

$$x + 2y = 3$$
$$-x + 3y = 15.$$

$$D = \begin{vmatrix} 1 & 2 \\ -1 & 3 \end{vmatrix} = 3 - (-2) = 5$$

$$x = \tfrac{1}{5} \begin{vmatrix} 3 & 2 \\ 15 & 3 \end{vmatrix} = \tfrac{1}{5}(9 - 30) = -\tfrac{21}{5}$$

$$y = \tfrac{1}{5} \begin{vmatrix} 1 & 3 \\ -1 & 15 \end{vmatrix} = \tfrac{1}{5}(15 + 3) = \tfrac{18}{5}.$$

You should check the solution $(-\tfrac{21}{5}, \tfrac{18}{5})$ in the *original* equations. (Do not use equations that you derived from the original ones. There may be a mistake in these derivations.)

(3) Solve the system:

$$x + y = 3$$
$$3x + 3y = 5.$$

$$D = \begin{vmatrix} 1 & 1 \\ 3 & 3 \end{vmatrix} = 3 - 3 = 0.$$

Here $D = 0$. The first equation is equivalent to $y = -x + 3$, a line of slope -1 and y-intercept 3; the second equation is equivalent to $y = -x + \tfrac{5}{3}$, a line of slope -1 and y-intercept $\tfrac{5}{3}$. The equations represent parallel lines. The system of equations has *no* solution.

When you examine the system of equations, you notice that the first one says $x + y = 3$; hence $3(x + y) = 9$. This contradicts the second equation, which states $3x + 3y = 5$. The equations contradict each other; this system of equations is *inconsistent* (Section 701, page 294).

(4) Solve the system:

$$\tfrac{2}{5}x - y = 3$$

$$-x + \tfrac{5}{2}y = -\tfrac{15}{2}.$$

$$D = \begin{vmatrix} \tfrac{2}{5} & -1 \\ -1 & \tfrac{5}{2} \end{vmatrix} = \tfrac{2}{5} \cdot \tfrac{5}{2} - (-1)(-1) = 1 - 1 = 0.$$

Here $D = 0$. The first equation is equivalent to $y = \tfrac{2}{5}x - 3$, a line of slope $\tfrac{2}{5}$ and y-intercept -3; the second equation is equivalent to $y = \tfrac{2}{5}x - 3$, a line of slope $\tfrac{2}{5}$ and y-intercept -3. The equations represent the same line. The system of equations has, as solutions, *every point* on either line.

Notice that the two equations of the system are equivalent; they are two sentences that convey the same information; this system of equations is *dependent* (Section 701, page 294).

Recall that $D \neq 0$ tells you that a pair of equations is consistent. They have just one solution. If, however, $D = 0$, the pair of equations may be either inconsistent (no solutions) or dependent (many solutions). How can you distinguish between inconsistent and dependent systems?

Consider the system:

$$a_{11}x_1 + a_{12}x_2 = c_1$$

$$a_{21}x_1 + a_{22}x_2 = c_2,$$

where $D = a_{11}a_{22} - a_{21}a_{12} = 0$. You have

$$0 \cdot x_1 = \begin{vmatrix} c_1 & a_{12} \\ c_2 & a_{22} \end{vmatrix} \quad \text{and} \quad 0 \cdot x_2 = \begin{vmatrix} a_{11} & c_1 \\ a_{21} & c_2 \end{vmatrix}.$$

If
$$\begin{vmatrix} c_1 & a_{12} \\ c_2 & a_{22} \end{vmatrix} \neq 0 \quad \text{or} \quad \begin{vmatrix} a_{11} & c_1 \\ a_{21} & c_2 \end{vmatrix} \neq 0,$$

you get a contradiction; $0 \cdot x_1 \neq 0$ or $0 \cdot x_2 \neq 0$. The system of conditions is inconsistent.

This leaves the case where

$$\begin{vmatrix} a_{11} & a_{12} \\ a_{21} & a_{22} \end{vmatrix} = \begin{vmatrix} c_1 & a_{12} \\ c_2 & a_{22} \end{vmatrix} = \begin{vmatrix} a_{11} & c_1 \\ a_{21} & c_2 \end{vmatrix} = 0;$$

that is, $a_{11}a_{22} = a_{21}a_{12}$, $c_1a_{22} = c_2a_{12}$, and $a_{11}c_2 = a_{21}c_1$. Up to this point we have not placed any restrictions upon the multipliers a_{ij} or c_i; but now the problem breaks up into many special cases depending upon whether one or more of these multipliers is zero.

The most interesting possibility, as we shall see, arises when every a_{ij} and every c_i is different from zero. Then

$$a_{11}a_{22} = a_{21}a_{12} \Rightarrow \frac{a_{11}}{a_{21}} = \frac{a_{12}}{a_{22}}$$

$$c_1a_{22} = c_2a_{12} \Rightarrow \frac{c_1}{c_2} = \frac{a_{12}}{a_{22}}.$$

Hence

$$\frac{a_{11}}{a_{21}} = \frac{a_{12}}{a_{22}} = \frac{c_1}{c_2};$$

that is, the multipliers in Equation (1) are *proportional* to the multipliers in Equation (2). Suppose that

$$\frac{a_{11}}{a_{21}} = \frac{a_{12}}{a_{22}} = \frac{c_1}{c_2} = k \neq 0;$$

then $a_{11} = ka_{21}$, $a_{12} = ka_{22}$, and $c_1 = kc_2$. Equation (1), $a_{11}x_1 + a_{12}x_2 = c_2$, becomes, by substitution, $ka_{21}x_1 + ka_{22}x_2 = kc_2$. This is equivalent to $a_{21}x_1 + a_{22}x_2 = c_2$, which is Equation (2). Equations (1) and (2) are *dependent*, in the sense that either equation can be derived from the other one. The two equations impose equivalent conditions upon the unknowns x_1 and x_2.

If one or more of the a_{ij} is zero, you get trivial cases. For example, if $a_{11} = 0$ the system of conditions becomes

$$a_{12}x_2 = c_1$$

$$a_{21}x_1 + a_{22}x_2 = c_2.$$

We shall not discuss this system of conditions because, in particular cases, it is trivial. It is easy to solve a system like

$$3y = 5$$

$$4x - 2y = 7.$$

Of course the determinant D of this system is $-12 \neq 0$. To get a system

$$0 \cdot x_1 + a_{12}x_2 = c_1$$

$$a_{21}x_1 + a_{22}x_2 = c_2$$

with $D = 0$, you must take $a_{21}a_{12} = 0$. If $a_{21} = 0$, you obtain two equations in the one unknown x_2; if $a_{12} = 0$ you obtain one equation in the two unknowns, x_1 and x_2. This is typical. Cases where one or more of the a_{ij} or the c_i is zero cause no trouble in particular problems, but to treat the general case is very tedious. Try it if you wish. It turns out that if

$$\begin{vmatrix} a_{11} & a_{12} \\ a_{21} & a_{22} \end{vmatrix} = \begin{vmatrix} c_1 & a_{12} \\ c_2 & a_{22} \end{vmatrix} = \begin{vmatrix} a_{11} & c_1 \\ a_{21} & c_2 \end{vmatrix} = 0,$$

the system of conditions is dependent.

This completes our discussion of systems of two linear equations in two unknowns. As you reexamine what we have said, you will notice that the case where $D \neq 0$ is simple and straightforward; but when $D = 0$ the discussion breaks down into many special cases that are tedious to handle. When this happens in a mathematical discussion, mathematicians have learned to look for a better way of expressing the problem. Such a "better way" can be based upon the ideas introduced in Section 706. It involves calling upon further abstractions of the idea of number to secure greater elegance and clarity of expression.

As we proceed to examine three linear equations in three unknowns, four linear equations in four unknowns, etc., we shall limit ourselves to generalizations of the case where $D \neq 0$. We need more powerful methods to attack generalizations of the case where $D = 0$.

The following exercises will help you to assimilate the ideas you have met so far.

EXERCISES §703

1. Given the system of equations $4x + y = 1$ and $3x - 2y = 9$. In the notation of the text, what is a_{21}? a_{12}? a_{22}? c_2?

2. Evaluate the following determinants:

(a) $\begin{vmatrix} 5 & 4 \\ 3 & 7 \end{vmatrix}$

(b) $\begin{vmatrix} 2 & 1 \\ 4 & -6 \end{vmatrix}$

(c) $\begin{vmatrix} 1 & -2 \\ 5 & 3 \end{vmatrix}$

(d) $\begin{vmatrix} 4 & -2 \\ 2 & -1 \end{vmatrix}$

(e) $\begin{vmatrix} -5 & -2 \\ -1 & -6 \end{vmatrix}$

(f) $\begin{vmatrix} a & -1 \\ 3 & 2a \end{vmatrix}$

(g) $\begin{vmatrix} 2x & 3x \\ 4 & 1 \end{vmatrix}$

(h) $\begin{vmatrix} x & y \\ -3 & 2 \end{vmatrix}$

(i) $\begin{vmatrix} r & t \\ -t & r \end{vmatrix}.$

Answers: (a) 23; (b) −16; (d) 0; (f) $2a^2 + 3$.

3. Solve the following systems by determinants. Be sure to check your answers.

(a) $7x - 2y = 4$
$\quad\;\, 3x + y = 11$

(b) $2x + 3y = 1$
$\quad\;\, 3x + 4y = 2$

(c) $5x - 2y = 3$
$\quad\;\, 4x - 3y = 6$

(d) $\frac{1}{2}x - y = 2$
$\quad\;\, 7x + 18y = -12$

(e) $2.2x + 1.7y = -4.8$
$\quad\;\, -1.6x + 0.5y = 8.7$

(f) $\sqrt{2}x + y = 5$
$\quad\;\, x + \sqrt{2}y = 4\sqrt{2}$

(g) $rx + sy = 5$
$\quad\;\, sx + ry = 5$

(h) $7x - 12y = a$
$\quad\;\, 4x + 7y = b.$

Answers: (a) (2,5); (c) (-3/7, -18/7); (f) ($\sqrt{2}$,3).

4. Use determinants to decide whether the systems of equations in Exercise 2 (page 297) are consistent, inconsistent, or dependent. Compare with your graphical solutions.

5. Find the solution set for each of the following conditions:

(a) $\begin{vmatrix} 2 & 3 \\ 5 & x \end{vmatrix} = 0$

(b) $\begin{vmatrix} 3 & -4 \\ 7x & 2x \end{vmatrix} = 0$

(c) $\begin{vmatrix} 2 & 4x \\ -1 & 3 \end{vmatrix} = 14$

(d) $\begin{vmatrix} 2x & 3 \\ 4 & x \end{vmatrix} = 0$

(e) $\begin{vmatrix} x+2 & x-3 \\ x & 5 \end{vmatrix} = -10$

(f) $\begin{vmatrix} x & y \\ 4 & 1 \end{vmatrix} = 0$

(g) $\begin{vmatrix} 2x & -3y \\ 1 & -6 \end{vmatrix} = 9$

(h) $\begin{vmatrix} 2y & 3x \\ x & 1 \end{vmatrix} = 4.$

Answers: (a) $\{7\frac{1}{2}\}$; (b) $\{0\}$; (e) $\{-2, 10\}$; (f) $\{(x,\frac{1}{4}x)\}$; (h) $\{(x,\frac{3}{2}x^2 + 2)\}$.

6. What type of graph is determined by each of the following conditions?

(a) $\begin{vmatrix} 2x & 3y \\ -5 & 7 \end{vmatrix} = 4$

(b) $\begin{vmatrix} y & x \\ (x-1) & 1 \end{vmatrix} = 0$

(c) $\begin{vmatrix} x^2 & y^2 \\ -2 & 2 \end{vmatrix} = 8$

(d) $\begin{vmatrix} 2x^2 & 3y^2 \\ -5 & 9 \end{vmatrix} = 12$

(e) $\begin{vmatrix} x^2 & 4 \\ y^2 & 9 \end{vmatrix} = 36$

(f) $\begin{vmatrix} 2x & 3y \\ 4 & 6 \end{vmatrix} = 0.$

Answers: (a) Straight line; (c) circle.

7. Show that if $a \neq 0$ and $b \neq 0$, then

$$\begin{vmatrix} x & y \\ a & b \end{vmatrix} = 0 \Leftrightarrow \frac{x}{a} = \frac{y}{b}.$$

That is, if the elements of a second-order determinant are not zero, then the value of the determinant is zero if and only if the elements in the rows are proportional.

8. Show that

$$\begin{vmatrix} a & b \\ c & d \end{vmatrix} = \begin{vmatrix} a + kb & b \\ c + kd & d \end{vmatrix},$$

where the range of k is L.

9. Show that

$$\begin{vmatrix} a & b \\ c & d \end{vmatrix} = - \begin{vmatrix} b & a \\ d & c \end{vmatrix}.$$

10. Illustrate the properties of Exercises 8 and 9 with $k = -2$ and the

determinant

$$\begin{vmatrix} 41 & 19 \\ 18 & 8 \end{vmatrix}.$$

Consider, now, the system of equations

(9) $$a_{11}x_1 + a_{12}x_2 + a_{13}x_3 = c_1$$

(10) $$a_{21}x_1 + a_{22}x_2 + a_{23}x_3 = c_2$$

(11) $$a_{31}x_1 + a_{32}x_2 + a_{33}x_3 = c_3.$$

We define the determinant of coefficients,

$$D = \begin{vmatrix} a_{11} & a_{12} & a_{13} \\ a_{21} & a_{22} & a_{23} \\ a_{31} & a_{32} & a_{33} \end{vmatrix}$$

$$= a_{11} \begin{vmatrix} a_{22} & a_{23} \\ a_{32} & a_{33} \end{vmatrix} - a_{21} \begin{vmatrix} a_{12} & a_{13} \\ a_{32} & a_{33} \end{vmatrix} + a_{31} \begin{vmatrix} a_{12} & a_{13} \\ a_{22} & a_{23} \end{vmatrix}$$

$$= a_{11}(a_{22}a_{33} - a_{32}a_{23}) - a_{21}(a_{12}a_{33} - a_{32}a_{13}) + a_{31}(a_{12}a_{23} - a_{22}a_{13}).$$

We call D a *third-order* determinant in contrast to the *second-order* determinants that you met previously. Notice how the definition expresses a third-order determinant in terms of three second-order determinants. Compare the expansions of second- and third-order determinants. In both cases you go down the first column, and multiply each element by what remains of the determinant after you delete the row and column that contain that element. You begin with a (+) sign; you alternate between (+) and (−) signs.

As you study the expansion of D, notice these effects of the definition: Each term in the expansion is a product of three elements of D. For example, $a_{11}a_{22}a_{33}$ and $-a_{21}a_{12}a_{33}$ are terms in the expansion. Each term in the expansion contains one element from each row and each column of D. For example, $-a_{11}a_{32}a_{23}$ contains an element from row 1 and column 1 (a_{11}), an element from row 3 and column 2 (a_{32}), and an element from row 2 and column 3 (a_{23}). The expansion contains six terms, each of the form $a_{1i}a_{2j}a_{3k}$, where (i,j,k) is some arrangement of the numbers (1,2,3). Three terms carry the (+) sign; three terms carry the (−) sign. Perhaps you can discover a rule to decide which three terms carry the (+) sign. When you write a term in the order $a_{1i}a_{2j}a_{3k}$, notice the order of arrangement of the values of i, j, and k. Can you connect this order of arrangement with the sign of the term?

It is often a tedious job to solve three linear equations in three unknowns by the method of addition and subtraction. You eliminate one unknown, say x_3, from Equations (9) and (10); then you eliminate x_3 from Equations (10) and (11); you get two equations in the unknowns x_1 and x_2; you eliminate x_2 from these two equations and solve for x_1. Then you continue the process to solve for x_2 and x_3.

People who have worked through this process found a convenient way to express their results using third-order determinants. Here is the pattern:

Calculate
$$D = \begin{vmatrix} a_{11} & a_{12} & a_{13} \\ a_{21} & a_{22} & a_{23} \\ a_{31} & a_{32} & a_{33} \end{vmatrix}.$$

If $D \neq 0$,

$$x_1 = \frac{1}{D}\begin{vmatrix} c_1 & a_{12} & a_{13} \\ c_2 & a_{22} & a_{23} \\ c_3 & a_{32} & a_{33} \end{vmatrix}, \qquad x_2 = \frac{1}{D}\begin{vmatrix} a_{11} & c_1 & a_{13} \\ a_{21} & c_2 & a_{23} \\ a_{31} & c_3 & a_{33} \end{vmatrix},$$

and

$$x_3 = \frac{1}{D}\begin{vmatrix} a_{11} & a_{12} & c_1 \\ a_{21} & a_{22} & c_2 \\ a_{31} & a_{32} & c_3 \end{vmatrix}.$$

If $D = 0$, there is something special about the system of equations. We shall not discuss the many possibilities for the general case; but you can use methods, somewhat like those you used previously, to study a particular system of equations.

Notice that the third-order case where $D \neq 0$ is a generalization of the second-order case where $D \neq 0$. Once you have learned the pattern for solving two equations in two unknowns, you can apply this same pattern to solve three equations in three unknowns. The following exercises will help you to do this:

EXERCISES §703 (cont.)

11. Given the system of equations

$$2x_1 + 7x_2 + 4x_3 = 8$$
$$-x_1 - 3x_2 + 2x_3 = 7$$
$$x_1 + \tfrac{1}{2}x_2 + 2x_3 = 10.$$

In the notation of the text, what is a_{11}? a_{23}? a_{32}? c_2? a_{31}?

12. Evaluate the determinants:

(a) $\begin{vmatrix} 3 & 2 & 5 \\ 1 & 6 & 0 \\ 2 & 1 & 3 \end{vmatrix}$ (b) $\begin{vmatrix} 4 & 1 & 3 \\ 0 & 7 & 4 \\ 5 & 1 & 1 \end{vmatrix}$

(c) $\begin{vmatrix} 2 & -1 & 0 \\ -1 & 5 & -4 \\ 3 & 1 & -2 \end{vmatrix}$ (d) $\begin{vmatrix} 2 & 7 & 4 \\ -1 & -3 & 2 \\ 1 & \tfrac{1}{2} & 2 \end{vmatrix}$

(e) $\begin{vmatrix} 3 & 4 & 5 \\ 6 & 7 & 8 \\ 9 & 10 & 11 \end{vmatrix}$ (f) $\begin{vmatrix} 2m & 1 & -4 \\ m & 3 & 2 \\ 5 & 4 & -1 \end{vmatrix}$

(g) $\begin{vmatrix} x & y & 1 \\ 2 & 3 & 1 \\ 4 & -2 & 1 \end{vmatrix}$ (h) $\begin{vmatrix} r & -2t & 0 \\ r & 0 & -r \\ t & r & -t \end{vmatrix}$.

Answers: (a) -7; (b) -73; (d) 24; (g) $5x + 2y - 16$.

13. Use determinants to solve the system of Exercise 11. Check the results. [Your solution of Exercise 12(d) may be useful here.]

14. Solve each of the following systems of equations, using determinants:

(a) $\begin{aligned} x_1 + x_2 + x_3 &= 2 \\ 2x_1 - x_2 - x_3 &= 1 \\ 4x_1 + 3x_2 - x_3 &= -5 \end{aligned}$ (b) $\begin{aligned} 2x_1 - x_2 + 2x_3 &= -2 \\ 5x_1 - 3x_2 - 3x_3 &= 1 \\ -3x_1 + 2x_2 - 4x_3 &= 6 \end{aligned}$

(c) $\begin{aligned} 3x + 5y - 18z &= 5 \\ x + 2y - 5z &= 3 \\ 2x + 4y - 9z &= 8 \end{aligned}$ (d) $\begin{aligned} 2r + 4t + 3s &= 1 \\ 3r - 2t - 5s &= 5 \\ 5r + 2t + 2s &= 2 \end{aligned}$

(e) $\begin{aligned} u + v - w &= 1 \\ 3u + v + 5w &= -1 \\ 7u + 3v - 6w &= 2 \end{aligned}$ (f) $\begin{aligned} 2x - y - 3z &= 5 \\ 4x + 7y + 2z &= 0 \\ 2x + 2y - 9z &= 1 \end{aligned}$

(g) $\begin{aligned} 0.7x + 0.9y + 1.1z &= 1.3 \\ 1.5x + 1.3y + 1.9z &= 2.1 \\ 0.6x + 1.2y + 0.8z &= 1.7 \end{aligned}$ (h) $\begin{aligned} 2x + y + z &= 5k \\ 3x + 5y + 6z &= 9k \\ 4x - 3y - 4z &= 10k. \end{aligned}$

Answers: (a) $(1,-2,3)$;   (c) $(17,-2,2)$;   (d) $(\frac{1}{2},\frac{3}{4},-1)$;   (f) $(\frac{79}{39}, -\frac{46}{39}, \frac{3}{39})$;   (g) $(0.62, 1.28, -.26)$;   (h) $(3k, -6k, 5k)$.

15. Try to solve the system of equations

$$5x_1 + 3x_2 - 8x_3 = 5$$

$$2x_1 + 4x_2 + x_3 = 1$$

$$-x_1 + x_2 + 4x_3 = 3$$

by the techniques of this section. Comment on your results. (Notice that if there were an answer for x_1, it would have to satisfy the condition $0 \cdot x_1 = 160$. Since this is impossible, the system is *inconsistent*. When $D = 0$, and at least one of the other three determinants is not zero, there is no solution to the system. Notice how this is a generalization of the second order case.)

16. Try to solve the system of equations

$$4x_1 - 3x_2 + 7x_3 = 5$$

$$3x_1 - 2x_2 + 4x_3 = 4$$

$$2x_1 + x_2 - 9x_3 = 5$$

by the techniques of this section.

Notice how *all four* determinants are zero. When this happens, the system may or may not have a solution. A complete discussion of this situation is beyond the scope of this book; however, we suggest ways to proceed. In two of the equations, replace one unknown by a parameter k. Consider the resulting system of two equations in the other two unknowns. For example, if $x_3 = k$ in the first two equations, you have

$$4x_1 - 3x_2 = 5 - 7k$$

$$3x_1 - 2x_2 = 4 - 4k.$$

Now if the determinant D of the coefficients of this second-order system is not zero, you can solve for x_1 and x_2 in terms of k. These values of x_1 and x_2, together with $x_3 = k$, constitute the solution. Under the conditions stated (all four third-order determinants of the original system are zero), any solution obtained in this fashion can be shown to satisfy the third equation for every real value of k. We call such a system *dependent*. There are many solutions; one for each real value of k. You should now proceed to:

(a) Solve the second order system above for x_1 and x_2 in terms of k, thus obtaining the general solution of the original system.
(b) Obtain specific solutions for these replacements of k: 1, 2, -1, and 0. Check each solution by substitution.
(c) Show that the general solution (in terms of k) satisfies all three equations.

Answers: (a) $(2 + 2k, 1 + 5k, k)$; (b) $k = 1$, $(4,6,1)$; $k = 2$, $(6,11,2)$.

Now examine a system of n linear equations in n unknowns:

$$a_{11}x_1 + a_{12}x_2 + \ldots + a_{1n}x_n = c_1$$
$$a_{21}x_1 + a_{22}x_2 + \ldots + a_{2n}x_n = c_2$$
$$\cdot \quad \cdot \quad \cdot \quad \cdot \quad \cdot \quad \cdot \quad \cdot$$
$$a_{n}x_1 + a_{n2}x_2 + \ldots + a_{nn}x_n = c_n.$$

We define the determinant of coefficients,

$$D = \begin{vmatrix} a_{11} & a_{12} & \cdots & a_{1n} \\ a_{21} & a_{22} & \cdots & a_{2n} \\ \cdot & \cdot & & \cdot \\ \cdot & \cdot & & \cdot \\ \cdot & \cdot & & \cdot \\ a_{n1} & a_{n2} & \cdots & a_{nn} \end{vmatrix}$$

$$= a_{11}\begin{vmatrix} a_{22} & a_{23} & \cdots & a_{2n} \\ a_{32} & a_{33} & \cdots & a_{3n} \\ \cdot & \cdot & & \cdot \\ \cdot & \cdot & & \cdot \\ a_{n2} & a_{n3} & \cdots & a_{nn} \end{vmatrix} - a_{21}\begin{vmatrix} a_{12} & a_{13} & \cdots & a_{1n} \\ a_{32} & a_{33} & \cdots & a_{3n} \\ \cdot & \cdot & & \cdot \\ \cdot & \cdot & & \cdot \\ a_{n2} & a_{n3} & \cdots & a_{nn} \end{vmatrix}$$

$$+ a_{31}\begin{vmatrix} a_{12} & a_{13} & \cdots & a_{1n} \\ a_{22} & a_{23} & \cdots & a_{2n} \\ a_{42} & a_{43} & \cdots & a_{4n} \\ \cdot & \cdot & & \cdot \\ \cdot & \cdot & & \cdot \\ a_{n2} & a_{n3} & \cdots & a_{nn} \end{vmatrix} \ldots + (-1)^{n+1}a_{n1}\begin{vmatrix} a_{12} & a_{13} & \cdots & a_{1n} \\ a_{22} & a_{23} & \cdots & a_{2n} \\ \cdot & \cdot & & \cdot \\ \cdot & \cdot & & \cdot \\ a_{n-1,2} & a_{n-1,3} & \cdots & a_{n-1,n} \end{vmatrix}.$$

We call D an nth-order determinant. Notice how the definition expresses the nth-order determinant in terms of n determinants of order $n - 1$. As before, we expanded the determinant in terms of its first column. As before, the effect is to get n times as many terms in the expansion as you get in expanding a determinant of order $(n-1)$. Each term is a product of n elements of D, one from each row and column of D.

It can be proved that the previously established pattern generalizes. Calculate D. If $D \neq 0$, then

$$
x_1 = \frac{1}{D}
\begin{vmatrix}
c_1 & a_{12} & \cdots & a_{1n} \\
c_2 & a_{22} & \cdots & a_{2n} \\
\cdot & \cdot & & \cdot \\
\cdot & \cdot & & \cdot \\
\cdot & \cdot & & \cdot \\
c_n & a_{2n} & \cdots & a_{nn}
\end{vmatrix}, \quad
x_2 = \frac{1}{D}
\begin{vmatrix}
a_{11} & c_1 & a_{13} & \cdots & a_{1n} \\
a_{21} & c_2 & a_{23} & \cdots & a_{2n} \\
\cdot & \cdot & \cdot & & \cdot \\
\cdot & \cdot & \cdot & & \cdot \\
\cdot & \cdot & \cdot & & \cdot \\
a_{n1} & c_n & a_{n3} & \cdots & a_{nn}
\end{vmatrix}, \quad \cdots,
$$

$$
x_n = \frac{1}{D}
\begin{vmatrix}
a_{11} & a_{12} & \cdots & a_{1,n-1} & c_1 \\
a_{21} & a_{22} & \cdots & a_{2,n-1} & c_2 \\
\cdot & \cdot & & \cdot & \cdot \\
\cdot & \cdot & & \cdot & \cdot \\
\cdot & \cdot & & \cdot & \cdot \\
a_{n1} & a_{n2} & \cdots & a_{n,n-1} & c_n
\end{vmatrix}.
$$

We shall not discuss the case where $D = 0$.

EXERCISES §703 (cont.)

17. Evaluate the following determinants:

(a)
$$
\begin{vmatrix}
2 & 1 & -2 & 3 \\
5 & 1 & -3 & 2 \\
0 & -2 & 2 & -3 \\
1 & 1 & -1 & 1
\end{vmatrix}
$$

(b)
$$
\begin{vmatrix}
2 & 1 & 0 & 2 \\
1 & -3 & 0 & -1 \\
0 & -2 & 4 & 1 \\
-1 & 1 & 5 & 0
\end{vmatrix}
$$

(c)
$$
\begin{vmatrix}
3 & -1 & 1 & 3 \\
-2 & 4 & 3 & 5 \\
2 & 0 & 1 & 3 \\
1 & 2 & -4 & -1
\end{vmatrix}
$$

(d)
$$
\begin{vmatrix}
2 & 5 & 7 & 17 \\
0 & 3 & 9 & 29 \\
0 & 0 & 1 & 12 \\
0 & 0 & 0 & -1
\end{vmatrix}
$$

Answers: (a) 4;   (b) 71;   (c) 0;   (d) −6.

18. Use determinants to solve the following systems of equations. Check your work by substitution.

(a) $x_1 + 2x_2 - 3x_3 + x_4 = 2$
    $-x_1 - x_2 + 7x_3 + x_4 = 5$
    $2x_1 + 4x_2 - 5x_3 + 3x_4 = 3$
    $x_2 + 5x_3 + 4x_4 = 1$

(b) $x_1 - x_3 + 2x_4 = 0$
    $2x_2 + x_3 + 3x_4 = 1$
    $x_1 + 3x_3 - 4x_4 = 0$
    $4x_1 + x_4 = 2$

(c) $x + 3y + 2z + 2w = 5$
    $2x - 4y - z - 3w = 7$
    $-2x + y + 4z + 2w = -6$
    $4x + 2y - 3z - w = -2.$

Answers: (a) $D = 1$, solution $(17,1,4,-5)$;   (b) $D = -8$, solution $(1,5,-3,$
$-2)$;   (c) $D = 24$, solution $\left(\dfrac{43}{4}, -\dfrac{71}{4}, -\dfrac{57}{8}, \dfrac{247}{8}\right).$

As n takes values greater than 3, the work of expanding the determinants soon becomes unmanageable. The expansion of a third order determinant contains $3 \times 2 \times 1 = 6$ terms; the expansion of a fourth order determinant contains $4 \times 3 \times 2 \times 1 = 24$ terms; the expansion of a tenth order determinant contains $10 \times 9 \times 8 \times 7 \times 6 \times 5 \times 4 \times 3 \times 2 \times 1 = 3{,}628{,}800$ terms. You may share the astonishment of an earlier mathematician at the rapid growth of these numbers. It is said that he named the product of the numbers from n to 1 inclusive *n-factorial*, and used the symbol $n!$ to register his astonishment! Hence $3! = 3 \cdot 2 \cdot 1 = 6$; $4! = 4 \cdot 3 \cdot 2 \cdot 1 = 24$; $10! = 10 \cdot 9 \cdot 8 \cdot 7 \cdot 6 \cdot 5 \cdot 4 \cdot 3 \cdot 2 \cdot 1 = 3{,}628{,}800$; etc. You can find other values of $n! = n(n-1)(n-2) \ldots 3 \cdot 2 \cdot 1$ in your tables.

Each of the 3,628,800 terms in the expansion of a tenth-order determinant is the product of ten numbers. In a practical problem, each of these numbers might be a number, like 31.862, that contains five significant figures.

As you think about actually doing these calculations, you may conclude that this whole question of solving systems of linear equations by determinants is a beautiful but useless theory. Experience shows that the escape from such a dilemma may lie in one of two directions. You look for properties of determinants that simplify the job of expanding them, and you try to use computing machinery to speed up your calculations.

Both of these methods of making the theory practical have been tried with good results. It is now possible to use electronic computers to expand higher-order determinants. You do run into problems of getting too many figures for even the biggest machines to handle. Methods of estimating the number of significant figures in the answers to such calculations are a topic of current research in applied mathematics. We ignore this question of machine calculation here, and proceed, in Section 704, to explore a few of the properties of determinants.

704. Some properties of determinants

We shall use determinants of order three to illustrate certain properties of determinants. Then we shall apply these properties to simplify the expansion of determinants of any order.

$$P\ 1: \qquad \begin{vmatrix} a_{11} & a_{12} & a_{13} \\ a_{21} & a_{22} & a_{23} \\ a_{31} & a_{32} & a_{33} \end{vmatrix} = \begin{vmatrix} a_{11} & a_{21} & a_{31} \\ a_{12} & a_{22} & a_{32} \\ a_{13} & a_{23} & a_{33} \end{vmatrix}.$$

In words, the value of a determinant is not affected by interchanging the rows and columns of the determinant.

To prove this property, you can expand each of the determinants, and use the properties of real numbers to show that the expansions are equal.

P 2: If you multiply each element of one row (or one column) of a determinant by k, the effect is to make the value of the determinant k times as large.

Take, for example, the determinant

$$\begin{vmatrix} 1 & 0 & 1 \\ 2 & 4 & 1 \\ 3 & 5 & 7 \end{vmatrix}.$$

Multiply each element of the second row by -2; you get the determinant

$$\begin{vmatrix} 1 & 0 & 1 \\ -4 & -8 & -2 \\ 3 & 5 & 7 \end{vmatrix} = -2 \begin{vmatrix} 1 & 0 & 1 \\ 2 & 4 & 1 \\ 3 & 5 & 7 \end{vmatrix}.$$

If you recall that each term in the expansion of a determinant contains just one element from each row and column of the determinant, this property may seem reasonable to you. You can check it in special instances. We shall not burden you with a general proof.

P 3: If each element of a row or column of a determinant is 0, the value of the determinant is 0.

Take, for example, the determinant

$$D = \begin{vmatrix} 1 & 0 & 1 \\ 2 & 0 & 1 \\ 3 & 0 & 7 \end{vmatrix}.$$

By P 2,
$$2D = \begin{vmatrix} 1 & 2 \cdot 0 & 1 \\ 2 & 2 \cdot 0 & 1 \\ 3 & 2 \cdot 0 & 7 \end{vmatrix} = \begin{vmatrix} 1 & 0 & 1 \\ 2 & 0 & 1 \\ 3 & 0 & 7 \end{vmatrix} = D;$$

but $2D = D \Rightarrow D = 0.$

P 4: If you interchange two rows (or two columns) of a determinant, you change the sign of the determinant. For example,

$$\begin{vmatrix} 1 & 4 & 7 \\ 2 & 5 & 8 \\ 3 & 6 & 9 \end{vmatrix} = - \begin{vmatrix} 3 & 6 & 9 \\ 2 & 5 & 8 \\ 1 & 4 & 7 \end{vmatrix}.$$

(Notice that we interchanged the first and third rows of the determinant.)

If you recall the way that we assigned $(+)$ and $(-)$ signs to the terms of the expansion of a determinant, this property may seem reasonable to you. You can check it in special instances; try this in the example above. Again, we omit the proof.

P 5: If two rows (or two columns) of a determinant are identical, the value of the determinant is 0.

Take, for example, the determinant

$$D = \begin{vmatrix} 1 & 4 & 4 \\ 2 & 5 & 5 \\ 3 & 6 & 6 \end{vmatrix}.$$

If you apply P 4 to interchange the second and third columns you obtain

$$-D = \begin{vmatrix} 1 & 4 & 4 \\ 2 & 5 & 5 \\ 3 & 6 & 6 \end{vmatrix} = D; \text{ but } -D = D \Rightarrow D = 0.$$

P 6: If you add the same multiple of each element of one row to the corresponding element of another row of the determinant, you do not change the value of the determinant. The corresponding statement for columns also holds. For example,

$$\begin{vmatrix} a & d & g \\ b & e & h \\ c & f & i \end{vmatrix} = \begin{vmatrix} a+kd & d & g \\ b+ke & e & h \\ c+kf & f & i \end{vmatrix}.$$

In this instance we added k times each element of the second column to the corresponding element of the first column. You can prove the equality of the two determinants by expanding them and applying properties of real numbers.

Here are some examples to help you learn to apply these six properties of determinants:

(1) Evaluate $\quad D = \begin{vmatrix} 1 & -17 & 0 \\ 2 & 6 & 0 \\ 5 & -3 & 0 \end{vmatrix}.$ $\quad$ By P 3, $D = 0$.

(2) Evaluate
$$D = \begin{vmatrix} 1 & -17 & 1 \\ 2 & 6 & 0 \\ 5 & -3 & 0 \end{vmatrix}.$$

We have
$$D = - \begin{vmatrix} 1 & -17 & 1 \\ 0 & 6 & 2 \\ 0 & -3 & 5 \end{vmatrix}$$

$$= - \left(1 \begin{vmatrix} 6 & 2 \\ -3 & 5 \end{vmatrix} - 0 \begin{vmatrix} -17 & 1 \\ -3 & 5 \end{vmatrix} + 0 \begin{vmatrix} -17 & 1 \\ 6 & 2 \end{vmatrix} \right)$$

$$= -[30 - (-6)] = -36.$$

(3) Evaluate
$$D = \begin{vmatrix} 5 & 2 & 1 \\ 1 & 2 & 4 \\ 4 & 6 & -3 \end{vmatrix}.$$

We have

$$D = \begin{vmatrix} 5 + (-5)(1) & 2 + (-5)(2) & 1 + (-5)(4) \\ 1 & 2 & 4 \\ 4 + (-4)(1) & 6 + (-4)(2) & -3 + (-4)(4) \end{vmatrix} \quad \text{(P 6 used twice)}$$

$$= \begin{vmatrix} 0 & -8 & -19 \\ 1 & 2 & 4 \\ 0 & -2 & -19 \end{vmatrix} = 2 \begin{vmatrix} 0 & -4 & -19 \\ 1 & 1 & 4 \\ 0 & -1 & -19 \end{vmatrix} \quad \text{(P 2)}$$

$$= 2 \begin{vmatrix} 0 & -4 & -19 \\ 1 & 1 & 4 \\ 0 + (-1)(0) & -1 + (-1)(-4) & -19 + (-1)(-19) \end{vmatrix}$$

$$= 2 \begin{vmatrix} 0 & -4 & -19 \\ 1 & 1 & 4 \\ 0 & 3 & 0 \end{vmatrix}.$$

You could continue to express the value of D in a great many ways. Once the first column of D contains two zeros, this reduces the number of terms in the expansion of D from 6 to 2. Thus

$$D = \begin{vmatrix} 0 & -8 & -19 \\ 1 & 2 & 4 \\ 0 & -2 & -19 \end{vmatrix} = -1 \begin{vmatrix} -8 & -19 \\ -2 & -19 \end{vmatrix} = -[152 - 38] = -114$$

and $\quad D = 2 \begin{vmatrix} 0 & -4 & -19 \\ 1 & 1 & 4 \\ 0 & 3 & 0 \end{vmatrix} = -2 \begin{vmatrix} -4 & -19 \\ 3 & 0 \end{vmatrix} = -2(57) = -114$

are two ways to expand D that involve about the same amount of calculation.

(4) Evaluate $\qquad D = \begin{vmatrix} 1 & 0 & 0 \\ 2 & 5 & -2 \\ 3 & 6 & 3 \end{vmatrix}.$

We have, by P 1, $\quad D = \begin{vmatrix} 1 & 2 & 3 \\ 0 & 5 & 6 \\ 0 & -2 & 3 \end{vmatrix} = 1 \begin{vmatrix} 5 & 6 \\ -2 & 3 \end{vmatrix} = 27.$

The following exercises give you further opportunities for practice in evaluating determinants.

EXERCISES §704

1. Verify P 1 by evaluating the determinants

$$\begin{vmatrix} 1 & 3 & -4 \\ 0 & -1 & 2 \\ 2 & 5 & 0 \end{vmatrix} \text{ and } \begin{vmatrix} 1 & 0 & 2 \\ 3 & -1 & 5 \\ -4 & 2 & 0 \end{vmatrix}.$$

2. Expand both determinants to show that

$$\begin{vmatrix} 34 & 17 \\ 3 & 9 \end{vmatrix} = (17)(3) \begin{vmatrix} 2 & 1 \\ 1 & 3 \end{vmatrix}.$$

What property is illustrated?

3. Without evaluating, show why each of the following determinants must be zero. Tell which properties you use.

(a) $\begin{vmatrix} 5 & -3 & 9 \\ 1 & 4 & 0 \\ 0 & 0 & 0 \end{vmatrix}$ (b) $\begin{vmatrix} 7 & -5 & 7 \\ 2 & 4 & 2 \\ 1 & 9 & 1 \end{vmatrix}$

(c)
$$\begin{vmatrix} 2 & 4 & 0 & 9 \\ 5 & 3 & 0 & 5 \\ 0 & 6 & 0 & -2 \\ -7 & -2 & 0 & 1 \end{vmatrix}$$

(d)
$$\begin{vmatrix} 1 & 2 & 5 \\ 1 & 2 & 7 \\ 1 & 2 & -9 \end{vmatrix}$$

(e)
$$\begin{vmatrix} -3 & 2 & 3 \\ -5 & 7 & 5 \\ 4 & 1 & -4 \end{vmatrix}$$

(f)
$$\begin{vmatrix} 3 & 6 & -3 & -9 \\ 2 & 4 & -7 & 3 \\ 9 & -1 & 5 & 2 \\ -2 & -4 & 2 & 6 \end{vmatrix}.$$

4. Without evaluating the determinants, show that the following statements are valid. Tell which properties you use. Then expand the determinants to verify the equations.

(a)
$$\begin{vmatrix} 2 & 4 \\ 3 & 5 \end{vmatrix} = - \begin{vmatrix} 4 & 2 \\ 5 & 3 \end{vmatrix}$$

(b)
$$\begin{vmatrix} x & 3y \\ 5 & 6 \end{vmatrix} = 3 \begin{vmatrix} x & y \\ 5 & 2 \end{vmatrix}$$

(c)
$$\begin{vmatrix} 6 & 14 \\ -3 & 5 \end{vmatrix} = 6 \begin{vmatrix} 1 & 7 \\ -1 & 5 \end{vmatrix}$$

(d)
$$\begin{vmatrix} 5 & 3 & 6 \\ 7 & 4 & 3 \\ 2 & -1 & 1 \end{vmatrix} = - \begin{vmatrix} 6 & 3 & 5 \\ 3 & 4 & 7 \\ 1 & -1 & 2 \end{vmatrix} = \begin{vmatrix} 6 & 3 & 5 \\ 1 & -1 & 2 \\ 3 & 4 & 7 \end{vmatrix}$$

(e)
$$\begin{vmatrix} 12 & 8 & -4 \\ 9 & 17 & -11 \\ -15 & 4 & 1 \end{vmatrix} = 12 \begin{vmatrix} 1 & 2 & -1 \\ 3 & 17 & -11 \\ -5 & 4 & 1 \end{vmatrix}$$

(f)
$$\begin{vmatrix} a & b \\ 2 & 3 \end{vmatrix} = \begin{vmatrix} a+2 & b+3 \\ 2 & 3 \end{vmatrix}$$

(g)
$$\begin{vmatrix} 12 & 16 \\ 3 & 4 \end{vmatrix} = \begin{vmatrix} 0 & 0 \\ 3 & 4 \end{vmatrix}$$

(h)
$$\begin{vmatrix} 57 & 65 \\ -5 & -6 \end{vmatrix} = \begin{vmatrix} 7 & 5 \\ -5 & -6 \end{vmatrix} = \begin{vmatrix} 2 & 5 \\ 1 & -6 \end{vmatrix}$$

(i)
$$\begin{vmatrix} 1 & 7 & 5 \\ -2 & 6 & -10 \\ 1 & 8 & 5 \end{vmatrix} = 0.$$

5. Explain how P 4 permits you to expand by the elements of any column of a determinant. Illustrate by interchanging columns, then expanding the determinant,

$$\begin{vmatrix} 5 & 0 & 4 \\ 7 & 2 & 1 \\ -9 & 0 & -5 \end{vmatrix}.$$

6. Is it possible to expand by the elements of any row? Explain.

7. State a reason for each step in the following evaluation of a determinant:

$$\begin{vmatrix} x & y & 1 \\ -1 & 5 & 1 \\ 2 & 3 & 1 \end{vmatrix} = \begin{vmatrix} x-2 & y-3 & 0 \\ -1 & 5 & 1 \\ 2 & 3 & 1 \end{vmatrix} = \begin{vmatrix} x-2 & y-3 & 0 \\ -3 & 2 & 0 \\ 2 & 3 & 1 \end{vmatrix}$$

$$= \begin{vmatrix} 0 & x-2 & y-3 \\ 0 & -3 & 2 \\ 1 & 2 & 3 \end{vmatrix} = \begin{vmatrix} x-2 & y-3 \\ -3 & 2 \end{vmatrix} = 2x + 3y - 13.$$

8. Given the determinant

$$\begin{vmatrix} 1 & 4 & -1 \\ -2 & 6 & 7 \\ 3 & 5 & 2 \end{vmatrix}.$$

(a) Expand, using the definition of the value of a third-order determinant.
(b) Multiply the elements of the first row by 2 and add to the corresponding elements of the second row. Then multiply the elements of the first row by −3 and add to those of the last row. Evaluate the resulting determinant and compare with part (a).
(c) Use the first column to get two zeros in the first row. Evaluate the resulting determinant.
(d) Evaluate the determinant by obtaining zeros at two places in the last column.

9. Evaluate the following determinants. Use the properties of determinants to simplify your work. Compare with your work in Exercises 12 (page 331) and 17 (page 334) when possible.

(a) $\begin{vmatrix} 3 & 2 & 5 \\ 1 & 6 & 0 \\ 2 & 1 & 3 \end{vmatrix}$
(b) $\begin{vmatrix} 4 & 1 & 3 \\ 0 & 7 & 4 \\ 5 & 1 & 1 \end{vmatrix}$
(c) $\begin{vmatrix} 2 & -1 & 0 \\ -1 & 5 & -4 \\ 3 & 1 & -2 \end{vmatrix}$

(d) $\begin{vmatrix} 2 & 7 & 4 \\ -1 & -3 & 2 \\ 1 & \frac{1}{2} & 2 \end{vmatrix}$
(e) $\begin{vmatrix} 3 & 4 & 5 \\ 6 & 7 & 8 \\ 9 & 10 & 11 \end{vmatrix}$
(f) $\begin{vmatrix} 2m & 1 & -4 \\ m & 3 & 2 \\ 5 & 4 & -1 \end{vmatrix}$

(g) $\begin{vmatrix} x & y & 1 \\ 2 & 3 & 1 \\ 4 & -2 & 1 \end{vmatrix}$ (h) $\begin{vmatrix} r & -2t & 0 \\ r & 0 & -r \\ t & r & -t \end{vmatrix}$ (i) $\begin{vmatrix} 1 & x & x^2 \\ 1 & y & y^2 \\ 1 & z & z^2 \end{vmatrix}$

(j) $\begin{vmatrix} 2 & 1 & -2 & 3 \\ 5 & 1 & -3 & 2 \\ 0 & -2 & 2 & -3 \\ 1 & 1 & -1 & 1 \end{vmatrix}$ (k) $\begin{vmatrix} 2 & 1 & 0 & 2 \\ 1 & -3 & 0 & -1 \\ 0 & -2 & 4 & 1 \\ -1 & 1 & 5 & 0 \end{vmatrix}$

(l) $\begin{vmatrix} 3 & -1 & 1 & 3 \\ -2 & 4 & 3 & 5 \\ 2 & 0 & 1 & 3 \\ 1 & 2 & -4 & -1 \end{vmatrix}$ (m) $\begin{vmatrix} 2 & -3 & 3 & 6 \\ 5 & 2 & 2 & 1 \\ 7 & 4 & -5 & 9 \\ 3 & -1 & 7 & 4 \end{vmatrix}$

(n) $\begin{vmatrix} 3 & -2 & 5 & 0 & 1 \\ -1 & 4 & 1 & 3 & 2 \\ 0 & 1 & 2 & 6 & 3 \\ 2 & 5 & -1 & -2 & 2 \\ 4 & 6 & 3 & -5 & 1 \end{vmatrix}$.

10. (a) By expanding

$$\begin{vmatrix} a & b \\ c & d \end{vmatrix} \quad \text{and} \quad \begin{vmatrix} a & c \\ b & d \end{vmatrix},$$

prove that P 1 is valid for second-order determinants.

(b) Prove P 1 for third-order determinants.

11. Prove the instance of P 6 for third-order determinants given in the text [See Exercise 8 (page 329) for an instance of this property applied to second-order determinants.]

12. P 4 states that

$$\begin{vmatrix} a & d & g \\ b & e & h \\ c & f & i \end{vmatrix} = - \begin{vmatrix} d & a & g \\ e & b & h \\ f & c & i \end{vmatrix}.$$

Prove this instance of P 4 by expanding both determinants.

13. Use the results of Exercises 11 and 12 to prove the instance of P 6 where a multiple of the elements of the first column is added to the elements of the second column.

We close this section with an application of the properties of determinants. We hope you will enjoy it as an intellectual game. As you develop and work with new mathematical symbols, you open the door to new insights. We use what you already know about determinants to illustrate this fact.

Recall the system of three linear equations in three unknowns:

(1) $$a_{11}x_1 + a_{12}x_2 + a_{13}x_3 = c_1$$
(2) $$a_{21}x_1 + a_{22}x_2 + a_{23}x_3 = c_2$$
(3) $$a_{31}x_1 + a_{32}x_2 + a_{33}x_3 = c_3.$$

We now apply **P 5**, with insight that a person working with properties of determinants might naturally acquire:

I want to eliminate x_2 and x_3 in order to solve for x_1. I know that

$$\begin{vmatrix} a_{12} & a_{12} & a_{13} \\ a_{22} & a_{22} & a_{23} \\ a_{32} & a_{32} & a_{33} \end{vmatrix} = \begin{vmatrix} a_{13} & a_{12} & a_{13} \\ a_{23} & a_{22} & a_{23} \\ a_{33} & a_{32} & a_{33} \end{vmatrix} = 0.$$

Suppose I write equations equivalent to (1), (2), and (3) as follows:

(4) $$a_{11}\begin{vmatrix} a_{22} & a_{23} \\ a_{32} & a_{33} \end{vmatrix}x_1 + a_{12}\begin{vmatrix} a_{22} & a_{23} \\ a_{32} & a_{33} \end{vmatrix}x_2 + a_{13}\begin{vmatrix} a_{22} & a_{23} \\ a_{32} & a_{33} \end{vmatrix}x_3 = c_1\begin{vmatrix} a_{22} & a_{23} \\ a_{32} & a_{33} \end{vmatrix}$$

(5) $$a_{21}\begin{vmatrix} a_{12} & a_{13} \\ a_{32} & a_{33} \end{vmatrix}x_1 + a_{22}\begin{vmatrix} a_{12} & a_{13} \\ a_{32} & a_{33} \end{vmatrix}x_2 + a_{23}\begin{vmatrix} a_{12} & a_{13} \\ a_{32} & a_{33} \end{vmatrix}x_3 = c_2\begin{vmatrix} a_{12} & a_{13} \\ a_{32} & a_{33} \end{vmatrix}$$

(6) $$a_{31}\begin{vmatrix} a_{12} & a_{13} \\ a_{22} & a_{23} \end{vmatrix}x_1 + a_{32}\begin{vmatrix} a_{12} & a_{13} \\ a_{22} & a_{23} \end{vmatrix}x_2 + a_{33}\begin{vmatrix} a_{12} & a_{13} \\ a_{22} & a_{23} \end{vmatrix}x_3 = c_3\begin{vmatrix} a_{12} & a_{13} \\ a_{22} & a_{23} \end{vmatrix}.$$

Now suppose I combine these equations as (4) $-$ (5) $+$ (6). I get

(7) $$Dx_1 + 0x_2 + 0x_3 = \begin{vmatrix} c_1 & a_{12} & a_{13} \\ c_2 & a_{22} & a_{23} \\ c_3 & a_{32} & a_{33} \end{vmatrix}.$$

Hence, if $D \neq 0$,

$$x_1 = \frac{1}{D}\begin{vmatrix} c_1 & a_{12} & a_{13} \\ c_2 & a_{22} & a_{23} \\ c_3 & a_{32} & a_{33} \end{vmatrix}.$$

In this way you can find multipliers for Equations (1), (2), and (3) to eliminate two of the three unknowns in one step. Repeat the process in a special instance to clinch the idea:

Eliminate y and z from the system,

(8) $$2x - 3y + 5z = 1$$
(9) $$x + y - z = 5$$
(10) $$3x - y + 2z = -3.$$

Follow the pattern above, and write the equivalent equations:

(11) $2\begin{vmatrix} 1 & -1 \\ -1 & 2 \end{vmatrix}x - 3\begin{vmatrix} 1 & -1 \\ -1 & 2 \end{vmatrix}y + 5\begin{vmatrix} 1 & -1 \\ -1 & 2 \end{vmatrix}z = 1\begin{vmatrix} 1 & -1 \\ -1 & 2 \end{vmatrix}$

(12) $1\begin{vmatrix} -3 & 5 \\ -1 & 2 \end{vmatrix}x + 1\begin{vmatrix} -3 & 5 \\ -1 & 2 \end{vmatrix}y - 1\begin{vmatrix} -3 & 5 \\ -1 & 2 \end{vmatrix}z = 5\begin{vmatrix} -3 & 5 \\ -1 & 2 \end{vmatrix}$

(13) $3\begin{vmatrix} -3 & 5 \\ 1 & -1 \end{vmatrix}x - 1\begin{vmatrix} -3 & 5 \\ 1 & -1 \end{vmatrix}y + 2\begin{vmatrix} -3 & 5 \\ 1 & -1 \end{vmatrix}z = -3\begin{vmatrix} -3 & 5 \\ 1 & -1 \end{vmatrix}.$

Now combine these equations by taking (11) − (12) + (13). This yields

(14) $\begin{vmatrix} 2 & -3 & 5 \\ 1 & 1 & -1 \\ 3 & -1 & 2 \end{vmatrix}x + \begin{vmatrix} -3 & -3 & 5 \\ 1 & 1 & -1 \\ -1 & -1 & 2 \end{vmatrix}y + \begin{vmatrix} 5 & -3 & 5 \\ -1 & 1 & -1 \\ 2 & -1 & 2 \end{vmatrix}z = \begin{vmatrix} 1 & -3 & 5 \\ 5 & 1 & -1 \\ -3 & -1 & 2 \end{vmatrix}.$

Notice that P 5 tells you that the multipliers of y and z in Equation (14) are both 0.

EXERCISES §704 (cont.)

14. Solve the following systems of equations, using determinants. Use whatever properties of determinants you need to simplify the computation. Check your solutions.

(a) $45x_1 + 73x_2 = 83$
$32x_1 + 52x_2 = 59$

(b) $329x - 321y = 133$
$265x - 259y = 107$

(c) $x_1 + 3x_2 - x_3 = 1$
$2x_1 - 4x_2 - 2x_3 = -2$
$5x_1 + 6x_2 - 7x_3 = 0$

(d) $5r + 2s + 8t = 6$
$7r + 3s + 9t = 2$
$2r + s + 3t = 2$

(e) $3x_1 + x_2 - 5x_3 = 13$
$4x_1 + x_2 + 7x_3 = 9$
$2x_1 - x_2 - 6x_3 = -8$

(f) $57x + 56y + 47z = 75$
$49x + 49y + 39z = 70$
$64x + 64y + 51z = 91$

(g) $x_1 + 2x_3 - x_4 = 3$
$3x_2 + 2x_3 + 3x_4 = 10$
$4x_1 + 5x_3 + 2x_4 = 9$
$x_1 + 3x_2 + x_3 + 7x_4 = 9$

(h) $2x + 3y - 4z + w = 2$
$5x - 7y + 2z = 7$
$-6x + 4y + z - 2w = -9$
$x + y + 3z - 3w = 0$

(i) $A + 3B - 2C = 8$
$B - 3C + 2D + 2E = -1$
$-A - 6C + 4D + 6E = -7$
$-C + 7D + 6E = 8$
$-2B + 3C + 5D = -2.$

Answers: (a) $D = 4$, $(\frac{9}{4}, -\frac{1}{4})$; (b) $D = -146$, $(\frac{50}{73}, \frac{21}{73})$; (c) $D = 20$, $(.5, .4, .7)$;

(e) $D = 71$, $(\frac{16}{71}, \frac{750}{71}, -\frac{25}{71})$; (f) $D = 3$, $(12, -5, -7)$; (g) $D = 9$, $(-2, \frac{1}{3}, 3, 1)$;

(h) $D = -189$, $(\frac{83}{63}, \frac{4}{63}, \frac{3}{7}, \frac{56}{63})$; (i) $D = 2$, $(-5, 7, 4, 0, 2)$.

15. A diagram of an electric circuit is shown in Fig. 7–24. The R's represent resistances (measured in ohms), the E's are voltages, and the I's indicate the amount of current (in amperes) that flows in the different branches of the circuit. By applying Kirchhoff's and Ohm's laws, the following conditions must hold:

$$I_1 - I_2 - I_3 = 0$$

$$(R_1 + R_4)I_1 + R_3I_3 = E_1$$

$$R_2I_2 - R_3I_3 = E_2.$$

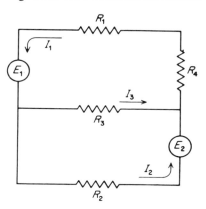

Fig. 7–24.

(a) If $R_1 = 5$ ohms, $R_2 = 10$ ohms, $R_3 = 15$ ohms, $R_4 = 25$ ohms, $E_1 = 10$ volts, and $E_2 = 20$ volts, determine the currents I_1, I_2, and I_3 flowing in each branch of the circuit. (Note: If negative values of I appear, we interpret this to mean that the current flows in the opposite direction to that indicated by the arrows on the diagram.)

(b) Replacing a voltage by its negative in the system of equations corresponds to reversing the connections where that voltage is applied to the system. What would be the effect on the currents in the different branches of the circuit if the connections of the voltage at E_2 in the diagram were reversed, but the rest of the system remained the same as in part (a)?

Answers: (a) $(.5, 1.5, -1)$; (b) $(.1, -1.3, 1.4)$.

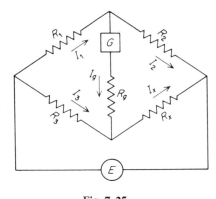

Fig. 7–25.

16. Figure 7–25 shows a diagram of a Wheatstone bridge, a circuit for measuring an unknown resistance R_x in terms of three known resistances, R_1, R_2, R_3. G is a galvanometer, a device for measuring current, with a resistance of R_g. The elements of the circuit must satisfy the following conditions.

$$I_1 - I_2 - I_g = 0$$

$$I_3 - I_x + I_g = 0$$

$$R_1I_1 + R_2I_2 - R_3I_3 - R_xI_x = 0$$

$$R_1I_1 - R_3I_3 + R_gI_g = 0$$

$$R_1I_1 + R_2I_2 = E.$$

The known resistances are adjusted until no current flows in the galvanometer $(I_g = 0)$.

(a) Considering the I's to be the unknown's, evaluate the determinant for the numerator of the unknown I_g in terms of E, R_1, R_2, R_3, and R_x.

(b) Show that when E and R_1 are not zero,

$$I_g = 0 \Leftrightarrow R_x = \frac{R_2 R_3}{R_1}.$$

Answer: (a) $E(R_2 R_3 - R_1 R_x)$.

17. Find multipliers that will enable you to eliminate all unknowns except x_1 in one step, using the system of equations of:

(a) Exercise 14(c).
(b) Exercise 14(e).
(c) Exercise 14(g).

18. Let (x_1,y_1) and (x_2,y_2) be the coordinates of any two points P_1 and P_2. Show that the graph of the condition

$$\begin{vmatrix} x & y & 1 \\ x_1 & y_1 & 1 \\ x_2 & y_2 & 1 \end{vmatrix} = 0$$

is the straight line that passes through P_1 and P_2. (*Suggestion:* If you expand by the first row, the condition takes the form $Ax + By + C = 0$; hence it is the equation of some line. Now show by direct substitution and P 5 that the line must pass through P_1 and P_2.)

19. Use the results of Exercise 18 to write the equation of the line that passes through $(2, -3)$ and $(-4,7)$. [See Exercise 7 (page 341) for an example of evaluating this type of determinant.]

20. (a) Show that the graph of the condition

$$\begin{vmatrix} (x^2 + y^2) & x & y & 1 \\ (x_1^2 + y_1^2) & x_1 & y_1 & 1 \\ (x_2^2 + y_2^2) & x_2 & y_2 & 1 \\ (x_3^2 + y_3^2) & x_3 & y_3 & 1 \end{vmatrix} = 0$$

is a circle that passes through the points (x_1,y_1), (x_2,y_2), and (x_3,y_3).

(b) Determine the equation of the circle that passes through the points $(0, -7)$, $(-1,0)$, and $(-2,-3)$.

Answer: $x^2 + y^2 - 6x + 6y - 7 = 0$.

21. The area of a triangle whose vertices are at (x_1,y_1), (x_2,y_2), and (x_3,y_3) is given by the absolute value of

$$\frac{1}{2}\begin{vmatrix} x_1 & y_1 & 1 \\ x_2 & y_2 & 1 \\ x_3 & y_3 & 1 \end{vmatrix}.$$

(You can prove this by considering the areas of the trapezoids formed by dropping perpendiculars from the three points to the x axis.)

(a) Find the area of the triangle whose vertices are at $(-1,3)$, $(5,1)$, and $(8,5)$.

(b) Show that three points are *collinear* (on the same straight line) if and only if the above determinant is zero. (Is this property also related to Exercise 18?)

(c) Show that the points $(3,5)$, $(-2,8)$, and $(13,-1)$ are collinear.

(d) Devise a condition, using a determinant, that the coordinates of four *concyclic* points must satisfy. (All the points lie on same circle.) (*Hint:* See Exercise 20.)

22. If there are many unknowns and the coefficients are not small whole numbers, the solution of systems of linear equations by determinants is very tedious. Moreover, it is impractical because there is no check on the correctness of the calculations until the solution is completed. This leads to much useless calculation when an arithmetical error is made. The method of *pivotal condensation* is a systematic technique that provides a check as the steps are carried out. Furthermore, it is well suited to use with calculating machines when the multipliers are awkward numbers. We illustrate with a third-order system. Consider the set of linear equations,

$$a_{11}x_1 + a_{12}x_2 + a_{13}x_3 = a_{14}$$

$$a_{21}x_1 + a_{22}x_2 + a_{23}x_3 = a_{24}$$

$$a_{31}x_1 + a_{32}x_2 + a_{33}x_3 = a_{34}.$$

(Notice the slight change in notation. The c_i are replaced by the parameters a_{i4}.)

First we write the system symbolically, representing the equal signs by a vertical line and indicating the unknown by the column in which the subscript appears. Next we add all the numbers in each row and place the sum at the right of the double line. (See the first three rows below.) Thus $a_{1T} = a_{11} + a_{12} + a_{13} + a_{14}$ is the total of all the numbers in the first row. The last column will be our check column.

(x_1)	(x_2)	(x_3)			*Totals*
a_{11}	a_{12}	a_{13}	a_{14}		a_{1T}
a_{21}	a_{22}	a_{23}	a_{24}		a_{2T}
a_{31}	a_{32}	a_{33}	a_{34}		a_{3T}
	b_{22}	b_{23}	b_{24}		b_{2T}
	b_{32}	b_{33}	b_{34}		b_{3T}
		c_{33}	c_{34}		c_{3T}
k_1	k_2	k_3			

The number in the upper left corner of the third-order system is our first *pivot*. To reduce to two equations in two unknowns, we operate on each a_{ij} that is not in the row or column of the pivot in the following fashion: Multiply the element by the pivot and then subtract the product of the element above it in the pivots-row by the element to the left of it in the pivots-column. Write this result below the line in a position corresponding to the position of the element being operated on. For example, a_{22} is not in the row or column of the pivot; hence we carry out the following calculations to get b_{22}: $b_{22} = a_{11}a_{22} - a_{21}a_{12}$. Notice that b_{22} is in a position below the line corresponding to a_{22}. To operate on a_{23}, we calculate: $b_{23} = a_{11}a_{23} - a_{21}a_{13}$.

In general, $b_{ij} = a_{11}a_{ij} - a_{i1}a_{1j}$. When we have operated on a_{22}, a_{23}, a_{24}, and a_{2T} to get b_{22}, b_{23}, b_{24}, and b_{2T}, we arrive at the first check point; the sum of the elements to the left of the double line in each row must equal the number to the right of the double line in that row. If $b_{2T} \neq b_{22} + b_{23} + b_{24}$, we look for the mistake immediately, before proceeding further. When this row checks, proceed to operate on the next row of a_{ij} and check it. The b's then, will be coefficients of a system of equations in x_2 and x_3 that have the same solution as before except that x_1 has been eliminated. Now choose b_{22} as the new pivot and repeat the process to get one equation in one unknown. (Note that there are only three elements to operate on in this case: b_{33}, b_{34}, and b_{3T}.)

Since $c_{33}x_3 = c_{34}$, $x_3 = c_{34}/c_{33}$. Divide c_{34} by c_{33} and write the quotient, say k_3, at the bottom of the x_3 column. Now move up to the b's. Since $b_{22}x_2 + b_{23}x_3 = b_{24}$, and we know that the value of x_3 is k_3, then

$$x_2 = \frac{b_{24} - b_{23}k_3}{b_{22}}.$$

Call the result of this calculation k_2, and write the number k_2 at the bottom of the x_2 column.

Moving up to the third-order system, and knowing $x_3 = k_3$ and $x_2 = k_2$, we calculate

$$x_1 = \frac{a_{14} - a_{13}k_3 - a_{12}k_2}{a_{11}} \quad \text{(Why?)}$$

and write the result, k_1, at the bottom of the x_1 column. Our solution is, then, the ordered number-triple, (k_1, k_2, k_3).

Comments: (1) In the forward-solution (determining the b's and c's) we systematically carry out the same type of calculation—the product of two numbers minus the product of two others, just like evaluating second-order determinants.

(2) In the back-solution (determining the k's) we could have used the second row of b's for k_2, or any one of the three rows of the a's for k_1. If there is a choice, choose the one with the easiest numbers. The other rows of that set can be used for a check if needed. Notice, also, that you always follow the same routine in the back-solution. Choose an equation of the set. From the number on the right of the vertical line, subtract the product of each k, previously determined, and its multiplier in that row, and divide by the last number on the left of the row.

(3) For a fourth-order system, first reduce to a third-order system, then to a second-order system, and finally to one equation in one unknown. The technique is the same, but there is one extra stage.

(4) You can evaluate determinants by this technique. Leave out the column of constants (a_{i4} in the example), but maintain a last column of totals for a check. At each stage after the second, every element will be exactly divisible by the pivot two stages back. After you make such divisions, the last number is the value of the determinant. In our example c_{33}/a_{11} is the value of the determinant formed by the nine a's in the upper left corner.

We illustrate this process numerically with the system of Exercise 14(c).

(x_1)	(x_2)	(x_3)			Totals
1	3	−1	1		4
2	−4	−2	−2		−6
5	6	−7	0		4
	−10	0	−4		−14
	−9	−2	−5		−16
		20	14		34
.5	.4	.7			

Now try your hand at the method of pivotal condensation. Do Exercise 14(g) and (i), as a starter.

We have suggested proofs for some of the properties of determinants. In the case of the method of pivotal condensation we gave you cookbook-type directions with no justification. We do not apologize for this. We wanted to suggest, in a brief section, the very extensive theory of determinants.

705. Systems of linear equations and matrices

You have learned to solve the system

$$a_{11}x_1 + a_{12}x_2 + a_{13}x_3 = c_1$$
$$a_{21}x_1 + a_{22}x_2 + a_{23}x_3 = c_2,$$
$$a_{31}x_1 + a_{32}x_2 + a_{33}x_3 = c_3,$$

$D \neq 0$, using third-order determinants. You should think of

$$D = \begin{vmatrix} a_{11} & a_{12} & a_{13} \\ a_{21} & a_{22} & a_{23} \\ a_{31} & a_{32} & a_{33} \end{vmatrix}$$

as a number that you get by expanding the determinant.
We now consider the square array of numbers

$$A = \begin{pmatrix} a_{11} & a_{12} & a_{13} \\ a_{21} & a_{22} & a_{23} \\ a_{31} & a_{32} & a_{33} \end{pmatrix}$$

and call this array the *matrix A*. We consider also the rectangular arrays of numbers

$$X = \begin{pmatrix} x_1 \\ x_2 \\ x_3 \end{pmatrix} \quad \text{and} \quad C = \begin{pmatrix} c_1 \\ c_2 \\ c_3 \end{pmatrix}.$$

These are matrices also. Mathematicians call these single-column matrices *vectors*.

Notice that matrices are something new. A determinant has a value, a single number that you get by expanding the determinant. A matrix is a rectangular array of numbers to which we are free to assign convenient properties.

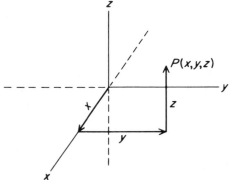

Fig. 7–26.

You have already met matrices as points. Recall that (3,2) represents an element of the cartesian product $L \times L$. You think of the symbol (3,2) as composed of the two numbers 3 and 2. Each of these numbers has meaning in itself; 3 is the x-coordinate and 2 is the y-coordinate of the point (3,2). Recall that we associated the point (3,2) with the complex number $3 + 2i$ in Section 104 (page 18). This number, $3 + 2i$, is a two-piece number with many of the properties of the one-piece, real numbers.

Think now of the cartesian product $(L \times L) \times L$. You pair each element (x,y) of the cartesian product $L \times L$ with an element z of the set L. This yields an ordered number-triple, (x,y,z). Geometrically, this represents a point in a space of three-dimensions. In Fig. 7–26 we drew an x-axis, a y-axis, and a z-axis. Look at the corner of the floor of a room. Label the line along which the wall on your left intersects the floor, the x-axis; label the line along which the wall on your right intersects the floor, the y-axis; label the line along which the two walls intersect, the z-axis. This is the framework that the figure represents. In the figure, we continued each axis by a dotted line. Notice that the axes separate three-space into eight *octants*, four above the xy-plane and four below the xy-plane. The cartesian product $(L \times L) \times L$ is the set of all points in three-space. You pair each point, (x,y) of the base plane with a real number z. This yields a point $P(x,y,z)$ like the one in Fig. 7–26. You can think of the ordered number-triple (x,y,z) as a one-rowed matrix.

It is harder to visualize the matrix (x_1,x_2,x_3,x_4) as a point. When you reason by analogy you come up with the idea of pairing each point (x_1,x_2,x_3) of three-space with a real number x_4; but you run out of directions to draw axes. Mathematicians like to call (x_1,x_2,x_3,x_4) a point in four-space. When they do this they are reasoning by analogy, and using geometric language to help them visualize a matrix. They are not pretending that there really is a mysterious fourth dimension in the physical world.

It is even harder to interpret a matrix like

$$\begin{pmatrix} 1 & 3 & 5 \\ 2 & 4 & 6 \end{pmatrix} \quad \text{or} \quad \begin{pmatrix} 3 & 8 & 6 \\ 5 & 2 & 6 \\ 7 & 1 & 4 \end{pmatrix}$$

as a single point, or number. People usually think of these matrices as rectangular arrays of separate numbers. Yet mathematicians have built an arithmetic of matrices that we shall explore briefly. This arithmetic of matrices provides an elegant way to attack the solution of systems of linear equations.

You may wish to compare the basic identities for matrices with the basic identities for real numbers, as given in Section 202 (page 63) and the basic identities for complex numbers, as given in Section 507 (page 212). Notice that the labeling of the properties of matrices parallels the labeling of properties of real numbers.

Definition of equality

D 1: $A = B$ means that the matrices A and B have the same numbers of rows and columns, and each element a_{ij} of A is equal to the corresponding element b_{ij} of B. For example,

$$\begin{pmatrix} 1 & 2 \\ 4 & 6 \\ 7 & 9 \end{pmatrix} = \begin{pmatrix} \frac{3}{3} & 6-4 \\ \frac{1}{3}(12) & 2+4 \\ (7)(1) & \frac{9}{1} \end{pmatrix}.$$

Definition of addition and multiplication

Addition: If A and B are matrices that have the same numbers of rows and columns, $A + B$ is defined to be a matrix with elements $a_{ij} + b_{ij}$ obtained by adding corresponding elements of A and B. For example:

$$(3 \quad 4 \quad 5) + (2 \quad -3 \quad -2) = (5 \quad 1 \quad 3).$$

Multiplication: If A has n rows and m columns and B has m rows and r columns, we define the product, AB, to be:

$$AB = \begin{pmatrix} a_{11} & a_{12} & \cdots & a_{1m} \\ a_{21} & a_{22} & \cdots & a_{2m} \\ \cdot & \cdot & & \cdot \\ \cdot & \cdot & & \cdot \\ \cdot & \cdot & & \cdot \\ a_{n1} & a_{n2} & \cdots & a_{nm} \end{pmatrix} \begin{pmatrix} b_{11} & b_{12} & \cdots & b_{1r} \\ b_{21} & b_{22} & \cdots & b_{2r} \\ \cdot & \cdot & & \cdot \\ \cdot & \cdot & & \cdot \\ \cdot & \cdot & & \cdot \\ b_{m1} & b_{m2} & \cdots & b_{mr} \end{pmatrix} =$$

$$\begin{pmatrix} a_{11}b_{11} + a_{12}b_{21} + \cdots + a_{1m}b_{m1} & a_{11}b_{12} + a_{12}b_{22} + \cdots + a_{1m}b_{m2} & \cdots & a_{11}b_{1r} + a_{12}b_{2r} + \cdots + a_{1m}b_{mr} \\ a_{21}b_{11} + a_{22}b_{21} + \cdots + a_{2m}b_{m1} & a_{21}b_{12} + a_{22}b_{22} + \cdots + a_{2m}b_{m2} & \cdots & a_{21}b_{1r} + a_{22}b_{2r} + \cdots + a_{2m}b_{mr} \\ \vdots & \vdots & & \vdots \\ a_{n1}b_{11} + a_{n2}b_{21} + \cdots + a_{nm}b_{m1} & a_{n1}b_{12} + a_{n2}b_{22} + \cdots + a_{nm}b_{m2} & \cdots & a_{n1}b_{1r} + a_{n2}b_{2r} + \cdots + a_{nm}b_{mr} \end{pmatrix}$$

Notice that AB is a matrix of n rows and r columns. Notice that the element in the ith row and jth column of AB is obtained by applying the ith row of A to the jth column of B and adding the products of the pairs of elements that touch. Study the following example to see how this works:

$$\begin{pmatrix} 2 & 3 & 4 \\ -1 & 2 & 1 \end{pmatrix} \begin{pmatrix} 1 & -3 \\ 2 & -1 \\ 3 & 4 \end{pmatrix}$$

$$= \begin{pmatrix} 2(1) + 3(2) + 4(3) & 2(-3) + 3(-1) + 4(4) \\ -1(1) + 2(2) + 1(3) & -1(-3) + 2(-1) + 1(4) \end{pmatrix} = \begin{pmatrix} 20 & 7 \\ 6 & 5 \end{pmatrix}.$$

Notice that this is not equal to the product,

$$\begin{pmatrix} 1 & -3 \\ 2 & -1 \\ 3 & 4 \end{pmatrix} \begin{pmatrix} 2 & 3 & 4 \\ -1 & 2 & 1 \end{pmatrix} = \begin{pmatrix} 5 & -3 & 1 \\ 5 & 4 & 7 \\ 2 & 17 & 16 \end{pmatrix}.$$

Notice that the product $\begin{pmatrix} 2 & 1 \\ 3 & 4 \end{pmatrix} \begin{pmatrix} 1 \\ 2 \end{pmatrix} = \begin{pmatrix} 4 \\ 11 \end{pmatrix}$

is defined, but not so the product $\begin{pmatrix} 1 \\ 2 \end{pmatrix} \begin{pmatrix} 2 & 1 \\ 3 & 4 \end{pmatrix}$.

When the definitions of addition and multiplication apply, the following properties can be proved:

PROPERTIES OF ADDITION (*When defined*)	PROPERTIES OF MULTIPLICATION (*When defined*)

Closure

A 1: For each A and B, there is a matrix C such that $A + B = C$.

M 1: For each A and B, there is a matrix C such that $AB = C$.

Uniqueness

A 2: $(A = C \text{ and } B = D)$
$\Rightarrow (A + B = C + D)$.

M 2: $(A = C \text{ and } B = D)$
$\Rightarrow (AB = CD)$.

Commutative

A 3: $A + B = B + A$.

M 3: There are pairs of matrices, A and B, such that $AB \neq BA$.

Associative

A 4: $(A + B) + C = A + (B + C)$.

M 4: $(AB)C = A(BC)$.

Identity (for square matrices)

A 5: There is a unique identity for addition, that we call O, such that $A + O = A$ for each n by n matrix A. (O is the n by n matrix, each of whose elements is zero).

M 5: There is a unique identity for multiplication, that we call I, such that $A \cdot I = I \cdot A = A$ for each n by n matrix A. (I is the n by n matrix with elements $x_{ij} = 0$, $i \neq j$, and $x_{ii} = 1$).

For example,

$$\begin{pmatrix} 1 & 2 \\ 3 & 4 \end{pmatrix} + \begin{pmatrix} 0 & 0 \\ 0 & 0 \end{pmatrix} = \begin{pmatrix} 1 & 2 \\ 3 & 4 \end{pmatrix};$$

For example,

$$\begin{pmatrix} 1 & 2 \\ 3 & 4 \end{pmatrix}\begin{pmatrix} 1 & 0 \\ 0 & 1 \end{pmatrix} = \begin{pmatrix} 1 & 0 \\ 0 & 1 \end{pmatrix}\begin{pmatrix} 1 & 2 \\ 3 & 4 \end{pmatrix}$$
$$= \begin{pmatrix} 1 & 2 \\ 3 & 4 \end{pmatrix}$$

$$\begin{pmatrix} 1 & 2 & 3 \\ 4 & 5 & 6 \\ 7 & 8 & 9 \end{pmatrix} + \begin{pmatrix} 0 & 0 & 0 \\ 0 & 0 & 0 \\ 0 & 0 & 0 \end{pmatrix} = \begin{pmatrix} 1 & 2 & 3 \\ 4 & 5 & 6 \\ 7 & 8 & 9 \end{pmatrix}.$$

$$\begin{pmatrix} 1 & 2 & 3 \\ 4 & 5 & 6 \\ 7 & 8 & 9 \end{pmatrix}\begin{pmatrix} 1 & 0 & 0 \\ 0 & 1 & 0 \\ 0 & 0 & 1 \end{pmatrix} = \begin{pmatrix} 1 & 0 & 0 \\ 0 & 1 & 0 \\ 0 & 0 & 1 \end{pmatrix}\begin{pmatrix} 1 & 2 & 3 \\ 4 & 5 & 6 \\ 7 & 8 & 9 \end{pmatrix} = \begin{pmatrix} 1 & 2 & 3 \\ 4 & 5 & 6 \\ 7 & 8 & 9 \end{pmatrix}.$$

Inverse Element (for square matrices)

A 6: For each square matrix, A, there is a unique inverse for addition, that we call $(-A)$, such that $A + (-A) = O$. (To obtain the matrix $(-A)$, you change the sign of each element of A).

M 6: For each square matrix, A, whose determinant $|A| \neq 0$, there is a unique inverse for multiplication, that we call A^{-1}, such that $A^{-1}A = I$. (We explain later how to find A^{-1} when $|A| \neq 0$).

Inverse Operation (for square matrices)

A 7: $A - B = A + (-B)$.

M 7: $|B| \neq 0 \Rightarrow A \div B = \dfrac{A}{B} = AB^{-1}.$*

* This defines what might be called a *right* quotient, AB^{-1}. The *left* quotient, $B^{-1}A$, is not necessarily the same. See M 3.

Order

A 8: The symbol $A < B$ is not defined for matrices. Hence Property A 8 is not meaningful for matrices.

M 8: The symbol $A < B$ is not defined for matrices. Hence Property M 8 is not meaningful for matrices.

PROPERTIES FOR COMBINING ADDITION AND MULTIPLICATION

D 1: $A(B + C) = AB + AC.$

D 2: $-A = (-I)A.$

D 3: $(A + B)C = AC + BC.$

D 4: $A(B - C) = AB - AC.$

D 5: $(A + B)(C + D) = AC + BC + AD + BD.$

D 6: $(A + B)^2 = A^2 + BA + AB + B^2$ $(BA + AB = AB + AB$ is *not* an identity for matrices).

D 7: $(A - B)^2 = A^2 - BA - AB + B^2.$

D 8: $(A + B)(A - B) = A^2 + BA - AB - B^2$ $(BA - AB = O$ is *not* an identity for matrices).

D 9: $A(B + C + D) = AB + AC + AD.$

D 10: $-(A + B + C) = (-A) + (-B) + (-C).$

You may be impressed, as mathematicians were, with the similar behavior of matrices and real numbers. Matrices behave even more like complex numbers in the sense that familiar properties of order break down. The big difference comes in M 3. Multiplication of matrices is not a commutative operation. This fact leads to the differences you notice in identities like D 6, D 7, and D 8.

This brings us back to the unanswered question of Chapter 1: What is a number? Whether or not you wish to call vectors (matrices of one row or one column) numbers is a matter of taste. If you wish to say points are numbers, and vectors are points, you may decide to call vectors numbers. Few mathematicians would wish to call all matrices numbers; but they must admit that matrices act a lot like numbers.

The following exercises give you opportunities to experiment with the arithmetic of matrices:

EXERCISES §705

1. Given the matrices

$$A = \begin{pmatrix} 2 & 1 & -4 \\ 5 & 0 & 1 \end{pmatrix}, \quad B = \begin{pmatrix} 1 & 6 \\ -3 & 0 \\ 3 & -2 \end{pmatrix}, \quad C = \begin{pmatrix} 2 & -4 \\ 1 & 1 \\ -2 & 3 \end{pmatrix}.$$

Calculate (a) $B + C$ and $C + B$;   (b) AB and BA;   (c) $A(B + C)$ and $AB + AC$.

2. Let

$$A = \begin{pmatrix} 5 & 4 & 2 \\ 7 & -1 & 5 \\ 2 & 3 & 0 \end{pmatrix} \quad \text{and} \quad I = \begin{pmatrix} 1 & 0 & 0 \\ 0 & 1 & 0 \\ 0 & 0 & 1 \end{pmatrix}.$$

Calculate IA and AI.

3. Let

$$A = \begin{pmatrix} 2 & 1 \\ 3 & -4 \end{pmatrix}, \quad B = \begin{pmatrix} -4 & -1 \\ 2 & 5 \end{pmatrix}, \quad C = \begin{pmatrix} 0 & 2 \\ -1 & 3 \end{pmatrix}.$$

Calculate $(AB)C$ and $A(BC)$.

4. Given

$$A = \begin{pmatrix} a_{11} & a_{12} & a_{13} & a_{14} \\ a_{21} & a_{22} & a_{23} & a_{24} \\ a_{31} & a_{32} & a_{33} & a_{34} \\ a_{41} & a_{42} & a_{43} & a_{44} \end{pmatrix}, \quad \text{and} \quad X = \begin{pmatrix} c_1 \\ c_2 \\ c_3 \\ c_4 \end{pmatrix}.$$

(a) Which of the following symbols are defined? $A + X$, $X + A$, AX, and XA.
(b) Use the definition to perform the operations that are defined.

5. Verify by matrix multiplication that

$$\text{if} \quad A = \begin{pmatrix} 1 & 1 & -2 \\ 3 & 7 & -3 \\ 1 & 2 & -1 \end{pmatrix}, \quad \text{then} \quad A^{-1} = \begin{pmatrix} -1 & -3 & 11 \\ 0 & 1 & -3 \\ -1 & -1 & 4 \end{pmatrix}.$$

6. When a matrix A has a multiplicative inverse, this inverse is always commutative with A in multiplication; i.e., if $A^{-1} \cdot A = I$, then $A \cdot A^{-1} = I$. Verify this property for the two matrices of Exercise 5.

7. For a square matrix of two rows and columns, whose determinant is not zero, the inverse can be found by a simple rule. Interchange the position of the diagonal elements (a_{11} and a_{22}), reverse the sign of the non-diagonal elements, then divide all four numbers by the determinant of the matrix. Thus, if

$$A = \begin{pmatrix} a & b \\ c & d \end{pmatrix}, \quad \text{then} \quad A^{-1} = \begin{pmatrix} d/D & -b/D \\ -c/D & a/D \end{pmatrix},$$

where $D = ad - bc$.

(a) Prove, by multiplication of A^{-1} and A as given above, that if $D \neq 0$, A^{-1} can be determined in this fashion.

(b) Find the inverse of $\begin{pmatrix} 7 & 3 \\ 4 & 2 \end{pmatrix}$. Check by matrix multiplication.

8. Find the inverses of the following matrices. (*Suggestion:* see Exercise 7.)

(a) $\begin{pmatrix} 3 & 4 \\ 5 & 7 \end{pmatrix}$ (b) $\begin{pmatrix} 6 & -5 \\ 3 & -2 \end{pmatrix}$

(c) $\begin{pmatrix} 5 & -2 \\ 4 & -3 \end{pmatrix}$ (d) $\begin{pmatrix} 0.3 & 2.2 \\ 0.5 & 4.0 \end{pmatrix}$.

Now examine the equation

$$\begin{pmatrix} a_{11} & a_{12} & a_{13} \\ a_{21} & a_{22} & a_{23} \\ a_{31} & a_{32} & a_{33} \end{pmatrix} \begin{pmatrix} x_1 \\ x_2 \\ x_3 \end{pmatrix} = \begin{pmatrix} c_1 \\ c_2 \\ c_3 \end{pmatrix}.$$

When you multiply the matrices on the left,

$$\begin{pmatrix} a_{11}x_1 + a_{12}x_2 + a_{13}x_3 \\ a_{21}x_1 + a_{22}x_2 + a_{23}x_3 \\ a_{31}x_1 + a_{32}x_2 + a_{33}x_3 \end{pmatrix} = \begin{pmatrix} c_1 \\ c_2 \\ c_3 \end{pmatrix}.$$

Applying the definition of equality of matrices, you recognize this as a system of three linear equations in the three unknowns, x_1, x_2, and x_3.

A shorter way to write this same equation is

$$AX = C,$$

where $A = \begin{pmatrix} a_{11} & a_{12} & a_{13} \\ a_{21} & a_{22} & a_{23} \\ a_{31} & a_{32} & a_{33} \end{pmatrix}$, $\quad X = \begin{pmatrix} x_1 \\ x_2 \\ x_3 \end{pmatrix}$, $\quad$ and $\quad C = \begin{pmatrix} c_1 \\ c_2 \\ c_3 \end{pmatrix}$.

Compare the equation $AX = C$ to the equation $ax = c$. We solved the equation $ax = c$ by applying properties of real numbers; the existence of $1/a$, $a \neq 0$, was crucial. We said:

$$ax = c$$

$$\frac{1}{a} = \frac{1}{a}\left(\frac{1}{a}\right) \text{ exists provided } a \neq 0 \text{ by}$$

$$\text{(M 6, page 63)}$$

$$\frac{1}{a}(ax) = \frac{1}{a} \cdot c \qquad \text{(M 2)}$$

$$\left(\frac{1}{a} \cdot a\right)x = \frac{c}{a} \qquad \text{(M 4)}$$

$$1 \cdot x = \frac{c}{a} \qquad \text{(M 6)}$$

$$x = \frac{c}{a}. \qquad \text{(M 5)}$$

Now we solve the equation $AX = C$ by applying properties of matrices; the existence of A^{-1}, $|A| \neq 0$, is crucial. We say:

$$AX = C$$
$$A^{-1} = A^{-1} \quad (A^{-1} \text{ exists for } |A| \neq 0, \text{ by M 6})$$
$$A^{-1}(AX) = A^{-1}C \qquad \qquad \text{(M 2)}$$
$$(A^{-1}A)X = A^{-1}C \qquad \qquad \text{(M 4)}$$
$$IX = A^{-1}C \qquad \qquad \text{(M 6)}$$
$$X = A^{-1}C. \qquad \qquad \text{(M 5)}$$

Notice that the solutions of the two equations, $ax = c$ and $AX = C$, are *formally* the same. The set of matrices and the set of real numbers have similar structures as far as this problem is concerned. The commutative law for multiplication and the properties of order do not enter into these solutions.

Practically speaking, we have not accomplished much toward solving systems of linear equations. The calculation of A^{-1} turns out to be as hard a problem as the solution of the corresponding system of equations. Our accomplishments are rather in the direction of a briefer way to express a problem, a new way of saying things that may lead to new insights, and the like.

The theory of matrices does provide elegant ways to explore the special cases where the determinant of the coefficients of a system of linear equations $|A| = 0$. It has other applications that you will meet in Section 706. For the time being, we are most eager to have you explore the similarities and differences between the structure of the set of real numbers and the structure of the set of matrices.

We close this section with a set of directions for finding A^{-1} when $|A| \neq 0$. You may wish to consult some of the references given at the end of Chapter 7 for proofs of these results. Others of the References will provide further reading on the solutions of systems of linear equations with matrices.

Given the n by n matrix,

$$A = \begin{pmatrix} a_{11} & a_{12} & \cdots & a_{1n} \\ a_{21} & a_{22} & \cdots & a_{2n} \\ \cdot & \cdot & & \cdot \\ \cdot & \cdot & & \cdot \\ \cdot & \cdot & & \cdot \\ a_{n1} & a_{n2} & \cdots & a_{nn} \end{pmatrix}$$

with determinant $|A| \neq 0$. To calculate A^{-1}, proceed as follows:
  (1) Calculate $|A|$.
  (2) Calculate the *cofactor*, A_{ij}, of each element, a_{ij}, of A. The cofactor of a_{ij} is the determinant, of order $n - 1$, that you get by deleting the row and

column of A that contain a_{ij}; you prefix this determinant by the sign, $(-1)^{i+j}$. An example will help: If

$$A = \begin{pmatrix} 1 & -1 & 5 \\ 2 & -3 & -5 \\ 3 & -2 & 6 \end{pmatrix},$$

the cofactor of -5 is the determinant,

$$A_{23} = (-1) \begin{vmatrix} 1 & -1 \\ 3 & -2 \end{vmatrix},$$

which you get by deleting the second row and the third column of A, and using the sign of $(-1)^{2+3} = (-1)^5 = -1$. Similarly, the cofactor of 5 is

$$A_{13} = \begin{vmatrix} 2 & -3 \\ 3 & -2 \end{vmatrix},$$

the cofactor of -3 is

$$A_{22} = \begin{vmatrix} 1 & 5 \\ 3 & 6 \end{vmatrix}, \quad \text{etc.}$$

(3) Form the matrix

$$A^{-1} = \begin{pmatrix} A_{11}/|A| & A_{21}/|A| & \cdots & A_{n1}/|A| \\ A_{12}/|A| & A_{22}/|A| & \cdots & A_{n2}/|A| \\ \cdot & \cdot & & \cdot \\ \cdot & \cdot & & \cdot \\ \cdot & \cdot & & \cdot \\ A_{1n}/|A| & A_{2n}/|A| & \cdots & A_{nn}/|A| \end{pmatrix},$$

in which the element in the ith row and jth column is the cofactor of the element in the jth row and ith column of A, divided by the determinant $|A|$.

For example, when

$$A = \begin{vmatrix} 1 & -1 & 5 \\ 2 & -3 & -5 \\ 3 & -2 & 6 \end{vmatrix}, \quad \text{then} \quad |A| = 24,$$

$A_{11} = -28$, $A_{12} = -27$, $A_{13} = 5$, $A_{21} = -4$, $A_{22} = -9$, $A_{23} = -1$, $A_{31} = 20$, $A_{32} = 15$, $A_{33} = -1$. Hence

$$A^{-1} = \begin{pmatrix} -28/24 & -4/24 & 20/24 \\ -27/24 & -9/24 & 15/24 \\ 5/24 & -1/24 & -1/24 \end{pmatrix}.$$

As a check, calculate

$$A^{-1}A = \begin{pmatrix} -28/24 & -4/24 & 20/24 \\ -27/24 & -9/24 & 15/24 \\ 5/24 & -1/24 & -1/24 \end{pmatrix} \begin{pmatrix} 1 & -1 & 5 \\ 2 & -3 & -5 \\ 3 & -2 & 6 \end{pmatrix} = \begin{pmatrix} 1 & 0 & 0 \\ 0 & 1 & 0 \\ 0 & 0 & 1 \end{pmatrix} = I.$$

To solve the system of equations,

$$x - y + 5z = 3$$
$$2x - 3y - 5z = 4$$
$$3x - 2y + 6z = 6,$$

write the *matrix equation*

$$\begin{pmatrix} 1 & -1 & 5 \\ 2 & -3 & -5 \\ 3 & -2 & 6 \end{pmatrix} \begin{pmatrix} x \\ y \\ z \end{pmatrix} = \begin{pmatrix} 3 \\ 4 \\ 6 \end{pmatrix}.$$

Multiply by the inverse for multiplication of the coefficient matrix. We found A^{-1} above. You get

$$I \begin{pmatrix} x \\ y \\ z \end{pmatrix} = \begin{pmatrix} x \\ y \\ z \end{pmatrix} = \begin{pmatrix} -28/24 & -4/24 & 20/24 \\ -27/24 & -9/24 & 15/24 \\ 5/24 & -1/24 & -1/24 \end{pmatrix} \begin{pmatrix} 3 \\ 4 \\ 6 \end{pmatrix} = \begin{pmatrix} 20/24 \\ -27/24 \\ 5/24 \end{pmatrix}.$$

Hence $x = 20/24 = 5/6$, $y = -27/24 = -9/8$, and $z = 5/24$. You should check these values of x, y, and z in the original equations.

EXERCISES §705 (cont.)

9. When you write the system of equations,

$$x + y - 2z = 4$$
$$3x + 7y - 3z = 6$$
$$x + 2y - z = 3,$$

in the matrix form $AX = C$, what is the matrix A? the matrix C?

10. The inverse of the matrix A of Exercise 9 is given in Exercise 5 (page 355). Use A^{-1} to solve the system of equations of Exercise 9.

11. Solve each system of equations with matrices. [Your answers to Exercise 8 (page 356) will be helpful.]

(a) $3x + 4y = 7$
   $5x + 7y = 2$

(b) $6x - 5y = 2$
   $3x - 2y = 4$

(c) $5x - 2y = 1$
   $4x - 3y = -3$

(d) $0.3x + 2.2y = 1.4$
   $0.5x + 4.0y = 2.5.$

12. Use the methods of the text to determine the inverses of the following matrices.

(a) $\begin{pmatrix} 1 & 2 & 0 \\ -1 & 1 & 4 \\ 2 & 3 & -1 \end{pmatrix}$ (b) $\begin{pmatrix} 2 & -1 & 2 \\ 1 & 1 & -2 \\ 4 & -2 & 5 \end{pmatrix}$

(c) $\begin{pmatrix} 1 & 1 & 1 \\ 2 & -1 & -1 \\ 4 & 3 & -1 \end{pmatrix}$ (d) $\begin{pmatrix} 5 & 3 & 3 \\ 7 & 4 & 1 \\ 3 & 2 & 4 \end{pmatrix}$

(e) $\begin{pmatrix} 1 & 0 & 2 & -1 \\ 0 & 3 & 2 & 3 \\ 4 & 0 & 5 & 2 \\ 1 & 3 & 1 & 7 \end{pmatrix}.$

Answers:

(a) $\begin{pmatrix} -13 & 2 & 8 \\ 7 & -1 & -4 \\ -5 & 1 & 3 \end{pmatrix}$ (b) $\begin{pmatrix} 1/3 & 1/3 & 0 \\ -13/3 & 2/3 & 2 \\ -2 & 0 & 1 \end{pmatrix}$

(d) $\begin{pmatrix} 14 & -6 & -9 \\ -25 & 11 & 16 \\ 2 & -1 & -1 \end{pmatrix}$ (e) $\begin{pmatrix} 22/3 & -3 & -7/3 & 3 \\ 55/9 & -2 & -19/9 & 7/3 \\ -14/3 & 2 & 5/3 & -2 \\ -3 & 1 & 1 & -1 \end{pmatrix}.$

13. Solve each system of equations with matrices. (Your answers to Exercise 12 will be helpful.)

(a) $x + 2y = 3$
$-x + y + 4z = 7$
$2x + 3y - z = 5$

(b) $2x - y + 2z = 1$
$x + y - 2z = 4$
$4x - 2y + 5z = 3$

(c) $x + y + z = 2$
$2x - y - z = 1$
$4x + 3y - z = -5$

(d) $5x + 3y + 3z = 2$
$7x + 4y + z = 0$
$3x + 2y + 4z = -1$

(e) $x + 2z - w = 3$
$3y + 2z + 3w = 10$
$4x + 5z + 2w = 9$
$x + 3y + z + 7w = 9.$

14. Using the inverse matrix of Exercise 12(b), determine the solution of the system

$$2x - y + 2z = r$$
$$x + y - 2z = s$$
$$4x - 2y + 5z = t$$

in terms of r, s, and t.

Answer: $(\frac{1}{3}r + \frac{1}{3}s, -\frac{13}{3}r + \frac{2}{3}s + 2t, -2r + t).$

706. Linear transformations and matrices

In Chapter 6, and up to this point in Chapter 7, we have used the word *unknown* as a special name for a variable. We have often used the word *parameter* as another special name for a variable. These words are convenient when you use variables in special ways. Now we take a new look at systems of linear equations, and remind you that parameters and unknowns are still variables.

When you see the system of equations

$$a_{11}x_1 + a_{12}x_2 + \ldots + a_{1n}x_n = c_1$$

$$a_{21}x_1 + a_{22}x_2 + \ldots + a_{2n}x_n = c_2$$

$$\vdots$$

$$a_{n1}x_1 + a_{n2}x_2 + \ldots + a_{nn}x_n = c_n$$

you think of x_i as an unknown and c_i a parameter. We now replace the symbol c_i by the symbol y_i, and interchange the right and left sides of each equation:

$$y_1 = a_{11}x_1 + a_{12}x_2 + \ldots + a_{1n}x_n$$

$$y_2 = a_{21}x_1 + a_{22}x_2 + \ldots + a_{2n}x_n$$

$$\vdots$$

$$y_n = a_{n1}x_1 + a_{n2}x_2 + \ldots + a_{nn}x_n.$$

With this change of notation, you begin to look at these n linear equations in a new way. You think of *transforming n numbers*, $(x_1, x_2, \ldots, x_n)$ into n new numbers $(y_1, y_2, \ldots, y_n)$ by means of this set of *linear transformations*.

When you use the briefer matrix notation, you write

$$Y = AX,$$

where

$$Y = \begin{pmatrix} y_1 \\ y_2 \\ \vdots \\ y_n \end{pmatrix}, \quad X = \begin{pmatrix} x_1 \\ x_2 \\ \vdots \\ x_n \end{pmatrix}, \quad \text{and} \quad A = \begin{pmatrix} a_{11} & a_{12} & \cdots & a_{1n} \\ a_{21} & a_{22} & \cdots & a_{2n} \\ \vdots & \vdots & & \vdots \\ a_{n1} & a_{n2} & \cdots & a_{nn} \end{pmatrix}.$$

One application of linear transformations is to coding and decoding secret messages. We use an application to cryptography to illustrate this: Suppose you assign letters of the alphabet to numbers as follows:

1	2	3	4	5	6	7	8	9	10	11	12	13	14	15	16	17	18
a	b	c	d	e	f	g	h	i	j	k	l	m	n	o	p	q	r

19	20	21	22	23	24	25	26	27	28	29	=	0
s	t	u	v	w	x	y	z	—	?	!		

The dash, question mark, and exclamation point are used as fillers. It is convenient to have a *prime* number like 29, and to *cast out multiples of 29;* that is, to set $29 = 0$, $30 = 1$, $31 = 2$, ..., $62 = 2(29) + 4 = 4$, etc.

Now we make some further agreements:

(1) Messages will be broken into groups of 3 letters each. Thus "Passengers are cold and hungry" becomes

PAS SEN GER SAR ECO LDA NDH UNG RY—.

This becomes

$$16, 1, 19 \quad 19, 5, 14 \quad 7, 5, 18 \quad 19, 1, 18 \quad 5, 3, 15 \quad 12, 4, 1$$
$$14, 4, 8 \quad 21, 14, 7 \quad 18, 25, 27.$$

(2) The *secret matrix* for coding will be

$$A = \begin{pmatrix} 5 & 3 & 1 \\ 0 & 4 & 3 \\ 2 & 3 & 1 \end{pmatrix}.$$

When $\quad X = \begin{pmatrix} x_1 \\ x_2 \\ x_3 \end{pmatrix} = \begin{pmatrix} 16 \\ 1 \\ 19 \end{pmatrix}$, $Y = \begin{pmatrix} y_1 \\ y_2 \\ y_3 \end{pmatrix} = AX$

$$= \begin{pmatrix} 5 & 3 & 1 \\ 0 & 4 & 3 \\ 2 & 3 & 1 \end{pmatrix} \begin{pmatrix} 16 \\ 1 \\ 19 \end{pmatrix} = \begin{pmatrix} 5 \times 16 + 3 \times 1 + 1 \times 19 \\ 0 \times 16 + 4 \times 1 + 3 \times 19 \\ 2 \times 16 + 3 \times 1 + 1 \times 19 \end{pmatrix} = \begin{pmatrix} 102 \\ 61 \\ 54 \end{pmatrix}.$$

When you cast out multiples of 29,

$$\begin{pmatrix} 102 \\ 61 \\ 54 \end{pmatrix} = \begin{pmatrix} 15 \\ 3 \\ 25 \end{pmatrix};$$

you can go back to letters now, and this becomes OCY. (15 is O, 3 is C, and 25 is Y).

Now you should try to code 19, 5, 14. Try it first yourself. Then compare your work to what follows to be sure you catch on to the system:

$$\begin{pmatrix} 5 & 3 & 1 \\ 0 & 4 & 3 \\ 2 & 3 & 1 \end{pmatrix} \begin{pmatrix} 19 \\ 5 \\ 14 \end{pmatrix} = \begin{pmatrix} 5 \times 19 + 3 \times 5 + 1 \times 14 \\ 0 \times 19 + 4 \times 5 + 3 \times 14 \\ 2 \times 19 + 3 \times 5 + 1 \times 14 \end{pmatrix} = \begin{pmatrix} 124 \\ 62 \\ 67 \end{pmatrix} = \begin{pmatrix} 8 \\ 4 \\ 9 \end{pmatrix}.$$

When you go back to letters, 8, 4, 9 becomes HDI. So far, the message

PAS SEN

becomes
OCY HDI.

You should continue to put the whole message into code. Here is what you should get:

GER   SAR   ECO   LDA   NDH   UNG   RY—

becomes
JPR   !!A   T?E   OSH   CKS   ISD   RGV

To make a code useful, the right people have to know how to decode the message. Think of trying to do this without knowing the system! Notice that the first S in the message became a Y. The second S became an H. One of the standard techniques for breaking codes is to count the frequency of certain letters. The letter E is the most frequent letter in a typical message. But the first E in our message turned into a D. The second one turned into a P. The third one turned into a T. Notice also that R turned into itself twice. But once it turned into an A. All these peculiarities make it hard for the person who tries to break the code.

If you know the secret matrix, you can decode the message by solving systems of equations. You receive the number-triple OCY. You write (15, 3, 25); then you set up the matrix equation

$$\begin{pmatrix} 5 & 3 & 1 \\ 0 & 4 & 3 \\ 2 & 3 & 1 \end{pmatrix} \begin{pmatrix} x_1 \\ x_2 \\ x_3 \end{pmatrix} = \begin{pmatrix} 15 \\ 3 \\ 25 \end{pmatrix}.$$

The next three letters, HDI, give you another system of equations with the same coefficient matrix, etc. This is a situation in which it will be especially helpful to know the inverse for multiplication of the coefficient matrix. Once you have calculated this inverse, you can decode the message very simply.

If $Y = AX$ is used for transforming the vector X into the vector Y, then

$$A^{-1}Y = A^{-1}(AX) = (A^{-1}A)X = IX = X$$

or $\qquad\qquad\qquad X = A^{-1}Y$

will transform the vector Y back to X.

You can use the methods of Section 705 (page 357) to calculate the inverse of the *coding* matrix. This *decoding* matrix will involve fractions that you can eliminate by the gimmick of casting out 29's. This is where it comes in handy to have a prime number like 29. We illustrate the process:

$$A = \begin{pmatrix} 5 & 3 & 1 \\ 0 & 4 & 3 \\ 2 & 3 & 1 \end{pmatrix}; \quad |A| = \begin{vmatrix} 5 & 3 & 1 \\ 0 & 4 & 3 \\ 2 & 3 & 1 \end{vmatrix} = -15;$$

$$A_{11} = \begin{vmatrix} 4 & 3 \\ 3 & 1 \end{vmatrix} = -5; \quad \frac{A_{11}}{|A|} = \frac{-5}{-15} = \frac{1}{3} = \frac{1+29}{3} = 10.$$

Mathematicians have developed a special arithmetic of sets of numbers in which two numbers are equal if they differ by a multiple of a prime number, like 29. They speak of the numbers *modulo* 29, and study the structure of this set of numbers as we studied the structure of the real numbers. An interesting feature of the set of numbers modulo 29 is that you can replace fractions, like 1/3, by integers, such as 10 (above).

The decoding matrix turns out to be

$$A^{-1} = \begin{pmatrix} 10 & 0 & 19 \\ 17 & 23 & 1 \\ 16 & 18 & 18 \end{pmatrix}.$$

As a check,

$$A^{-1}A = \begin{pmatrix} 10 & 0 & 19 \\ 17 & 23 & 1 \\ 16 & 18 & 18 \end{pmatrix} \begin{pmatrix} 5 & 3 & 1 \\ 0 & 4 & 3 \\ 2 & 3 & 1 \end{pmatrix} = \begin{pmatrix} 88 & 87 & 29 \\ 87 & 146 & 87 \\ 116 & 174 & 88 \end{pmatrix} = \begin{pmatrix} 1 & 0 & 0 \\ 0 & 1 & 0 \\ 0 & 0 & 1 \end{pmatrix}.$$

The person who knows the system, and the decoding matrix, proceeds as follows: OCY is 15, 3, 25. Then

$$\begin{pmatrix} 10 & 0 & 19 \\ 17 & 23 & 1 \\ 16 & 18 & 18 \end{pmatrix} \begin{pmatrix} 15 \\ 3 \\ 25 \end{pmatrix} = \begin{pmatrix} 16 \\ 1 \\ 19 \end{pmatrix}.$$

Hence you interpret OCY to mean PAS.

You can decode the rest of the message in the same way. But do not lose the main idea among the details. The matrix A^{-1} undoes what the matrix A does. You use A to perform a linear transformation; you use the inverse of A, A^{-1}, to undo this transformation.

We return now to a geometric interpretation of the linear transformation, $Y = AX$. In Fig. 7–27, we drew two sets of axes. $P(x_1, x_2, x_3)$ is a point in three-space referred to the axes labeled x_1, x_2, and x_3. $Q(y_1, y_2, y_3)$ is a point in three-space referred to the axes labeled y_1, y_2, and y_3. You can think of the point Q as the *transform* of P. Each point P is transformed into a new point Q by the linear transformation $Y = AX$.

Take, for example,

$$y_1 = 2x_1 - 3x_2 + x_3$$
$$y_2 = -x_1 + x_2 - 2x_3$$
$$y_3 = 5x_1 - 2x_2 - 3x_3,$$

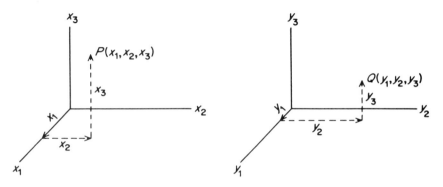

Fig. 7–27.

or $Y = \begin{pmatrix} 2 & -3 & 1 \\ -1 & 1 & -2 \\ 5 & -2 & -3 \end{pmatrix} X$. For the point $P(1,1,1)$, $X = \begin{pmatrix} 1 \\ 1 \\ 1 \end{pmatrix}$; then

$$Y = \begin{pmatrix} 2 & -3 & 1 \\ -1 & 1 & -2 \\ 5 & -2 & -3 \end{pmatrix} \begin{pmatrix} 1 \\ 1 \\ 1 \end{pmatrix} = \begin{pmatrix} 0 \\ -2 \\ 0 \end{pmatrix};$$

hence the transform of P is the point $Q(0,-2,0)$. In this way you can transform each point P into a new point Q.

Notice the similarity of this process to the process of alibi that we introduced in Chapter 4. The point $Q(y_1,y_2,y_3)$ is the point $P(x_1,x_2,x_3)$ in a different position.

You may wish to explore this topic of linear transformations further, using the references at the end of the chapter. We turn now to some special linear transformations in two-space:

(1) Consider the transformation

$$\begin{aligned} y_1 &= 0x_1 + x_2 \\ y_2 &= x_1 + 0x_2, \end{aligned} \quad \text{or} \quad Y = \begin{pmatrix} 0 & 1 \\ 1 & 0 \end{pmatrix} X.$$

Figure 7–28 gives the geometric interpretation. Notice that $y_1 = x_2$, and $y_2 = x_1$. A graph in the x_1x_2-plane will become a graph in the y_1y_2-plane; y_1 plays the role that x_2 played before; y_2 plays the role that x_1 played before. Hence the graph of $x_2 = 3x_1^2$ becomes the graph of $y_1 = 3y_2^2$. The effect is to transform each relation, like $\{(x_1,x_2) \mid x_2 = 3x_1^2\}$ above, into the inverse relation, like $\{(y_1,y_2) \mid y_1 = 3y_2^2\}$ above. (See Chapter 5, p. 177.)

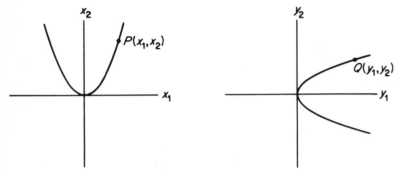

Fig. 7–28.

Now let

$$z_1 = 0y_1 + y_2 \qquad \text{or} \qquad Z = \begin{pmatrix} 0 & 1 \\ 1 & 0 \end{pmatrix} Y.$$
$$z_2 = y_1 + 0y_2,$$

This transforms the point $Q(y_1,y_2)$ into a new point $R(z_1,z_2)$. We get

$$Z = \begin{pmatrix} 0 & 1 \\ 1 & 0 \end{pmatrix} Y = \begin{pmatrix} 0 & 1 \\ 1 & 0 \end{pmatrix} \begin{pmatrix} 0 & 1 \\ 1 & 0 \end{pmatrix} X = \begin{pmatrix} 1 & 0 \\ 0 & 1 \end{pmatrix} X = X.$$

The new (z_1,z_2) are the original (x_1,x_2). That is, the inverse of the inverse of the relation, is the original relation.

(2) Consider the transformation

$$y_1 = -x_1 + 0x_2 \qquad \text{or} \qquad Y = \begin{pmatrix} -1 & 0 \\ 0 & -1 \end{pmatrix} X.$$
$$y_2 = 0x_1 - x_2,$$

You will recognize this transformation as a *reflection in the origin*. Again you will notice that applying the transformation twice brings you back where you started; that is,

$$Z = \begin{pmatrix} -1 & 0 \\ 0 & -1 \end{pmatrix} Y = \begin{pmatrix} -1 & 0 \\ 0 & -1 \end{pmatrix} \begin{pmatrix} -1 & 0 \\ 0 & -1 \end{pmatrix} X = \begin{pmatrix} 1 & 0 \\ 0 & 1 \end{pmatrix} X = X.$$

(3) Consider the transformation,

$$Y = \begin{pmatrix} -1 & 0 \\ 0 & 1 \end{pmatrix} X.$$

You will recognize this transformation as a *reflection in the vertical axis*. When you apply this transformation twice, you get the identity transformation, that is, $Z = X$.

These are special linear transformations in two-space. Notice that these transformations, and the more general ones we discussed earlier, all transform the origin (0,0,0) into the new origin. That is, if $Y = AX$, and

$$X = \begin{pmatrix} 0 \\ 0 \\ \cdot \\ \cdot \\ 0 \end{pmatrix}, \quad \text{then} \quad Y = \begin{pmatrix} 0 \\ 0 \\ \cdot \\ \cdot \\ 0 \end{pmatrix}.$$

Hence the translations of the origin that you met in Chapter 4 (page 122) are not included. Such translations of the origin require special treatment. (See Exercises §1000, page 506.)

You will meet an especially useful linear transformation in Chapter 10. This is the transformation called *rotation* of axes. Exercises §1000 treat rotation of axes in the matrix notation and suggest certain generalizations. But the general question of linear transformations provides ample material for a separate course.

As you look back over Sections 705 and 706, we hope you will glimpse the possibilities of building a powerful symbolism for stating problems briefly and conveniently. We have introduced determinants and matrices to illustrate these possibilities. Perhaps your imagination will carry you even further. Perhaps you see how symbols like matrices make it possible to look more deeply into problems of geometry. Perhaps you see how modern mathematics (for example, the theory of matrices) finds applications to problems that, at first examination, seem to have no connection with arithmetic or geometry. The example from the field of cryptography is an instance.

EXERCISES §706

1. Finish coding the message, PASSENGERS ARE COLD AND HUNGRY, using the coding matrix of the text. Decode the entire message to check your work.

2. Code a message of your own choice using the coding matrix given in the text. Check your work by decoding with the inverse matrix.

3. A message, that has been coded with the coding matrix given in the text, reads: AFT   JAO   PTM   Q—H   TDQ   F!T   L!? Decode this message.

4. Choose any third-order matrix. Check to see that the determinant is not zero. Determine the inverse matrix modulo 29. Check your inverse by matrix multiplication. Use the first matrix to code the message given in the text and compare the two coded messages. Check your work by decoding with your inverse matrix.

5. The transformation matrix $A = \begin{pmatrix} k & 0 \\ 0 & k \end{pmatrix}$ changes the scale on the two axes by a factor of k. For example, if $k = 3$,

$$\begin{pmatrix} y_1 \\ y_2 \end{pmatrix} = \begin{pmatrix} 3 & 0 \\ 0 & 3 \end{pmatrix} \begin{pmatrix} x_1 \\ x_2 \end{pmatrix}.$$

Each coordinate on the $y_1 y_2$-plane is 3 times the corresponding coordinate on the $x_1 x_2$-plane.

    (a) Using $k = 3$, what is the transformed point, Q_i, if P_i is: $P_1(1,2)$; $P_2(-2,3)$; $P_3(1/3,-4)$?

    (b) Plot each point P_i on a coordinate system, and the corresponding point Q_i on a different coordinate system.

    (c) What is the matrix of the inverse transformation?

6. What is the geometric significance of the transformation matrix $\begin{pmatrix} k & 0 \\ 0 & h \end{pmatrix}$, where $k \neq h$?

7. What happens to the points on the ellipse $x_1^2/4 + x_2^2/9 = 1$ under the transformation $\begin{pmatrix} 0 & 1 \\ 1 & 0 \end{pmatrix}$? What equation will the transformed points satisfy in the $y_1 y_2$-plane?

8. The transformation $\begin{pmatrix} y_1 \\ y_2 \end{pmatrix} = \begin{pmatrix} \frac{1}{4} & 0 \\ 0 & \frac{1}{2} \end{pmatrix} \begin{pmatrix} x_1 \\ x_2 \end{pmatrix}$ is applied to the points on a circle of radius 1 and center $(0,0)$ in the $x_1 x_2$-plane $[x_1^2 + x_2^2 = 1]$. What is the appearance of the graph of the transformed points in the $y_1 y_2$-plane? What is the equation that the transformed points satisfy? What is the matrix of the inverse transformation?

9. The transformation $\begin{pmatrix} y_1 \\ y_2 \end{pmatrix} = \begin{pmatrix} \frac{1}{2} & -\frac{1}{2}\sqrt{3} \\ \frac{1}{2}\sqrt{3} & \frac{1}{2} \end{pmatrix} \begin{pmatrix} x_1 \\ x_2 \end{pmatrix}$ has the effect of rotating the points of the $x_1 x_2$-plane about the origin through an angle of $60°$.

    (a) Determine the coordinates of the transformed points in the $y_1 y_2$-plane corresponding to each of the following points in the $x_1 x_2$-plane; $P_1(2,0)$; $P_2(4,0)$; $P_3(6,0)$; $P_4(2,2)$; $P_5(4,4)$; $P_6(0,1)$; $P_7(-4,6)$; $P_8(-6,-8)$.

    (b) Plot each P_i on an $x_1 x_2$-plane and the corresponding Q_i on a $y_1 y_2$-plane.

10. Find the inverse of the transformation matrix of Exercise 9 and thus determine the transformation that rotates points through an angle of $-60°$ about the origin.

11. If $Y = AX$ and $Z = BY$, then by substitution, $Z = B(AX) = (BA)X = CX$, where C is the product of the matrices B and A. Thus to determine the single matrix that will have the combined effect of the transformation A followed by the transformation B, we take $C = BA$.

    (a) What single transformation matrix corresponds to an interchange of axes followed by a stretching by a factor of 2?

    Suggestion: Take

$$A = \begin{pmatrix} 0 & 1 \\ 1 & 0 \end{pmatrix} \quad \text{and} \quad B = \begin{pmatrix} 2 & 0 \\ 0 & 2 \end{pmatrix}.$$

(b) Given the transformation matrix of Exercise 9, that rotates the points through an angle of 60° about the origin, determine a transformation matrix that rotates the points through an angle of 120° about the origin.

12. Given the linear transformations:

$$y_1 = 2x_1 - x_2 \quad \text{and} \quad z_1 = -y_1 + y_2$$
$$y_2 = 3x_1 - 2x_2 \qquad\qquad z_2 = 2y_1 - y_2$$

(a) Determine the z_i in terms of x_i by substitutions of the y_i from the first set of equations into the second set. Simplify the results.

(b) Determine the matrix of the first transformation and the matrix of the second transformation. By matrix multiplication (see Exercise 11), determine the matrix of the combined transformation. Compare with your answer to part (a). (Notice how matrix multiplication omits the unessentials, but automatically carries out the proper multiplications and additions of the important numbers.)

Answer: $A = \begin{pmatrix} 2 & -1 \\ 3 & -2 \end{pmatrix}$, $B = \begin{pmatrix} -1 & 1 \\ 2 & -1 \end{pmatrix}$, and $C = BA = \begin{pmatrix} 1 & -1 \\ 1 & 0 \end{pmatrix}$.

REFERENCES

1. Albert, A. A., *Introduction to Algebraic Theories.* Chicago: The University of Chicago Press, 1941. Chapters II to IV.

2. Birkhoff, G., and MacLane, S., *A Brief Survey of Modern Algebra.* New York: The MacMillan Co., 1953. Chapters VII to IX.

3. MacDuffee, C. C., *Vectors and Matrices.* LaSalle, Ill.: Open Court Publishing Co., 1943.

4. Olmsted, J., *Solid Analytic Geometry.* New York: Appleton-Century Co., 1947. Applications of matrices to the geometry of three dimensions. Chapters III, VI to IX.

5. Weiss, M. J., *Higher Algebra for the Undergraduate.* New York: John Wiley and Sons, 1949. Chapters 6 and 7.

8

Exponential and
Logarithmic Functions

We introduced you to exponential functions in Chapter 4. Much of your study of powers and roots of real numbers in Chapter 5 was directed toward constructing the continuous function $\{(x,y) \mid y = b^x,\ b > 0 \text{ and } b \neq 1\}$. Now we return to these exponential functions, and their inverses, the so-called logarithmic functions. We want to familiarize you with these functions as mathematical models that are useful for describing the world of your experiences. We want to help you develop the techniques and skills you need to apply these models effectively.

800. The number e as a natural base

As you work with the condition $y = b^x$, $b > 0$ and $b \neq 1$, you may begin to wonder whether some bases, b, are more convenient than others. From the standpoint of calculations, recall the advantages of the base 10. In the work of Section 503, page 186, it made things easier to have

$$1.454 \doteq 10^{.16256}$$

$$14.54 \doteq 10^{1.16256}$$

$$14540 \doteq 10^{4.16256}$$

$$.01454 \doteq 10^{-2+.16256}$$

The convenience of the base ten for the exponential function clearly depends upon the fact that we use the base ten as we count and as we write numbers. Historians have concluded that people began to use the base ten for counting because they happened to have ten fingers. From this point of view, a different anatomy would have led to a different base for the number system: eight fingers, base eight; twelve fingers, base twelve; etc.

The base ten has no theoretical advantage. Our preference for it arises out of the custom of using this base for our number system.

Now recall the choice of base that Bürgi made (Section 407, page 139). He used $b = 1.0001$ because the values of $(1.0001)^n$, $n \in N$, lie close enough together to give a practical table for performing calculations in exponential form. The disadvantages of $b = 1.0001$ are also evident: it turns out that $(1.0001)^{15,000} \doteq 4.6$; hence the base 1.0001 requires large exponents, $15,000$ to produce 4.6, for example.

At some point of history, between the times of Bürgi (c. 1600) and Euler (c. 1750), mathematicians began to see the advantages of a base like $b = (1.0001)^{10,000}$. It is easy to calculate $(1.0001)^1$, $(1.0001)^2$, ..., $(1.0001)^{10,000}$; these powers of 1.0001 lie close together; it is easy to calculate other powers of 1.0001 from these, for example, $(1.0001)^{15,000} = (1.0001)^{10,000} \cdot (1.0001)^{5000}$; each power of 1.0001 is also a power of $(1.0001)^{10,000}$, for example, $(1.0001)^{15,000} = [(1.0001)^{10,000}]^{1.5}$. Hence you can apply what you know about powers of 1.0001 to work with powers of $(1.0001)^{10,000}$; then you can use smaller exponents, 1.5 instead of $15,000$, for example.

Although the powers of 1.0001 lie close together, there are still gaps, between 1.0001^{10} and 1.0001^{11}, for example. To a mathematician, this suggests studying powers of the *binomial* $1 + 1/n$, and taking a close look at the value of $(1 + 1/n)^n$ for large values of $n \in N$. Notice that $(1 + 1/n)^n$ is a natural generalization of $(1.0001)^{10,000} = (1 + 1/10,000)^{10,000}$. If the powers of 1.0001 are not close enough together, you can study powers of 1.00001; continuing this line of reasoning leads you to study powers of $1 + 1/n$, where $n \in N$ is large enough to give you the precision you need.

Of course the binomial $1 + 1/n$ takes values closer to 1 as you assign larger values to n. For example, when $n = 1,000,000,000$, $1 + 1/n = 1 + 1/1,000,000,000$. Now what happens to $(1 + 1/n)^n$? For example, what is $(1 + 1/1,000,000,000)^{1,000,000,000}$? It turns out that the *limit as n becomes infinite*,

$$\lim_{n \to \infty} \left(1 + \frac{1}{n}\right)^n,$$

exists, and is an irrational number between 2 and 3. This number comes up so often in their work that mathematicians, since the time of Euler, have given it a special name. They call it e.

Recall the irrational number π, which represents the ratio of the circumference to the diameter of a circle; recall the imaginary number i. The numbers e, π, and i occur often enough to justify the special letter symbols that mathematicians have given them. One of the dramatic accomplishments of Euler was the proof of the identity $e^{2\pi i} = 1$. This simple-looking formula contains, besides the numbers 1 and 2, the three numbers, e, π, and i, so fundamental in mathematical analysis.

You know that $(1 + 1/n)^2 = 1 + 2/n + 1/n^2$. You can easily prove that

$(1 + 1/n)^3 = (1 + 1/n)^2(1 + 1/n) = 1 + 3/n + 3/n^2 + 1/n^3$. You can continue, in this way, to evaluate $(1 + 1/n)^4$, $(1 + 1/n)^5$, etc. In fact, it can be shown that

$$n \in N \Rightarrow \left(1 + \frac{1}{n}\right)^n = 1 + \frac{n}{1} \cdot \frac{1}{n} + \frac{n(n-1)}{1 \cdot 2} \cdot \frac{1}{n^2}$$
$$+ \frac{n(n-1)(n-2)}{1 \cdot 2 \cdot 3} \cdot \frac{1}{n^3} + \ldots + \frac{1}{n^n}.$$

When n is a large number, the *expansion* of $(1 + 1/n)^n$ contains a large number of terms, each term smaller than the preceding one. This expansion can be written in the form

$$\left(1 + \frac{1}{n}\right)^n = 1 + 1 + \frac{1}{2!}\left(1 - \frac{1}{n}\right) + \frac{1}{3!}\left(1 - \frac{3}{n} + \frac{2}{n^2}\right) + \ldots .$$

Then it is proved that

$$e = \lim_{n \to \infty} \left(1 + \frac{1}{n}\right)^n = 1 + 1 + \frac{1}{2!} + \frac{1}{3!} + \frac{1}{4!} + \ldots .$$

Recall, from Section 703 (page 335) the symbols $2! = 2 \cdot 1$, $3! = 3 \cdot 2 \cdot 1$, ... Recall that $10! = 3,628,800$. In the *series*

$$e = 1 + 1 + \frac{1}{1 \cdot 2} + \frac{1}{1 \cdot 2 \cdot 3} + \frac{1}{1 \cdot 2 \cdot 3 \cdot 4} + \ldots,$$

the terms become smaller and smaller. In decimal form,

$$e = 1 + 1 + 0.5 + (0.16666 \ldots) + (0.04166 \ldots)$$
$$+ (0.00833 \ldots) + (.00138 \ldots) + \ldots .$$

The value of e is approximately 3 (1 significant figure), 2.7 (2 significant figures), 2.72 (3 significant figures), etc. The number e, like the number π, cannot be expressed exactly as a decimal. But, by adding more and more terms of the series, you can get closer and closer decimal approximations to e. Your book of tables gives $e = 2.71828183$.

Mathematicians speak of the number e as the *natural* base for the exponential function $y = b^x$. They call $y = e^x$ *the* exponential function. They tabulate values of e^x and e^{-x} for many values of x. Find, in your book of tables, the facts

$$e^{1.33} = 3.7810 \quad \text{and} \quad e^{-1.21} = .29820,$$

for example.

We suggest two more approaches (besides the historical approach from Bürgi's $b = 1.0001$) to the selection of a natural base for the exponential function. Each of these approaches leads us again to the base e.

(1) In Fig. 8–1, we drew a graph of $y = 2^x$, and a tangent line to the graph at the point $P(x,y)$. The slope of this tangent line is $QP/TQ = y/TQ = 2^x/TQ$. As you select other points $P(x,y)$, you might expect to get different

lengths, TQ, corresponding to each choice of P. The values of the variable, directed-distance TQ, are all positive. As you select points $P(x,y)$ closer to the x-axis, the slope of the tangent line is a smaller number; but the line-segment TP is shorter.

Prepare a graph of $y = 2^x$. Try different positions of the point $P(x,y)$. Notice that the directed-distance TQ is, in each instance, about 1.4. This means that the slope of the tangent line to the graph of $y = 2^x$ is approximately $2^x/1.4$ for each point $P(x,y)$.

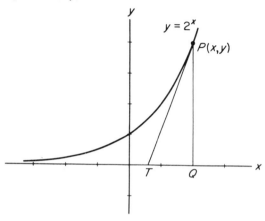

Fig. 8–1.

You should repeat this for the graph of $y = 3^x$ and find that the slope of the tangent line to the graph is approximately $3^x/.9$ for each point $P(x,y)$.

The question arises whether there is a base b such that the graph of $y = b^x$ has a slope $b^x/1 = b^x$? Mathematicians have found that the answer is yes. When $b = e$, the slope of the graph of $y = e^x$ is simply e^x.

When you think of the condition $y = e^x$ as expressing a law of growth, the slope of the tangent line is a measure of the rate at which y changes as x changes. The fact that this slope is e^x means that y grows at a rate equal to its size.

When you use the language of Section 603 (page 265) you say

$$y' = e^x.$$

The table emphasizes the meaning of this equation. The rate of change of y (the slope of the tangent line) is equal to y.

x	-1	$-.5$	0	$.5$	1	2
$y = e^x$	.37	.61	1	1.65	2.72	7.39
$y' = e^x$	.37	.61	1	1.65	2.72	7.39

(2) For a second approach, we return to the problem of finding the amount of $1 invested at a rate of compound interest i per year.

The idea of compound interest is to add the interest to the principal, and hence to earn interest on your interest. In everyday affairs it is common to add interest to principal once each year, once each half-year, or once each quarter. What would happen if you added interest to principal once a day, once a minute, once a second, or still more often? Intuitively, this is the fairest plan. You do not allow your interest to accumulate for a whole year, or even for a quarter year, before it begins earning interest. As you go to the limit, you add interest to principal *instantaneously*, as the actuaries say.

To find the amount of $1 invested for n years at a rate i per year, you use the formula

$$A = (1 + i)^n, \quad \text{when you compound interest yearly,}$$

$$A = \left(1 + \frac{i}{2}\right)^{2n}, \quad \text{when you compound interest half-yearly,}$$

$$A = \left(1 + \frac{i}{4}\right)^{4n}, \quad \text{when you compound interest quarterly,}$$

and $\quad A = \left(1 + \frac{i}{k}\right)^{kn}, \quad$ when you compound interest k times a year.

Now $$A = \left(1 + \frac{i}{k}\right)^{kn} = \left[\left(1 + \frac{i}{k}\right)^{k/i}\right]^{ni}.$$

Write $k/i = t$. Then

$$\frac{i}{k} = \frac{1}{t}, \quad \text{and} \quad A = \left[\left(1 + \frac{1}{t}\right)^{t}\right]^{ni}.$$

If k becomes infinite, then t becomes infinite, and

$$\lim_{t \to \infty} \left(1 + \frac{1}{t}\right)^{t} = e.$$

Hence, when you compound interest instantaneously, $A = e^{ni}$. This is the formula for the amount, in n years, of $1 that earns interest at a rate i per year, compounded instantaneously.

To study the effects of the interest period upon the compound amount, suppose you invest $1 for 10 years at 4% per year. Use your tables to check the following statements: Compounded yearly, $A = (1.04)^{10} = 1.4802$; compounded half-yearly, $A = (1 + .04/2)^{(2)(10)} = (1.02)^{20} = 1.4859$; compounded quarterly, $A = (1.01)^{40} = 1.4889$; compounded instantaneously, $A = e^{(10)(.04)} = e^{.4} = 1.4918$. Notice that the differences are not large. As you would expect, your principal accumulates more rapidly when you compound interest more often.

Notice how you can reduce all compound interest calculations to calculations that involve powers of e when you decide to compound interest instantaneously. For example, to find the amount of $1 at $3\frac{1}{2}\%$ per year for 30 years, interest compounded instantaneously, $A = e^{30(.035)} = e^{1.05} = 2.8577$. If the principal is $100 instead of $1, $A = 100e^{1.05} = \$285.77$. Actuaries and accountants can use this scheme to simplify their theoretical calculations. You can use it to get fairly good approximations to the answers based upon converting interest yearly, half-yearly, quarterly, or the like.

The second example illustrates the way in which the number e appears "naturally" in calculations that involve *continuous* growth. You will meet further examples of continuous growth (or decay), at a rate proportional to size, in Section §805.

Exercises §800 give you further opportunities to explore calculations with powers of e.

EXERCISES §800

1. Use your tables of the exponential function to evaluate:

(a) $e^{0.37}$ (b) $e^{2.51}$ (c) $e^{-1.42}$

(d) $e^{-0.04}$ (e) $e^{-5.3}$ (f) $4e^3$

(g) $(e^{-1.8})^2$ (h) $(e^{1.75})^4$ (i) $\sqrt{e^{2.64}}$

Answers: (a) 1.4477; (c) .24171; (g) $e^{-3.6} = .02732$.

2. Prepare a carefully drawn graph of $y = e^x$ for $-4 \leq x \leq 3$. At several points on the curve, draw tangent lines. Determine, graphically, a numerical approximation for the slope of each tangent line (see Fig. 8–1, page 373). Compare with the value of the y coordinate of this point.

3. Repeat Exercise 2 with the graph of $y = 3^x$. Compare the slope of each tangent with $3^x/.9$.

4. Use your tables of the exponential function to estimate the value, or values, of the unknown that satisfy each equation.

(a) $y = 3e^{1.4}$ (b) $e^a = 1.31$ (c) $.07 = e^x$

(d) $64 = 25e^k$ (e) $3 = e^{2x}$ (f) $N = (-3.4)e^{2y}$,

(g) $512 = 125e^{3t}$ (h) $e^{-\frac{1}{4}x^2} = .375$.   where $y = 1.02$

Answers: (b) $a = .27$; (d) $k = .94$; (h) $x = \pm 1.4$.

5. Make up a table of values of $(1 + 1/n)^n$ for $n = 1, 2, 3, 4, 5, 10, 20, 50$. Notice that even when n is as large as 50, the value of $(1 + 1/n)^n$ is an approximation for e accurate to only two significant figures.

Hint: For small values of n, rewrite $(1 + 1/n)^n$ in the form $(n + 1)^n/n^n$. For large values of n, compound interest tables are helpful. For example, $(1 + 1/20)^{20} = (1 + .05)^{20}$.

6. Approximate the value of e, accurate to six significant figures, by adding decimal approximations for the first nine terms of the series

$$e = 1 + \frac{1}{1!} + \frac{1}{2!} + \frac{1}{3!} + \frac{1}{4!} + \frac{1}{5!} + \dots .$$

7. The approximation $(1 + i/k)^{kn} \doteq e^{in}$ is better for larger values of k. Let $i = .12$ and $n = 4$. Use tables of the exponential function for the right-hand side and compound interest tables for the left side to check the approximation for each of the following values of k: $k = 2$, $k = 4$, and $k = 12$.

8. A small-loan company charges interest at the rate of $2\frac{1}{2}\%$ per month, (30% per year compounded monthly). How much will $100 amount to at the end of three years if no part of the loan is repaid during this time? Give the exact amount from the compound interest table, and the approximate amount from the tables of the exponential function.

Answers: $243.25; $245.96.

9. (a) If $i = 1$, the equation $y = \lim\limits_{k\to\infty} (1 + 1/k)^{kx} = e^x$ expresses continuous growth *at the rate of 100%* per year. Show that the *effective yearly rate* of growth is approximately 172%. [*Hint:* The change in y from the xth year to the $(x + 1)$th year is $e^{x+1} - e^x$. This is $(e^{x+1} - e^x)/e^x \cdot 100$ per cent of the amount in the xth year.]

(b) Let $y = 2^x$. Show that the effective yearly rate of growth is 100%, i.e., y doubles every year.

10. Draw the graph of $y = ae^{bx}$ for the following values of the parameters a and b.

(a) $a = 2$, $b = 1$ (b) $a = 2$, $b = 2$
(c) $a = -2$, $b = 1$ (d) $a = 1.3$, $b = 0.4$
(e) $a = 0.8$, $b = -1.6$ (f) $a = -1.2$, $b = -.64$.

11. Show that the conditions $y = 2^x$ and $y = e^{0.693x}$ are approximately equivalent. [*Hint:* $e^{0.693} \doteq 2$.] Graph $y = e^{0.693x}$ and compare with $y = 2^x$.

801. The inverse conditions, $y = e^x$ and $y = \log_e x$

Recall that the inverse of $y = x^3$ is $x = y^3$. Interchanging the roles of x and y in a condition gives you the inverse of the condition. Geometrically, the effect is a reflection in the line $y = x$.

An equation like $x = y^3$ is not convenient as a formula for expressing the values of y that correspond to the values you assign to x. That is why we *solve the equation for y*, and write $y = \sqrt[3]{x}$. The root-notation ($\sqrt[3]{x}$) enables you to express the inverse of the condition $y = x^3$ in the form $y = \sqrt[3]{x}$.

We turn now to the condition $y = e^x$, and its inverse $x = e^y$. The graph of $x = e^y$ is the reflection in the line $y = x$ of the graph of $y = e^x$.

The equation $x = e^y$ is not convenient as a formula for expressing the values of y that correspond to the values you assign to x. Mathematicians have adopted a standard notation for expressing this same condition in a more convenient form. They define

$$x = e^y \Longleftrightarrow y = \log_e x.$$

They read the expression $\log_e x$ as *the logarithm of x to base e*.

Study Fig. 8–2 as you try to visualize the inverse conditions $y = e^x$ and $y = \log_e x$.

More generally, the inverse of $y = b^x$ is $x = b^y$. For $b > 0$ and $b \neq 1$, we define

$$x = b^y \Leftrightarrow y = \log_b x.$$

Hence the phrase *logarithm to base b*, like the phrase cube root, is merely a convenient way of expressing the inverse of a familiar condition. The phrase cube root of x enables you to express the inverse of the phrase cube of x.

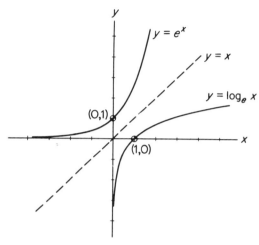

Fig. 8–2.

The phrase *logarithm of x to base b* enables you to express the inverse of the phrase b *exponent x*.

In your book of tables you find $e^{3.45} \doteq 31.500$. Another way to say this is $\log_e 31.500 \doteq 3.45$. Also, in the compound interest table, $(1.05)^{34} \doteq 5.2533$. Another way to say this is $\log_{1.05} 5.2533 \doteq 34$.

You can also translate familiar facts into the language of logarithms. For example, you know that $5^3 = 125$; hence $\log_5 125 = 3$; since $10^5 = 100,000$, $\log_{10} 100,000 = 5$.

If you want to find $\log_3 81$, let $\log_3 81 = t$. Then you know that $3^t = 81$. Since $3^4 = 81$, and $3^t = 81$, $t = 4$ is the value of $\log_3 81$; you may write $\log_3 81 = 4$.

It is not usually so easy to find the logarithm of a number. For example, $\log_5 30 = t$ means that $5^t = 30$; but how do you solve this equation for t? Of course you can make a table of powers of 5; but this is a slow job that involves some difficult calculations. To find $5^{2.5} = 5^{5/2} = \sqrt{5^5} = \sqrt{3125}$ is not difficult. Your book of tables gives $\sqrt{3120} \doteq 55.857$, and $\sqrt{3130} \doteq 55.946$; by interpolation, $\sqrt{3125} \doteq 55.901$. Hence $5^{2.5} \doteq 55.901$. It is harder to find $5^{2.2} = 5^{11/5}$. Try it!

You will study properties of logarithms in Section 802, and learn to perform logarithmetic calculations with a table in base 10 in Section 803. Then you will find, in Section 804, that the task of computing a good approximation to $\log_5 30$ is comparatively easy.

Exercises §801 will help you to assimilate the definition $\log_b x = y \Leftrightarrow b^y = x$; they will help you get the feel of the language of logarithms, learn to make estimates of answers to questions involving logarithms, and so forth.

EXERCISES §801

1. Draw the graph of $y = 2^x$. By reflection in the line $y = x$, sketch the graph of $y = \log_2 x$.

2. Write each of the following conditions in the equivalent exponential form; then determine the value of y.

(a) $y = \log_2 8$ (b) $y = \log_2 \frac{1}{2}$ (c) $y = \log_3 9$

(d) $y = \log_5 625$ (e) $y = \log_7 \sqrt{7}$ (f) $y = \log_4 8$

(g) $y = \log_{1/2} 4$ (h) $y = \log_6 6$ (i) $y = \log_b b$

(j) $y = \log_{10} 10^3$ (k) $y = \log_{1000} 10$ (l) $y = \log_2 (.25)$.

Answers: (a) $2^y = 8$, $y = 3$; (e) $7^y = 7^{1/2}$, $y = \frac{1}{2}$; (g) $(\frac{1}{2})^y = 4$, $y = -2$.

3. Write each of the following conditions in the equivalent exponential form; then determine the value of the unknown.

(a) $3 = \log_3 x$ (b) $\frac{1}{4} = \log_{16} x$ (c) $-\frac{1}{2} = \log_{25} N$

(d) $5 = \log_{10} y$ (e) $-1.2 = \log_e x$ (f) $2 = \log_b 49$

(g) $.75 = \log_b 27$ (h) $-\frac{1}{4} = \log_a 9$ (i) $\log_{10} M = 1$

(j) $\log_{10} R = -1$ (k) $\log_3 27 = 2x - 1$ (l) $\log_2 (2x - 1) = 16$.

Answers: (a) $3^3 = x$, $x = 27$; (c) $25^{-1/2} = N$, $N = \frac{1}{5}$; (k) $3^{2x-1} = 27$, $x = 2$.

4. Determine the value of each unknown with the help of your compound interest tables.

(a) $\log_{1.02} (1.741) = y$ (b) $\log_{1.05} (7.04) = L$

(c) $\log_{1.03} x = 25$ (d) $\log_{1.06} x = 41$

(e) $\log_{1.04} x = -34$ (f) $\log_{1.01} (.665) = z$.

Answers: (a) 28; (c) 2.0938; (e) .26355.

5. Use the tables of the exponential function to approximate the following logarithms. Interpolate if necessary.

(a) $\log_e 1.6$ (b) $\log_e 5$ (c) $\log_e 0.6$

(d) $\log_e 0.08$ (e) $\log_e 20$ (f) $\log_e e$.

Answers: (a) .47; (c) $-.511$.

6. From tables of the exponential function, $e^{1.61} \doteq 5$. Hence $5^{2.5} \doteq (e^{1.61})^{2.5} = e^{4.025}$. Estimate $5^{2.5}$ from the tables of the exponential function and compare with the value given in the text. Estimate $5^{2.2}$ by this method.

Answer: $5^{2.2} \doteq 34.5$.

7. Show that $5^y \doteq e^{1.61y}$. The solution of the exponential equation $5^y = 30$ is $y = \log_5 30$. Determine an approximation for $\log_5 30$ by solving the equivalent equation $e^{1.61y} = 30$.

Answer: $\log_5 30 \doteq 2.11$.

8. Show that $y = e^{-x}$ and $y = \log_e (1/x)$ are inverse conditions. Sketch the graph of $y = e^{-x}$ and obtain the graph of $y = \log_e (1/x)$ by reflection in the line $y = x$.

802. Properties of logarithms

As you would expect, the properties of logarithms parallel to the corresponding properties of exponents. The definition

$$\log_b x = y \Leftrightarrow b^y = x$$

makes it clear that logarithms *are* exponents.

Suppose, for example, that

$$\log_b M = s \quad \text{and} \quad \log_b N = t.$$

Then $b^s = M \quad \text{and} \quad b^t = N.$

By the laws of exponents, $b^s \cdot b^t = b^{s+t}$. Hence

$$M \cdot N = b^{s+t}.$$

When you translate this statement into the language of logarithms, it becomes

$$\log_b MN = s + t$$
$$= \log_b M + \log_b N.$$

The equation $\log_b MN = \log_b M + \log_b N$ states that the logarithm of a product (in base b) is the sum of the logarithms of the factors (in base b). This corresponds to the fact that the product of two powers of b is the power of b whose exponent is the sum of the exponents.

The table below gives the properties of exponents on a base b, $b > 0$ and $b \neq 1$ (Section 502, page 184), and the corresponding properties of logarithms to base b, $b > 0$ and $b \neq 1$. Recall the importance of the restrictions $b > 0$ and $b \neq 1$. Powers of a negative base may be positive $[(-2)^4 = 16]$, negative $[(-2)^5 = -32]$, or undefined in the set L $[(-2)^{1/2} \notin L]$; this leads to serious complications in working with the condition $y = b^x$ when $b < 0$. Powers of 1 are all equal to 1; $(y = b^x$ and $b = 1) \Rightarrow (y = 1)$; also $(y = \log_b x$ and $b = 1) \Rightarrow (x = 1)$. We shall restrict the base b to a positive number different from 1.

Properties of Exponents ($b > 0$ and $b \neq 1$)	*Properties of Logarithms* ($b > 0$ and $b \neq 1$)
E 1: $b^x \cdot b^y = b^{x+y}$	L 1: $\log_b (MN) = \log_b M + \log_b N$
E 2: $(b^x)^y = b^{xy}$	L 2: $\log_b M^t = t \log_b M$
E 3: $\dfrac{b^x}{b^y} = b^{x-y}$	L 3: $\log_b \left(\dfrac{M}{N}\right) = \log_b M - \log_b N$

We have proved L 1 already. To prove L 2, let $\log_b M = s$. Then $b^s = M$ and $(b^s)^t = b^{st}$ (by E 2). Hence $M^t = b^{st}$ and $\log_b M^t = st$, that is,

$$\log_b M^t = t \log_b M.$$

You should prove L 3, using our proof of L 1 as a guide. The following examples illustrate these properties of logarithms:

(1) Given $\log_{10} 2 \doteq .3010$, and $\log_{10} 3 \doteq .4771$, calculate $\log_{10} 6$.

$$\log_{10} 6 = \log_{10} 3 \cdot 2 = \log_{10} 3 + \log_{10} 2 \qquad\qquad \text{(L 1)}$$
$$\doteq .4771 + .3010 = .7781.$$

(2) Given $\log_{10} 2 \doteq .3010$, calculate $\log_{10} 16$.

$$\log_{10} 16 = \log_{10} 2^4 = 4 \log_{10} 2 \qquad\qquad \text{(L 2)}$$
$$\doteq 1.2040.$$

When you use your table of logarithms to check this result, you find

$$\log_{10} 1.6 \doteq .20412 \quad \text{(corresponding to } 10^{.20412} \doteq 1.6)$$
$$\log_{10} 16 \doteq 1.20412 \quad \text{(corresponding to } 10^{1.20412} \doteq 16).$$

Hence $\log_{10} 16 = 1.2041$ to the nearest .0001, and the previous result, $\log_{10} 16 \doteq 1.2040$, is in error. The explanation is apparent. We used $\log_{10} 2 \doteq .3010$, whereas a better approximation is $\log_{10} 2 \doteq .30103$. Such rounding errors are always present in logarithmic calculations.

(3) Given $\log_{10} 5 \doteq .69897$, calculate $\log_{10} 5000$.

$$\log_{10} 5000 = \log_{10} 5 \cdot 1000 = \log_{10} 5 + \log_{10} 1000 \qquad \text{(L 1)}$$
$$\doteq .69897 + 3 \qquad (\log_{10} 1000 = 3)$$
$$= 3.69897.$$

Notice, again, the advantages of the base 10 for calculation ($\log_{10} 1000 = 3$).

(4) Given $\log_{10} 5 \doteq .6990$, calculate $\log_{10} \sqrt[10]{5}$.

$$\log_{10} \sqrt[10]{5} = \log_{10} 5^{1/10} = \tfrac{1}{10} \log_{10} 5 \qquad\qquad \text{(L 2)}$$
$$\doteq \tfrac{1}{10}(.6990)$$
$$= .06990.$$

(5) Given $\log_{10} 21 \doteq 1.32222$ and $\log_{10} 3 \doteq .47712$, calculate $\log_{10} 7$.

$$\log_{10} 7 = \log_{10} (21/3) = \log_{10} 21 - \log_{10} 3 \qquad \text{(L 3)}$$
$$\doteq 1.32222 - .47712$$
$$= .84510.$$

We now prove six other properties of logarithms:

L 4 $$\log_b b = 1.$$

This is, by definition, equivalent to the statement $b^1 = b$.

L 5 $\log_b 1 = 0$.

This is, by definition, equivalent to the statement $b^0 = 1$.

L 6 $\log_b (b^N) = N$.

Perhaps this property of logarithms is obvious to you. It says the exponent on b that yields b^N is N. Most people find that such "obvious" statements tax their powers of concentration. Hence we reduce the proof to a sequence of easy steps:

$$\log_b (b^N) = N \log_b b \qquad \text{(L 2)}$$
$$= N \cdot 1 = N. \qquad \text{(L 4)}$$

L 7 $b^{\log_b N} = N$.

This is another "obvious" property of logarithms. It says the exponent cn b that yields N when used as an exponent on b yields N. Again we reduce the proof to a sequence of easy steps:

Suppose that $b^s = N$.

Then, by definition, $\log_b N = s$.

By substitution for s, $b^{\log_b N} = N$.

As examples of L 7, $2^{\log_2 5} = 5$, $10^{\log_{10} 1.4} = 1.4$, and $e^{\log_e 7} = 7$.

L 8 $\log_b \left(\dfrac{1}{N}\right) = -\log_b N$.

You know that $\log_b \dfrac{1}{N} = \log_b 1 - \log_b N \qquad \text{(L 3)}$

$$= 0 - \log_b N \qquad \text{(L 5)}$$
$$= -\log_b N.$$

L 8 is useful when you wish to change divisions into multiplications. For example, suppose you want to calculate P from the formula

$$P = \frac{M \times N \times T^2}{R \times S}.$$

You can set up a *computing form* as follows:

$$\left.\begin{array}{l} \log M = \\ \log N = \\ 2\log T = \log T^2 = \end{array}\right\} \text{Add} \qquad\qquad \left.\begin{array}{l} \log R = \\ \log S = \end{array}\right\} \text{Add}$$

$$\log R \times S =$$

$$\left.\begin{array}{l} \log M \times N \times T^2 = \\ \log R \times S = \end{array}\right\} \text{Subtract}$$

$$\log P = \log \frac{M \times N \times T^2}{R \times S} =$$

Notice that $\log M \times N \times T^2 = \log M + \log N + \log T^2$

and $\log R \times S = \log R + \log S.$

Then $\log P = \log (M \times N \times T^2) - \log (R \times S).$

It is often more convenient to set up a computing form as follows:

$$\left.\begin{array}{r} \log M = \\ \log N = \\ 2 \log T = \log T^2 = \\[6pt] \log \dfrac{1}{R} = -\log R = \\[10pt] \log \dfrac{1}{S} = -\log S = \\[6pt] \hline \end{array}\right\} \text{Add}$$

$$\log P = \log MNT^2 \left(\frac{1}{R}\right)\left(\frac{1}{S}\right) =$$

This second procedure is a time-saver in many practical calculations. We shall discuss it further in Section 803.

L 9 $\log_b N = (\log_a N)(\log_b a) = \log_a N/\log_a b.$

This important property of logarithms enables you to calculate logarithms in one base when you know logarithms in another base. To prove it, suppose $\log_a N = s$, so that $N = a^s$. Take logarithms of each side, using base b. You get

$$\log_b N = \log_b a^s$$
$$= s \log_b a \qquad\qquad\qquad\qquad (\text{L } 2)$$
$$= (\log_a N)(\log_b a). \qquad (\text{Substitution for } s)$$

This proves the first part of L 9.

Now apply this equation to the instance in which $N = b$. You get

$$\log_b b = (\log_a b)(\log_b a).$$

Since $\log_b b = 1,$ $(\text{L } 4)$
$$1 = (\log_a b)(\log_b a).$$

Hence $\log_b a = 1/\log_a b,$

and $\log_b N = (\log_a N)(\log_b a) = (\log_a N)/(\log_a b).$

We shall apply these nine properties of logarithms to perform numerical calculations in Section 803. Exercises §802 are intended to familiarize you with these properties.

EXERCISES §802

1. Determine the values of $\log_2 \frac{1}{2}$, $\log_2 2$, $\log_2 4$, $\log_2 8$, and $\log_2 32$ from the definition of logarithms. Using these values, verify that:

(a) $\log_2 4 + \log_2 8 = \log_2 32$ (b) $\log_2 2^3 = 3 \log_2 2$
(c) $\log_2 \frac{1}{2} = -\log_2 2$ (d) $\log_2 8 - \log_2 4 = \log_2 2$
(e) $\log_2 4^{1/2} = \frac{1}{2} \log_2 4$.

State which property of logarithms is illustrated in each part.

Answer: (a) $2 + 3 = 5$, P 1.

2. Prove L 3.

3. Given that $\log_5 2 \doteq .4307$, $\log_5 3 \doteq .6826$, and $\log_5 5 = 1$, find the values of:

(a) $\log_5 6$ (b) $\log_5 4$ (c) $\log_5 10$
(d) $\log_5 (1.5)$ (e) $\log_5 27$ (f) $\log_5 (2/3)$.

Hint: $\log_5 6 = \log_5 (2 \cdot 3) = \log_5 2 + \log_5 3$, etc.
Answers: (a) 1.1133;   (d) .2519.

4. Given that $\log_{10} 7.2 \doteq .85733$, write the logarithm of each number.

(a) $\log_{10} 72$ (b) $\log_{10} 720$ (c) $\log_{10} 0.72$
(d) $\log_{10} 72,000$ (e) $\log_{10} 0.0072$ (f) $\log_{10} (7.2)^2$
(g) $\log_{10} (72)^3$ (h) $\log_{10} (1/7.2)$ (i) $\log_{10} \sqrt[3]{7.2}$.

Answers: (b) 2.85733;   (c) $-.14267$;   (h) $-.85733$.

5. Use the properties of logarithms to write each expression as a single logarithm.

(a) $\log_b M + \log_b N$ (b) $\log_b M + 2 \log_b R$
(c) $\frac{1}{2} \log_b S - \log_b T - 3 \log_b R$ (d) $3 \log_b M - 2 \log_b T + \frac{1}{2} \log_b N$
(e) $\log_b M^2 - \log_b \sqrt{M}$.

Answers: (b) $\log_b MR^2$;   (d) $\log_b M^3 \sqrt{N}/T^2$.

6. Expand using the properties of logarithms.

(a) $\log_b (R^2 T)$ (b) $\log_b (N \sqrt[3]{S})$
(c) $\log_b (M^2 \sqrt{R}/T)$ (d) $\log_b (M^{-1} R^{1/4} T^{-1/2})$
(e) $\log_e e^{2.3}$ (f) $\log_b (M^2 - N^2)$.

Answers: (b) $\log_b N + \frac{1}{3} \log_b S$;   (f) $\log_b (M + N) + \log_b (M - N)$.

7. Set up a computing form for determining each logarithm in parts (a) through (d) of Exercise 6 in terms of the logarithms of M, N, R, S, and T.

8. Evaluate:

(a) $2^{\log_2 8}$ (b) $5^{\log_5 25}$ (c) $7^{\log_7 15}$
(d) $e^{\log_e 1.7}$ (e) $b^{\log_b 25}$ (f) $3^{\log_3 1}$
(g) $4^{\log_2 8}$ (h) $(\frac{1}{2})^{\log_2 8}$ (i) $(\frac{1}{2})^{\log_2 7}$.

Answers: (a) 8;   (d) 1.7;   (h) $\frac{1}{8}$.

9. Write out L 9 with $a = 4$, $b = 2$, and $N = 64$. Verify that L 9 holds in this instance by evaluating all the logarithms in the equation using the definition of logarithms. Repeat with the same values of a and b, but with $N = \frac{1}{2}$.

803. Logarithmic calculations in base 10

When you used the table of logarithms to perform calculations in Section 503 (page 189), you expressed the numbers as powers of 10. You could continue to do your calculations in this way; but it is much more convenient to use the language of logarithms, and to apply what you have learned about the laws of logarithms. It this section we give you tips that will help you to make logarithmic calculation a practical and efficient technique.

First recall the method of finding $\log 218.6$ (base 10, understood) in a table of logarithms. The table gives you $\log 2.186 \doteq 0.33965$. You know that $\log 100 = \log 10^2 = 2\log 10 = 2$. Hence $\log 218.6 = \log[(2.186) \cdot (100)] = \log 2.186 + \log 100 \doteq 2.33965$.

We shall call the decimal (like 0.33965) that you get from the table the *mantissa* of the logarithm. We shall call the whole number (like 2) that represents the logarithm of a power of 10 the *characteristic* of the logarithm. Logarithms in base 10 are called *common logarithms*.

Every number is the product of a number between 1 and 10 and a power of 10. For example, $218.6 = 2.186 \times 10^2$, $21,860 = 2.186 \times 10^4$, $2.186 = 2.186 \times 10^0$, $.02186 = 2.186 \times 10^{-2}$, $.00002186 = 2.186 \times 10^{-5}$, etc. The characteristic of the common logarithm is simply the exponent of the power of 10. To get the characteristic, you count the number of places from the decimal point for a number between 1 and 10, to the decimal point as it actually appears. Then you make the characteristic positive for numbers greater than 10, 0 for numbers between 1 and 10, and negative for numbers between 0 and 1. For example,

Number	Characteristic of the common logarithm
716.2	2
81,697,000	7
26.8	1
9.4287	0
.006281	$-3 = 7.00000 - 10$
.2246	$-1 = 9.00000 - 10$
.00000298	$-6 = 4.00000 - 10$
etc.	

It is convenient to keep the mantissas of logarithms positive decimals. For example,

$$\log .0007628 \doteq -4 + 0.88241$$

(that is, $.0007628 = 10^{-4} \times 7.628 \doteq 10^{-4} \times 10^{0.88241}$).

The mantissa, 0.88241, is a positive decimal. For the purposes of most calculations it is better to express the logarithm of a number between 0 and 1 using the pattern:

$$\log .0007628 \doteq -4 + 0.88241$$
$$= 6.88241 - 10.$$

For one thing, this avoids the confusion between $-4 + 0.88241$ (a number between -4 and -3) and -4.88241 (a number between -5 and -4).

For another thing, expert computers find it unnecessary to write the -10. In practical calculations there is little likelihood of confusing 6.88241 and $6.88241 - 10$. The first is the logarithm of 7,628,000; the second is the logarithm of .0007628. You are not apt to make a mistake of 10 places in the position of a decimal point!

The following examples will help you to acquaint yourself with this new way of writing the characteristic of the logarithm of a number between 0 and 1:

(1) $$\log .6284 \doteq 9.79824 - 10.$$

(2) $$\log .018357 \doteq 8.26380 - 10.$$

This last calculation involves interpolation. The table gives

$$7 \begin{bmatrix} \log 1.8350 \doteq .26364 \\ \log 1.8357 \\ \log 1.8360 \doteq .26387 \end{bmatrix} 23; \qquad .7 \times 23 \doteq 16.$$

Hence $\log 1.8357 \doteq .26364 + .00016 = .26380.$

(3) $$\log .000048882 \doteq 5.68915 - 10.$$

You should check the interpolation between $\log 4.8880 \doteq 0.68913$ and $\log 4.8890 \doteq 0.68922$. Notice the opportunity to use the *proportional parts* given in the table to speed up the interpolation. The proportional parts table for a difference of 9 gives you $.2 \times 9 = 1.8 \doteq 2$.

In certain calculations, even this new way of writing the characteristic of the logarithm of a number requires careful handling. The following examples illustrate the pitfalls and give you techniques for avoiding them.

(4) Calculate $N = 286.31 \div .0046719$.

$$\log 286.31 \doteq 2.45684$$
$$\log .0046719 \doteq 7.66949 - 10$$
$$\log N = \log 286.31 - \log .0046719. \qquad (L\ 3)$$

If you subtract directly, you get negative signs in your answer. To avoid this you think as follows:

$$\log 286.31 \doteq 12.45684 - 10$$
$$\log .0046719 \doteq \underline{\ 7.66949 - 10}$$
$$\log N \doteq \ \ 4.78735.$$

From the table:

$$.4 \begin{bmatrix} \log 6.128 = .78732 \\ .78735 \\ \log 6.129 = .78739. \end{bmatrix} \begin{matrix} 3 \\ \end{matrix} \Big] 7$$

You conclude that $\log 6.1284 \doteq .78735$. (You can use proportional parts of 7, as given in the table, to find that $3/7 \doteq .4$.) Hence

$$N \doteq 61{,}284.$$

In problems that call for subtracting a larger number from a smaller number ($2.45684 - 7.66949$, above), add and subtract 10 in the *minuend* (make 2.45684 into $12.45684 - 10$, above).

(5) Calculate $N = (.004283)^6$.

$$\log .004283 \doteq 7.63175 - 10,$$

$$\log N = 6 \log .004283 \doteq 45.79050 - 60,$$

Hence $$\log N \doteq 5.79050 - 20.$$

Hence $N \doteq .000\ 000\ 000\ 000\ 006\ 173$ or, more conveniently expressed, $N \doteq 6.173 \times 10^{-15}$.

The trick here is to avoid the wrong answer, $N \doteq .00006173$. When you see $\log N \doteq 45.79050 - 60$, it is tempting to write $\log N \doteq 5.79050 - 10$ instead of $\log N \doteq 5.79050 - 20$. You must be alert when you work with powers of numbers like .004283. It is easier when you work with practical problems, where you have the feel of the problem and know about what size answer to expect. In such problems you are not apt to misplace a decimal point by 10 places.

(6) Calculate $N = \sqrt[7]{.0004888}$.

$$\log .0004888 \doteq 6.68913 - 10$$

$$\log N = \tfrac{1}{7} \log .0004888 \doteq \tfrac{1}{7}(66.68913 - 70)$$

$$\doteq 9.52702 - 10$$

$$N \doteq .3365.$$

The trick here is to avoid dividing $6.68913 - 10$ by 7; $\tfrac{1}{7}(6.68913 - 10) \doteq 0.95559 - 1.42857$. This gets complicated; so you write $6.68913 - 10 = 66.68913 - 70$. Then it is easy to divide by 7.

You are now ready to do any logarithmic calculation. We picked some of the tricky ones for the examples above. Most calculations are comparatively straightforward. You have only to learn the tricks of organizing your calculations to get maximum efficiency, and hence to speed up your calculations and reduce your errors to a minimum.

Expert computers like to set up a computing form before they plunge into the details of calculation. This separates thinking the problem from performing the calculations. It also saves turning pages in the table of logarithms as the following examples will show.

(7) You are working with the formula $N = 2\pi\sqrt[3]{S/T}$. Set up a convenient

computing form and use it to calculate the value of N that corresponds to $S = 181.7$, $T = 19.64$.

$$\log 2\pi \doteq 0.79818$$
$$S = 181.7 \qquad \log S \doteq 2.25935 \qquad \tfrac{1}{3}\log S \doteq 0.75312 \quad \Big\}\ \text{Add}$$
$$\overline{\quad\quad\quad 1.55130 \quad}$$
$$T = 19.64 \qquad \log T \doteq 1.29314 \qquad \tfrac{1}{3}\log T \doteq 0.43105 \quad \Big\}\ \text{Subtract}$$
$$N \doteq 13.19 \qquad\qquad\qquad\qquad \log N \doteq 1.12025.$$

At first you think $\log N = (\log 2\pi + \tfrac{1}{3}\log S) - \tfrac{1}{3}\log T$. Then you arrange a computing form like the one above. Study the details of this form.

You get $\log 2\pi$ from a special Table of Important Constants. If you printed up some copies of this computing form, you would include the value of $\log 2\pi$; you would leave the other spaces blank until you assigned values to S and T.

Notice the convenience of getting $\log S$ and $\log T$ while you have the table of logarithms open; then you take one third of each of these logarithms; then you do the addition and subtraction; then you use the table backwards to get the value of N.

Here is another computing form for the same formula:

$$S = 181.7 \qquad\qquad \log S \doteq 2.25935 \quad \Big\}\ \text{Subtract}$$
$$T = 19.64 \qquad\qquad \log T \doteq 1.29314$$
$$\qquad\qquad\qquad \log S/T = 0.96621$$

$$\qquad\qquad\qquad \tfrac{1}{3}\log S/T \doteq 0.32207 \quad \Big\}\ \text{Add}$$
$$\qquad\qquad\qquad \log 2\pi \doteq 0.79818$$
$$N = 13.19 \qquad\qquad \log N \doteq 1.12025.$$

This comes from thinking $\log N = \tfrac{1}{3}(\log S - \log T) + \log 2\pi$.

Here is a third computing form, that comes from thinking

$$\log N = \log 2\pi + \tfrac{1}{3}\log S + \tfrac{1}{3}\log \frac{1}{T}.$$

$$\log 2\pi \doteq 0.79818$$
$$S = 181.7 \qquad \log S \doteq 2.25935 \qquad \tfrac{1}{3}\log S \doteq 0.75312 \quad \Big\}$$
$$T = 19.64 \qquad \log \frac{1}{T} \doteq 28.70686 - 30 \qquad \tfrac{1}{3}\log \frac{1}{T} \doteq 9.56895 - 10 \quad \Big\}\ \text{Add}$$
$$N \doteq 13.19 \qquad\qquad\qquad\qquad \log N \doteq 1.12025.$$

This third computing form has the advantage of eliminating subtraction. But it introduces some new subtleties in finding $\tfrac{1}{3}\log 1/T$. The table of logarithms gives $\log T = \log 19.64 \doteq 1.29314$. Hence $\log 1/T = -\log T$

(L 8, page 381) $\doteq$ −1.29314. To make this the sum of an integer and a positive decimal, write

$$\log \frac{1}{T} \doteq (10.00000 - 1.29314) - 10$$

$$\doteq 8.70686 - 10.$$

With a little practice, you can do subtractions from 10 mentally. Instead of saying 4 from 10, 1 from 9, etc., you look at 1.29314 and write 8.70686. You say $1 + 8 = 9$, $2 + 7 = 9$, $9 + 0 = 9$, $3 + 6 = 9$, $1 + 8 = 9$, and, finally $6 + 4 = 10$. Some computers call log $1/T$ the *cologarithm* of T, and write colog $T =$ colog $19.64 \doteq 8.70686 - 10$. Once you master this technique, you can add the cologarithm rather than subtract the logarithm. Now log $1/T \doteq 8.70686 - 10 = 28.70686 - 30$, and $\frac{1}{3} \log 1/T \doteq 9.56895 - 10$.

From now on we shall give only one computing form. It is good experience to try several different forms. In practical calculation, a very small saving of time may be important when you do a great many similar calculations.

(8) You are working with the formula $P = A^3 BC/\sqrt{D}$, calculating values of P that correspond to values assigned to A, B, C, and D. Set up a convenient computing form and use it to calculate the value of P that corresponds to $A = .3264$, $B = 46.85$, $C = .04936$, and $D = 856.1$.

$A = .3264$	$\log A \doteq 9.51375 - 10$	$3 \log A \doteq 8.54125 - 10$ ⎤
$B = 46.85$		$\log B \doteq 1.67071$ ⎬ Add
$C = .04936$		$\log C \doteq 8.69338 - 10$ ⎦
		$\log A^3 BC \doteq \overline{8.90534 - 10}$ ⎤
		⎬ Subtract
$D = 856.1$	$\log D \doteq 2.93252$	$\frac{1}{2} \log D \doteq 1.46626$ ⎦
$P \doteq .002748$		$\log P \doteq 7.43908 - 10.$

You should carry through these calculations and show that log $P \doteq 7.43908 - 10$. Notice, again, how the computing form saves you time: You look up all the logarithms; then you perform the calculations to get log P; then you use the table backwards to get the values of P.

Exercises §803 give you practice in calculations with common logarithms. As you begin to work on them, keep in mind that you should plan your solution before you perform any calculations. Recall that:

(1) $\log (A + B)$ can not be expressed simply in terms of log A and log B. Hence formulas that involve additions (or subtractions) do not lend themselves to logarithmic calculation.
(2) $\log AB = \log A + \log B$
(3) $\log A/B = \log A - \log B$
(4) $\log A^t = t \log A$.

You will use logarithmic calculations again in Section 805 and as you work with the trigonometric equations in Chapter 9. You should think of the techniques of using a table of logarithms as an extension of the techniques of elementary arithmetic. They are basic to the calculations that arise in elementary analysis.

EXERCISES §803

1. State the characteristic of each of the following common logarithms:

(a) log 3.12   (b) log 31.2   (c) log .0312
(d) log 312   (e) log 7468   (f) log 7000
(g) log .0002   (h) log .0065   (i) log 4.1372
(j) log 89.239   (k) log 10^9 (l) log .56313
(m) log 10^{-5} (n) log 100,000   (o) log 627.5
(p) log .00001.

Answers: (a) 0;   (f) 3;   (h) −3.

2. Find the mantissa, and then write the complete logarithm for each part of Exercise 1.

Answers: (a) 0.49415;   (f) 3.84510;   (h) 7.81291 − 10.

3. Find the numbers whose common logarithms are given.

(a) log x = .77988   (b) log x = .93822   (c) log M = 1.30103
(d) log S = 2.53719   (e) log y = 8.72477 − 10 (f) log R = 1.12314
(g) log N = 3.2   (h) log x = 9.89532 − 10 (i) log y = 6.42157 − 10
(j) log N = −3.57843   (k) log z = −.41556   (l) log x = 5.67421.

Answers: (a) 6.024;   (d) 344.5;   (g) 1584.9;   (j) .00026398.

4. Evaluate

(a) $10^{.60206}$ (b) $10^{1.81245}$ (c) $10^{3.52952}$
(d) $10^{8.63498-10}$ (e) $10^{-1.36502}$ (f) $10^{-.52714}$.

Answers: (b) 64.93;   (d) .04315;   (f) .29707.

5. Solve for x.

(a) 10^x = 7.36   (b) 10^x = 736   (c) 10^x = .4316
(d) 10^x = .0032   (e) 10^{2x} = 51.43   (f) 10^{-x} = 6.547.

Answers: (b) 2.86688;   (d) −2.49485;   (f) −.81604.

6. Carry out the following calculations with help of logarithms:

(a) (23.1)(5.94)   (b) (.4981)(81.7)   (c) (543.8)/(65.36)
(d) $\sqrt{8235}$ (e) $\sqrt[3]{47.421}$ (f) (49.57)/(67.32)
(g) $\sqrt{0.3472}$ (h) $\sqrt[5]{0.018262}$ (i) (0.00668)/(0.439).

Answers: (b) 40.695;   (e) 3.6196;   (i) .015217.

7. Show that colog 4 = (−1) log 4 = log .25 by the properties of logarithms. Evaluate colog 4 by two methods and compare results.

8. Calculate $427.9/[(65.61)(89.32)]$ by (a) subtracting logarithms, (b) the use of cologarithms.

9. Carry out the following calculations with logarithms. Set up a computing form in each case. For divisions use cologarithms or subtract logarithms of divisors, whichever seems more convenient.

(a) $\sqrt{\dfrac{288.36}{623.14}}$

(b) $(6.7521)^2/(.94316)(1.6254)$

(c) $\sqrt[4]{.0058742}$

(d) $\sqrt[3]{4290\sqrt{769}}$

(e) $(8.9413)^{3/4}$

(f) $\left(\dfrac{763.13}{8.9426\sqrt{641.52}}\right)^3$

(g) $(8.315)^2(69.43)^{-1}(961.3)^{-1/2}$

(h) $(.65812)\sqrt[3]{15.326/.27642}$

(i) $(54.316)^4(6.1592)^{-2}(213.47)^{-3}$

(j) $[(429.26)^{-1/4}(62.789)]^{-1/2}$.

Answers: (a) .68026; (b) 29.740; (c) .27685; (d) 49.182; (e) 5.1707; (f) 38.249; (g) .032117; (h) 2.5095.

10. Evaluate

(a) $3^{2.4}$

(b) $7^{-1.6}$

(c) $5^{2.2}$

(d) $(\sqrt{3})^{1.8}$

(e) π^3

(f) $\pi^{1.7}$.

Answers: (a) 13.966; (b) .044447; (d) 2.6879; (f) 7.0008.

11. Use common logarithms to evaluate $e^{3.4}$. Compare with the value found in the tables of the exponential function.

12. Which is larger, e^π or π^e?

13. The formula $P = 0.00161\,V^2L/D$ gives the pressure (pounds per square inch) needed to force water through a pipe at a velocity of V ft/sec. L is the length (ft) and D is the diameter (in.) of the pipe. Set up a convenient computing form for calculating P when V, L, and D are given. Evaluate P when

(a) $V = 6.72$, $L = 2435$, $D = 6$
(b) $V = 12.5$, $L = 3750$, $D = 12$
(c) $V = 12.5$, $L = 165$, $D = \frac{1}{2}$.

Answers: (a) 29.5; (b) 78.6; (c) 83.0.

14. For large values of n, it is tedious to find the exact value of $n!$ Sterling's formula, $n! \doteq n^n e^{-n}\sqrt{2\pi n}$ gives a good approximation when n is large.

(a) Set up a computing form for using logarithms to estimate $n!$ with this formula.

(b) Estimate $n!$ for $n = 10, 15, 20,$ and 100. Compare with the values found in a table of factorials.

15. The average life of a certain type of light bulb when operated at its normal voltage of 115 volts is 2875 hr. If the voltage is increased to V volts, the average life is given by $L = 2875(V/115)^{-12.4}$. Determine L when $V = 125$ volts; when $V = 100$ volts.

16. The formula $M = 1.769(T + 393)^{2.51}(10^{-5})$ gives the average molecular weight M of a petroleum fraction in terms of the temperature, T, in degrees centigrade of its atmospheric boiling point. Determine M when $T = 175°$.

Answer: 144.93.

17. From more extensive tables of logarithms we find $\log 1.01 = .004321374$, $\log 1.001 = .000434077$, and $\log 1.0001 = .000043427$. Estimate e with logarithms using the formula $e \doteq (1 + 1/t)^t$, and $t = 100$, $t = 1000$, and $t = 10,000$.

804. Logarithmic calculations in bases other than ten

When you use logarithms in base 10, you may wonder who made the tables, and how. Calculations like those of Bürgi came first. Then mathematicians developed formulas for calculating logarithms in base e. In your book of tables, you will find formulas like

$$e^x = 1 + x + \frac{x^2}{2!} + \frac{x^3}{3!} + \frac{x^4}{4!} + \cdots$$

and

$$(0 < x \le 2) \Rightarrow \log_e x = (x - 1) - \tfrac{1}{2}(x - 1)^2 + \tfrac{1}{3}(x - 1)^3 - \cdots.$$

The development of such formulas requires the techniques of calculus that were developed by Newton (1642–1727), Leibniz (1646–1716) and their successors. We shall call logarithms in base e *natural logarithms* in contrast to common logarithms that are based upon 10.

Once you have a table of natural logarithms, you can calculate common logarithms by L 9 (page 382). Thus

$$\log_{10} N = \frac{\log_e N}{\log_e 10} = \log_e N \log_{10} e.$$

From your book of tables, $\log_e 10 \doteq 2.30258509299404568402$, and $\log_{10} e \doteq 0.43429448190325182765$. Given that $\log_e 223.0 \doteq 5.40717$, you can calculate

$$\log_{10} 223.0 \doteq \frac{5.40717}{2.302585} \doteq (5.40717)(0.4342945).$$

Even today, a person who needs a more accurate value of the logarithm of a number in base 10 than he has available in a set of tables begins by calculating an accurate value of the logarithm in base e; then he uses the extremely accurate value of $\log_e 10$, or $\log_{10} e$, as given in the tables; then he uses L 9.

The more usual situation is to have a table of logarithms in base 10 that is accurate enough for practical purposes. It is rare to need more than seven-place logarithms, and tables of seven-place logarithms are widely available. Even the five-place tables in your book of tables are good enough for most purposes. The fact that accurate tables in base 10 are so widely available leads to a curious reversal of history. When you need a natural logarithm, you use the tables in base e if you have an accurate enough table available; but often you use the table in base 10 as follows:

$$\log_e 218.68 = (\log_{10} 218.68)(\log_e 10) \doteq (2.33981)(2.302585) \doteq 5.38761.$$

From the base e table you find

$$\left.\begin{array}{l} \log_e 218 \doteq 5.38450 \\ \log_e 219 \doteq 5.38907 \end{array}\right] .00457.$$

By *unsafe* interpolation, $\log_e 218.68 \doteq 5.38450 + .68(.00457)$
$$\doteq 5.38761.$$

The chance of getting a wrong answer, like 5.38760 or 5.38762, is rather likely when you interpolate between $\log_e 218$ and $\log_e 219$ to get $\log_e 218.68$.

The technique of getting logarithms in other bases from logarithms in base 10 is important in certain applied problems. The most common situation calls for finding logarithms in base e from logarithms in base 10. We give you some examples to study. Then we give you some further questions to explore in Exercises §804.

(1) Find $\log_2 17$.

$$\log_2 17 = \frac{\log_{10} 17}{\log_{10} 2} \doteq \frac{1.23045}{.30103}.$$

To avoid the long division, we proceed as follows:

$$\left.\begin{array}{l} \log 1.23045 \doteq 10.09007 - 10 \\ \log .30103 \doteq 9.47861 - 10 \end{array}\right\} \text{Subtract}$$

$$\overline{}$$

$$\log \log_2 17 \doteq 0.61146$$
$$\log_2 17 \doteq 4.0875.$$

Notice the appearance, in this example, of logarithms of logarithms. When you recall that logarithms are numbers, you will recognize that there is nothing to prevent your taking logarithms of logarithms; and it was convenient to avoid long division here.

(2) Recall from Section 801 (page 377) the question of finding $\log_5 30$. You are now ready to tackle this question efficiently:

$$\log_5 30 = \frac{\log_{10} 30}{\log_{10} 5} \doteq \frac{1.47712}{0.69897}.$$

$$\left.\begin{array}{l} \log 1.47712 \doteq 10.16941 - 10 \\ \log 0.69897 \doteq 9.84446 - 10 \end{array}\right\} \text{Subtract}$$

$$\overline{}$$

$$\log \log_5 30 \doteq 0.32495$$
$$\log_5 30 \doteq 2.1132.$$

You should check this result against the discussion in Section 801 (page 377) to see whether it is a reasonable answer.

(3) Find $\log_e 4263$. When you follow the same approach that we used above, you get

$$\log_e 4263 = \frac{\log_{10} 4263}{\log_{10} e} \doteq \frac{3.62972}{0.43429}$$

$$\left. \begin{array}{l} \log 3.62972 \doteq 10.55987 - 10 \\ \log 0.43429 \doteq 9.63778 - 10 \end{array} \right\} \text{Subtract}$$

$$\log \log_e 4263 \doteq \overline{0.92209}$$

$$\log_e 4263 \doteq 8.3578.$$

You can also use the table of natural logarithms as follows: The table gives

$$\log_e 426.3 \doteq 6.05514$$

(by interpolation between $\log 426.0$ and $\log 427.0$). Also,

$$\log_e 10 \doteq 2.30259.$$

Hence
$$\log_e 4263 = \log_e (426.3 \times 10)$$

$$= \log_e 426.3 + \log_e 10$$

$$\doteq 6.05514 + 2.30259$$

$$= 8.35773.$$

You should contrast this answer with the previous one, 8.3578, to notice the sources of rounding errors and interpolation errors in each answer. Notice that when a table of natural logarithms is available, it is convenient. When the natural logarithm you want is not in the table, you may be able to adapt the table to fit your needs. As further examples:

(4)
$$\log_e 39,700 = \log_e 397 + \log_e 100$$

$$\doteq 5.98394 + 4.60517$$

$$= 10.58911.$$

(5)
$$\log_e .00468 = \log_e \frac{4.68}{1000}$$

$$= \log_e 4.68 - \log_e 1000$$

$$\doteq 1.54330 - 6.90776$$

$$= 4.63554 - 10.$$

When you find it difficult to adapt your table of natural logarithms to the problem in hand you can always use tables in base 10.

EXERCISES §804

1. Use a table of logarithms in the base 10 to calculate the following logarithms. Check results by referring to a table of natural logarithms.

(a) $\log_e 4$ (b) $\log_e 67$ (c) $\log_e 8.73$
(d) $\log_e 227.9$ (e) $\log_e 0.81$ (f) $\log_e 0.09$
(g) $\log_e 5.714$ (h) $\log_e 936.5$ (i) $\log_e 0.6543$.

2. Use a table of natural logarithms to calculate the following logarithms. Check results by referring to a table of common logarithms.

(a) $\log_{10} 5.76$ (b) $\log_{10} 429$ (c) $\log_{10} .51$
(d) $\log_{10} 6.752$ (e) $\log_{10} 100$ (f) $\log_{10} 742.3$.

3. Evaluate:

(a) $\log_e 8350$ (b) $\log_e 64{,}000$ (c) $\log_e 0.0042$
(d) $\log_e 0.0627$ (e) $\log_e 5921$ (f) $\log_e 429{,}000$.

Answers: (a) 9.03002;   (c) 4.52732 − 10;   (f) 12.96922.

4. Determine $\log_2 8$ from the definition of logarithms. Then use the change of base formula to evaluate $\log_2 8$ with base-10 tables and with base-e tables. Compare the three results.

5. Evaluate:

(a) $\log_2 9$ (b) $\log_2 25$ (c) $\log_3 47$
(d) $\log_3 1.29$ (e) $\log_5 483$ (f) $\log_{17} 192$
(g) $\log_{1/2} 17$ (h) $\log_{1/2} 0.432$ (i) $\log_{0.3} 12$.

Answers: (a) 3.1699;   (e) 3.8399;   (f) 1.8557;   (h) 1.2109.

6. Since $e^x = N \Leftrightarrow x = \log_e N$, the tables of the exponential function can be used backwards to approximate $\log_e N$. Estimate the following logarithms by this method. Check your answers with a table of natural logarithms.

(a) $\log_e 1.6$ (b) $\log_e 2.56$ (c) $\log_e 5.207$
(d) $\log_e 9.5$ (e) $\log_e .2466$ (f) $\log_e .08$.

7. The equivalence of the conditions in Exercise 6 also enables you to estimate e^x, when x is given, by using a table of natural logarithms. Estimate the following values of e^x by this method; then compare with the values found in the tables of the exponential function.

(a) $e^{.47}$ (b) $e^{1.79}$ (c) $e^{5.60}$
(d) $e^{-.51}$ (e) $e^{-1.66}$ (f) $e^{5.743}$.

8. Determine $\log_5 30$, using logarithms in the base e. Show that this is equivalent to the approximation method of solving an exponential equation suggested in Exercise 7 (page 379). Compare also with Example (2) of this section.

9. Carry out the following calculations in two ways, with common logarithms and with natural logarithms. Which type of logarithms seems better suited for computation?

(a) $(3.47)(65.9)$ (b) $(28.3)/(5.09)$ (c) $\sqrt{8.752}$
(d) $2613/4179$ (e) $\sqrt{.764}$ (f) $\sqrt[3]{9136}$.

10. Show that the points $(1,0)$, $(b,1)$, $(b^2,2)$, $(b^{-1},-1)$, (b^k,k) are on the graph of $y = \log_b x$.

11. Prove

(a) $\log_b a > 1$ and $b > 1 \Rightarrow a > b$
(b) $\log_b a = 1 \Leftrightarrow a = b$
(c) $\log_b a < 1$ and $b > 1 \Rightarrow a < b$
(d) $\log_b a < 0$ and $b > 1 \Rightarrow a < 1$
(e) $\log_b a < 0$ and $0 < b < 1 \Rightarrow a > 1$
(f) $\log_b x > \log_a x > 0$ and $b > 1 \Rightarrow a > b$.

12. The change of base formula shows that the equations $y = \log_b x$ and $y = (\log_b e)(\log_e x)$ are equivalent. Hence the graphs $y = \log_b x$ and $y = \log_e x$ have the same shape with a different scale for the y-axis, the scale factor being $\log_b e$. (What happens to the graph when the scale factor is negative?) Hence the graph of $y = \log_b x$ can easily be sketched by locating a few strategic points on the graph (see Exercise 10). Sketch

(a) $y = \log_5 x$ (b) $y = \log_7 x$ (c) $y = \log_{1/2} x$
(d) $y = \log_{15} x$ (e) $y = \log_{1/4} x$ (f) $y = \log_{0.1} x$.

13. Compare the appearance of the graphs of $y = \log_4 x$ and $y = \log_{1/4} x$.

14. Show that $y = (1/0.47) \log_e x$ and $y = \log_{1.6} x$ have the same graph.

805. Conditions that involve logarithms

You have already met simple conditions that involve logarithms. For example, $\log_{10} x = 2.63879$; $\log_2 8 = x$; and $3e^{-0.2x^2} = 15$. As you look for the solution set of one of these conditions, you expect to use a table of logarithms; thus you expect to get approximations to the solutions.

(1) $\log_{10} x = 2.63879$ yields $x \doteq 435.30$.

(2) $\log_2 8 = x \Leftrightarrow 2^x = 8$ yields $x = 3$. This condition is an exception; you get the exact solution, $x = 3$.

(3) $3e^{-0.2x^2} = 15$, $e^{-0.2x^2} = 5$;

$$-0.2x^2 \log_{10} e = \log_{10} 5$$

$$x^2 = -\frac{\log_{10} 5}{0.2 \log_{10} e} \doteq -\frac{0.69897}{(0.2)(.43429)}.$$

Since this condition defines x^2 as a negative number, $x \notin L$. The set of real numbers that satisfy the condition is the null set $\{\ \}$.

(4) $15e^{-0.2x^2} = 3$, $e^{-0.2x^2} = \frac{1}{5} = 0.2$

$$-0.2x^2 \log_{10} e = \log_{10} 0.2$$

$$x^2 = -\frac{\log_{10} 0.2}{0.2 \log_{10} e} \doteq -\frac{9.30103 - 10}{0.2(.43429)},$$

$$x^2 \doteq -\frac{-0.69897}{0.086858} = \frac{0.69897}{0.086858} \doteq 8.$$

Hence $x \doteq \pm\sqrt{8}$. The set of real numbers,

$$\{x \mid 15e^{-0.2x^2} = 3\} = \{\pm\sqrt{8} \text{ (approx.)}\}.$$

You can simplify the calculations in this example by using natural logarithms instead of common logarithms. Thus

$$e^{-0.2x^2} = 0.2, \qquad -0.2x^2 \log_e e = \log_e 0.2.$$

Using the table of natural logarithms, and the fact that $\log_e e = 1$, you get

$$x^2 \doteq \frac{8.391 - 10}{-0.2} = \frac{-1.609}{-0.2} \doteq 8.04.$$

Hence $x \doteq \pm\sqrt{8.04}$. The solution set is $\{\pm\sqrt{8.04} \text{ (approx.)}\}$.

Conditions that involve logarithms commonly arise in problems of growth and decay. When, for example, you study the decay of a quantity of radium, or any radioactive substance, it is convenient to express the law of decay as follows:

$$N_t = N_0 e^{-\lambda t}$$

In this equation N_0 represents the number of atoms of radioactive material present at the beginning (when $t = 0$); N_t represents the number of atoms of radioactive material present at time t (t years, or t hours, or t seconds, or t microseconds after time 0. You choose a unit of time that is convenient to the problem. Some substances decay slowly; others, like the materials in an atomic bomb, decay very rapidly). λ is a constant whose value is characteristic of the material under study.

A typical problem is the following: A radioactive substance loses one-half of its weight in 5 yr. Find λ.

We shall assume that the number of atoms of the substance decreases from N_0 to $N_0/2$ in 5 yr. Hence $N_5 = N_0/2$. The equation becomes

$$\frac{N_0}{2} = N_0 e^{-5\lambda}$$

$$\tfrac{1}{2} = e^{-5\lambda}$$

$$\log_e \tfrac{1}{2} = -5\lambda \log_e e,$$

$$-\log_e 2 = -5\lambda$$

$$\lambda = \frac{\log_e 2}{5} \doteq \frac{0.69315}{5}$$

$$\doteq .139.$$

With this value of the constant λ you can write the law of decay for this substance as

$$N_t = N_0 e^{-0.139t}.$$

As you apply this law you get three types of problems as follows:

(5) How many atoms will be left when you begin with 3.46×10^8 atoms and wait for 10 yr? The answer is

$$N_{10} = (3.46 \times 10^8)e^{(-0.139)(10)}.$$

According to your tables, $e^{-1.39} \doteq 0.24908$. Hence $N_{10} \doteq (3.46 \times 10^8) \times (0.24908)$. It is more convenient to use logarithms and proceed as follows:

$$N_{10} = \frac{3.46 \times 10^8}{e^{1.39}}$$

$$\log 3.46 \times 10^8 \doteq 8.53908$$

$$\log e^{1.39} \qquad \doteq 0.60367 \qquad \text{(Using the table for } \log_{10} e^x\text{)}$$

$$\log N_{10} \qquad \doteq 7.93541$$

$$N_{10} \doteq 8.618 \times 10^7$$

$$\doteq 8.62 \times 10^7.$$

Notice that

$$\frac{N_{10}}{N_0} \doteq \frac{8.62 \times 10^7}{3.46 \times 10^8} \doteq .25.$$

Recall that the substance loses one-half its weight in 5 yr; continuing at this rate, it loses one-half of its remaining weight in 5 more yr. Hence $N_{10} = \frac{1}{2}N_5 = \frac{1}{2}(\frac{1}{2}N_0) = \frac{1}{4}N_0$.

(6) How many atoms were there 100 yr ago, if there are 2.85×10^6 atoms now? The answer is N_0, where

$$2.85 \times 10^6 = N_0 e^{(-0.139)(100)}.$$

This yields

$$N_0 = (2.85 \times 10^6)e^{13.9}.$$

Your table does not contain the value of $e^{13.9}$. You may proceed as follows

$$N_0 = (2.85 \times 10^6)e^{10} \cdot e^{3.9}$$

$$\log (2.85 \times 10^6) \doteq 6.45484$$

$$\log e^{10} \qquad \doteq 4.34294$$

$$\log e^{3.9} \qquad \doteq 1.69375$$

$$\log N_0 \qquad \doteq 12.49153$$

$$N_0 \doteq 3.10 \times 10^{12}.$$

Notice that we gave the answer to three significant figures. This may appear reasonable in light of the given data, $N_{100} = 2.85 \times 10^6$. Using $\lambda \doteq .13863$ yields $N_0 \doteq 2.99 \times 10^{12}$, correct to three significant figures. Geologists have used the technique of this problem as they studied the ages of rock formations.

(7) How long will it take for 9.63×10^8 atoms to decay to 2.54×10^5 atoms? The answer is t (years), where

$$(2.54 \times 10^5) = (9.63 \times 10^8)e^{-0.139t}.$$

This yields
$$e^{-0.139t} = \frac{2.54 \times 10^5}{9.63 \times 10^8}.$$

More conveniently,
$$e^{0.139t} = \frac{9.63 \times 10^8}{2.54 \times 10^5}$$

$$= \frac{9.63 \times 10^3}{2.54}$$

$$.139t \log_e e = \log_e 9.63 + \log_e 10^3 - \log_e 2.54$$

$$.139t \doteq 2.26488 + 6.90776 - 0.93216 = 8.24048$$

$$t \doteq \frac{8.24048}{.139} \doteq 59.3.$$

Hence it will take 59.3 yr, or about 59 yr, for the decay to take place.

You can also use a *slide rule*, which has the log-log scales, to estimate t quickly and conveniently.

You will find further illustrations of exponential and logarithmic conditions in Exercises §805.

EXERCISES §805

1. Solve the following equations for x:

(a) $e^{4x} = 7$ (b) $e^{-\frac{1}{2}x} = 6.34$

(c) $1.32e^{3x} = 29.74$ (d) $14e^{x^2} = 350$

(e) $\log_e 2x = 6.542$ (f) $\log_e (75x) = 11.293$

(g) $\log_e 8(x + 4) = 9$ (h) $\log_e (4x^2) = 15$

(i) $1.32e^{1.7x} - 46.84 = 0$ (j) $46.84e^{-1.7x} - 1.32 = 0$

(k) $\log_{37} x = 1.9342$ (l) $7^x = 41$

(m) $(2.6)^{x^2} = (3.1)^x$ (n) $\log_e (e^{\frac{1}{2}x} + 25) = 3.65$

(o) $(2\pi)^{-\frac{1}{2}}e^{-\frac{1}{2}x^2} = 0.16.$

Answers: (a) .4865;   (b) -3.6938;   (c) 1.0383;   (d) ±1.7942;   (e) 346.8; (g) 1008.9;   (h) ±904.0;   (k) 1079;   (l) 1.9084;   (m) 0, 1.1841;   (n) 5.2018; (o) ±1.3518.

2. A radioactive substance decomposes according to the condition $G = 10e^{-.03t}$, where G is the number of grams remaining after t years.

(a) What is the initial amount of radioactive substance (when $t = 0$)?

(b) How much will remain after 9 yr? after 18 yr?

(c) Find the time when only half the original amount remains. (We call this time the *half-life* of the radioactive material.)

Answers: (a) 10 grams;   (b) 7.63 grams, 5.83 grams;   (c) 23.1 yr.

3. The time t for which $N_t = \frac{1}{2}N_0$ in the law of decay, $N_t = N_0e^{-\lambda t}$, is called the half-life of the material. Show that the half-life in terms of λ is $(1/\lambda) \log_e 2$.

4. For radiocarbon, a radioactive substance used in dating historical objects, the value of λ (when t is measured in years) is approximately $1.24(10^{-4})$. Determine the half-life of radiocarbon (see Exercise 3).

Answer: Approximately 5600 yr.

5. An experiment with bacteria begins with a culture of 100 bacteria. At the end of 4 days there are 332 bacteria. The equation $y = ae^{rx}$, where y is the number of bacteria after x days have elapsed, provides a good mathematical model for this situation.

(a) Determine values for the parameters a and r from the data given ($y = 100$ when $x = 0$, and $y = 332$ when $x = 4$).

(b) If the growth of the bacteria continues to obey this condition, how many bacteria may be expected in 10 days?

(c) In how many days will the number of bacteria double?

6. In Exercise 6 of Section 407 (page 144), the equation $y = 128(1.5)^x$ expresses the number of bacteria present (y), in terms of the number of days that have elapsed (x), when the number of bacteria in the culture increases by 50% each day. Rewrite this equation in the form $y = ae^{rx}$. (*Suggestion:* Let $a = 128$ and solve $e^r = 1.5$ for r.)

Answer: $y = 128e^{.405x}$.

7. Rewrite the condition, $y = 10(.8)^x$, in the form $y = ae^{rx}$.

Answer: $y = 10e^{-.223x}$.

8. The pH of a solution is a measure of acidity of the solution and is defined to be the common logarithm of the reciprocal of the hydrogen ion concentration, $[H^+]$. That is, $pH = \log_{10}(1/[H^+])$. If the solution is neutral, $[H^+] = 1.0(10^{-7})$, and $pH = \log(1/10^{-7}) = \log 10^7 = 7$. A pH of less than 7 indicates an acid solution, while pH greater than 7 indicates that the solution is alkaline.

(a) Determine the pH of a solution if $[H^+] = 4.2 \times 10^{-5}$.

(b) Determine $[H^+]$ for a solution whose pH is 8.23.

Answers: (a) $pH \doteq 4.38$;   (b) $[H^+] \doteq 5.89(10^{-9})$.

9. Solve $pH = \log_{10}(1/[H^+])$ for $[H^+]$. Express the results as an exponential with the base 10, also as an exponential with the base e.

10. The condition $y = (2\pi)^{-\frac{1}{2}}e^{-\frac{1}{2}x^2}$ is important in the theory of probability. Solve for x in terms of y. What is the range of y?

Answer: $x = \pm\sqrt{-2 \log_e y - \log_e 2\pi}$ for $0 < y \leq (2\pi)^{-1/2}$.

11. Solve each of the following equations for the variable indicated.

(a) $u = \log_{10} 2z$ for z.   (b) $e^{\frac{1}{2}x} = M$ for x.

(c) $ae^{ny} = T$ for y.   (d) $x = \frac{1}{4}\log_e (y/a)$ for y.

(e) $\log_e (y + 1)^2 = x$ for y.   (f) $\log_x 5 = 3$ for x.

(g) $e^{z^2} = A$ for z.   (h) $at^{x+3} = b$ for x.

Answers: (a) $z = \frac{1}{2}(10^u)$;   (b) $x = 2 \log_e M$;   (c) $y = (1/n)(\log_e T - \log_e a)$; (d) $y = ae^{4x}$; (e) $y = e^{\frac{1}{2}x} - 1$; (f) $x = \sqrt[3]{5}$; (g) $z = \pm\sqrt{\log_e A}$; (h) $x = -3 + \log_t b - \log_t a$.

806. The logarithmic scale

When you draw the graphs of exponential functions and perform logarithmic calculations, you may be able to save time by working graphically rather than arithmetically. You use the logarithmic scale that appears on slide rules, and special kinds of graph paper.

It is easy to construct a logarithmic scale either with or without a table of logarithms. Suppose you want to make a scale that is 10 in. long. You can use the table of logarithms to find that log 2 $\doteq$ 0.3010. You mark the left end of the scale 1. You place the point 2 at a distance $(.3010)10 = 3.010$ in.

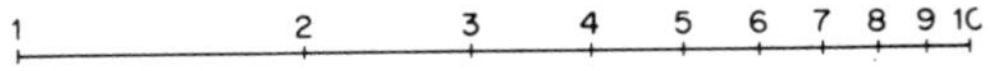

Fig. 8–3.

to the right of 1. You place the point 3 at a distance $(\log 3)10 \doteq (.4771)10 = 4.771$ in. to the right of 1, etc. You get a scale that looks like Fig. 8–3. You can fill in as many intermediate points as you wish. For example, you place the point 3.5 at a distance $(\log 3.5)10 \doteq 5.440$ in. to the right of 1.

It may strengthen your intuitive understanding of logarithms to proceed in another way. Suppose a quantity grows 20% per year. For convenience, begin with the quantity 1 and trace its growth in the table below:

t (years)	0	1	2	3	4	5	6
Q (quantity)	1.00	1.20	1.44	1.73	2.07	2.49	2.99

t (years)	7	8	9	10	11	12	13
Q (quantity)	3.58	4.30	5.16	6.19	7.43	8.92	10.70

The quantity Q obeys the condition

$$Q = (1.2)^t;$$

that is,

$$\log_{1.2} Q = t.$$

This means that $\log_{1.2} 1.00 = 0$, $\log_{1.2} 1.20 = 1$, $\log_{1.2} 1.44 = 2$, etc. Now examine Fig. 8–4 and notice that the numbers below the scale are the logarithms, in base 1.2, of the numbers above the scale. The upper numbers form a logarithmic scale on which equal distances represent the same ratio. Thus

$$\frac{1.20}{1.00} \doteq \frac{1.44}{1.20} \doteq \frac{1.73}{1.44}, \text{ etc.}$$

At the end of each year Q is 20% more than it was at the beginning of the year. When you interpolate to place the numbers 1, 2, 3, ..., 10 in the upper set, you get a scale like the one in Fig. 8–4. The fact that these logarithms are in the base 1.2 is unimportant, for

$$\log_{1.2} N = \frac{\log_{10} N}{\log_{10} 1.2}.$$

Logarithms in base 1.2 are logarithms in base 10 multiplied by $1/\log_{10} 1.2$. The effect is a change of scale, a change in the distance between 1 and 10.

To get a more accurate logarithmic scale you could work with base 1.1 (10% increase), or with base 1.01 (1% increase), or even with base 1.0001 as Bürgi did.

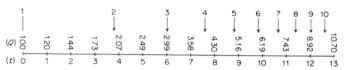

Fig. 8–4.

We now proceed to a brief introduction to the practical applications of the logarithmic scale. Then we suggest further exploratory activities in Exercises §806. In order to follow what we have to say, you will need some equipment. You need at least an inexpensive 10-in. slide rule and sheets of semi-log and full-log graph paper. It is also helpful to have access to some sort of circular slide rule.

Recall from Section 410, page 162, the function $\{(a,\alpha)\}$ for the arc-length a and the angle measured in degrees, α, at the center of a circle of radius r. You used proportions like

$$\frac{\alpha}{a} = \frac{180}{\pi r}$$

to calculate corresponding values of a and α. For example, when $r = 5$ and $\alpha = 152°$,

$$\frac{152}{a} = \frac{180}{5\pi}.$$

Hence
$$a = \frac{5\pi(152)}{180} = \frac{38\pi}{9} \doteq 13.2$$

when $r = 5$ and $a = 60$,
$$\frac{\alpha}{60} = \frac{180}{5\pi}.$$

Hence
$$\alpha = \frac{(180)(60)}{5\pi} = \frac{2160}{\pi} \doteq 690°.$$

Such direct proportions are very common in applied mathematics. They are especially convenient when you use a slide rule. First examine the C and D scales of a slide rule. These are logarithmic scales that run from 1 to 10, or from 10 to 100, or from 100 to 1000, or from .01 to .1. You interpret the numbers on the scale to fit the problem in hand. Study the scales to locate numbers like 224, 3.14, .00586, etc.

Now set 180 on the C scale above $5\pi \doteq 15.7$ on the D scale. With this setting of the rule, the numbers on the C scale are angles measured in degrees; below each angle appears the corresponding arc of a circle of radius 5. Some values of (α, a) that you can read are: ((180, 15.7), (200, 17.5), (400, 34.9), (900, 78.5), (1000, 87.3). Of course you can interpret (200, 17.5) as (2, .175), or as (.02, .00175), etc. This is equivalent to multiplying the numerator and denominator of the fraction α/a by a power of 10; on the scale it is equivalent to interpreting the numbers on the scales as running from 1 to 10 rather than from 100 to 1000, or from .01 to .1, etc.

To see why the slide rule works as a ratio-machine, you should think again about the way that logarithmic scales are constructed. Set 2 on the C scale above 3 on the D scale. Notice that 1 on the C scale is above 1.5 on the D scale. As you look at the slide rule in this position, notice that it says $\log 3 - \log 2 = \log 1.5 - \log 1$. That is, the distance $0.4771 - 0.3010$ equals the distance $0.1761 - 0.0000$. In this position it also says $\log 6 - \log 4 = \log 9 - \log 6$, etc.

Hence fractions equal to 2/3, like 1/1.5, 4/6, 6/9, etc., appear on the rule with numerators on the C scale and denominators on the D scale. Of course you run off the scale finally. At the right end of the D scale you read 6.67/10; numerators like 7, on the C scale, are beyond the end of the D scale. Some slide rules provide *folded* scales (a CF and a DF scale) to let you read fractions equal to 2/3 with numerators beyond 667. On other slide rules, you must move the C scale to place its right hand *index* (the figure 1 at the right of the C scale) over 1.5 on the D scale. Then you can read fractions with numerators from 667 to 999.

To make the slide rule a useful tool, you need to use it and study its possibilities. The manuals, which most manufacturers provide with new slide rules, are helpful even when you understand the principle of the slide rule. They point out short cuts and special tricks that you are not apt to discover when you learn to use a slide rule on your own.

We give you two more useful proportions that arise in the geometry of circles. They concern the area of a *segment* of a circle as shown in Fig. 8–5. You can use these proportions to practice with your slide rule as a ratio-machine.

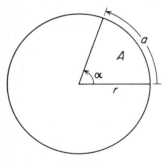

Fig. 8–5.

$$\frac{A}{\alpha} = \frac{\pi r^2}{360} \quad \text{and} \quad \frac{A}{a} = \frac{\pi r^2}{2\pi r} = \frac{r}{2}.$$

These proportions say that the area-measure of a segment of a circle, A, is proportional to the degree-measure of the angle, α, or the measure of the arc, a, of the segment. When $r = 8$ and $a = 12$, $A/12 = 8/2$. When you set 8 above 2; you read 48 above 12.

Notice that the second proportion is more convenient than the first one. When $r = 8$ and $\alpha = 70°$, $A/70 = \pi(8^2)/360$. You have to find the value of $\pi(8^2)$ in order to set the slide rule. You get $\pi(8^2) \doteq 201$; hence $A/70 = 201/360$. When you set 201 above 360, you read 49 above 70.

You should experiment with other instances of these proportions for slide rule practice. Then consider the question: if a pilot flies 46 mi in 8 min, how long will it take him to travel 300 mi at this same *rate*. The proportion is

$$\frac{d}{t} = \frac{46}{8}$$

where d is measured in miles and t is measured in minutes. On your slide rule, set 46 over 8; then read the number of minutes below the number 300. You get $t \doteq 52$ min. Notice that this one setting of your slide rule enables you to read the number of minutes the pilot takes to go various distances, and the number of miles he will travel in various times, when he maintains a rate of 46 mi per 8 min.

When you ask how far will the pilot go in 15 min, the number 15 on the D scale is beyond the end of the C scale. You can move the right index of the C scale to the position occupied by the left index of the C scale. Then you read 86 on the C scale above 15 on the D scale. Thus the pilot goes about 86 mi in 15 min. Pilots like to use circular slide rules to solve problems of this sort. The circular slide rule avoids the difficulty of running over the end of a scale. Examine a circular slide rule to see how it works.

When you want to graph an equation like $y = ab^x$, you can use ordinary graph paper and get an exponential curve. For example, the graph of $A = 2(1.05)^t$ gives you the amount of \$2 at 5% interest compounded yearly for t years.

You can also use logarithms and express the condition $y = ab^x$ in the form

$$\log y = \log a + x \log b = (\log b)x + \log a.$$

If you plot the set of number-pairs, $\{(x, \log y)\}$, you get a straight line of slope $\log b$, and $(\log y)$-intercept $\log a$.

It is convenient to accomplish this straightening-out of the graph of an exponential function in another way. When you plot y on a logarithmic scale, vertical distances represent logarithms of y. Hence the graph of $y = ab^x$ on *semi-log* graph paper is a straight line. Figure 8–6 shows the general appearance of the semi-log graph paper; but you should examine several samples of commercially made papers also.

Notice that the distances from 1 to 2, 10 to 20, etc., are equal on the logarithmic scale. Also, you can interpret the range from 1 to 10 as a range from 100 to 1000, etc.

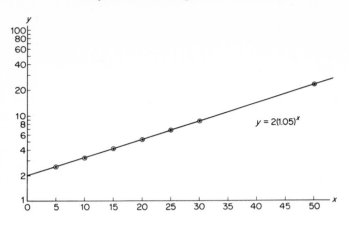

Fig. 8–6.

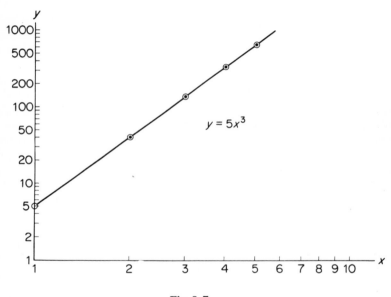

Fig. 8–7.

Notice how the graph of $y = 2(1.05)^x$ shows the amounts (y) of \$2 invested at 5% interest compounded yearly for x years. You can use the 5% compound-interest table to check the figures below:

x	0	5	10	15	20	25	...	50
y	2.00	2.55	3.26	4.16	5.31	6.77	...	22.93

Then check the plotted points in the figure.

As you work with semi-log graph paper, you may begin to wonder what full-log graph paper is good for. When you plot a simple power function like $\{(x,5x^3)\}$ on ordinary graph paper you get a curve. If you take logarithms, in the condition $y = 5x^3$,

$$\log y = \log 5 + 3 \log x$$
$$= 3(\log x) + \log 5.$$

The graph of the set of number-pairs, $\{(\log x, \log y)\}$ is a straight line of slope 3, and $(\log y)$-intercept $\log 5$. This $(\log y)$-intercept corresponds to $\log x = 0$, that is, to $x = 1$.

If you use full-log paper the distances along the x- and y-axes are really logarithms of x and y. Hence the graph looks like Fig. 8–7.

This brief introduction to applications of the logarithmic scale may stimulate you to investigate further. We leave it to you to decide how far to go. The slide rule, logarithmic graph paper, and other applications of logarithmic scales are practical consequences of theoretical investigations of powers and roots of real numbers, and the exponential function.

EXERCISES §806

1. Construct a logarithmic scale 10 in. long like Fig. 8–3 (page 400). Mark every half-unit from 1 to 10 on the scale. (Do not forget to account for the fact that most rulers are not marked with tenths of inches.) Compare your finished scale with the C scale on a slide rule.

2. From the 6% column of a compound-interest table, construct a logarithmic scale in the base 1.06 on a sheet of graph-paper.

3. If I is the length of an object in inches and C is the length in centimeters, then $I/C = 1/2.54$. Set up this ratio on a slide rule, then calculate:

(a) I, when $C = 5.08$; 8.5; 57; 320; .9; .075.

(b) C, when $I = 3$; 29; 3700; 6; 73.5; .082.

Answers: (a) 2.00; 3.35; 22.4; 126; .354; .0295.

4. If M is the velocity in *miles per hour* and F is the same velocity in *feet per second*, then $F/M = 22/15$. Determine:

(a) F, when $M = 60$; 40; 100; 558; 2000.

(b) M, when $F = 1$; 3.21; 32.1; 167; 750.

Answers: (b) .682; 2.19; 21.9; 114; 511.

5. Make a table of values of $y = 6.2e^{0.5x}$ for $x = 1, 2, 3, ..., 10$. Plot on ordinary graph paper and on semi-log graph paper. Compare results.

6. Repeat Exercise 5 with $y = 2000e^{-0.4x}$.

7. The following table shows the amount of sales of an industrial corporation for the first 11 years of business.

x (year)	1	2	3	4	5	6	7	8	9	10	11
y (sales in millions of dollars)	1.5	1.8	2.2	2.6	3.1	3.7	4.5	5.5	6.5	7.7	9.2

(a) Plot on semi-log graph paper.

(b) Draw the line that appears to fit the points best.

(c) An equation of the form $y = ab^x$ will fit the data reasonably well. From the line of part (b), estimate a and b. (*Hint:* You have the graph of $\log y = (\log b)x + \log a$. Hence when $x = 0$, $y = a$; a is the number on the logarithmic scale where the line intersects it. To estimate b, choose any two points reasonably far apart, and $\dfrac{\log y_2 - \log y_1}{x_2 - x_1} = \log b$.)

(d) Rewrite the equation of part (c) in the form $y = ae^{rx}$, i.e., solve $e^r = b$ for r. From the tables of the exponential function, estimate y when $x = 10$ and compare with the value in the table.

(e) Assuming that the corporation continues to grow in this fashion, estimate from the graph, and from your equation, the amount of sales in the 12th and 15th years.

Approximate results: (c) $y = 1.26(1.20)^x$; $y = 1.26e^{.182x}$; (e) 11.1, 19.3.

8. If a slide rule has the necessary scales, you can use it to perform many types of calculations. Use the following problems for practice. The answers are given to three significant digits for use with a 10-in. rule.

(a) $\sqrt{2.79}$ (b) $\sqrt{27.9}$ (c) $\sqrt{279}$

(d) $(2.78)(3.36)$ (e) $(17.9)(22.5)$ (f) $(.861)(94.3)$

(g) $(2.56)\sqrt{8.43}$ (h) $\sqrt{(6.40)(9.37)}$ (i) $\dfrac{82.5}{29.7}$

(j) $\dfrac{34.2}{1.52}$ (k) $\dfrac{\sqrt{85.6}}{7.52}$ (l) $\sqrt[3]{8.35}$

(m) $\sqrt[3]{83.5}$ (n) $\sqrt[3]{835}$ (o) $(2.37)\sqrt[3]{7.94}$

(p) $(46)\sqrt[3]{235}$ (q) $\dfrac{(3.29)(4.26)}{17.3}$ (r) $\dfrac{(46.5)(29.6)}{(81.7)(11.3)}$

(s) $\tan 29°$ (t) $\cos 75°$ (u) $\sin 37.5°$

(v) $(34.6)\sin 13°$ (w) $(19.6)\cos 52.4°$ (x) $\dfrac{425}{\sin 18°}$

(y) $\dfrac{61.5}{\cos 32°}$ (z) $86 \tan 37°$ (θ) $(22.1)\tan 65°$.

Answers: (a) 1.67; (b) 5.28; (c) 16.7; (d) 9.34; (e) 403; (f) 81.2; (g) 7.43; (h) 7.74; (i) 2.78; (j) 22.5; (k) 1.23; (l) 2.03; (m) 4.37; (n) 9.42; (o) 4.73; (p) 284; (q) .810; (r) 1.49; (s) .554; (t) .259; (u) .609; (v) 7.78; (w) 12.0; (x) 1380; (y) 72.5; (z) 64.8; (θ) 47.4.

9

Trigonometry

You may recognize, in the word *trigonometry*, the Greek roots for *triangle* and *measure*. Historically, the study of trigonometry means the measurement of triangles.

The Greeks of the time of Thales (640–546 B.C.) and Pythagoras (c. 550 B.C.) traveled to Egypt and to Babylonia and learned a great deal about practical geometry. Geometry meant measurement of the earth; triangles are the natural building-blocks for earth-measurement.

In the hands of the Greeks, geometry became a model of deductive thinking. Euclid (c. 330 B.C.) reduced geometry to a system of statements, called theorems, which he proved from a few definitions and reasonable-looking assumptions. His method of proof relied upon logical deduction; the rules of logic, as formulated by Aristotle (384–322 B.C.) are essentially the ones you have been using in previous chapters. Only in very recent years have scholars refined them.

As geometry grew more theoretical, and further removed from its original job of earth-measurement, trigonometry continued to grow. The theorems of geometry were applied to the measurement of triangles. The astronomers were especially successful. Eratosthenes (c. 250 B.C.) measured the circumference of the earth long before Columbus sailed westward to try to find the East Indies. Ptolemy (c. 140 A.D.) carried the science of astronomy to a level of perfection that we can still admire. These achievements were made possible by applying geometry, and developing techniques of calculation adapted to the demands of trigonometry.

Modern applications of trigonometry to astronomy, surveying, and navigation require little more theoretical knowledge than the Greeks had. There have been big advances in calculation. Logarithms and computing machines have made life easier for the people who measure triangles. They can solve problems now that would have been *practically* impossible in Ptolemy's time. There have been big advances in tools of measurement too. These new measuring devices have opened the way to practical applications of theories. Yet the necessary geometric theories were already developed, ready for use, before the birth of Christ.

There is another important part of the study of trigonometry that is modern. As they developed geometry to a high level of perfection, the Greeks left arithmetic and algebra in a primitive state as compared to what we call arithmetic and algebra today. In modern times, following Descartes (1596–1650), mathematicians have learned to combine geometry and algebra to develop what they call analytic methods. You have been studying elementary analysis, looking at problems both algebraically and graphically. With this approach, you can investigate, very simply, some of the problems that required the best genius of Greek thought; and you can go further. You can study the trigonometric functions and apply your findings to the study of periodic phenomena like the cycle of heart beats, seasonal variations in business activity, and the variation of voltage in an alternating-current circuit.

That is why we approach trigonometry in a modern way. Our approach gives us what the Greeks knew about trigonometry; it gives us much more besides.

900. Six interdependent ratios of trigonometry

In Section 410, page 169, you learned that

$$\sin \theta = \frac{y}{r}$$

$$\cos \theta = \frac{x}{r}$$

$$\tan \theta = \frac{y}{x}.$$

Corresponding to each point $P(x,y)$, except the origin ($r \neq 0$), there are ratios $\sin \theta = y/r$ and $\cos \theta = x/r$; corresponding to each point $P(x,y)$ not on the y-axis ($x \neq 0$), there is a ratio $\tan \theta = y/x$.

Since

$$\frac{y}{x} = \frac{y/r}{x/r},$$

I
$$\tan \theta = \frac{\sin \theta}{\cos \theta}.$$

This *identity* is an instance of the interdependence of the trigonometric ratios. A word of caution is in order at this point. The ratio $\tan \theta = y/x$ is not defined when $x = 0$. Recall that $\tan \theta$ is not defined when $\theta = \pi/2$, or $3\pi/2$, or an angle that differs from one of these angles by a multiple of 2π.

When we call the equation $\tan \theta = \sin \theta/\cos \theta$ an identity, we mean that *the equality holds whenever tan θ and sin θ/cos θ are defined.* It would become tiresome to list all of the exceptions whenever we use such an equation. Hence we shall agree that our formulas, from now on, are subject to such restrictions.

We now define three more trigonometric ratios as follows:

II $$\csc \theta = \frac{r}{y} \qquad\qquad \csc \theta = \frac{1}{\sin \theta}$$

III $$\sec \theta = \frac{r}{x} \qquad \text{hence} \qquad \sec \theta = \frac{1}{\cos \theta}$$

IV $$\cot \theta = \frac{x}{y} \qquad\qquad \cot \theta = \frac{1}{\tan \theta}.$$

Notice that csc θ is not defined when $y = 0$, sec θ is not defined when $x = 0$, and cot θ is not defined when $y = 0$.

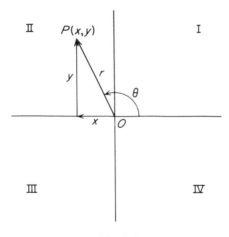

Fig. 9–1.

It is evident that these ratios are unnecessary from a mathematical point of view. Yet, in practice, it is convenient to have names (and tables) for the *reciprocals* of sin θ (*cosecant θ* or csc $\theta = 1/\sin \theta$), cos θ (*secant θ* or sec $\theta = 1/\cos \theta$), and tan θ (*cotangent θ* or cot $\theta = 1/\tan \theta$).

Equations (1) through (6) define the trigonometric ratios of an angle θ, placed in standard position, in terms of the coordinates of a point $P(x,y)$ on its terminal side, and the distance $OP = r$. You should study Fig. 9–1 as you think about this statement. Then study the effect of other placements of the point $P(x,y)$. It is evident that sin θ and csc θ are positive in quadrants I and II, negative in quadrants III and IV; cos θ and sec θ are positive in quadrants I and IV, negative in quadrants II and III; $\tan \theta$ and $\cot \theta$ are positive in quadrants I and III, negative in quadrants II and IV.

Other identities that follow readily from the definitions of the six trigonometric ratios are:

V $$\cot \theta = \frac{\cos \theta}{\sin \theta}$$

VI $$\sin^2 \theta + \cos^2 \theta = 1$$

VII $$1 + \tan^2 \theta = \sec^2 \theta$$

VIII $$1 + \cot^2 \theta = \csc^2 \theta.$$

The expression $\sin^2 \theta$ is an abbreviation for $(\sin \theta)^2 = (\sin \theta)(\sin \theta)$; similarly, $\cos^2 \theta = (\cos \theta)^2$, and so forth.

To prove these identities, express each trigonometric ratio in terms of the coordinates of a point $P(x,y)$ on the terminal side of angle θ and the distance $OP = r$. For example:

$$1 + \tan^2 \theta = 1 + \left(\frac{y}{x}\right)^2$$

$$= \frac{x^2 + y^2}{x^2}$$

$$= \frac{r^2}{x^2} \quad \text{(By the theorem of Pythagoras)}$$

$$= \sec^2 \theta.$$

You should prove the other identities. Then you should locate them in your book of mathematical tables. You will find these identities and many others listed in the section on trigonometry.

It is essential to memorize at least a few trigonometric identities; then you can prove many other identities, beginning with the ones you know. The following examples, and Exercises §900, illustrate the procedure. You should not be surprised to find that you can often simplify a complicated-looking expression by applying the identities.

(1) Prove that $$(\csc \alpha)\left(\sin \alpha + \frac{\sin^3 \alpha}{\cos^2 \alpha}\right) = \sec^2 \alpha.$$

We agree to interpret these directions as a briefer way to say: "Prove that $(\csc \alpha)(\sin \alpha + \sin^3 \alpha/\cos^2 \alpha) = \sec^2 \alpha$ for each value of α for which both sides of the equation are defined." Recall that $\csc \alpha = r/y$ is not defined when $\alpha = 0°$; for $\alpha = 0°$ makes $y = 0$. Also, $\alpha = 180°$ makes $\csc \alpha = r/0$, and $\csc 180°$ is not defined. We shall not stop, in each example, to list the restrictions on the variables. We shall take it for granted that suitable restrictions are understood.

$$(\csc \alpha)\left(\sin \alpha + \frac{\sin^3 \alpha}{\cos^2 \alpha}\right) = \frac{1}{\sin \alpha}\left(\sin \alpha + \frac{\sin^3 \alpha}{\cos^2 \alpha}\right) \qquad \left[\csc \alpha = \frac{1}{\sin \alpha}\right]$$

$$= 1 + \frac{\sin^2 \alpha}{\cos^2 \alpha} \qquad \text{[distributive law]}$$

$$= 1 + \left(\frac{\sin \alpha}{\cos \alpha}\right)^2 \qquad \left[\frac{a^n}{b^n} = \left(\frac{a}{b}\right)^n\right]$$

$$= 1 + \tan^2 \alpha \qquad \left[\tan \alpha = \frac{\sin \alpha}{\cos \alpha}\right]$$

$$= \sec^2 \alpha. \qquad [1 + \tan^2 \alpha = \sec^2 \alpha]$$

Notice the form of this argument. We took the more complicated-looking expression, $(\csc \alpha)(\sin \alpha + \sin^3 \alpha/\cos^2 \alpha)$, and reduced it by a sequence of known identities to the less complicated-looking expression. As you acquire the technique, you will find it much more convenient to work with trigonometric expressions than to rewrite these expressions as ratios that involve x, y, and r.

(2) Prove that $\cos \theta \tan \theta \csc \theta = 1$.

$$\cos \theta \tan \theta \csc \theta = \cos \theta \cdot \frac{\sin \theta}{\cos \theta} \cdot \frac{1}{\sin \theta} = 1.$$

(3) Prove that $\dfrac{\cos^2 \theta}{1 + \sin \theta} = 1 - \sin \theta$.

$$\frac{\cos^2 \theta}{1 + \sin \theta} = \frac{1 - \sin^2 \theta}{1 + \sin \theta} \qquad [\sin^2 \theta + \cos^2 \theta = 1]$$

$$= \frac{(1 - \sin \theta)(1 + \sin \theta)}{1 + \sin \theta} \qquad [a^2 - b^2 = (a - b)(a + b)]$$

$$= 1 - \sin \theta. \qquad \left[\frac{ab}{b} = a\right]$$

(4) Prove that $\dfrac{\sin \theta - \cos \theta}{\sin \theta + \cos \theta} = \dfrac{1 - 2 \sin \theta \cos \theta}{\sin^2 \theta - \cos^2 \theta}$.

$$\frac{\sin \theta - \cos \theta}{\sin \theta + \cos \theta} = \frac{(\sin \theta - \cos \theta)(\sin \theta - \cos \theta)}{(\sin \theta + \cos \theta)(\sin \theta - \cos \theta)} \qquad \left[\frac{a}{b} = \frac{ac}{bc}\right]$$

$$= \frac{\sin^2 \theta - 2 \sin \theta \cos \theta + \cos^2 \theta}{\sin^2 \theta - \cos^2 \theta} \qquad \begin{array}{l}[(a - b)^2 = a^2 - 2ab + b^2; \\ (a - b)(a + b) = a^2 - b^2)]\end{array}$$

$$= \frac{(\sin^2 \theta + \cos^2 \theta) - 2 \sin \theta \cos \theta}{\sin^2 \theta - \cos^2 \theta}$$

$$= \frac{1 - 2 \sin \theta \cos \theta}{\sin^2 \theta - \cos^2 \theta}. \qquad [\sin^2 \theta + \cos^2 \theta = 1]$$

The question arises, "How do you know what step to take next?" This is, of course, the unanswerable question about proof in mathematics, and about creative work in any field of endeavour. In proving trigonometric identities, as in factoring and in solving equations, you acquire the tricks of the trade by experience. At first you proceed by trial and error; then you begin to recognize patterns, and forms of expressions that suggest something useful that you can do next. We provide a sequence of easy identities for you to prove in Exercises §900.

(5) Suppose you have derived the formula

$$S = |\tan t| \sqrt{1 + \cot^2 t}$$

for measuring the displacement of a particle from a point at time t. You wonder whether you can simplify the formula to make it easier to apply. You proceed as follows.

$$S = |\tan t| \sqrt{1 + \cot^2 t}$$
$$= |\tan t| \sqrt{\csc^2 t}$$
$$= |\tan t| \cdot |\csc t|$$
$$= \left|\frac{\sin t}{\cos t}\right| \cdot \left|\frac{1}{\sin t}\right|$$
$$= \left|\frac{1}{\cos t}\right|$$
$$= |\sec t|.$$

The formula $S = |\sec t|$ is simpler than the original one.

EXERCISES §900

1. Let θ be an angle in standard position. If you know the coordinates of a point $P(x,y)$ on the terminal side of θ, it is easy to calculate r. (How?) In the following exercises, $P(x,y)$ is given. Draw the angle θ; determine r; then give the values of the six trigonometric ratios.

(a) $P(3,4)$ (b) $P(7,7)$ (c) $P(-2,5)$
(d) $P(6,-4)$ (e) $P(-1,-1)$ (f) $P(3,\sqrt{7})$
(g) $P(-\sqrt{13},-6)$ (h) $P(-2.3,3.2)$ (i) $P(\frac{1}{2},-\frac{1}{2}\sqrt{3})$
(j) $P(-5,-12)$ (k) $P(h,k)$ (l) $P(-\frac{1}{4}\sqrt{15},\frac{1}{4})$.

Answers: (a) $r = 5$, $\sin \theta = 4/5$, $\cos \theta = 3/5$, $\tan \theta = 4/3$, etc.; (c) $r = \sqrt{29}$, $\sin \theta = 5/\sqrt{29}$, $\cos \theta = -2/\sqrt{29}$, $\tan \theta = -2.5$, etc.

2. Verify that the ratios for each angle, computed in Exercise 1, satisfy the identities: $\tan \theta = \sin \theta/\cos \theta$, $\sin^2 \theta + \cos^2 \theta = 1$, and $1 + \tan^2 \theta = \sec^2 \theta$.

3. Is $1 + \tan^2 \pi/2 = \sec^2 \pi/2$? Explain why this is *not* an instance of the identity $1 + \tan^2 \theta = \sec^2 \theta$.

4. Prove the basic identities, V, VI, and VIII (page 410).

5. Make up a table with four columns, one for each of the quadrants, and six rows, one for each of the trigonometric ratios, to indicate whether each ratio is positive or negative in each quadrant. Then find a similar table in your book of tables.

6. In what quadrant must the terminal side of the angle θ lie if:

(a) $\sin \theta > 0$ and $\cos \theta < 0$ (b) $\cot \theta < 0$ and $\cos \theta > 0$
(c) $\tan \theta > 0$ (d) $\sec \theta < 0$ and $\cos \theta > 0$
(e) $\sin \theta > 0$.

7. From each condition on angle θ, determine the values of each of the six trigonometric ratios:

(a) $\tan \theta = 1/3$ and θ is a first-quadrant angle. (*Hint:* In Fig. 9–2, the point (3,1) lies on the terminal side of angle θ. Hence $r = \sqrt{10}$; hence $\sin \theta = 1/\sqrt{10}$, $\cos \theta = 3/\sqrt{10}$, etc.)

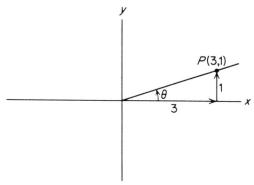

Fig. 9–2.

(b) $\sin \theta = 0.6$ and $\cos \theta < 0$. (*Hint:* θ lies in quadrant II; there is a point $P(x,y)$ on the terminal side of angle θ, such that $y = 6$ and $r = 10$; for this point, $x = -8$. Hence $\cos \theta = -0.8$, $\tan \theta = -3/4$, etc.)
(c) $\cos \theta = 2/7$ and $\cot \theta < 0$.
(d) $\sec \theta = 1$.
(e) $\cot \theta = -0.75$ and $\sin \theta < 0$.

Prove the identities in Exercises 8 through 31:

8. $\sec \theta \cot \theta = \csc \theta$.

9. $\dfrac{\sin^2 \theta}{1 - \cos \theta} = 1 + \cos \theta$.

10. $\dfrac{\cos \theta}{\cot \theta} = \sin \theta$.

11. $\sec^2 x - \tan^2 x = 1$.

12. $\sin \theta \sec \theta = \tan \theta$.

13. $\cot x = \dfrac{\csc x}{\sec x}$.

14. $\tan x \csc x = \sec x$.

15. $(\csc x - 1)(\csc x + 1) = \cot^2 x$.

16. $(\tan \alpha + \sec \alpha)\cos \alpha = 1 + \sin \alpha$.

17. $\dfrac{\cos \alpha}{\sin \alpha \cot \alpha} = 1$.

18. $(\sec^2 x - 1)\cos^2 x = \sin^2 x$.

19. $\tan \theta(1 - \sin^2 \theta) = \cos \theta \sin \theta$.

20. $\dfrac{1 + \tan^2 \alpha}{1 + \cot^2 \alpha} = \tan^2 \alpha$.

21. $\tan \theta + \cot \theta = \sec \theta \csc \theta$.

22. $\dfrac{\sin^2 A}{\tan^2 A} + \sin^2 A = 1$.

23. $\cos t + \sin t \tan t = \sec t$.

24. $1 + 2 \cos \theta \sin \theta = (\sin \theta + \cos \theta)^2$.

25. $\tan \theta + \sec \theta = \dfrac{\cos \theta}{1 - \sin \theta}$.

26. $\dfrac{1 + \sin \theta}{\cos \theta} = \dfrac{\cos \theta}{1 - \sin \theta}$.

27. $2 \sin^2 T + \cos^2 T \tan^2 T = 3 \sin^2 T$.

28. $\sin \theta \cos \theta(\tan \theta + \cot \theta) = 1$.

29. $\sin^4 y - \cos^4 y = \sin^2 y - \cos^2 y$.

30. $\dfrac{\sin^2 M}{1 - \cos M} + \dfrac{\sin^2 M}{1 + \cos M} = 2$.

31. $(1 + \sec a)(1 - \cos a) = \sin a \tan a$.

32. Test each identity (Exercises 8 through 31) with the values of the trigonometric ratios found for one of the angles in Exercise 1.

Simplify the formulas in Exercises 33 to 37:

33. $R = \dfrac{\sin \theta}{\tan \theta}$.

34. $V = \cos \theta(\tan \theta + \sec \theta) - 1$.

35. $y = \sin x(\cot x + \tan x)$.

36. $M = |\cot r| \sqrt{1 - \cos^2 r}$.

37. $X = \tan \theta + \cot \theta - \csc \theta \sec \theta$.

Answers: **33.** $R = \cos \theta$;   **34.** $V = \sin \theta$;   **35.** $y = \sec x$;   **37.** $X = 0$.

You have studied identities that follow easily from the definitions of the trigonometric ratios; these identities establish an interdependence of the six ratios. The names of the six trigonometric ratios suggest another sort of interdependence. Why sine and *co*sine, tangent and *co*tangent, secant and *co*secant? In geometry, you call the angles A and B *complementary* when $B = 90° - A$. Study Fig. 9-3. Recall that $Q(b,a)$ is the reflection in the line $y = x$ of $P(a,b)$. Triangles RCP and SOQ are congruent; when angle $POR = A$, angle $QOR = 90° - A$; when $OP = r$, $OQ = r$.

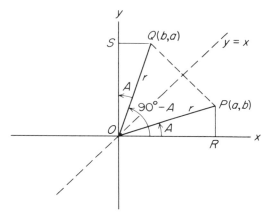

Fig. 9-3.

Notice in the figure that $\sin A = \dfrac{b}{r} = \cos (90° - A)$, $\tan A = \dfrac{b}{a} =$ cot $(90° - A)$, and $\sec A = \dfrac{r}{a} = \csc (90° - A)$. Hence, for this placement of angle A, each trigonometric ratio for angle A equals the co-trigonometric ratio of the complement of angle A.

We shall prove, in Section 903, that these identities hold for each placement of the angle A. Let us agree that co-cos $A = \sin A$, co-cot $A = \tan A$, and co-csc $A = \sec A$; let us use $t(A)$ to symbolize any one of the six trigonometric ratios, as we previously used $p(x)$ to symbolize any polynomial. Then

$$t(A) = \text{co-}t(90° - A) \quad \text{or} \quad t(\theta) = \text{co-}t\left(\frac{\pi}{2} - \theta\right)$$

for each angle A measured in degrees, or θ measured in radians, and for each trigonometric ratio $t(A)$ or $t(\theta)$. For example: $\sin 40° = \cos (90° - 40°)$ $= \cos 50°$; $\tan \frac{3}{8}\pi = \cot (\frac{1}{2}\pi - \frac{3}{8}\pi) = \cot \frac{1}{8}\pi$; $\sec 320° = \csc (90° - 320°) =$ csc $-(230°)$; $\cos 120° = $ co-cos $(90° - 120°) = \sin (-30°)$; $\cot \frac{5}{6}\pi =$ co-cot $(\frac{1}{2}\pi - \frac{5}{6}\pi) = \tan (-\frac{1}{3}\pi)$; etc.

The identity

$$t(A) = \text{co-}t(90° - A)$$

is especially useful when $45° < A \leq 90°$. For example: sin 50° = cos 40°; cos 90° = sin 0°; tan 80° = cot 10°; etc. This makes it unnecessary to tabulate the trigonometric ratios of angles A in the range $45° < A \leq 90°$. You look in the table for the co-trigonometric ratio of the complement of A.

Now examine the tables of trigonometric ratios in your book of tables. Notice that the tables cover the range $0° \leq A \leq 45°$; you use the same table to read the trigonometric ratios of angles in the range $45° < A \leq 90°$. Some tables help you to do this by reading from the top when you want angles in the range $0° \leq A \leq 45°$, and reading from the bottom when you want angles in the range $45° < A \leq 90°$; but notice that this amounts to using the same table entry for tan 52° and cot 38°, for csc 68° and sec 22°, etc.

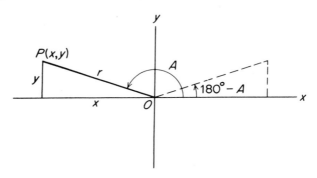

Fig. 9–4.

To find the trigonometric ratios for angles whose terminal sides are in quadrants II, III, or IV, you can still use the tables for the range $0° \leq A \leq 45°$. Figure 9–4 suggests the technique.

You know that sin $A = y/r$, cos $A = x/r$, tan $A = y/x$, etc. In the figure, x is negative, y is positive, and r is positive (see Section 104, page 19). Hence sin $A > 0$, cos $A < 0$, tan $A < 0$, etc. We have

$$\sin A = \sin (180° - A) \qquad \csc A = \csc (180° - A)$$
$$\cos A = -\cos (180° - A) \qquad \sec A = -\sec (180° - A)$$
$$\tan A = -\tan (180° - A) \qquad \cot A = -\cot (180° - A).$$

These equations express the trigonometric ratios for angles in the second quadrant (like A in the figure) in terms of the trigonometric ratios for angles in the first quadrant. For example,

$$\sin 170° = \sin (180° - 170°) \doteq \sin 10° \doteq 0.1736$$

and $$\cot 100° = -\cot (180° - 100°) = -\cot 80°.$$

Since cot 80° = tan (90° − 80°) = tan 10°, you can use the tables with the range $0° \leq A \leq 45°$. You get cot 100° = −tan 10° $\doteq$ −0.1763. In this way you can find any trigonometric ratio, $t(A)$, for an angle A whose terminal side falls in quadrant II.

The following examples extend this technique to angles whose terminal sides lie in quadrant III or quadrant IV:

(6) Use tables to find cos 215°. First make a sketch (Fig. 9–5). You see that $\cos 215° = x/r$. From the sketch, x is negative, and

$$\cos 215° = -\cos 35° \doteq -0.8192.$$

(7) Use tables to find cot 256°. First make a sketch (Fig. 9–6). You see that $\cot 256° = x/y$, x is negative, y is negative, and

$$\cot 256° = \cot 76°;$$

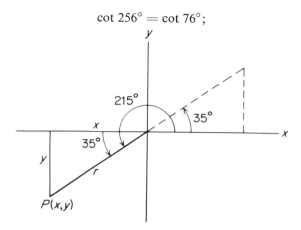

Fig. 9–5.

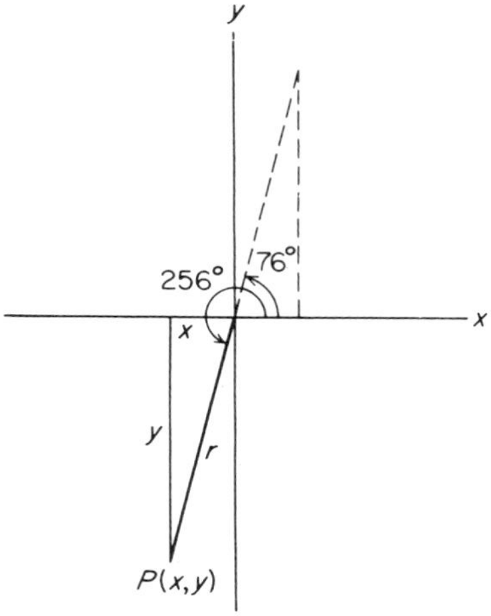

Fig. 9–6. 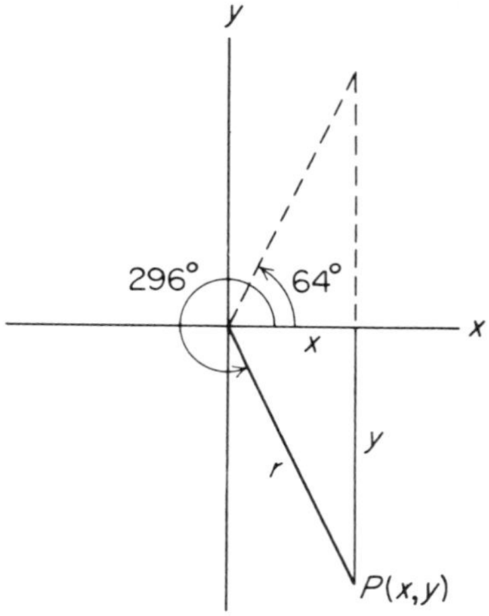   **Fig. 9-7.**

but cot $76° =$ tan $14°$, and hence

$$\text{cot } 256° = \text{tan } 14° \doteq 0.2493.$$

(8) Use tables to find sec $296°$. First make a sketch (Fig. 9–7). You see that sec $296° = r/x$, x is positive, and sec $296° =$ sec $64° =$ csc $26° \doteq 2.2812$.

(9) Use tables to find sin $328°$. First make a sketch (Fig. 9–8). You see that sin $328° = y/r$, y is negative and sin $328° = -$sin $32° \doteq -0.5299$.

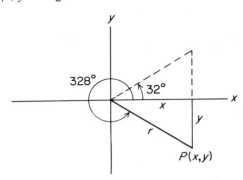

Fig. 9–8.

EXERCISES §900 (cont.)

38. Express each of the following in terms of angles between $0°$ and $45°$; then find the value with the help of a book of tables.

(a) tan $78°$ (b) sin $(-12°)$ (c) csc $114°$ (d) cos $156°$
(e) cos $320°$ (f) cos $(-346°)$ (g) cot $285°$ (h) sec $(-307°)$
(i) sin $205°$ (j) tan $251°$ (k) sin $96°$ (l) cot $(-192°)$
(m) sin $(-260°)$ (n) cos $800°$ (o) sec $(-415°)$ (p) sin $2426°$.

39. Find at least four different angles for which:

(a) cos $\theta = \frac{1}{2}$ (b) sin $\theta = 0$ (c) tan $\theta = -1$
(d) sin $\theta \doteq .43837$ (e) tan $\theta \doteq -1.1918$ (f) csc $\theta = 2$.

Answers: (a) $-60°$, $300°$, $420°$, $660°$; (e) $-50°$, $130°$, $310°$, $490°$.

40. Decide whether each statement is true or false.

(a) sin $(-315°) =$ sin $45°$ (b) sin $(-50°) = -$sin $50°$
(c) cos $(-50°) = -$cos $50°$ (d) tan $800° =$ tan $80°$
(e) cot $800° =$ cot $10°$ (f) $(x = y) \Rightarrow (\sin^2 x + \cos^2 y = 1)$
(g) $(\sin^2 x + \cos^2 y = 1) \Rightarrow (x = y)$ (h) $(\sin^2 x + \cos^2 y \neq 1) \Rightarrow (x \neq y)$
(i) $\sin^2 12° + \cos^2 168° = 1$ (j) tan $(180° + 20°) =$ tan $180° +$ tan $20°$
(k) tan $(50° + 20°) =$ tan $50° +$ tan $20°$ (l) tan $(x + y) =$ tan $x +$ tan y
(m) $\cos^2 35° + \cos^2 55° = 1$ (n) $(\sin x = \sin y) \Leftrightarrow (x = y)$.

41. Given that A is a first quadrant angle. Write each of the following, using A alone:

(a) cos (180° − A)   (b) tan (90° + A)   (c) sec (360° − A)
(d) sin (270° + A)   (e) cos (A − 270°)   (f) cos (−A)
(g) tan (180° + A)   (h) sin (−A)   (i) csc (270° − A).

Answers: (a) −cos A; (b) −cot A; (c) sec A; (e) −sin A.

42. Simplify the expression $\dfrac{3 \cos 75° \sin 195° + \sin 165° \sin 15°}{\cos 255°}$ by writing in terms of sin 15°.

Answer: 2 sin 15°.

901. Measurement of a right triangle

Before we explore the algebra of the trigonometric ratios further, we pause to examine some applications of the ratios to classical trigonometry.

We shall make free use of the tables of trigonometric ratios, and their logarithms, as given in your book of tables. You should realize, as you use

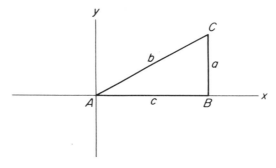

Fig. 9–9.

your tables, that we have not explained how the tables were made. So, for the time being, you are in the position of a person who uses an instrument (a telephone, for example) without a full understanding of its design.

First we defined trigonometric ratios as certain vectors associated with the unit circle. Then we freed ourselves from the unit circle, and began to identify the trigonometric ratios as ratios that involve the coordinates of a point $P(x,y)$ on the terminal side of the angle θ, and the distance of P from the origin. Now consider the angle A in a triangle ABC that has a right angle at B (Fig. 9–9).

We placed triangle ABC with the vertex A at the origin, and the vertex of the right angle, B, on the positive x-axis. If $A = 0°$ or $A = 90°$, the triangle degenerates into a line segment. Since $A + B + C = 180°$ and $B = 90°$, $0° < A < 90°$.

Notice how we labeled triangle *ABC*. Capital letters designate the *vertices*, or the *angles*, of the triangle; corresponding small letters designate the *sides* opposite these vertices or angles of the triangle. We also use these letters for the measures of the angles or sides of the triangle.

As a special instance of our previous definitions,

$$\sin A = \frac{a}{b} = \frac{\text{side opposite angle } A}{\text{hypotenuse}}$$

$$\cos A = \frac{c}{b} = \frac{\text{side adjacent to angle } A}{\text{hypotenuse}}$$

$$\tan A = \frac{a}{c} = \frac{\text{side opposite angle } A}{\text{side adjacent to angle } A}.$$

You should write out the corresponding equations for the reciprocal ratios, csc *A*, sec *A*, and cot *A*.

Many books on trigonometry begin with these six equations as definitions of the trigonometric ratios. Then they extend these definitions to make the more general definitions that we made earlier.

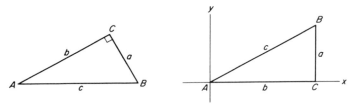

Fig. 9–10.

The case $0° < A < 90°$, and $C = 90°$, is similar (Fig. 9–10). You can flip the triangle *ABC* over and place it in the position of the second triangle, *ACB*; in this way you get a triangle congruent to triangle *ABC*, and in standard position. Then

$$\sin A = \frac{a}{c}, \quad \cos A = \frac{b}{c}, \quad \tan A = \frac{a}{b}, \quad \text{etc.}$$

It is not always convenient to move triangles into the standard position. Hence it is worthwhile to learn to think of the trigonometric ratios in a right triangle as

$$\sin A = \frac{\text{side opposite angle } A}{\text{hypotenuse}}, \quad \sec A = \frac{\text{hypotenuse}}{\text{side adjacent to angle } A}, \quad \text{etc.}$$

Notice that this way of thinking of the trigonometric ratios is consistent with the earlier way of visualizing them; and it saves you the trouble of always having to place the right triangle in standard position.

With these ideas in mind, we proceed to illustrate the *solution of right triangles.* It turns out that you can find all the *parts* (sides and angles) of a right triangle when you know the right angle, a side, and one other part of the triangle. We call this *solving the triangle.*

(1) In triangle ABC, $B = 90°$, $a = 50$ ft, and $A = 28°$. Solve the triangle. (Assume that the given values of B, a, and A are exact; then this is a theoretical triangle that belongs to the mathematical model for trigonometry.) First make a rough sketch. To draw the triangle to scale, begin with angle A (Fig. 9–11).Use a protractor to make $A = 28°$. Then decide on a scale, say

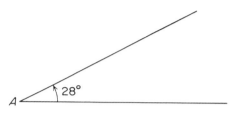

Fig. 9–11.

1 cm represents 10 ft. With this scale, 5 cm represents 50 ft. Place a ruler marked in centimeters at right angles to the horizontal side of angle A. Slide the ruler until the distance between the sides of angle A is 5 cm. Draw and label side a (Fig. 9–12). Now complete the solution of triangle ABC

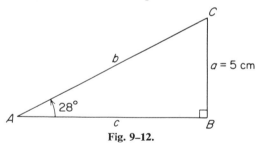

Fig. 9–12.

by measuring its parts on the *scale drawing.* You find $c \doteq 9.4$ cm, or 94 ft; $b \doteq 10.7$ cm, or 107 ft; $C = 62°$.

It takes time to make a good scale drawing. Also, your solution of a triangle by scale drawing is limited to the accuracy of the scale drawing. It is usually faster to use the tables of trigonometric ratios. Then the accuracy of your solution is limited to the accuracy of the tables; but you can get more accurate tables if the problem you are solving requires them.

Notice, then, that $\qquad$ $\tan 28° \doteq .5317$ $\qquad$ (From tables)

$$\doteq \frac{50}{c}.$$ $\qquad$ (Fig. 9–12)

When you solve the condition $.5317 \doteq 50/c$ to find c, $.5317c \doteq 50$, or $c \doteq 50/.5317$; to complete the calculation requires the division $50 \div .5317$.

It is easier to proceed as follows:

$$\cot 28° \doteq 1.8807 \doteq \frac{c}{50}; \qquad c \doteq (50)(1.8807) \doteq 94.04 \text{ ft.}$$

This is an example of the convenience of having tables for the reciprocals of the trigonometric ratios. In this exercise, using tan 28° leads to a division; it is more convenient to use the reciprocal ratio, cot 28°, and perform a multiplication.

To find b, $\csc 28° \doteq 2.1301 \doteq b/50$; $b \doteq 50(2.1301) \doteq 106.51$ ft. Compare this method of finding b with saying $\sin 28° \doteq .4695 \doteq 50/b$; also compare it to saying $\cos 28° \doteq .8829 \doteq 94.04/b$, or $\sec 28° \doteq 1.1326 \doteq b/94.04$. The first method avoids division; it also avoids using the calculated side, $c \doteq 94.04$, and thus an unnecessary risk of errors of calculation.

To find C, recall that $A + B + C = 180°$ in any triangle ABC. Since $B = 90°$, $A + C = 90°$.

$$C = 90° - A = 90° - 28° = 62°.$$

The values of c and b are approximations; the value of C is exact.

(2) In triangle ABC, $C = 90°$, $c = 126$ ft, and $a = 28.4$ ft. Solve the triangle.

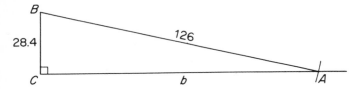

Fig. 9–13.

First make a sketch (Fig. 9–13); then, to help you visualize the way that the given parts of the triangle *determine* the triangle, make an accurate scale drawing. Draw C first; then lay off 28.4 ft in the scale you decide to use. This determines the vertex B of the triangle. Place the point A at a distance of 126 ft (to scale) from the point B, and on the other *arm* of angle C. You can now measure A, B, and b.

To solve triangle ABC by calculation, you can use the theorem of Pythagoras to find b. Thus $b^2 + (28.4)^2 = (126)^2$. It is convenient to use a table of squares and square roots to speed up the calculation. Try this, and check your result against the solution given below. Notice that you still have to calculate A and B.

An easier way to proceed is:

$$\sin A = \frac{28.4}{126} \doteq 0.2254.$$

Using a table for sin A,

$$A \doteq 13.0° \quad \text{(nearest 0.1 degree)}$$

$$B \doteq 90.0° - 13.0° = 77.0°.$$

$$\cos A = \frac{b}{126} \doteq \cos 13.0° \doteq 0.9744$$

$$b \doteq (126)(0.9744) \doteq 122.8 \text{ ft.}$$

You should experiment with other possible procedures, some of them just as good as the one we have followed. Notice, in this example, the division $28.4 \div 126$ and the multiplication $(126)(0.9744)$. To avoid these calculations, you can use logarithms. This is especially convenient because it takes no longer to look up the logarithms of the trigonometric ratios than to look up the trigonometric ratios themselves.

Logarithms have the disadvantage of making it harder to check your calculations by estimation. It is easier, with logarithms, to miss a crude error in calculation. This makes it even more important to organize your work carefully, and to check your results against a sketch of the triangle.

Here is a well-organized logarithmic solution of triangle ABC.

$\sin A = \dfrac{a}{c}$:	log 28.4	$\doteq 11.45332 - 10$ ⎫
	log 126	$\doteq \underline{\ 2.10037\qquad}$ ⎬ (Subtract)
		⎭
	log sin A	$\doteq\ 9.35295 - 10$
	A	$\doteq 13°02'$ (nearest minute).
$B = 90° - A$:	B	$\doteq 89°60' - 13°02' = 76°58'$
$b = c \cos A$:	log 126	$\doteq 2.10037$ ⎫
	log cos $13°02' \doteq 9.98867 - 10$	⎬ (Add)
		⎭
	log b	$\doteq 2.08904$
	b	$\doteq 122.8$ ft.

(3) In triangle ABC, $B = 90°$, $a = 486.9$ m, and $c = 866.2$ m.

Notice (Fig. 9–14) how easy it is to make a scale drawing of this triangle. Notice that you can use the theorem of Pythagoras to calculate b. Thus:

$$b^2 = (866.2)^2 + (486.9)^2.$$

This method is easy and convenient when you have a desk calculator and know how to use it. It is not at all convenient when you work with paper and pencil; even with your table of squares you will find that the interpolations are awkward.

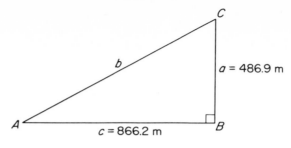

Fig. 9–14.

Here is a well-organized solution of triangle ABC, using logarithms:

$$\tan A = \frac{a}{c}: \quad \left.\begin{array}{ll} \log 486.9 & \doteqdot 12.68744 - 10 \\ \log 866.2 & \doteqdot \quad 2.93762 \end{array}\right\} \text{(Subtract)}$$

$$\begin{array}{ll} \log \tan A & \doteqdot \quad 9.74982 - 10 \\ A & \doteqdot 29°20' \end{array}$$

$$C = 90° - A: \qquad C \doteqdot 89°60' - 29°20' = 60°40'$$

$$\sin A = \frac{a}{b}, \qquad \left.\begin{array}{ll} \log 486.9 & \doteqdot 12.68744 - 10 \\ \log \sin 29°20' & \doteqdot \quad 9.69010 - 10 \end{array}\right\} \text{(Subtract)}$$

$$\text{or } b = \frac{a}{\sin A}: \quad \log b \qquad \doteqdot \quad 2.99734$$

$$b \qquad \qquad \doteqdot 993.9 \text{ ft.}$$

Notice, in finding b, that it is as easy to subtract logarithms as to add logarithms. Hence there is no need to use $b = a \csc A$ to avoid division.

(4) A ground radar station located at A picks up a bogey at a range of 12,860 yd, angle of elevation 19°39'. What is the altitude of the plane above the radar station?

An application like this one involves two new difficulties not present in the previous examples. First, there is the new lingo of the radar operators. Second, there is the question of precision of measurements. You must interpret the language of the question to know what you are asked to do. You must also be concerned about the effect upon your answer of approximation in the measurements; answers to practical problems are not useful until you know their precision.

Figure 9–15 interprets this problem for you. A *bogey* is simply an unidentified aircraft. Notice the meanings of the phrases *range, angle of elevation*, and *altitude*. Range means *line of sight* distance; angle of elevation is measured from the horizontal (level) line upward; *angle of depression* is measured from the horizontal line downward (the angle of depression of the radar station as seen from the plane equals the angle of elevation of the plane as seen from the radar station); *ground distance* is the horizontal distance between the radar station and the plane; altitude of the plane above the radar station is measured vertically.

We interpret the given data as follows: 12,860 yd means 12,860 ± 5 yd (that is, range is measured to the nearest 10 yd); 19°39′ means 19°39′ ± 0.5′ (that is, angle of elevation is measured to the nearest minute). In practice, it is very difficult to measure the angle of elevation to this precision, and easy to measure range to this precision.

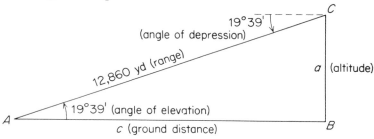

Fig. 9–15.

With these understandings, the problem is reduced to finding a in triangle ABC:

$$\log \sin 19°39′ = 9.52669 - 10$$

$$\sin A = \frac{a}{b}, \qquad \log 12,860 \quad = 4.10924 \qquad \Big\} \text{(Add)}$$

$$\text{or } a = b \sin A: \quad \log a \quad = 3.63593$$

$$a \qquad = 4324 \text{ yd.}$$

It is customary to express the altitude in feet. Hence we interpret the answer $a = 4324$ yd to mean that the altitude of the plane is $3 \times 4324 = 12,972 \doteq 12,970$ ft.

We emphasize one other contrast between mathematical exercises and practical problems. When you make an error in a mathematical exercise, no one gets hurt. When you make an error in a real-life situation, people may get hurt, or it may cost your boss a lot of money. Hence it is customary to *check* the solutions of practical problems. For example:

$$C = 90° - A: \qquad C = 89°60′ - 19°39′ = 70°21′ \quad \text{and}$$

$$\log 4324 \quad = 13.63589 - 10$$

$$\cos C = \frac{a}{b}: \quad \log 12,860 = \quad 4.10924 \qquad \Big\} \text{(Subtract)}$$

$$\log \cos C \ = 9.52665 - 10$$

$$C = 70°21′.$$

This is a rather convincing check, but it is still not good enough to satisfy a surveyor or an astronomer. He would object that we used the same parts of triangle *ABC* in the solution and in the check. We used log 12,860 in both places. Even when you look up log 12,860 twice, you are not sure; it is easy to make the same error twice. Hence the people for whom the results of calculations are really important try to devise checking procedures that are practically foolproof. We shall return to this question in Section 909.

EXERCISES §901

1. Estimate a solution from a scale drawing, then solve each triangle. (Round the trigonometric ratios from the tables to three significant digits and answers to two significant digits. Give angles to the nearest degree. Logarithms are not necessary.)

(a) $B = 90°$, $C = 17°$, $c = 30$ (b) $A = 90°$, $B = 65°$, $c = 80$
(c) $B = 90°$, $b = 36$, $a = 27$ (d) $B = 90°$, $c = 6.8$, $A = 33°$
(e) $C = 90°$, $a = 28$, $b = 35$ (f) $A = 90°$, $a = 4.2$, $B = 21°$
(g) $C = 90°$, $c = 560$, $a = 320$ (h) $C = 90°$, $A = 58°$, $a = 0.26$
(i) $B = 90°$, $C = 45°$, $b = 7.4$.

Answers: (a) $A = 73°$, $a = 98$, $b = 103$; (c) $A = 49°$, $C = 41°$, $c = 24$; (e) $A = 39°$, $B = 51°$, $c = 45$; (g) $A = 35°$, $B = 55°$, $b = 460$.

2. Estimate a solution from a scale drawing; then solve each triangle. (Use logarithms. Determine the angles to the nearest minute and the lengths of sides to four significant digits.)

(a) $A = 90°$, $B = 67°21'$, $b = 49.76$ (b) $C = 90°$, $A = 34°29'$, $b = 8.322$
(c) $C = 90°$, $A = 51°46'$, $c = 2359$ (d) $B = 90°$, $c = 563.2$, $a = 129.8$
(e) $C = 90°$, $c = .9247$, $a = .8115$ (f) $A = 90°$, $B = 8°50'$, $c = 5.663$
(g) $B = 90°$, $b = 16.23$, $c = 5.569$ (h) $B = 90°$, $C = 73°12'$, $c = 3621$
(i) $A = 90°$, $b = .7291$, $c = .06457$.

Answers: (a) $C = 22°39'$, $a = 53.92$, $c = 20.76$; (c) $B = 38°14'$, $a = 1853$, $b = 1460$; (d) $A = 12°59'$, $C = 77°1'$, $b = 578.0$; (g) $A = 20°4'$, $C = 69°56'$, $a = 15.24$.

3. Determine the hypotenuse of the triangle $C = 90°$, $a = 52.63$, $b = 19.47$, using: (a) the Pythagorean theorem, and (b) trigonometric ratios, and compare results.

4. A boy scout, standing 53 ft from the base of a vertical cliff, finds the angle of elevation to the top to be 41°. How high is the cliff above the level of his eye?

Answer: 46 ft.

5. A building 75 ft tall casts a 32-ft shadow. What is the angle of elevation of the sun?

6. A television tower is braced by guy wires fastened in the ground 24 ft from the center of the base of the tower. At what height is the other end fastened to the tower if the angle of elevation of the guy wire is 78°50′? What is the length of one of the guy wires?

7. To drive from town *A* to town *B*, one must drive 47 mi south, then 83 mi east. What is the air-line distance from *A* to *B*? In what direction should a plane fly from *A* to *B*?

Answer: 95 mi, 60.5° east of south.

8. From a point on level ground 72 ft from the base of a smokestack, the angle of elevation to the top is 66°. How tall is the smokestack?

9. An extension ladder, 12 ft long, leans against a building with its foot 5 ft from the base of the building. How steep (angle of elevation) is the ladder? How steep is the ladder when it is extended to a length of 26 ft? Will the ladder now reach a window sill 25 ft above the ground?

Answer: 65°, 79°, yes.

10. A gable roof has a rise of 11 ft with a run of 14 ft (see Fig. 9–16). What is the pitch (angle of elevation) of the roof? How long should the roof rafters be cut?

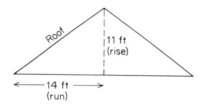

Roof

11 ft (rise)

14 ft (run)

Fig. 9–16.

11. The diameter *AB* of a circle is 18 cm. For each point *C* on the circle, triangle *ABC* is a right triangle. (Why?) Determine the legs of the right triangle, *AC* and *BC*, if angle *BAC* is: 10°; 20°; 30°; 40°; 50°.

12. Show that the length of one side of a regular octagon inscribed in a circle of radius *R* is given by: $L = 2R \sin 22\frac{1}{2}°$.

13. Show that the length of one side of a regular polygon of *n* sides inscribed in a circle of radius *R* is given by: $L = 2R \sin (180°/n)$. Calculate the length of one side of a regular polygon of seven sides inscribed in a circle of radius 5 cm. Draw the figure with a compass as a check.

14. Show that the length of the arc of a circle of radius *R* is $R(\theta - 2 \sin \frac{1}{2}\theta)$ longer than the corresponding chord, where θ is the measure of the central angle (in radians) subtending the arc.

15. A ship observes a lighthouse in a direction 37° from its course. After the ship has traveled 3.6 mi, the lighthouse is on the ship's beam (at an angle of 90° from the ship's course). How far is the ship from the lighthouse at this time?

Answer: 2.7 mi.

16. A ship observes a lighthouse in a direction of 19° from its course. After the ship has traveled 2.4 mi, the lighthouse is in a direction of 26° from the course of the ship. If the ship follows the same course, how close will it come to the lighthouse? How far away was the lighthouse when the last angle was measured?

Answer: 2.8 mi, 6.4 mi.

902. Measurement of any triangle

We proceed to the solution of any triangle in which the known parts determine the triangle (Fig. 9–17). We placed triangle ABC with the vertex A at the origin, and the vertex B on the positive x-axis. If $A = 0°$ or $A = 180°$, the triangle degenerates into a line segment. Hence $0° < A < 180°$. The angle A may be *acute* $(0° < A < 90°)$ as in the first triangle, or *obtuse* $(90° < A < 180°)$ as in the second triangle, or a *right* angle $(A = 90°)$. In each case, if the coordinates of C are (x,y), $\cos A = x/b$ and $\sin A = y/b$. Hence $x = b \cos A$ and $y = b \sin A$; we labeled the point $C(b \cos A, b \sin A)$ in the figure.

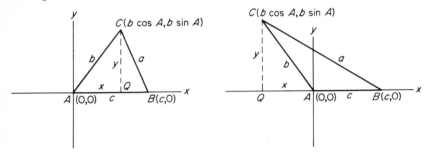

Fig. 9–17.

We shall label each triangle ABC with the vertices $A(0,0)$, $B(c,0)$, and $C(b \cos A, b \sin A)$, arranged counterclockwise. As before, capital letters will designate vertices or angles; corresponding small letters will designate sides opposite these vertices or angles. It is convenient to standardize the notation in this way as we develop formulas for the general triangle.

For the point C, $y = b \sin A$; also, in the right triangle CQB, $\sin B = y/a$ yields $y = a \sin B$. Hence

$$b \sin A = a \sin B \quad \text{or} \quad \frac{a}{\sin A} = \frac{b}{\sin B}.$$

By placing triangle ABC with the vertex C at the origin and the vertex A on the positive x-axis, the vertex B has coordinates $(a \cos C, a \sin C)$: proceeding as before, you find that

$$a \sin C = c \sin A \quad \text{or} \quad \frac{a}{\sin A} = \frac{c}{\sin C}.$$

Combining these results yields the *law of sines:*

I
$$\frac{a}{\sin A} = \frac{b}{\sin B} = \frac{c}{\sin C}.$$

That is: *In any triangle the sides are proportional to the sines of the opposite*

angles. This formula holds in any triangle, right or *oblique.* In particular, if
$B = 90°$, sin $B = 1$, and

$$\frac{a}{\sin A} = \frac{b}{1} = \frac{c}{\sin C};$$

that is, sin $A = a/b$ and sin $C = c/b$ as in Section 901 (page 420).

We shall not plunge you at once into a detailed study of all the possible
cases of solutions of oblique triangles. Rather, we shall rely upon sketches
and scale drawings to decide whether the given data determine a triangle.
When the given data determine a triangle, it is always possible to *solve the
triangle* (to find the unknown parts of the triangle) by scale drawing or by
calculation. The next example illustrates one method of solution based on
the law of sines.

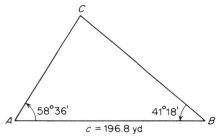

Fig. 9–18.

(1) In triangle ABC, $c = 196.8$ yd, $A = 58°36'$, and $B = 41°18'$. Solve
the triangle.

First make a sketch (Fig. 9–18). When you draw c first, and then place
A and B at the ends of the line segment c, it is clear that the given data determine a triangle ABC. If you choose a convenient scale, like 1 cm represents
10 yd, you can prepare a scale drawing and solve triangle ABC by measuring
to scale. You should do this to see how *two angles and the included side
determine a triangle.*

When you know two angles of a triangle you can always calculate the
third angle from the formula $A + B + C = 180°$; hence *one side and any
two angles determine a triangle.*

We now use the law of sines to solve triangle ABC:

$A + B + C = 180°$

$\left.\begin{matrix} A = \ \ 58°36' \\ B = \ \ 41°18' \end{matrix}\right\}$ Add

$\overline{A + B = \ \ 99°54'}$

$\left.\begin{matrix} A + B + C = 179°60' \\ A + B = \ \ \ \ 99°54' \end{matrix}\right\}$ Subtract

$C = \ \ \ \ 80°06'$

$\dfrac{a}{\sin A} = \dfrac{c}{\sin C}$ yields $\dfrac{a}{\sin 58°36'} = \dfrac{196.8}{\sin 80°06'}$

$$\left.\begin{array}{l} \log 196.8 \doteq 2.29403 \\ \log \sin 58°36' \doteq 9.93123 - 10 \end{array}\right\} \text{Add}$$

$$\left.\begin{array}{l} 12.22526 - 10 \\ \log \sin 80°06' \doteq 9.99348 - 10 \end{array}\right\} \text{Subtract}$$

$$\log a \doteq 2.23178$$

$$a \doteq 170.5 \text{ yd}$$

$$\frac{b}{\sin B} = \frac{c}{\sin C} \quad \text{yields} \quad \frac{b}{\sin 41°18'} = \frac{196.8}{\sin 80°06'}$$

$$\left.\begin{array}{l} \log 196.8 \doteq 2.29403 \\ \log \sin 41°18' \doteq 9.81955 - 10 \end{array}\right\} \text{Add}$$

$$\left.\begin{array}{l} 12.11358 - 10 \\ \log \sin 80°06' \doteq 9.99348 - 10 \end{array}\right\} \text{Subtract}$$

$$\log b \doteq 2.12010$$

$$b \doteq 131.9 \text{ yd.}$$

This first example on oblique triangles is an especially important one. In the standard method of *surveying by triangulation*, a civil engineer directs a crew of men to make a careful measurement of a base line, like the side c of our triangle.* Then he selects a convenient point C and measures angles A and B. He calculates a and b and uses one of them as a new base line from which to continue his triangulation. Thus the surveyor solves hundreds of triangles by the law of sines on a single job. This makes it worthwhile to print a special computing form to apply the law of sines and check the solution. We need some special formulas, to be developed in Section 909, to illustrate the surveyor's method of checking his solutions.

EXERCISES §902

1. Draw a figure for an approximate solution; then solve by the law of sines:

(a) $A = 39°$, $B = 64°$, $b = 32$
(b) $C = 42°17'$, $B = 71°28'$, $c = 6.438$
(c) $a = 3218$, $B = 63°24'$, $C = 49°12'$
(d) $c = 82.4$, $A = 38°40'$, $C = 114°10'$
(e) $a = 5.791$, $A = 47°26'$, $B = 24°7'$.

Answers: (a) $C = 77°$, $a = 22$, $c = 35$; (b) $A = 66°15'$, $b = 9.073$, $a = 8.759$; (d) $B = 27°10'$, $a = 56.4$, $b = 41.2$.

* "Men Who Measure the Earth," *National Geographic Magazine*, vol. CIX, No. 3, March 1956, page 335.

2. Two fire towers, *A* and *B*, are 16.5 mi apart. The forest rangers wish to determine the location of a forest fire which at station *A* is seen in the direction of 46°10′ from the straight line *AB* connecting the stations, and in the direction of 68°30′ from *BA* at station *B*. Find the distance of the fire from the nearer tower.

Answer: 13.1 mi from *B*.

3. A motorist traveling north observes a mountain peak in the direction of 34° west of north. After he has traveled 21 mi, the peak is 81° west of north. How far away is the peak at this time?

4. *A* and *B* are two points on opposite sides of a river. A third point *C* is on the same side as *A* and 175.2 ft downstream from *A*. Angle *CAB* is measured and found to be 78°13′, while angle *ACB* is 46°49′. How far is it across the river from *A* to *B*?

Answer: 156.0 ft.

5. Prove that, in any triangle, the area is one-half the product of two sides multiplied by the sine of the included angle. If the sides are *b* and *c* and the included angle is *A*, then area = $\frac{1}{2}bc \sin A$. (*Hint:* In Fig. 9–17, the altitude drawn to side *c* is the *y*-coordinate of point *C*.)

6. A triangular plot of ground has two sides of length 145 ft and 219 ft with angle between these sides 61°20′. Determine the area of the plot.

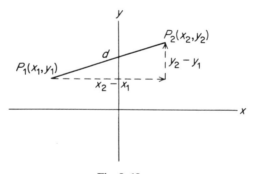

Fig. 9–19.

To develop a second important formula connecting the sides and angles of a general triangle, recall from Section 702 (page 304) the formula for the distance between two points in the cartesian plane. Figure 9–19 will help you to recall this important *distance formula*. The horizontal distance from $P_1(x_1,y_1)$ to $P_2(x_2,y_2)$ is $x_2 - x_1$; the vertical distance is $y_2 - y_1$. Hence the length of P_1P_2 is:

$$d = \sqrt{(x_2 - x_1)^2 + (y_2 - y_1)^2}.$$

When applied to Fig. 9–17, this distance formula yields, for the distance *a* between $C(b \cos A, b \sin A)$ and $B(c,0)$:

$$a = \sqrt{(c - b \cos A)^2 + (0 - b \sin A)^2}$$

$$= \sqrt{c^2 - 2cb \cos A + b^2 \cos^2 A + b^2 \sin^2 A}$$

$$= \sqrt{c^2 - 2cb \cos A + b^2(\cos^2 A + \sin^2 A)}$$

$$= \sqrt{c^2 - 2cb \cos A + b^2}.$$

Hence

II(a) $$a^2 = b^2 + c^2 - 2bc \cos A.$$

You should draw triangle ABC with the vertex B at the origin and prove the formula

II(b) $$b^2 = c^2 + a^2 - 2ca \cos B;$$

then place the vertex C at the origin and prove that

II(c) $$c^2 = a^2 + b^2 - 2ab \cos C.$$

This is the *law of cosines*. It states: *In any triangle the square of one side is the sum of the squares of the other two sides less twice the product of these sides and the cosine of the angle between them.*

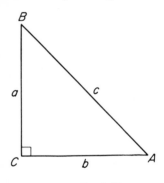

Fig. 9–20.

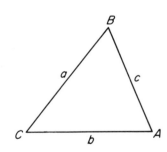

Fig. 9–21.

The theorem of Pythagoras is a special case of the law of cosines:
If $C = 90°$ (Fig. 9–20),

$$c^2 = a^2 + b^2 - 2ab \cos 90°$$

$$= a^2 + b^2 - 2ab(0)$$

$$= a^2 + b^2.$$

If $0° < C < 90°$ (Fig. 9–21), $a^2 + b^2$ is *decreased* by $2ab \cos C$, and $c^2 = a^2 + b^2 - 2ab \cos C$; clearly, $c^2 < a^2 + b^2$.

If $90° < C < 180°$ (Fig. 9–22), $\cos C = -\cos (180° - C)$ is negative; $c^2 = a^2 + b^2 - 2ab \cos C = a^2 + b^2 + 2ab \cos (180° - C)$; clearly, $c^2 > a^2 + b^2$.

Study the three figures to get a better "feel" for the law of cosines.

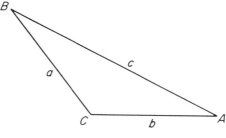

Fig. 9–22.

To continue the examples:

(2) In triangle ABC, $a = 54.80$ m, $b = 37.26$ m, and $C = 26°14'$. Solve the triangle.

First, make a sketch (Fig. 9–23). When you draw b first, then C, and mark off $a = 54.80$, you find that the given data determine a triangle ABC. If you choose a convenient scale, you can prepare a scale drawing to solve the triangle. You should do this to see how *two sides and the included angle determine a triangle*.

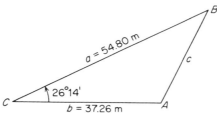

Fig. 9–23.

We now use the law of cosines to solve triangle ABC:

$c^2 = a^2 + b^2 - 2ab \cos C$:

$$\left.\begin{array}{l} a^2 = 54.80^2 \doteq 3003.0 \\ b^2 = 37.26^2 \doteq 1388.3 \end{array}\right\} \text{Add}$$

$$\left.\begin{array}{l} a^2 + b^2 \doteq 4391.3 \\ 2ab \cos C \doteq 3663.1 \end{array}\right\} \text{Subtract}$$

$$c^2 \doteq 728.2$$

$$c \doteq 26.99.$$

Notice the awkwardness of this calculation. You perform interpolations in your table of squares to find the squares of a and b, and then to find the square root of c^2; you multiply to find $2(54.80)(37.26)(0.8970)$. Of course you can use logarithms to find squares and square roots, and to calculate $2ab \cos C$; but you need the values of a^2 and b^2 (*not* their logarithms) to calculate $a^2 + b^2$; and you need the value of $2ab \cos C$ (*not* its logarithm) to calculate $(a^2 + b^2) - (2ab \cos C)$. Hence the logarithmic solution is much less efficient for the law of cosines than for the law of sines. Try it!

You need a desk calculator to make the law of cosines a convenient and efficient formula. We shall develop formulas in Section 904, and use these formulas in Section 909, to achieve an efficient logarithmic solution of a triangle in which two sides and the included angle are known; but, when you have a desk calculator and know how to use it, the law of cosines becomes an efficient formula.

Now that you have $c \doteq 26.99$ it is easy to calculate A and B using the law of sines:

$$\frac{a}{\sin A} = \frac{c}{\sin C}, \quad \text{or}$$

$$\sin A = \frac{a \sin C}{c}:$$

$$\left.\begin{array}{ll} \log 54.80 & \doteq 1.73878 \\ \log \sin 26°14' \doteq & 9.64545 - 10 \end{array}\right\} \text{Add}$$

$$\left.\begin{array}{ll} & 11.38423 - 10 \\ \log 26.99 & \doteq 1.43120 \end{array}\right\} \text{Subtract}$$

$$\log \sin A \quad \doteq 9.95303 - 10$$

Either $A \doteq 63°50'$, or $A \doteq 179°60' - 63°50' = 116°10'$. From Fig. 9–23, $A \doteq 116°10'$.

$$\frac{b}{\sin B} = \frac{c}{\sin C}, \quad \text{or}$$

$$\sin B = \frac{b \sin C}{c}:$$

$$\left.\begin{array}{ll} \log 37.26 & \doteq 1.57124 \\ \log \sin 26°14' \doteq & 9.64545 - 10 \end{array}\right\} \text{Add}$$

$$\left.\begin{array}{ll} & 11.21669 - 10 \\ \log 26.99 & \doteq 1.43120 \end{array}\right\} \text{Subtract}$$

$$\log \sin B \quad \doteq 9.78549 - 10$$

Either $B \doteq 37°36'$ or $B \doteq 179°60' - 37°36' = 142°24'$. From Fig. 9–23, $B \doteq 37°36'$.

As a check, $A + B + C = 180°$. We have

$$116°10' + 37°36' + 26°14' = 180°00'.$$

As you look back over the solution, you may be surprised at the precision of the result, $A + B + C \doteq 180°00'$. You will find rounding errors in the calculation of c; you cannot expect to always have your checks come out "on the nose."

EXERCISES §902 (cont.)

7. Plot each pair of points and use the distance formula to determine the distance between them:

(a) $(2,3)$; $(4,7)$ (b) $(-3,1)$; $(1,2)$ (c) $(2,-1)$; $(5,3)$

(d) $(7,3)$; $(-1,0)$ (e) $(4,-3)$; $(-4,3)$ (f) $(-5,-2)$; $(7,3)$

(g) $(-2\frac{1}{2},3)$; $(-4\frac{1}{2},1)$ (h) $(3\frac{1}{4},-2\frac{1}{2})$; $(-1\frac{1}{2},-5\frac{1}{4})$ (i) $(\frac{8}{3},-\frac{16}{3})$; $(\frac{4}{9},\frac{4}{3})$

(j) $(4\sqrt{3},4)$; $(-\sqrt{3},-1)$ (k) $(\sqrt{6},\sqrt{3})$; $(\sqrt{2},-2)$ (l) $(0,0)$; (a,b)

(m) $(a,-b)$; $(-a,b)$ (n) (r,t); (r,m) (o) $(-k,k)$; (h,h)

(p) $(a\cos\theta, a\sin\theta)$; $(b\cos\theta, b\sin\theta)$.

8. Draw a figure for an approximate solution; then solve with the help of the law of cosines:

(a) $b = 47$, $c = 52$, $A = 69°$

(b) $a = 3.4$, $b = 8.9$, $C = 142°$

(c) $a = 312$, $c = 573$, $B = 56°20'$

(d) $a = 21.25$, $b = 33.83$, $C = 37°15'$

(e) $b = 249.8$, $c = 1163$, $A = 136°14'$.

Answers: (a) $a = 56$, $B = 51°$, $C = 60°$; (b) $c = 11.8$, $A = 10°$, $B = 28°$; (d) $c = 21.25$, $A = 37°15'$, $B = 105°30'$.

9. A parallelogram has sides of 72 and 45 in. One interior angle is 65°. Determine the lengths of the diagonals.

10. Find the area of the parallelogram in Exercise 9 (see Exercise 5).

11. Show that the sum of the squares of the two diagonals of a parallelogram is equal to twice the sum of the squares of the non-parallel sides.

12. Two forces of magnitude f_1 and f_2 act upon an object with an angle of α between their lines of action. If r is the magnitude of the resultant force, show that

$$r = \sqrt{f_1^2 + f_2^2 + 2f_1 f_2 \cos\alpha}.$$

13. What is the magnitude of the single force that will replace two forces of 167 and 182 lb acting on an object with an angle of 75° between their lines of action?

14. A formation of airplanes is flying at a speed of 420 knots (nautical miles per hour). If a plane, leaving the formation, flies at an angle of 37° from the direction of the remainder of the formation and with a speed of 490 knots, what will be its distance from the formation in 30 min?

15. A light plane is heading east with a speed of 85 knots. It travels in a wind of 35 knots blowing toward a direction of 78° north of east. What is the velocity and direction of the plane's travel relative to the ground?

16. A and B are on opposite sides of an inaccessible swamp. From a third point C, angle ACB is found to be $37°19'$, while $CA = 626.3$ ft and $CB = 712.8$ ft. Determine the distance across the swamp from A to B.

We pause to summarize what we have said, so far, about the solution of oblique triangles:

Case (1): Generalizing from Example (1), given one side and two angles, you can solve a triangle by the law of sines. You calculate the third angle of the triangle by the formula $A + B + C = 180°$; then you use the formula

$$\frac{a}{\sin A} = \frac{b}{\sin B} = \frac{c}{\sin C},$$

and take advantage of the convenience of logarithms.

There is no restriction upon the length of the given side; but the two given angles are restricted by the condition $A + B + C = 180°$. You cannot have two angles of a triangle whose sum is 180° or more.

Case (2): Generalizing from Example (2), given two sides and the included angle, you can find the third side of the triangle by the law of cosines; then you can calculate the remaining angles by the law of sines. It is inconvenient to use logarithms with the law of cosines.

There is no restriction upon the lengths of the given sides; the given angle is restricted to be greater than 0° and less than 180°.

This leaves the cases where you know two sides and an angle, not the included angle, or three sides, or three angles. We dispose of these cases now:

Case (3): Given a, b, and $A < 90°$, solve the triangle. (We assume that the given angle $A < 90°$. The case of $A \geq 90°$ is left for an exercise.)

This may, or may not, be possible, as Fig. 9–24 suggests. As you try to

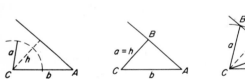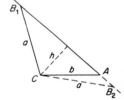

Fig. 9–24.

draw triangle ABC, the distance a may be too short to give you a triangle; the distance a may be just long enough to give you a triangle, which appears to have a right angle at B; the distance a may be long enough to yield two triangles, AB_1C and AB_2C, both of which have the given parts a, b, and A; the distance a may yield two triangles, AB_1C and AB_2C, one with the given parts a, b, and A, and one with the parts a, b, and $180° - A$. Here, then, are the four possibilities:

(a) No triangle ABC
(b) A unique triangle ABC, with $B = 90°$
(c) Two triangles ABC, a so-called *ambiguous case*
(d) A unique triangle ABC, with $B \neq 90°$.

When you are given two sides of a triangle, and one angle not the included angle, you should make a careful sketch. If the decision as to which of the possibilities arises is a close one, your analysis of the problem will enable you to decide. Notice, in the figure, that when $A < 90°$ the possibilities are:

  (a) $h = b \sin A > a$
  (b) $h = b \sin A = a$
  (c) $h = b \sin A < a$, and $b > a$
  (d) $h = b \sin A < a$, and $b < a$.

In practice, you make a sketch first. Then you apply the law of sines, using the given parts a, b, and A, to find B.

$$\frac{a}{\sin A} = \frac{b}{\sin B} \quad \text{yields} \quad \sin B = \frac{b \sin A}{a}.$$

Corresponding to possibility:

  (a) A value of $\sin B$ (or of $\log \sin B$) that is impossible
  (b) $\sin B = 1$ (or $\log \sin B = 0$), and hence $B = 90°$
  (c) and (d) $0 < \sin B < 1$ (or $\log \sin B < 0$); then there are two values of B, one *acute* ($0° < B < 90°$) and one *obtuse* ($90° < B < 180°$). If $b > a$, you have possibility (c), with two triangles AB_1C and AB_2C. If $b < a$, only the acute angle B obeys the conditions of the problem.

You will study these possibilities further as you work Exercises §902.

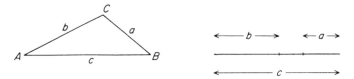

Fig. 9–25.

Case (4): Given a, b, and c, solve the triangle. This is always possible provided no one of the lengths a, b, and c is greater than or equal to the sum of the other two lengths. See Fig. 9–25. If one length is greater than or equal to the sum of the other two lengths, say $c \geq a + b$, there will be no triangle ABC. Otherwise the parts a, b, and c determine a triangle ABC.

The formula $c^2 = a^2 + b^2 - 2ab \cos C$ (or $a^2 = b^2 + c^2 - 2bc \cos A$, or $b^2 = a^2 + c^2 - 2ac \cos B$) enables you to calculate C (or A, or B). For example,

$$2ab \cos C = a^2 + b^2 - c^2$$

and

$$\cos C = \frac{a^2 + b^2 - c^2}{2ab}.$$

Then you can use the law of sines to calculate A and B.

Case (5): Given A, B, and C, solve the triangle. This is always impossible, as Fig. 9–26 shows. We call a pair of triangles, like $A_1B_1C_1$ and $A_2B_2C_2$, *similar*. Their angles are equal in pairs, and hence they have the same shape. But knowing the three angles of a triangle does not provide any information about its size.

The remaining Exercises §902 give you an opportunity to apply what you have learned about the solution of right triangles and oblique triangles. We return, in Section 909, to the question of efficient solutions of triangles and to foolproof methods of checking solutions.

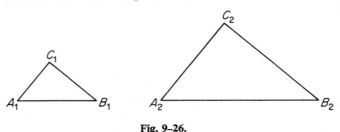

Fig. 9–26.

The following comments will help you to assess the accuracy of your solutions of triangles:

For a theoretical triangle, whose sides are given exactly, the accuracy of your solution is limited only by the accuracy of the tables of the trigonometric ratios that you use. In most applications of trigonometry to solving triangles, however, the data are measurements, and the results of the solution should be rounded to correspond to the accuracy of the measurements. The following table gives generally reasonable working rules for corresponding accuracy between sides and angles.

Sides, number of significant digits:	2	3	4	5
Angle to the nearest:	1°	10′	1′	0.1′

Exercise 17 is intended to make these working rules appear reasonable. In all remaining problems, round your answers to make them compatible with the given data. Use logarithms when they simplify the calculations.

EXERCISES §902 (cont.)

17. Suppose the condition $\sin A = .83$ is the result of calculations with sides of a triangle, where the number .83 is accurate only to two significant digits. This means that $.825 < \sin A < .835$, which, if A is a first-quadrant angle, implies that $55°35' < A < 56°37'$. It may seem reasonable to report A as $56°$ with the understanding that it is accurate to the nearest degree. In the following conditions, consider the numbers given to be accurate only to the number of significant digits shown. Find *bounds* for a first-quadrant angle. Notice that you obtain different results in different parts of the table.

(a) $\cos A = .88$ (b) $\cos A = .882$ (c) $\cos A = .8823$
(d) $\cot B = 1.9$ (e) $\cot B = 1.87$ (f) $\cot B = 1.872$
(g) $\sin \theta = .14$ (h) $\sin \theta = .144$ (i) $\sin \theta = .1440$
(j) $\sin \phi = .97$ (k) $\sin \phi = .968$ (l) $\sin \phi = .9681$.

Answers: (a) $27°44' < A < 28°58'$; (b) $28°2' < A < 28°11'$; (c) $28°4' < A < 28°6'$.

18. The following four triangles differ only in the length of side *a*. Draw a figure carefully for each triangle, then solve by the law of sines:

(a) $A = 32°$, $a = 1.2$, $b = 3.4$ (b) $A = 32°$, $a = 1.8$, $b = 3.4$
(c) $A = 32°$, $a = 2.8$, $b = 3.4$ (d) $A = 32°$, $a = 4.5$, $b = 3.4$.

Answers: (a) No solution;   (b) $B = 90°$, $c = 2.9$ $C = 58°$;   (c) $B_1 = 40°$, $c_1 = 5.0$ $C_1 = 108°$ or $B_2 = 140°$, $c_2 = 0.7$ $C_2 = 8°$;   (d) $B = 24°$, $c = 7.0$, $C = 124°$.

19. Draw a figure for an approximate solution; then solve with the help of the law of cosines:

(a) $a = 11$, $b = 15$, $c = 13$ (b) $a = 4.23$, $b = 6.61$, $c = 9.82$
(c) $a = 27.6$, $b = 56.5$, $c = 49.3$.

Answers: (b) $A = 19°40'$, $B = 31°50'$, $C = 128°30'$.

20. For each triangle, draw a figure, determine a method of solution, then solve:

(a) $A = 53°48'$, $C = 41°7'$, $b = 65.58$
(b) $B = 72°36'$, $a = 9.356$, $b = 14.723$
(c) $C = 35°40'$, $b = 557$, $c = 214$
(d) $A = 126°21'$, $C = 18°37'$, $b = 7.946$
(e) $B = 59°10'$, $b = 43.2$, $c = 48.1$
(f) $A = 42°13.7'$, $a = 1.8258$, $b = 2.7166$
(g) $B = 78°30'$, $a = 242$, $c = 312$
(h) $C = 26°55'$, $a = 134.2$, $b = 289.6$
(i) $A = 14°25.2'$, $B = 22°43.5'$, $c = 0.81546$
(j) $C = 74°18'$, $b = 4.532$, $c = 3.984$
(k) $A = 164°40'$, $b = 15.4$, $c = 20.3$
(l) $A = 110°$, $a = 35$, $b = 36$
(m) $B = 8°20'$, $b = 2.57$, $c = 8.26$
(n) $C = 147°36'$, $a = 6347$, $c = 9865$.

Answers: (b) $A = 37°20'$, $C = 70°4'$, $c = 14.50$;   (c) no solution;   (d) $B = 35°2'$, $c = 4.419$, $a = 11.15$;   (e) $A_1 = 47°50'$, $C_1 = 73°$, $a_1 = 37.3$ or $A_2 = 13°50'$, $C_2 = 107°$, $a_2 = 12.0$;   (f) $B = 90°$, $C = 47°46.3'$, $c = 2.0116$;   (g) $b = 355$, $A = 42°$, $C = 59°30'$.

21. Show that $\left(\cos C = \dfrac{a^2 + b^2 - c^2}{2ab} \text{ and } c > a + b \right) \Rightarrow (\cos C < -1)$, thus proving analytically that no triangle can exist when $c > a + b$.

22. Two sides and the angle opposite one of the sides of the triangle are given. Determine necessary conditions for a solution and the number of solutions, when the angle is equal to or greater than 90°.

Answer: If the sides and angle are denoted by a, b, and $A \geq 90°$, there is one and only one solution when $a > b$, no solution when $a \leq b$.

903. Trigonometric ratios of sums and products

We return now to the algebra of the trigonometric ratios to examine expressions like $\sin (A + B)$, $\cos 3A$, and $(\cos \theta + i \sin \theta)^3$.

In Fig. 9–27, A and B are two angles in standard position. The points

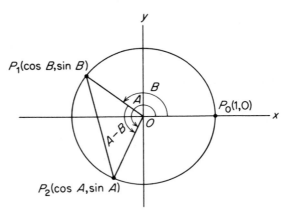

Fig. 9–27.

P_0, P_1, and P_2 are points on a unit circle. Since OP_2 is the terminal side of A, and OP_1 is the terminal side of B, $A - B$ is the amount of rotation from OP_1 to OP_2.

By definition of the trigonometric ratios, the points P_1 and P_2 on the unit circle have coordinates $P_1(\cos B, \sin B)$ and $P_2(\cos A, \sin A)$. We use the distance formula, as in Section 902 (page 431), to express the length of P_1P_2:

$$P_1P_2 = \sqrt{(\cos A - \cos B)^2 + (\sin A - \sin B)^2}$$

$$= \sqrt{(\cos^2 A + \sin^2 A) + (\cos^2 B + \sin^2 B) - 2(\cos A \cos B + \sin A \sin B)}$$

$$= \sqrt{2 - 2(\cos A \cos B + \sin A \sin B)};$$

then we use the law of cosines (page 432) in the triangle OP_1P_2 ($OP_1 = OP_2 = 1$) to express the length of P_1P_2:

$$P_1P_2 = \sqrt{1^2 + 1^2 - 2 \cdot 1 \cdot 1 \cdot \cos (A - B)}$$

$$= \sqrt{2 - 2 \cos (A - B)}.$$

From $(P_1P_2)^2 = (P_1P_2)^2$, we conclude

$$2 - 2(\cos A \cos B + \sin A \sin B) = 2 - 2 \cos (A - B).$$

Hence

I $$\cos (A - B) = \cos A \cos B + \sin A \sin B.$$

This basic formula states that the cosine of a difference of two angles is the sum of the product of the cosines of the two angles and the product of the sines of the two angles. From this formula, we can develop many other formulas. We illustrate the method:

(1) $$\cos (90° - A) = \cos 90° \cos A + \sin 90° \sin A$$
$$= 0 \cdot \cos A + 1 \cdot \sin A$$
$$= \sin A.$$

This is simply a replacement instance of the formula, in which you replace A by 90° and B by A. It is an easy proof of a formula that you used in Section 900 (page 415). Recall that

$$\cos (90° - A) = \text{co-cos } A = \sin A.$$

(2) Prove that $\cos (-B) = \cos B$. You can rely upon pictures, as in Section 900. To prove this identity analytically:

$$\cos (-B) = \cos (0 - B)$$
$$= \cos 0 \cos B + \sin 0 \sin B$$
$$= 1 \cdot \cos B + 0 \cdot \sin B$$
$$= \cos B.$$

(3) Prove that $\sin (-B) = -\sin B$.

$$\sin (-B) = \cos [90° - (-B)]$$
$$= \cos (90° + B)$$
$$= \cos [B - (-90°)]$$
$$= \cos B \cos (-90°) + \sin B \sin (-90°)$$
$$= \cos B \cdot (0) + \sin B \cdot (-1)$$
$$= -\sin B.$$

(4) $$\cos (A + B) = \cos [A - (-B)]$$
$$= \cos A \cos (-B) + \sin A \sin (-B)$$
$$= \cos A \cos B - \sin A \sin B. \quad \text{[Using (2) and (3)]}$$

This is our second basic formula:

II $$\cos (A + B) = \cos A \cos B - \sin A \sin B.$$

(5) Prove that $\sin (90° - A) = \cos A$.

$$\sin (90° - A) = \cos [90° - (90° - A)] \qquad \text{[using (1)]}$$

$$= \cos A.$$

(6) $\sin (A + B) = \cos [90° - (A + B)]$ [using (1)]

$$= \cos [(90° - A) - B]$$

$$= \cos (90° - A) \cos B + \sin (90° - A) \sin B$$

$$= \sin A \cos B + \cos A \sin B. \qquad \text{[using (1) and (5)]}$$

This is our third basic formula:

III $\sin (A + B) = \sin A \cos B + \cos A \sin B.$

You can now prove the following identities, as adaptations of the ones we have proved above:

IV $\sin (A - B) = \sin A \cos B - \cos A \sin B$

V $\sin 2A = \sin (A + A) = 2 \sin A \cos A$

VI $\cos 2A = \cos (A + A) = \cos^2 A - \sin^2 A$

$$= 1 - 2 \sin^2 A$$

$$= 2 \cos^2 A - 1.$$

You can go on to prove identities for $\sin 3A = \sin (2A + A)$, $\cos 5A = \cos (3A + 2A)$, etc. You will find a listing of these identities in your book of tables. You will prove some of them as you work Exercises §903.

Among the identities in your book of tables, notice particularly:

VII $\tan (A - B) = \dfrac{\tan A - \tan B}{1 + \tan A \tan B}$

VIII $\tan (A + B) = \dfrac{\tan A + \tan B}{1 - \tan A \tan B}$

IX $\tan 2A = \dfrac{2 \tan A}{1 - \tan^2 A}.$

We prove identity VII:

$$\tan (A - B) = \frac{\sin (A - B)}{\cos (A - B)}$$

$$= \frac{\sin A \cos B - \cos A \sin B}{\cos A \cos B + \sin A \sin B}.$$

Dividing numerator and denominator by cos *A* cos *B* yields

$$\tan (A - B) = \frac{\dfrac{\sin A \cos B}{\cos A \cos B} - \dfrac{\cos A \sin B}{\cos A \cos B}}{1 + \dfrac{\sin A \sin B}{\cos A \cos B}}$$

$$= \frac{\tan A - \tan B}{1 + \tan A \tan B}.$$

EXERCISES §903

1. Use Formula I to prove that cos (180° − *A*) = −cos *A*.

2. Use Formula II to prove that cos (π/2 + *A*) = −sin *A*.

3. Use Formula III to prove that sin (180° + *A*) = −sin *A*.

4. Use Formula IV to prove that sin (270° − *A*) = −cos *A*.

5. Use Formula VII to prove that tan (π − *A*) = −tan *A*.

6. Draw figures to illustrate Exercises 1 through 5; that is, use some replacement of *A* as you draw the figure. For example, in Exercise 4, sin (270° − *A*) = −*c*/*b* = −cos *A* (see Fig. 9–28).

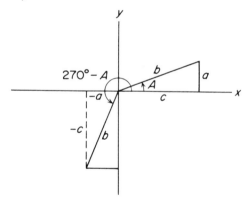

Fig. 9–28.

7. Prove Formula IV. Verify this identity for *A* = 180° and *B* = 90°; for *A* = π/2 and *B* = π/2.

8. (a) Prove Formula V. Verify this identity for *A* = 180°.

(b) Now replace *A* by 45° to get sin 2(45°) = 2 sin 45° cos 45°. Draw a unit circle, and notice that sin 2(45°) = sin 90° = 1;

$$\sin 45° = \cos 45° = \frac{1}{\sqrt{2}}.$$

Hence this replacement instance of Identity V reduces to

$$1 = 2\left(\frac{1}{\sqrt{2}}\right)\left(\frac{1}{\sqrt{2}}\right).$$

9. (a) Prove Formula VI. Notice that

$$\cos^2 A - \sin^2 A = (1 - \sin^2 A) - \sin^2 A = 1 - 2\sin^2 A$$
$$= \cos^2 A - (1 - \cos^2 A) = 2\cos^2 A - 1.$$

(b) Verify this identity for $A = \pi/2$.

(c) Now replace A by $\pi/4$, and show that Identity VI reduces to

$$0 = \frac{1}{2} - \frac{1}{2} = 1 - 2\left(\frac{1}{2}\right) = 2\left(\frac{1}{2}\right) - 1.$$

10. Prove Formula VIII. (*Hint:* Use the proof of Identity VII as a model.)

11. Prove Formula IX.

12. Prove: (a) $\sin 3A = \sin A\,(3 - 4\sin^2 A)$
              (b) $\cos 3A = \cos A\,(4\cos^2 A - 3)$.

904. More about the algebra of the trigonometric ratios

The basic formulas of Sections 900 and 903 imply many further trigonometric identities. We prove some of these further identities, and comment upon their peculiarities and possible applications. For a more complete listing of the trigonometric identities, you should consult your book of mathematical tables.

(1) Since
$$\cos 2A = 2\cos^2 A - 1,$$
$$\cos^2 A = \frac{1 + \cos 2A}{2}.$$

Think of this formula as $\cos^2\left(\dfrac{\alpha}{2}\right) = \dfrac{1 + \cos \alpha}{2}$, replacing A by $\dfrac{\alpha}{2}$. The formula

X
$$\cos\frac{\alpha}{2} = \pm\sqrt{\frac{1 + \cos \alpha}{2}}$$

is one of the *half-angle* formulas. You will find it, and others like it, in your book of tables. We shall use half-angle formulas to check the solutions of triangles in Section 909.

(2) $\sin (A + B) = \sin A \cos B + \cos A \sin B$

and $\sin (A - B) = \sin A \cos B - \cos A \sin B$

yield by addition $\sin (A + B) + \sin (A - B) = 2 \sin A \cos B$.
Hence

XI $\sin A \cos B = \frac{1}{2} \sin (A + B) + \frac{1}{2} \sin (A - B)$.

This curious formula expresses the *product* of $\sin A$ and $\cos B$ as a *sum* of two trigonometric ratios. Some historians believe that formulas of this kind led Napier (1550–1617) to the discovery of logarithms. You will recall how the identity $a^m \cdot a^n = a^{m+n}$ enabled us to multiply numbers by adding exponents. The modern notation for exponents had not yet been developed at the time of Napier, but trigonometric identities were well-known. It is possible that Napier discovered logarithms, as a means to multiply by adding, as he pondered identities like $\sin A \cos B = \frac{1}{2}\sin(A+B) + \frac{1}{2}\sin(A-B)$. Perhaps this will be clearer if you look at this identity in a slightly different way. Let $A + B = C$ and $A - B = D$. By addition, $2A = C + D$, and $A = \frac{1}{2}(C+D)$; by subtraction, $2B = C - D$, and $B = \frac{1}{2}(C-D)$. Substitution yields

$$\tfrac{1}{2}\sin C + \tfrac{1}{2}\sin D = \sin \tfrac{1}{2}(C+D) \cdot \cos \tfrac{1}{2}(C-D), \quad \text{or}$$

XII
$$\sin C + \sin D = 2\sin \tfrac{1}{2}(C+D) \cdot \cos \tfrac{1}{2}(C-D).$$

Notice that this identity has the effect of *factoring* the phrase $\sin C + \sin D$; it replaces the sum $\sin C + \sin D$ by the product $2\sin \frac{1}{2}(C+D) \cdot \cos \frac{1}{2}(C-D)$. This may have suggested to Napier the idea of replacing sums of numbers by products of numbers and, hence, the idea of logarithms.

Now recall the law of cosines, $c^2 = a^2 + b^2 - 2ab\cos C$. We used this law to solve a triangle ABC in which the parts a, b, and C are known. Other forms of the law of cosines enable you to solve any triangle ABC in which two sides and the included angle are known. But the law of cosines is not adapted to calculations with logarithms. We need a formula that replaces additions by multiplications. In Section 909 we shall develop such a formula, making use of factoring identities like XII.

You should study the trigonometric identities in your book of tables. Prove the identity

XIII
$$\sin A \cdot \sin B = \tfrac{1}{2}\cos(A-B) - \tfrac{1}{2}\cos(A+B),$$

using the identities for $\cos(A-B)$ and $\cos(A+B)$ somewhat as we used the identities for $\sin(A+B)$ and $\sin(A-B)$. Then derive the factoring identity

XIV
$$\cos C - \cos D = -2\sin \tfrac{1}{2}(C+D) \cdot \sin \tfrac{1}{2}(C-D).$$

The examples that follow give you a chance to experiment with trigonometric identities; they may also give you insight into a way to build tables of the trigonometric ratios.

$$(3) \qquad \cos 45° = \cos\left(\frac{90°}{2}\right) = \sqrt{\frac{1 + \cos 90°}{2}}$$

(using X and discarding the negative sign since $\cos 45°$ is positive)

$$= \sqrt{\frac{1+0}{2}}$$

$$= \frac{1}{\sqrt{2}} = \frac{\sqrt{2}}{2}.$$

$$(4) \qquad \sin 45° = \cos 45° = \frac{\sqrt{2}}{2}.$$

(Use the formula $\sin(90° - A) = \cos A$ to conclude that $\sin 45° = \cos 45°$.)

(5) In an equilateral triangle, the altitude bisects the base. In Fig. 9-29, we let $a = b = c = 2$; hence $|AD| = \frac{1}{2}c = 1$, and $h_c = \sqrt{b^2 - (\frac{1}{2}c)^2} = \sqrt{3}$. Also, the altitude bisects the vertex angle. Hence angle $ACD = \frac{1}{2}C = 30°$.

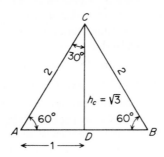

Fig. 9-29.

Use the figure to verify the following statements:

$$\cos 60° = \frac{1}{2}, \quad \sin 60° = \frac{\sqrt{3}}{2}, \quad \text{and} \quad \tan 60° = \sqrt{3};$$

$$\cos 30° = \frac{\sqrt{3}}{2}, \quad \sin 30° = \frac{1}{2}, \quad \text{and} \quad \tan 30° = \frac{1}{\sqrt{3}}.$$

To verify these statements analytically, consider the identity

$$\cos A \, (4\cos^2 A - 3) = \cos 3A.$$

For the replacement $A = 30°$,

$$\cos 30°(4\cos^2 30° - 3) = \cos 90° = 0.$$

Hence $\cos 30° = 0$ or $4\cos^2 30° - 3 = 0$ $[ab = 0 \Leftrightarrow (a = 0 \text{ or } b = 0)]$

Since $\cos 30° > 0$, $\cos^2 30° = \dfrac{3}{4}$ and $\cos 30° = \dfrac{\sqrt{3}}{2}$.

Hence $\cos 60° = \cos 2(30°) = 2\cos^2 30° - 1 = 2\left(\dfrac{3}{4}\right) - 1 = \dfrac{1}{2};$

$$\sin 30° = \cos(90° - 30°) = \frac{1}{2};$$

$$\sin 60° = \cos(90° - 60°) = \frac{\sqrt{3}}{2};$$

$$\tan 30° = \frac{\sin 30°}{\cos 30°} = \frac{1}{\sqrt{3}};$$

$$\tan 60° = \frac{\sin 60°}{\cos 60°} = \sqrt{3}.$$

(6) $\sin 75° = \sin (45° + 30°) = \sin 45° \cos 30° + \cos 45° \sin 30°$

$$= \frac{\sqrt{2}}{2} \cdot \frac{\sqrt{3}}{2} + \frac{\sqrt{2}}{2} \cdot \frac{1}{2}$$

$$= \frac{\sqrt{6} + \sqrt{2}}{4}.$$

(7) $\qquad \cos 5A = \cos (3A + 2A)$

$$= \cos 3A \cos 2A - \sin 3A \sin 2A.$$

Now use identities from your book of tables to write

$\cos 5A = \cos A \, (4 \cos^2 A - 3)(1 - 2 \sin^2 A)$

$$- \sin A \, (3 - 4 \sin^2 A)(2 \sin A \cos A)$$

$$= \cos A\{[4(1 - \sin^2 A) - 3](1 - 2 \sin^2 A) - (6 \sin^2 A - 8 \sin^4 A)\}$$

$$= \cos A \, (1 - 12 \sin^2 A + 16 \sin^4 A).$$

For the replacement $A = 18°$, $5A = 90°$, $\cos 5A = 0$, and

$$0 = \cos 18°(1 - 12 \sin^2 18° + 16 \sin^4 18°).$$

Hence $\cos 18° = 0$, or $16 \sin^4 18° - 12 \sin^2 18° + 1 = 0$. Since $\cos 18° \neq 0$, $16(\sin^2 18°)^2 - 12(\sin^2 18°) + 1 = 0$. This quadratic equation in $\sin^2 18°$ has discriminant $\Delta = 144 - 64 = 80$. Hence

$$\sin^2 18° = \frac{12}{32} \pm \frac{\sqrt{80}}{32} = \frac{3}{8} \pm \frac{\sqrt{5}}{8}.$$

By scale drawing, $\sin 18° \doteq .3$; hence $\sin^2 18° \doteq .10$, and $\sin^2 18° \neq 3/8 + \sqrt{5}/8 \doteq .65$. Hence $\sin^2 18° = 3/8 - \sqrt{5}/8 \doteq .10$. Since $\sin 18° > 0$,

$$\sin 18° = \sqrt{\frac{3}{8} - \frac{\sqrt{5}}{8}}.$$

Notice that the formulas of Examples (3) through (7) enable you to calculate values of the trigonometric ratios of 45°, 60°, 30°, 75°, and 18° to any desired accuracy. Then you can use half-angle formulas to calculate the trigonometric ratios of angles like $22\frac{1}{2}°$, $11\frac{1}{4}°$, 15°, 9°, and $4\frac{1}{2}°$. In this way, given a great deal of time and patience, you could build a table of the trigonometric ratios.

EXERCISES §904

1. From your knowledge of $\cos 45° = \frac{1}{2}\sqrt{2} = \sin 45°$, $\cos 60° = \frac{1}{2} = \sin 30°$, and $\cos 30° = \frac{1}{2}\sqrt{3} = \sin 60°$, prepare a table of $\sin A$ and $\cos A$ for $A = 0°$, 30°, 45°, ..., 360° (all multiples of 30° and 45° from 0° to 360°). Verify your results using the graphs of the sine and cosine functions. Your book of mathematical tables may have a similar table to use for a second check.

2. Prove that $\sin \frac{1}{2}\theta = \pm\sqrt{(1 - \cos\theta)/2}$. [*Hint:* Use $\cos 2A = 1 - 2\sin^2 A$.] Explain how to decide when to use the positive and when to use the negative sign.

3. Prove the following identities for converting products to sums:

(a) $\sin A \cos B = \frac{1}{2}\sin(A + B) + \frac{1}{2}\sin(A - B)$ (XI)

(b) $\sin A \sin B = \frac{1}{2}\cos(A - B) - \frac{1}{2}\cos(A + B)$ (XIII)

(c) $\cos A \cos B = \frac{1}{2}\cos(A + B) + \frac{1}{2}\cos(A - B)$.   (XV)

4. Prove the following identities for converting sums to products:

(a) $\sin A + \sin B = 2\sin \frac{1}{2}(A + B)\cos \frac{1}{2}(A - B)$ (XII)

(b) $\cos A - \cos B = -2\sin \frac{1}{2}(A + B)\sin \frac{1}{2}(A - B)$ (XIV)

(c) $\sin A - \sin B = 2\cos \frac{1}{2}(A + B)\sin \frac{1}{2}(A - B)$ (XVI)

(d) $\cos A + \cos B = 2\cos \frac{1}{2}(A + B)\cos \frac{1}{2}(A - B)$.   (XVII)

Hints: Replace B by $-B$ in XII to prove XVI. Use Exercise 3, XV and XIII, to prove XIV and XVII.

5. Convert each product to a sum, and each sum to a product. (See Exercises 3 and 4.)

(a) $\cos 82\frac{1}{2}° \cos 37\frac{1}{2}°$ (b) $\sin 21° \sin 39°$

(c) $\sin 3\pi/4 \cos \pi/4$ (d) $\sin(\theta + \pi)\cos(\theta - \pi)$

(e) $\cos(135° - \theta)\cos(45° + \theta)$ (f) $\sin 40° + \sin 80°$

(g) $\sin 125° - \sin 15°$ (h) $\cos 27° + \cos 19°$

(i) $\sin(60° + \theta) - \sin(60° - \theta)$ (j) $\cos(60° - A) + \cos(60° + A)$.

Answers: (a) $\frac{1}{2}(\cos 120° + \cos 45°) = (-1 + \sqrt{2})/4$; (d) $\frac{1}{2}(\sin 2\theta + \sin 2\pi) = \frac{1}{2}\sin 2\theta$; (h) $2\cos 23° \cos 4°$; (i) $2\cos 60° \sin\theta = \sin\theta$.

6. Give reasons for each step in the following proof:

$$\tan \frac{1}{2}\theta = \frac{\sin \frac{1}{2}\theta}{\cos \frac{1}{2}\theta}$$

$$= \frac{2\sin \frac{1}{2}\theta \cos \frac{1}{2}\theta}{2\cos^2 \frac{1}{2}\theta}$$

$$= \frac{\sin\theta}{1 + \cos\theta}.$$

7. Prove: (a) $\tan \frac{1}{2}\theta = \dfrac{1 - \cos\theta}{\sin\theta}$

(b) $\tan \frac{1}{2}\theta = \csc\theta - \cot\theta$

(c) $\tan \frac{1}{2}\theta = \pm\sqrt{\dfrac{1 - \cos\theta}{1 + \cos\theta}}$.

8. From the exact values of $\sin 75°$ and $\sin 18°$, given in terms of radicals in the text, compute decimal approximations accurate to five significant digits. Compare with your book of tables.

9. Determine the exact value of $\cos 18°$. (*Hint:* $\cos\theta = \pm\sqrt{1 - \sin^2\theta}$.)

10. Determine the exact value of $\sin 9°$. (*Hint:* See Ex. 2 and Ex. 9.)

11. Determine the exact value of each of the following:

(a) $\cos 75°$ (b) $\sin 105°$ (c) $\tan 75°$

(d) $\sin 15°$ (e) $\cos 15°$ (f) $\cos 37\frac{1}{2}°$

(g) $\sin 7\frac{1}{2}°$ (h) $\cos 82\frac{1}{2}°$ (i) $\cot (-15°)$

(j) $\tan 15°$ (k) $\tan 7\frac{1}{2}°$ (l) $\sin (-82\frac{1}{2}°)$.

Answers: (a) $(\sqrt{6} - \sqrt{2})/4$;   (c) $2 + \sqrt{3}$;   (f) $\sqrt{(4 + \sqrt{6} - \sqrt{2})/8}$; (k) $\sqrt{6} + \sqrt{2} - \sqrt{3} - 2$.

12. Simplify each expression:

(a) $\cos (\pi - \theta)$ (b) $1 - \sin (\frac{1}{2}\pi - \theta) \cos \theta$

(c) $\tan (\pi + \theta)$ (d) $\sin \theta \cos (-\theta)$

(e) $[\sin (90° - A) + \sin A][\cos A - \cos (90° - A)]$

(f) $(1 + \cos \frac{1}{2}\theta)(2 \cos \frac{1}{2}\theta - 1) - \cos \frac{1}{2}\theta$

(g) $\dfrac{\sin 2A}{2 \sin A}$ (h) $\dfrac{\sin 3A + \sin A}{\cos 3A + \cos A}$.

Answers: (b) $\sin^2 \theta$;   (d) $\frac{1}{2} \sin 2\theta$;   (e) $\cos 2A$;   (g) $\cos A$;   (h) $\tan 2A$.

905. Trigonometric functions and their inverses

You met three of the trigonometric functions in Section 409 (page 152). For example, you studied the set of number-pairs $\{(x,\sin x)\}$ and drew the graph of this function. You also graphed the functions $\{(x,\cos x)\}$ and $\{(x,\tan x)\}$. Now you are ready to look more deeply into the behavior of these functions, and to examine functions that involve the reciprocal-ratios csc x, sec x, and cot x.

You will also study the inverses of the trigonometric functions. For example, the rule $y = \sin x$ enables you to construct number-pairs (x,y) that belong to the set $\{(x,\sin x)\}$. The inverse rule, $x = \sin y$, enables you to construct number-pairs (x,y) that belong to the set $\{(x,\text{number whose sine is } x)\}$. In the first set, x represents a number, and y is the number that is the sine of x. In the second set, x is a number and y is a number whose sine is x.

Figure 9–30 displays the graphs of the six trigonometric functions. Check these graphs for different values of x, using your tables of the trigonometric ratios.

For the purposes of these graphs, the units of measure on the x-axis are radians. Recall that

$$x \text{ (radians)} = \frac{a \text{ (length units)}}{r \text{ (length units)}}.$$

You can also use degrees as a unit of measurement on the x-axis. This amounts to a change of scale on the x-axis, since

$$\frac{x}{\alpha} = \frac{\pi}{180°}.$$

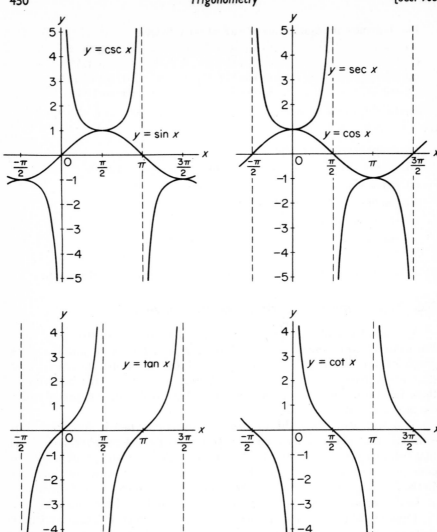

Fig. 9–30.

If, however, you use 1° as a unit of measure on the x-axis, it is inconvenient to use equal units of measure on the x- and y-axes. In the graph of $y = \sin x$, for example, as x increases from 0° to 90°, y increases from 0 to 1. When you use equal units of measure on the x- and y-axes, the sine curve either runs off the paper or has such small amplitude that it almost merges with the x-axis.

Notice the reciprocal character of $\sin x$ and $\csc x$, $\cos x$ and $\sec x$, and $\tan x$ and $\cot x$; notice the asymptotes of the graphs of $y = \csc x$, $y = \sec x$, $y = \tan x$, and $y = \cot x$.

A study of the graphs reveals that the graphs of $y = \sin x$ and $y = \cos x$ are graphs of functions, with the range of x the set L of real numbers; the rest of the graphs are graphs of functions, with the range of x restricted to avoid certain isolated values. For example, when $x = 0$, $\csc x$ and $\cot x$ are not defined; when $x = \pi/2$, $\sec x$ and $\tan x$ are not defined. We shall speak of the trigonometric functions $\{(x,t(x))\}$; each replacement of x by a real number yields a unique value of $y = t(x)$, except that certain values of x may yield no corresponding value of y. (In this connection, recall the graph of $y = 1/x$; y is not defined when $x = 0$.)

For each graph, the range of x is the set L of real numbers, except that you must exclude certain isolated values of x. For example, when $x = -\pi/2$, $\tan x$ is not defined. The range of y for the different graphs is of interest:

$$y = \sin x \Rightarrow -1 \le y \le 1 \qquad y = \csc x \Rightarrow y \le -1 \text{ or } y \ge 1$$
$$y = \cos x \Rightarrow -1 \le y \le 1 \qquad y = \sec x \Rightarrow y \le -1 \text{ or } y \ge 1$$
$$y = \tan x \Rightarrow y \in L \qquad\qquad y = \cot x \Rightarrow y \in L.$$

We drew the graphs with equal units of measure along the x- and y-axes. This makes it easier to discuss the graphs of the inverse relations as reflections in the line $y = x$ of the corresponding direct functions. Unless you use equal units of measure on the two axes, you destroy the symmetry of the graphs.

The inverse of the rule $y = \sin x$ is $x = \sin y$. The roles of x and y are interchanged, so that a point $P(a,b)$ on the graph of $y = \sin x$ corresponds to a point $P(b,a)$ on the graph of $x = \sin y$. We solve the condition $x = \sin y$ for y by inventing a new phrase. We say

$$x = \sin y \Leftrightarrow y = \arcsin x.$$

This *defines* the condition "y is a number whose sine is x," or $y = \arcsin x$, to mean $x = \sin y$. The sentence "$y = \arcsin x$" is often read "y is an angle whose sine is x" because people often visualize y as an angle.

In the same way, for each of the six trigonometric functions,

$$x = t(y) \Leftrightarrow y = \text{arc } t(x).$$

For example, $x = \sec y \Leftrightarrow y = \text{arcsec } x$.

Figure 9–31 displays the graphs of three of the six inverse trigonometric relations. Check these graphs as reflections in the line $y = x$ of the graphs of the corresponding trigonometric functions. Check these graphs, also, by using your tables of trigonometric ratios backwards. For example, when $x = 0.5$, $\arccos x = \pm\pi/3 + k(2\pi)$, where k is an element of the set I of integers, $\{\ldots, -2, -1, 0, 1, 2, \ldots\}$.

You should prepare graphs of $y = \text{arccsc } x$, $y = \text{arcsec } x$, and $y = \text{arccot } x$. Think of these graphs as reflections in the line $y = x$ of the graphs of the corresponding direct functions.

Notice that none of the graphs represent functions. Each replacement of x yields either many values of y or no value of y. This corresponds to the

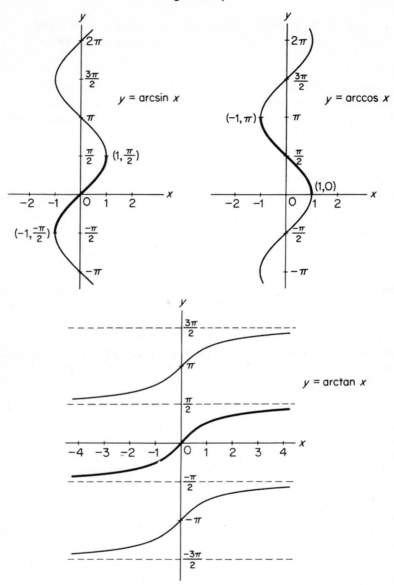

Fig. 9–31.

familiar fact that many angles, or no angle at all, may have a given sine, cosine, etc. For example, if $\sin y = .5$, $y = \pi/6 + k(2\pi)$ or $y = 5\pi/6 + k(2\pi)$, where $k \in I$; there are two values of y for each value of $k \in I$ (see the graph of $y = \arcsin x$). If $\sin y = 1.5$, there is no value of y that satisfies this condition.

To get inverse trigonometric *functions*, we select a *principal value* of $y = $ arc $t(x)$. The heavy line in each graph represents the set of *principal values* of y that correspond to the range of values of x. We use a capital letter, and write $y = $ Arc $t(x)$, as the condition that corresponds to the inverse trigonometric function $\{(x, \text{Arc } t(x))\}$. Then for

$$y = \text{Arcsin } x, \; -1 \leq x \leq 1, \text{ and } -\frac{\pi}{2} \leq y \leq \frac{\pi}{2},$$

$$y = \text{Arccos } x, \; -1 \leq x \leq 1, \text{ and } 0 \leq y \leq \pi,$$

$$\text{and } y = \text{Arctan } x, \; x \in L, \text{ and } -\frac{\pi}{2} < y < \frac{\pi}{2}.$$

Corresponding statements can be made concerning the other three inverse trigonometric functions. With these understandings, $\{(x, \text{Arc } t(x))\}$ is the inverse function that corresponds to the trigonometric function $\{(x, t(x))\}$; in each instance the range of x is as indicated above.

The most important inverse trigonometric relations are $\{(x, \text{arcsin } x)\}$, $\{(x, \text{arccos } x)\}$, and $\{(x, \text{arctan } x)\}$. You should become familiar with their graphs, and with the portions of these graphs that display the principal values of y.

EXERCISES §905

1. We return to the unit circle to picture the trigonometric functions as periodic functions with periods of 2π (the sine, cosine, cosecant, and secant) or π (the tangent and cotangent). Figure 9–32 suggests a graphic way to think of an element of a trigonometric function $\{(\theta, t(\theta))\}$: In the figure, $QP = \sin \theta$, $OQ = \cos \theta$, $P_0T = \tan \theta$, $OR = \csc \theta$, $OT = \sec \theta$, and $P_1R = \cot \theta$.

(a) Verify, for the replacement of θ shown in the figure, that $\csc \theta = 1/\sin \theta$, $\sec \theta = 1/\cos \theta$, and $\cot \theta = 1/\tan \theta$. (*Hint:* $\csc \theta = OR/SR = OR/1 = OP/QP = 1/\sin \theta$.)

(b) Draw a figure that corresponds to a replacement of θ by a second-quadrant angle. Notice that $\csc \theta = OR/1$ as before; but $\sec \theta = OT/-1 = -OT$, and $\cot \theta = P_1R < 0$.

(c) Draw figures that correspond to replacements of θ by third- and fourth-quadrant angles. Check the algebraic signs of $\csc \theta$, $\sec \theta$, and $\cot \theta$ against your previous knowledge of these ratios.

(d) Check the graphs of the six trigonometric functions (page 450), using the methods of this exercise to visualize number-pairs that belong to each function.

2. On a piece of graph paper make a drawing of Fig. 9–32 with $\theta = 65°$. Choose the unit distance so that the figure will be large enough to measure QP, OQ, P_0T, etc. Compare these lengths with the values of the six trigonometric ratios for $65°$ found in your book of tables.

3. Repeat Exercise 2 with $\theta = 140°$.

4. Determine the subset of the set of real numbers for which each of the following is not defined:

(a) tan *x*   (b) cot *x*   (c) sec *x*

(d) cos *x*   (e) csc *x*.

5. Draw the graphs of:

(a) $y = \text{arccot } x$ (b) $y = \text{arcsec } x$ (c) $y = \text{arccsc } x$.

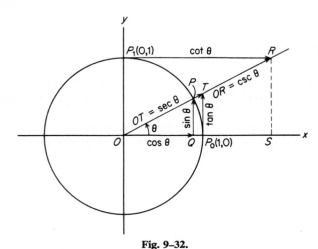

Fig. 9–32.

6. Explain why it would not be suitable to define principal values of arcsin *x* as $y = \text{Arcsin } x$ and $0 \le y \le \pi$. Would $0 \le \text{Arctan } x \le \pi$ be suitable for principal values of the arctangent function? (*Hint:* Is the graph of $y = \text{arcsin } x$ and $0 \le y \le \pi$ the graph of a function? Is the range of *x* for this graph the same as the range of *x* for the graph of $y = \text{arcsin } x$?)

7. Find:

(a) arcsin $\frac{1}{2}$ (b) Arcsin $\frac{1}{2}$ (c) Arctan (-1)

(d) Arccos 0   (e) arctan $\sqrt{3}$ (f) arcsec 1

(g) Arccot 2   (h) Arcsin $(-.5)$ (i) Arccos .829

(j) Arcsin .698   (k) Arccos $(-.42104)$ (l) arccos $(-.42104)$

(m) arcsin .27815   (n) arctan .94400   (o) arctan (-1.28).

Answers (in radians): (a) $\pi/6 + k(2\pi)$ or $5\pi/6 + k(2\pi)$; (b) $\pi/6$; (e) $\pi/3 + k\pi$; (i) 0.593; (l) 2.00538 + $k(2\pi)$ or 4.27780 + $k(2\pi)$.

(In degrees): (a) $30° + k(360°)$ or $150° + k(360°)$; (b) 30°; (e) $60° + k(180°)$; (i) 34°; (l) $114°54' + k(360°)$ or $245°6' + k(360°)$.

8. Explain why cos (Arcsin *x*) is never negative.

9. Explain why sin (Arcsin *x*) = sin (arcsin *x*) = *x* is an identity, but Arcsin (sin *x*) = *x* is *not* an identity.

We proceed to some examples that will help you assimilate the symbolism of inverse trigonometric conditions. We include some alternative ways of expressing the inverse trigonometric relations. This is to prepare you to read books that use other symbols.

(1) Find sin (arcsin .863). Clearly, sin (arcsin .863) = .863, since the sine of the angle whose sine is .863 must be .863. This is like saying $(\sqrt{2})^2 = 2$, since the square of the number whose square is 2 must be 2.

(2) Find arctan (tan θ). In words, find the angle whose tangent is the tangent of θ. Clearly, arctan (tan θ) = $\theta + k\pi$, $k \in I$. Notice that many

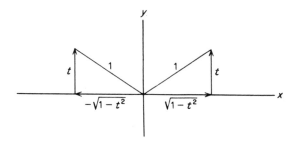

Fig. 9–33.

angles have the same tangent; tan θ = tan $(\theta + k\pi)$. This is somewhat like saying "Find a number whose square is the square of 2." The answer is either 2 or -2, for $2^2 = (-2)^2 = 4$.

(3) Find $\cot^{-1} 2$. We interpret this to mean "Find arccot 2." This notation is widely used, despite the possibility of confusion with the symbol $(\cot 2)^{-1} = 1/\cot 2$. When you see the symbol $\cot^{-1} 2$, replace it by the symbol arccot 2, which means the same thing. Similarly, $\sin^{-1} .8$ means arcsin .8, $\cos^{-1} .3$ means arccos .3, and in general, $t^{-1}(\theta)$ means arct (θ), for each trigonometric ratio $t(\theta)$.

We have $\cot^{-1} 2 = $ arccot 2. According to the tables, cot θ = 2 when $\theta \doteq 26°34'$, or 0.464 radian. When you examine the graph of $y = \cot x$, or the graph of $y = $ arccot x, you find that $\theta \doteq 26°34' + k(180°)$ or $\theta \doteq 0.464 + k(\pi)$, $k \in I$. Hence $\cot^{-1} 2 = $ arccot 2 $\doteq 0.464 + k\pi$ radians, or $26°34' + k(180°)$. Of course the principal value is $\text{Cot}^{-1} 2 = $ Arccot 2 $\doteq 0.464$ radian, or $26°34'$.

(4) Find tan $[\text{Cot}^{-1} (-\sqrt{3})]$. A sketch will help you to interpret this problem. You will find $\text{Cot}^{-1} (-\sqrt{3}) = $ Arccot $(-\sqrt{3}) = -\pi/6$ radian, or $-30°$. Then tan $[\text{Cot}^{-1} (-\sqrt{3})] = $ tan $(-\pi/6) = -1/\sqrt{3}$.

(5) Find cos (arcsin t). Let $\theta = $ arcsin t. Then sin $\theta = t$ and cos (arcsin t) = cos θ = $\pm\sqrt{1 - \sin^2 \theta} = \pm\sqrt{1 - t^2}$. A sketch like Fig. 9–33 will help you to visualize cos (arcsin t) = $\pm\sqrt{1 - t^2}$.

(6) A boy swings a rock in an old-fashioned sling. He lets the sling revolve at an angular speed of 9 revolutions per second; the distance from his hand

to the center of the rock is 10 in. Find the value of θ that gives the rock a horizontal velocity of 25 ft/sec (see Fig. 9–34).

In 1 revolution the rock travels $2\pi(10) = 20\pi$ in.; in 1 sec the rock travels $9(20\pi) = 180\pi$ in.; this is a speed of $180\pi/12 = 15\pi$ ft/sec. At any instant, the rock has a speed of 15π ft/sec in the direction of the tangent to the circle. The horizontal speed is $15\pi \sin \theta$, and the vertical speed is $15\pi \cos \theta$ ft/sec.

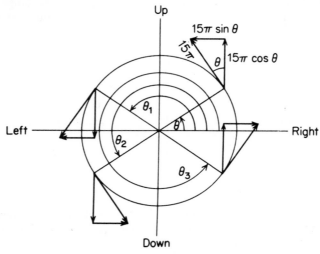

Fig. 9–34.

We must solve the condition

$$15\pi \sin \theta = \pm 25$$

$$\sin \theta = \pm \frac{5}{3\pi} \doteq \pm 0.53.$$

The solutions are $\theta = \arcsin (\pm 5/3\pi) \doteq \arcsin (\pm 0.53)$; that is, $\theta \doteq 32°$, 148°, 212°, 328°, etc; larger values of θ correspond to letting the sling revolve more than once before releasing the rock. You may be interested in calculating $15\pi \sin \theta = \pm 25$, and interpreting the $\pm$ symbols in terms of horizontal velocity to the left versus horizontal velocity to the right.

EXERCISES §905 (cont.)

10. Find:

(a) $\sin (\text{Arcsin } \frac{1}{2})$ (b) $\sin (\arcsin \frac{1}{2})$ (c) $\cos (\arccos .65)$
(d) $\tan (\arctan -1)$ (e) $\text{Arcsin} (\sin \pi/2)$ (f) $\text{Arcsin} (\sin 5\pi/2)$
(g) $\text{Arccos} (\cos 32°)$ (h) $\text{Arccos} (\cos -32°)$ (i) $\tan (\tan^{-1} .321)$
(j) $\text{Cos}^{-1} (\cos 800°)$ (k) $\sec (\text{arcsec } .22)$ (l) $\arctan (\tan 30°)$
(m) $\arcsin (\sin 315°)$ (n) $\arccos (\cos \pi/2)$ (o) $\arcsin (\sin -500°)$.

Answers: (a) $\frac{1}{2}$; (b) $\frac{1}{2}$; (e) $\pi/2$; (f) $\pi/2$; (l) $30° + k(180°)$.

11. Find:

(a) sin (Arctan 1)   (b) cos (Arcsin $\frac{1}{2}$)   (c) cos (Arcsin $-\frac{1}{2}$)
(d) tan (Arcsin $\frac{1}{2}$)   (e) cot (tan^{-1} 3)   (f) sin (Arccos .8)
(g) sec (arccos .2)   (h) cos (Arctan 1)   (i) tan (Arccos 1).

Answers: (a) $\frac{1}{2}\sqrt{2}$;   (c) $\frac{1}{2}\sqrt{3}$;   (e) $\frac{1}{3}$;   (f) .6;   (g) 5.

12. Evaluate in terms of x:

(a) sin (arccos x)   (b) cot (arccos x)   (c) cos (arccos x)
(d) sec (arccos x)   (e) csc (arccos x)   (f) cos (tan^{-1} x)
(g) sin (tan^{-1} x)   (h) cot (tan^{-1} x)   (i) tan (cot^{-1} x).

Answers: (a) $\pm\sqrt{1-x^2}$;   (b) $\pm x/\sqrt{1-x^2}$;   (f) $\pm 1/\sqrt{1+x^2}$.

13. Find:

(a) sin (Arcsin $\frac{1}{2}$ + Arccos $\frac{1}{2}$)   (b) cos (Arcsin .6 + Arcsin .8)
(c) sin (2 Arccos .6)   (d) sin ($\frac{1}{2}$ cos^{-1} .4).

(*Hint* for part (a): sin $(A + B)$ = sin A cos B + cos A sin B.)
Answers: (a) 1;   (c) .96.

14. Prove the identities:

(a) cos (2 arccos x) = $2x^2 - 1$ (b) sin (2 arccos y) = $\pm 2y\sqrt{1-y^2}$
(c) Arcsin t + Arccos t = $\pi/2$ (d) tan (arccot z) = $1/z$.

Once you know how to graph $y = t(x)$, it is easy to graph $y = bt(x)$. For example, the graph of $y = 3$ sin x is the graph of $Y = $ sin x, where $y = 3Y$; the graph of $y = -\frac{1}{2}$ cos x is the graph of $Y = $ cos x, where $y = -\frac{1}{2}Y$.

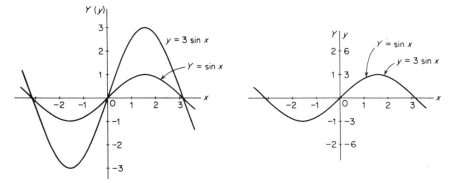

Fig. 9–35.

Similarly, the graph of $y = $ Arc $t(x)$ is easily adapted to graph $y = b$ Arc $t(x)$. For example, the graph of $y = -2$ Arctan x is the graph of $Y = $ Arctan x, where $y = -2Y$; the graph of $y = 60$ Arcsin x is the graph of $Y = $ Arcsin x, where $y = 60Y$.

The effect of the transformation $y = bY$, or $Y = y/b$, is to make each value of y b times as large as the corresponding value of Y. To graph $y = 3$ sin x, first visualize the graph of $Y = $ sin x. Then multiply each value of

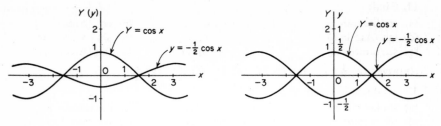

Fig. 9–36.

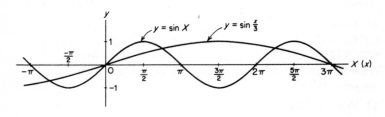

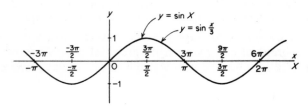

Fig. 9–37.

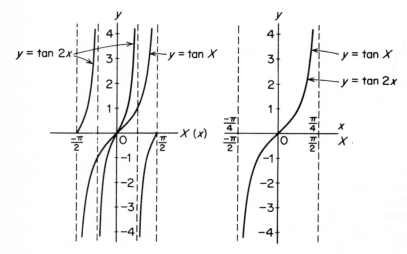

Fig. 9–38.

Y by 3, or else make the units of measurement in the y-direction one third as large. Figure 9–35 shows the effect of these two ways of thinking.

One way is to stretch the graph in the y-direction; the other way is to shrink the units of measurement in the y-direction. You should now sketch the graphs of $y = -\frac{1}{2} \cos x$, $y = -2$ Arctan x, and $y = 60$ Arcsin x. Notice, in the graph of $y = -\frac{1}{2} \cos x$, that you reflect the graph of $Y = \cos x$ in the x-axis, and then multiply each value of Y by $\frac{1}{2}$; or you multiply each value of Y by $\frac{1}{2}$, and then reflect the graph in the x-axis. The results are shown in Fig. 9–36.

When you graph $y = 60$ Arcsin x, you will find it convenient to change the units of measurement rather than stretch the curve in the y-direction. It is awkward to show the graphs of $y = 60$ Arcsin x and $Y =$ Arcsin x using the same units of measurement in the y-direction.

Consider next the graph of $y = t(x/a)$. For example, sketch the graph of $y = \sin(x/3)$. To do this, first visualize $y = \sin X$; then apply the transformation $X = x/3$ or $x = 3X$. The effect of the transformation $x = 3X$, or $X = x/3$ is to make each value of x three times as large as the corresponding value of X.

Study Fig. 9–37 and notice the two ways to accomplish this result. Observe that the period of $y = \sin(x/3)$ is 6π rather than 2π. In general, if $y = t(x)$ has period p, then $y = t(x/a)$ will have a period of ap.

Often it is more convenient to shrink the units in the x-direction, rather than to stretch the curve in the x-direction.

To graph $y = \tan 2x$, first visualize the graph of $y = \tan X$, then apply the transformation $X = 2x$, or $x = \frac{1}{2}X$. The effect of the transformation is to make each value of x half as large as the corresponding value of X; or you may accomplish the same result by making the unit of measurement in the x-direction twice as large. Study Fig. 9–38. What is the period of $y = \tan 2x$?

In summary, notice that

(a) $y = bt(x)$, or $y/b = t(x)$, is the same as $Y = t(x)$, where $y = bY$.
(b) $y = t(x/a)$ is the same as $y = t(X)$, where $x = aX$.

To accomplish the transformation $y = bY$, make each value of y b times the corresponding value of Y, or make the units of measurement in the y-direction $1/b$ as large; to accomplish the transformation $x = aX$, make each value of x a times the corresponding value of X, or make the unit of measurement in the x-direction $1/a$ times as large.

EXERCISES §905 (cont.)

15. Draw the graphs of $y = \cos x$, $y = 2 \cos x$, and $y = -3 \cos x$ on the same coordinate system.

16. Draw the graphs of $y = \sin x$, $y = \sin \frac{1}{2}x$, and $y = \sin 2x$ on the same coordinate system. What is the period of each function?

17. Draw the graph of $y = 2 \sin 2x$.

18. Graph $y = 2 + \sin x$. (*Hint:* This is the same as $Y = \sin x$, where $Y = y - 2$.)

19. Graph $y = \sin (x - \pi/2)$. (*Hint:* This is the same as $y = \sin X$, where $X = x - \pi/2$.)

20. Graph $y = -\cos x$ and compare with the graph of Exercise 19. Explain, with the help of trigonometric identities, the similarities of the two graphs.

21. Graph $y = \cos (x + \pi)$. [*Hint:* $x + \pi = x - (-\pi)$.]

22. Graph $y = \sqrt{2} \sin (x + \pi/4)$.

23. Graph $y = \sin x + \cos x$. (*Hint:* Graph $Y_1 = \sin x$ and $Y_2 = \cos x$, then, for each x, $y = Y_1 + Y_2$.) Compare with the graph of Exercise 22. Use trigonometric identities to explain the similarity.

24. Graph:

(a) $y = -3 \sin 2x$

(b) $y = \cos (x - \pi/3)$

(c) $y = \sin x - \cos x$

(d) $y = 3 \sin x + \cos x$

(e) $y = 3 \sin x - 2 \cos x$

(f) $y = \sin \frac{1}{2}x + \cos x$

(g) $y = \cos 2x + \cos x$

(h) $y = x + \sin x$.

25. If there is a replacement of p such that, for each x, and $x \in L$, $t(x + p) = t(x)$, then $y = t(x)$ is said to have period p. (See Chapter 4, page 153.) Show that if $y = t(x)$ has period p, then $y = t(x/a)$ has period ap.

Hint:

$$t\left(\frac{x + ap}{a}\right) = t\left(\frac{x}{a} + p\right) = t\left(\frac{x}{a}\right).$$

Before you leave this discussion of the trigonometric functions, examine some formulas that appear in your book of tables. In the section on differential calculus, you will find formulas like

$$\sin x = x - \frac{x^3}{3!} + \frac{x^5}{5!} - \frac{x^7}{7!} + \cdots$$

$$\text{Tan}^{-1} x = \text{Arctan } x = x - \tfrac{1}{3}x^3 + \tfrac{1}{5}x^5 - \tfrac{1}{7}x^7 + \cdots, \text{ etc.}$$

When you study calculus you will learn to prove that the derivative of $\sin x$ is $\cos x$; that is, the slope of the graph of $y = \sin x$ at the point (x, y) is $\cos x$. This result, and the background of knowledge of the trigonometric functions you have acquired here, will enable you to derive and use these formulas.

For example, when $x = .3$ radian,

$$\sin .3 = .3 - \frac{(.3)^3}{3!} + \frac{(.3)^5}{5!} - \frac{(.3)^7}{7!} + \cdots.$$

You can find the value of $\sin .3$ to any desired decimal precision by using enough terms of this series. Try this to see how many terms of the series you must use to get the four-place precision of your tables of trigonometric ratios. This is a modern way to construct a table of trigonometric ratios.

Also, when $x = 1$, Arctan $1 = \pi/4$; hence

$$\frac{\pi}{4} = \text{Arctan } 1 = 1 - \tfrac{1}{3}(1)^3 + \tfrac{1}{5}(1)^5 + \tfrac{1}{7}(1)^7 + \cdots .$$

This gives $\pi/4 = 1 - 1/3 + 1/5 - 1/7 + \ldots$, and enables you to calculate a value of π to any desired decimal precision. There are better series for calculating the value of π. These other series *converge* more rapidly; hence, fewer terms yield a desired decimal precision.

These ideas about the trigonometric functions are key ideas for people who want to work in pure mathematics; they are also key ideas for people who want to use the models of mathematics to explore the world of experience. You should experiment with them whenever the opportunity arises. The more different ways you can find to look at the trigonometric functions, the better.

If you look further among the formulas in your book of tables you will find formulas like $\cos x = (e^{ix} + e^{-ix})/2$, where $i^2 = -1$. These formulas suggest, and further study of the trigonometric and exponential functions confirms, a close connection between the trigonometric and exponential functions. Such formulas are of great theoretical and practical value. They are products of modern analysis; they represent a big advance since the trigonometry of the time of Ptolemy.

EXERCISES §905 (cont.)

26. Calculate sin .3, using the first three terms of the series. Compare with the value given in a book of tables.

27. Calculate sin 1, using the first three terms of the series. How precise is this result? Add the fourth term to see if the precision is improved.

28. Calculate sin 10°, using the first two terms of the series. (Note: The angle must be converted to radians to use this series.) Check with a book of tables.

29. Find a series for $\cos x$ in a book of tables and calculate the cosine of 1 radian.

30. Use the series given in the text for Arctan x to determine, in radians, the angle whose tangent is 0.2. Convert the angle to degrees and minutes, then look up its tangent as a check.

906. Polar coordinates

You have plotted the point $P(a,b)$ by moving a units along the x-axis and b units parallel to the y-axis. We call a and b the *rectangular coordinates* of P; a is the x-coordinate and b the y-coordinate of P.

There are other ways to locate a point in the plane. One of the simplest, and most useful, is the system of *polar coordinates*. As a basis for polar coordinates, we select a point, O, of the plane as the *pole*. We draw a half-line from the pole toward the right, and call it the *polar axis*. Then the point $P(r,\theta)$ is defined to be the point at distance r from the pole in a direction θ, measured counterclockwise from the polar axis (Fig. 9–39).

Once you decide the units of measurement, a unique point of the plane

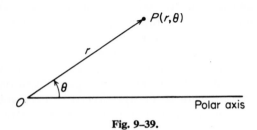

Fig. 9–39.

corresponds to each number-pair (r,θ), $\theta \in L$ and $r \in L$. For example, measure θ in radians and r in quarter-inches; then the points in Fig. 9–40 illustrate plotting points in polar coordinates. Notice that $(6,\pi/3)$ is 6 units in the direction $\pi/3$; $(-4,-\pi/6)$ is -4 units in the direction $-\pi/6$; etc.

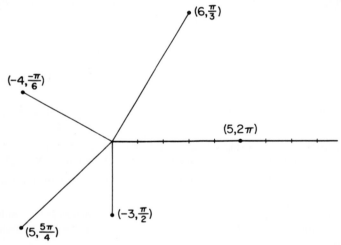

Fig. 9–40.

Each point of the plane has many pairs of polar coordinates. For example, the point $(6,\pi/3)$ also has coordinates $(-6,4\pi/3)$, $(6,7\pi/3)$, $(-6,10\pi/3)$, etc. In some ways, this is a disadvantage of polar coordinates as compared with rectangular coordinates; the same point corresponds to many different number-pairs. In other ways it is an advantage; you would expect, for example, to find simpler graphs for some of the periodic functions. Notice, in particular, that the pole corresponds to any element of the set $\{(0,\theta)\}$.

You have probably seen printed sheets of *polar coordinate paper*. These are convenient because they include equally spaced circles around the pole and equally spaced radii of these circles. You should secure sheets of polar coordinate paper and gain experience in using it.

EXERCISES §906

1. Plot each of the following points in polar coordinates:

(a) $(3, \pi/4)$ (b) $(1, 3\pi/4)$ (c) $(-1, -3\pi/4)$ (d) $(-1, 3\pi/4)$
(e) $(1, -3\pi/4)$ (f) $(2, 5\pi)$ (g) $(2, 20°)$ (h) $(2, -20°)$
(i) $(-2, 20°)$ (j) $(-2, -20°)$ (k) $(5, 786°)$ (l) $(0, 512°)$
(m) $(4, 5)$ (n) $(2, 2)$ (o) $(-2, 2)$ (p) $(-2, -2)$
(q) $(2, -2)$.

Hint for part (m): Interpret this to mean 5 radians, rather than 5 degrees, or 5 of some other unit of angle-measurement. This is simply a convenient agreement. When we mean units other than radians, we shall state this fact explicitly.

Notice that you can plot points in polar coordinates once you know how to measure angles; you do not need a knowledge of trigonometry. But the

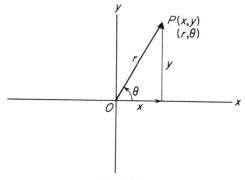

Fig. 9–41.

language of trigonometry provides convenient formulas for changing from rectangular to polar coordinates and vice versa; the trigonometric functions provide some of the more interesting polar graphs. Hence it is expedient to study polar coordinates here.

Consider the point P with rectangular coordinates (x, y) and polar coordinates (r, θ) (Fig. 9–41). Notice that

$$x = r \cos \theta; \qquad y = r \sin \theta.$$

These equations enable you to find the rectangular coordinates of a point whose polar coordinates are given. For example, the point $(5, 20°)$ has rectangular coordinates $(5 \cos 20°, 5 \sin 20°)$, approximately $(4.698, 1.710)$.

They also enable you to write the condition upon the polar coordinates of a point that corresponds to a given condition upon the rectangular coordinates of the point, that is, to write the polar condition for the graph of a given rectangular condition. For example, the equations $x = 5$ and $r \cos \theta = 5$ have the same graph; the equations $y = 3x + 2$ and $r \sin \theta = 3r \cos \theta + 2$ have the same graph; etc.

Also, from the figure,

$$r = \sqrt{x^2 + y^2}; \qquad \theta = \arctan \frac{y}{x}.$$

These equations are less convenient than the previous ones. For example, to find the polar coordinates of the point P whose rectangular coordinates are $(-3,7)$:

$$r = \sqrt{9 + 49} = \sqrt{58}$$

$$\theta = \arctan \frac{7}{-3}.$$

First we interpret the condition $\theta = \arctan 7/(-3)$ to define a second-quadrant angle. Then $\theta \doteq 113° + k(360°)$, and the polar coordinates of P are $(\sqrt{58}, 113° + k[360°])$. Other polar coordinates of P are $(-\sqrt{58}, -113° + k[360°])$. You will probably prefer to choose the coordinates $(\sqrt{58}, 113°)$ as the simplest ones; but notice again the lack of uniqueness of polar coordinates.

Notice that you can write the rectangular condition for the graph of a given polar condition. For example, $r = 5\theta$ becomes $\sqrt{x^2 + y^2} = 5 \arctan y/x$.

Often it is unwise to apply the formulas mechanically; you may avoid complications by using other conditions that involve some of the variables x, y, r, and θ. For example:

(1) Write in polar form, $x^2 + y^2 = 4x$. Proceeding mechanically,

$$(r \cos \theta)^2 + (r \sin \theta)^2 = 4(r \cos \theta)$$
$$r^2(\cos^2 \theta + \sin^2 \theta) = 4r \cos \theta$$
$$r^2 = 4r \cos \theta$$
$$r = 4 \cos \theta.$$

It is easier to notice that $x^2 + y^2 = r^2$; then $x^2 + y^2 = 4x$ becomes $r^2 = 4r \cos \theta$. You save the intermediate step.

(2) Write in rectangular form, $r = 5 \sec \theta$. Proceeding mechanically,

$$\sqrt{x^2 + y^2} = 5 \sec \left(\arctan \frac{y}{x} \right).$$

This equation is not easy to simplify; but you can use the methods of Section 905 (page 455) to show that

$$5 \sec \left(\arctan \frac{y}{x} \right) = 5 \left(\pm \frac{\sqrt{x^2 + y^2}}{x} \right)$$

and argue that only the positive sign should be used here. The equation reduces to $x\sqrt{x^2 + y^2} = 5\sqrt{x^2 + y^2}$, that is, $x = 5$. It is easier to notice that $\sec \theta = r/x$; then $r = 5 \sec \theta$ becomes $r = 5 \cdot r/x$, that is, $xr = 5r$. Since $r = 5 \sec \theta$, $r \neq 0$. Hence you may divide by r and reduce $xr = 5r$ to $x = 5$.

EXERCISES §906 (cont.)

2. Find the rectangular coordinates of each point whose polar coordinates are given:

(a) $(2,30°)$ (b) $(1,270°)$ (c) $(3,-60°)$

(d) $(8,225°)$ (e) $(4,35°)$ (f) $(6,750°)$

(g) $(-5,60°)$ (h) $(2,\pi/2)$ (i) $(8,\pi/3)$

(j) $(3\sqrt{2},3\pi/4)$ (k) $(4,-3\pi/2)$ (l) $(7,\pi)$

(m) $(7,-\pi)$ (n) $(1,1)$ (o) $(-2,1)$

(p) $(-3,-2)$.

Answers: (a) $(\sqrt{3},1)$; (c) $(\frac{3}{2},-\frac{3}{2}\sqrt{3})$; (e) $(3.28,2.29)$; (h) $(0,2)$; (j) $(-3,3)$; (n) $(.54,.84)$.

3. Find the polar coordinates of each point whose rectangular coordinates are given. Select the polar coordinates (r,θ) such that $0° \leq \theta \leq 360°$, $r \geq 0$.

(a) $(2,2)$ (b) $(3,-3)$ (c) $(0,5)$

(d) $(7,0)$ (e) $(-6,0)$ (f) $(-3\sqrt{3},3)$

(g) $(2,7)$ (h) $(-3,4)$ (i) $(5,12)$

(j) $(-1,-6)$ (k) $(4,-2)$ (l) $(-5,-8)$.

Answers: (a) $(2\sqrt{2},45°)$ or $(2\sqrt{2},\pi/4)$; (e) $(6,180°)$ or $(6,\pi)$; (g) $(\sqrt{53},74°3')$ or $(7.28,1.29)$; (j) $(\sqrt{37},260°32')$ or $(6.08,4.55)$.

4. Write a polar condition for the graph of each rectangular condition. Try to select the simplest polar condition:

(a) $y = 5$ (b) $y = 3x$

(c) $x = 7$ (d) $y = 2x - 3$

(e) $x^2 + y^2 = 16$ (f) $x^2 + y^2 = 7y$

(g) $x^2 + y^2 - 2x + 6y = 0$ (h) $(x^2 + y^2)^2 = 8xy$

(i) $y = \frac{1}{2}x^2$ (j) $x^2 + y^2 = \sqrt{x^2 + y^2} + 3x$.

Answers: (b) $\theta = \arctan 3$; (d) $r(2 \cos \theta - \sin \theta) = 3$; (f) $r = 7 \sin \theta$; (i) $r = 2 \tan \theta \sec \theta$.

5. Find a rectangular condition for the graph of each polar condition. Try to select the simplest rectangular condition.

(a) $r = 6 \csc \theta$ (b) $r = 5$

(c) $r = 9 \sec \theta$ (d) $r = 2 \sin \theta$

(e) $r = -3 \cos \theta$ (f) $r = 5 \cos \theta - 4 \sin \theta$

(g) $\theta = 2$ (h) $r = \dfrac{1}{2(1 + \sin \theta)}$

(i) $r^2 = 6 \csc 2\theta$.

Answers: (a) $y = 6$; (b) $x^2 + y^2 = 25$; (e) $x^2 + y^2 + 3x = 0$; (g) $y = (\tan 2)x$; (h) $y = \frac{1}{4} - x^2$.

We proceed to study graphs of polar conditions. As you would expect, sometimes the polar condition is simpler to graph than the corresponding cartesian condition, and sometimes the opposite is true.

Recall that the simplest graphs in cartesian coordinates are the graphs of the conditions $x = a$ and $y = b$. These are families of lines parallel to the coordinates axes. The simplest graphs in polar coordinates are the graphs of the conditions $r = a$ and $\theta = b$. As examples, $r = 5$ is a circle of radius 5 about the pole, and $\theta = \pi/4$ is the radial line in Fig. 9–42. More generally,

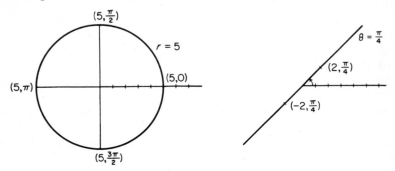

Fig. 9–42.

$r = a$ is a family of circles with centers at the pole; $\theta = b$ is a family of lines through the pole. Notice a characteristic of these lines; to make the lines run both directions from the pole, we permit r to represent a signed number. For example, on the line $\theta = \pi/4$, we have points $(-2,\pi/4)$ and $(2,\pi/4)$. These points correspond respectively to walking 2 units *backward* in the direction $\theta = \pi/4$, and 2 units *forward* in the direction $\theta = \pi/4$.

(3) Consider, now, the graph of $r = \sin \theta$. First prepare a table:

θ	0	$\dfrac{\pi}{6}$	$\dfrac{\pi}{4}$	$\dfrac{\pi}{3}$	$\dfrac{\pi}{2}$	$\dfrac{2}{3}\pi$	$\dfrac{3}{4}\pi$	$\dfrac{5}{6}\pi$	π	$\dfrac{7}{6}\pi$	$\dfrac{5}{4}\pi$	$\dfrac{4}{3}\pi$	$\dfrac{3}{2}\pi$	...
r	0	$\dfrac{1}{2}$	$\dfrac{\sqrt{2}}{2}$	$\dfrac{\sqrt{3}}{2}$	1	$\dfrac{\sqrt{3}}{2}$	$\dfrac{\sqrt{2}}{2}$	$\dfrac{1}{2}$	0	$-\dfrac{1}{2}$	$\dfrac{-\sqrt{2}}{2}$	$\dfrac{-\sqrt{3}}{2}$	-1	...

Then plot the points in polar coordinates (Fig. 9–43). When you join the points by a smooth curve, the graph is the *sine circle* of the figure; notice that values of θ in the range $0 \le \theta < \pi$ yield the complete sine circle. For values of θ in the range $\pi < \theta < 2\pi$, r is negative; you get points like $(-\tfrac{1}{2}, \tfrac{7}{6}\pi)$ that have the same location as points previously plotted; $(-\tfrac{1}{2}, \tfrac{7}{6}\pi)$ is the same point as $(\tfrac{1}{2}, \tfrac{1}{6}\pi)$, for example. The sine circle is repeated again and again as you assign larger values to θ.

As you study the graph of $r = \sin \theta$, we hope you will get a new **feel for the periodicity** of the sine function. It is worth noticing, too, that the sine

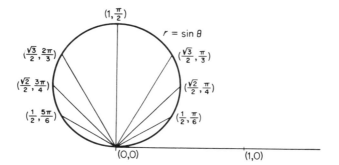

Fig. 9-43.

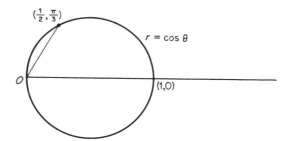

Fig. 9-44.

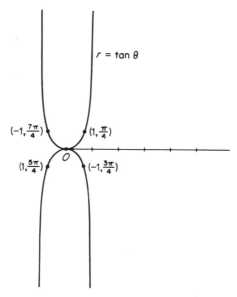

Fig. 9-45.

function is not the same thing as its graph in cartesian coordinates. Basically, the sine function is a set of number-pairs. Some of these number-pairs are recorded in the table above. There are many ways to express this set of number-pairs, for example, the cartesian graph, the polar graph, the equation $y = \sin x$, the equation $r = \sin \theta$, etc. But the function itself is a set of number-pairs.

(4) Figure 9–44 displays the graph of $r = \cos \theta$. Check this graph of the *cosine circle* by preparing a table of number-pairs, $\{(r, |\theta) \; r = \cos \theta\}$.

(5) The graph of $r = \tan \theta$ is more complicated, as you might expect, and it is mathematically less interesting than the graphs of $r = \sin \theta$ and $r = \cos \theta$. You should check Fig. 9–45 as an exercise in plotting polar graphs.

Practically speaking, the simplest polar graphs are the most useful ones. We shall not trouble you with the polar graphs of the inverse trigonometric functions, because they are complicated and somewhat confusing. The following exercises will help you to assimilate the examples of graphs of polar conditions that you have already met. Then we shall provide further examples of polar conditions with interesting graphs.

EXERCISES §906 (cont.)

6. Sketch graphs for the following conditions, using a polar coordinate system:

(a) $r = 3$ (b) $r = \frac{1}{2}$ (c) $r = 4$
(d) $r = -4$ (e) $\theta = \pi/2$ (f) $\theta = 0$
(g) $\theta = 4.2$ (h) $\theta = 120°$ (i) $\theta = -60°$.

7. Make a table of number-pairs, $\{(r,\theta)\}$, for $r = 3 \cos \theta$; then plot on a polar coordinate system (see Example 4).

8. Explain why the graph of $r = a \sin \theta$ will be a circle like the graph of $r = \sin \theta$, except that the diameter of the circle will be a units. Graph:

(a) $r = 2 \sin \theta$ (b) $r = 5 \sin \theta$
(c) $r = 3 \cos \theta$ (d) $r = \frac{1}{2} \cos \theta$
(e) $r = -4 \sin \theta$ (f) $r = -5 \cos \theta$.

9. Make a table of number pairs for $r = 5 \tan \theta$ and plot the graph (see Example 5).

10. The graphs of $r = a \sec \theta$ and $r = a \csc \theta$ are straight lines. (Why?) Graph:

(a) $r = \sec \theta$ (b) $r = 3 \sec \theta$
(c) $r = -3 \sec \theta$ (d) $r = \csc \theta$
(e) $r = 5 \csc \theta$ (f) $r = -5 \csc \theta$.

11. Make a table of number-pairs for $r = \cos (\theta - \pi/4)$ and plot the graph. Compare with the graph of $r = \cos \theta$. Formulate a general statement concerning the graph of $r = \cos (\theta - t)$, where t is a parameter.

12. Change the polar equation $r = 4 \sin \theta$ to the corresponding rectangular equation, $x^2 + y^2 = 4y$. Complete the square to write the equivalent equation $x^2 + (y - 2)^2 = 4$. Compare the polar and rectangular graphs of the two circles.

Your experience, thus far, with graphing equations in polar coordinates is very limited. The purpose of the remainder of this section is to acquaint you with graphs in polar coordinates.

Some of these graphs have found recent application to radiation problems. An antenna that is built to emit, or to receive, radio waves has a characteristic pattern. Some antennas are *directional*; they have maximum power in one particular direction; as you turn away from this maximum-power direction the strength of radiation falls off rapidly. Figure 9–46 suggests such a

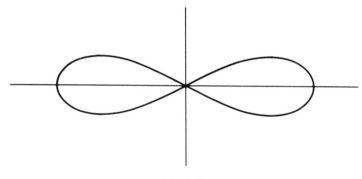

Fig. 9–46.

radiation pattern. You get maximum power in the $0°$ and the $180°$ directions; as you turn away from these directions the power decreases rather rapidly.

This graph has been a mathematical curiosity for centuries. Mathematicians call it a *lemniscate*. The possibility of applying it to the study of radiation patterns is one of those unforeseen dividends that the investigation of mathematical curiosities so often produces.

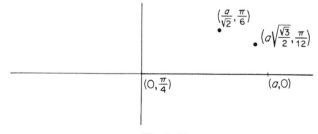

Fig. 9–47.

(6) Graph the equation $r^2 = a^2 \cos 2\theta$. As with the graphing of rectangular equations, the basic method is to prepare a table. As you do this, you look

for special characteristics of the equation that you can use as time-savers. Perhaps you can discover symmetry in the equation that leads to corresponding symmetry in the graph. Perhaps you can limit the *extent* of the curve by finding sets of values of one of the variables that fail to yield real values of the other variable; etc.

Here is a short table:

θ (radians)	0	$\pi/12$	$\pi/6$	$\pi/4$	$\pi/3$	$5\pi/12$	$\pi/2$
2θ	0	$\pi/6$	$\pi/3$	$\pi/2$	$2\pi/3$	$5\pi/6$	π
$\cos 2\theta$	1	$\sqrt{3}/2$	$1/2$	0	$-1/2$	$-\sqrt{3}/2$	-1
$r^2 = a^2 \cos 2\theta$	a^2	$a^2\sqrt{3}/2$	$a^2/2$	0	$-a^2/2$	$-a^2\sqrt{3}/2$	$-a^2$
r (length units)	a	$a\sqrt{\sqrt{3}/2}$	$a/\sqrt{2}$	0	...	...	...

Figure 9–47 shows the corresponding points of the graph. Notice that $\pi/4 < \theta < 3\pi/4 \Rightarrow \cos 2\theta < 0$; since there is no real number r such that $r^2 < 0$, there is no point on the graph in a direction θ such that $\pi/4 < \theta < 3\pi/4$.

Other values of θ yield other points $P(r,\theta)$ on the graph. Some of these points are easy to find from the values already tabulated. Since $\cos(-\theta) = \cos\theta$, and the point $(a\sqrt{\sqrt{3}/2},\pi/12)$ lies on the graph, the point $(a\sqrt{\sqrt{3}/2},-\pi/12)$ also lies on the graph. In this way you get the points $(a\sqrt{\sqrt{3}/2},-\pi/12)$, $(a/\sqrt{2},-\pi/6)$ and $(0,-\pi/4)$ without the need for additional calculations. Continuing the table:

θ	$7\pi/12$	$2\pi/3$	$3\pi/4$	$5\pi/6$	$11\pi/12$	π
r	...	...	0	$a/\sqrt{2}$	$a\sqrt{\sqrt{3}/2}$	a

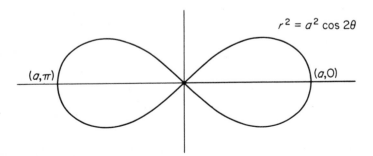

$$r^2 = a^2 \cos 2\theta$$

(a,π) $(a,0)$

Fig. 9–48.

As before, you get the points $(0,-3\pi/4)$, $(a/\sqrt{2},-5/6\pi)$, $(a\sqrt{\sqrt{3}/2},-11\pi/12)$ and $(a,-\pi)$ without further calculations. It becomes clear that the complete graph is the lemniscate of Fig. 9–48. Notice that the graph is symmetrical about the polar axis [$\cos\theta = \cos(-\theta)$], and that no real values of r correspond to values of θ in the ranges $\pi/4 < \theta < 3\pi/4$ and $-3\pi/4 < \theta < -\pi/4$.

(7) Graph the equation $r = a\cos\theta + b$. We begin with the instance where $a = 2$ and $b = 1$,

$$r = 2\cos\theta + 1.$$

θ	0	$\pi/6$	$\pi/3$	$\pi/2$	$2\pi/3$	$5\pi/6$	π
$2\cos\theta$	2	$\sqrt{3}$	1	0	-1	$-\sqrt{3}$	-2
r	3	$1+\sqrt{3}$	2	1	0	$1-\sqrt{3}$	-1

You can continue the table, and plot more points, to get the graph in Fig. 9–49. You can also use the fact that $\cos(-\theta) = \cos\theta$ as before; since $(2,\pi/3)$ lies on the graph, $(2,-\pi/3)$ will also lie on the graph; etc.

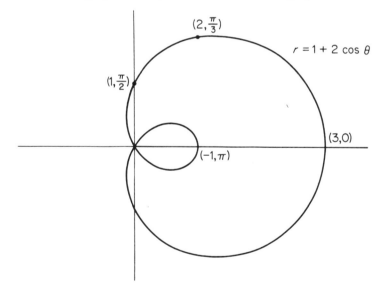

$(2,\frac{\pi}{3})$

$r = 1 + 2\cos\theta$

$(1,\frac{\pi}{2})$

$(3,0)$

$(-1,\pi)$

Fig. 9–49.

This graph is called a *limaçon*. You should try other values of the parameters a and b. The instance in which $a = b$ yields an interesting curve called a *cardioid*. Figure 9–50 displays the graph of the cardioid

$$r = 2\cos\theta + 2.$$

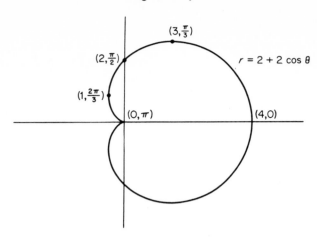

Fig. 9–50.

EXERCISES §906 (cont.)

13. Use polar-coordinate paper to draw the graph of each equation in polar coordinates. To draw the graph of an equation, assign a convenient numerical value to the parameter a.

(a) $r = a \sec \theta$ (b) $r = a \csc \theta$

(c) $r = 2 \sec (\theta - \pi/3)$ (d) $r^2 = a^2 \sin 2\theta$

(e) $r = 3 \cos \theta + 2$ (f) $r = 4 \cos \theta + 4$

(g) $r = 4 \cos \theta - 4$ (h) $r = 4 \sin \theta - 4$

(i) $r = 2 \cos \theta + 3$ (j) $r = a \cos \frac{1}{2}\theta$

(k) $r = a \csc^2 \frac{1}{2}\theta$ (l) $r = a \cos 2\theta$

(m) $r = a \cos 3\theta$ (n) $r = 2 \cos 6\theta + 3$

14. Graph, in polar coordinates, the set of points determined by each of the following conditions.

(a) $0 < r < 3$ (b) $\pi/6 < \theta < \pi/3$

(c) $0 < r < 3$ and $\pi/6 < \theta < \pi/3$ (d) $0 < r < 3$ or $\pi/6 < \theta < \pi/3$

(e) $0 < r < 4 \cos \theta$ (f) $0 < r < 4 \cos \theta$ and $0 < r < 3$

(g) $0 < r < 4 \cos \theta$ or $0 < r < 3$ (h) $0 < r < 4 \cos \theta$ and $\pi/6 < \theta < \pi/3$

(i) $r^2 < 4 \cos 2\theta$ (j) $0 < r < 2 \cos \theta + 2$

(k) $0 < r - 2 < 2 \cos \theta$ (l) $r = 2$ and $r = 4 \cos \theta$

(m) $r = 2 \cos \theta + 2$ and $r = 2\sqrt{3} \sin \theta$ (n) $0 < r < a \cos 3\theta$.

15. Let $P_1(r_1, \theta_1)$ and $P_2(r_2, \theta_2)$ be two points whose polar coordinates are given. Show that the distance between P_1 and P_2 is given by the formula

$$d = \sqrt{r_1^2 + r_2^2 - 2r_1 r_2 \cos (\theta_1 - \theta_2)}.$$

Suggestion: Apply the law of cosines to the triangle whose vertices are P_1, P_2 and the pole, O.

16. Find the distance between P_1 and P_2 for each of the following (see Exercise 15).

(a) $P_1(2,0)$; $P_2(2,\pi/2)$ (b) $P_1(2,0)$; $P_2(2,\pi)$
(c) $P_1(3,\pi/2)$; $P_2(4,-\pi/2)$ (d) $P_1(4,5\pi/6)$; $P_2(1,\pi/6)$
(e) $P_1(5,5\pi/4)$; $P_2(2,\pi/2)$ (f) $P_1(3,1.5)$; $P_2(4,0.8)$.

Answers: (a) $2\sqrt{2}$;   (c) 7;   (d) $\sqrt{21}$.

17. A circle of radius a has its center at $C(k,\omega)$. With the help of the distance formula of Exercise 15, show that the polar equation of the circle is

$$r^2 - 2kr \cos(\theta - \omega) + k^2 = a^2.$$

18. Write the polar equation of the circles whose radii and centers are given (see Exercise 17).

(a) a; $(a,\pi/2)$ (b) a; $(a,0)$
(c) 4; $(4,\pi/6)$ (d) 6; $(2,-\pi/3)$.

Answers: (a) $r = 2a \sin \theta$;   (c) $r = 4\sqrt{3} \cos \theta + 4 \sin \theta$.

907. Complex numbers as vectors

You learned, in Section 104, (page 18) to picture a complex number $x + yi$ as a *directed line segment*, or *vector*, from the origin to the point (x,y); you can also picture a complex number as a vector from the pole to the point (r,θ). You learned, in Section 105, (page 22) to add vectors by laying them end to end, and to multiply vectors by multiplying their lengths and adding their amplitudes.

Notice, in Fig. 9–51, the vector from the origin to the point (x,y). Notice how you add the vector from the origin to (c,d) to the vector from the origin to (a,b): You *translate* it (move it without changing its length or direction) to make its initial point (a,b) rather than $(0,0)$.

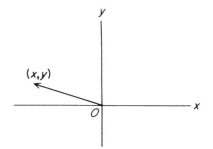 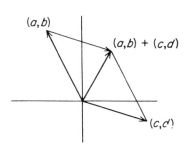

Fig. 9–51.

Notice, in Fig. 9–52, the vector from the pole to the point (r,θ). For this vector, $x = r \cos \theta$ and $y = r \sin \theta$; hence it corresponds to the complex number

$$x + yi = r \cos \theta + ir \sin \theta$$
$$= r(\cos \theta + i \sin \theta).$$

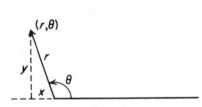 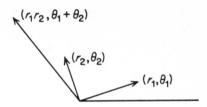

Fig. 9–52.

For the terminal point of the vector, we choose polar coordinates, (r,θ), such that $0° \leq \theta < 360°$ and $r \geq 0$. Then we call $r(\cos \theta + i \sin \theta)$ the *polar form* of the complex number $x + yi$; this polar form displays polar coordinates $r(r \geq 0)$ and $\theta(0° \leq \theta < 360°)$ of the terminal point of the corresponding vector. We call r the *magnitude* and θ the *amplitude* of the vector.

Further useful definitions are

$$r = |x + yi| = \sqrt{x^2 + y^2}$$

$$\theta = \arctan \frac{y}{x}.$$

We speak of $r = |x + yi|$ as the magnitude, or *absolute value*, of $x + yi$. Notice how the absolute value of a complex number, like the absolute value of a real number (page 204), is a non-negative real number.

Notice how you multiply the vectors to (r_1,θ_1) and (r_2,θ_2): The product of these vectors is a vector from the pole to the point $(r_1r_2,\theta_1 + \theta_2)$; that is, the magnitude of the product is the product of the magnitudes and the amplitude of the product is the sum of the amplitudes.

Now the question arises whether the correspondence between the sets of vectors and complex numbers is *preserved* under addition and multiplication. That is, when you add vectors, does the sum correspond to the sum of the corresponding complex numbers? When you multiply vectors, does the product correspond to the product of the corresponding complex numbers?

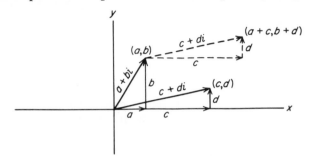

Fig. 9–53.

We consider addition first (see Fig. 9–53):

Vector to $\begin{matrix}(a,b)\\(c,d)\end{matrix}$ corresponds to   *complex number* $\begin{matrix}a+bi\\c+di\end{matrix}$

Sum of these vectors is vector to $(a+c, b+d)$

Sum of these complex numbers is $(a+c)+(b+d)i$

The vector to $(a+c, b+d)$ corresponds to the complex number $(a+c)+(b+d)i$. Hence the sum of the two vectors corresponds to the sum of the corresponding complex numbers; that is, the correspondence is *preserved under addition*.

You should learn to use the simpler diagram (Fig. 9–54). Notice how much like addition of real numbers this is. Addition of real numbers corresponds to laying vectors end to end with due regard for absolute value and sign. Addition of complex numbers corresponds to laying vectors end to end with due regard for absolute value and amplitude.

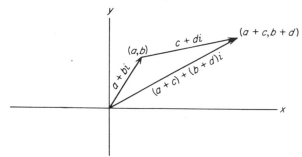

Fig. 9–54.

You can interpret the subtraction

$$(a+bi) - (c+di)$$

as the vector from (c,d) to (a,b). You can also change the sign of the subtrahend and change subtraction to addition; that is (see Fig. 9–55),

$$(a+bi) - (c+di) = (a+bi) + [(-c) + (-d)i].$$

EXERCISES §907

1. Draw vectors to the following points. Find the polar coordinates of the terminal point of each vector. Then write the rectangular form and the polar form of the corresponding complex number.

    (a) $(0,2)$ (b) $(2,0)$ (c) $(-7,0)$ (d) $(4,4)$ (e) $(-3,-3)$
    (f) $(0,-5)$ (g) $(1,5)$ (h) $(-2,4)$ (i) $(3,-2)$ (j) $(-3,-5)$.

    Answers: (c) $-7 + 0i$, $7(\cos 180° + i \sin 180°)$; (g) $1 + 5i$, $\sqrt{26}(\cos 78°41' + i \sin 78°41')$.

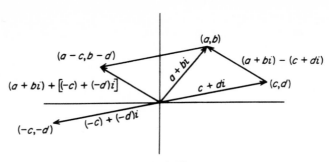

Fig. 9–55.

2. Determine the absolute values of the complex numbers $3 + 4i$ and $2 - 2i$. Find the product $(3 + 4i)(2 - 2i)$ and the absolute value of the product. Verify that the absolute value of the product is the product of the absolute values.

3. Draw graphs for the following additions or subtractions of vectors:

(a) $(2 + i) + (3 - i)$ (b) $(3 - 2i) - (4 + i)$
(c) $(-5 + 3i) + (7 - i)$ (d) $(-2 - i) - (3 + 2i)$
(e) $(2 + i) + (-1 + 3i) - (-2 + i)$.

4. Do you find it more convenient to subtract a vector or to add the negative of the vector? You should know how to get the result either way; hence you should do Exercises 3(b) and 3(d) both ways. In Exercise 3(e), it is probably easiest to proceed as follows: $(2 + i) + (-1 + 3i) + (2 - i)$. But you can get the result in several other ways, for example, $(2 + i) - (1 - 3i) - (-2 + i)$. Try this.

5. Repeat Exercise 3, working with the corresponding complex numbers. For example, in 3(c),

$$(-5 + 3i) + (7 - i) = (-5 + 7) + (3 - 1)i = 2 + 2i.$$

Check your results against the corresponding results for vectors.

6. Let $z_1 = 5 + 2i$ and $z_2 = -3 + i$. Make one vector diagram for $z_1 + z_2$, and another for $z_2 + z_1$. Give a geometric interpretation of the commutative law for addition.

7. Make a drawing to show that the vector $a + bi$ may be thought of as the sum of the vectors $(a + 0i)$ and $(0 + bi)$. Hence *every vector can be resolved into its horizontal and vertical components.*

8. Carry out the multiplication $(a + 0i)(c + di)$. Show that if a is positive, this corresponds geometrically to stretching (or shrinking) $c + di$ by a factor of a, keeping the direction the same. What happens if a is negative?

9. A geometrical construction of the product $(a + bi)(c + di)$ can be made as follows. Draw the two vectors. Form a triangle by joining the tip of one vector to the point $(1,0)$ on the real axis. Construct a triangle similar to this one, using the other vector as the side corresponding to the unit distance of the first triangle. The side of the second triangle that corresponds to the first vector will be the product vector. Show that the product vector so constructed has these properties: (a) its amplitude is the sum of the amplitudes of the factors; and (b) its magnitude is the product of the magnitudes of the factors. Try this construction with the product $(2 + 2i)(1 + 3i)$.

10. A plane heads north with an air speed of 500 mph. There is a 100-mph wind blowing from the west. The velocity of the plane relative to the ground can be represented by the complex number $V = 100 + 500i$. The magnitude of the ground speed of the plane is $|V|$, and direction of travel can be determined from the amplitude of V. Make a sketch and calculate the magnitude of the ground speed.

11. Forces are conveniently expressed by vectors. Suppose two forces $F_1 = 3 + 2i$ and $F_2 = -5 + i$ act on an object at the origin. Determine the magnitude of each of these forces. Find the single force (the vector sum) that is equivalent to these two forces acting together. What is the magnitude of the resultant force? What single force will balance the two so that the resultant is zero?

Now consider multiplication. We use the polar form of the complex numbers:

$$\text{\textit{Vector to} } \begin{matrix} (r_1, \theta_1) \\ (r_2, \theta_2) \end{matrix} \text{ corresponds to \textit{complex number} } \begin{matrix} r_1(\cos\theta_1 + i\sin\theta_1) \\ r_2(\cos\theta_2 + i\sin\theta_2) \end{matrix}$$

Product of these vectors is vector to $(r_1 r_2, \theta_1 + \theta_2)$

Product of these complex numbers is
$$r_1 r_2[(\cos\theta_1\cos\theta_2 - \sin\theta_1\sin\theta_2) + i(\sin\theta_1\cos\theta_2 + \cos\theta_1\sin\theta_2)] = r_1 r_2[\cos(\theta_1 + \theta_2) + i\sin(\theta_1 + \theta_2)]$$

The vector to $(r_1 r_2, \theta_1 + \theta_2)$ corresponds to the complex number

$$r_1 r_2[\cos(\theta_1 + \theta_2) + i\sin(\theta_1 + \theta_2)].$$

Hence the product of the two vectors corresponds to the product of the corresponding complex numbers; that is, the correspondence is *preserved under multiplication*.

A one-to-one correspondence that is preserved under addition and multiplication is especially useful. In the case of vectors and complex numbers, you can work with vectors and interpret your results in terms of complex numbers, or vice versa. Because of its usefulness, mathematicians give such a correspondence a special name; they call it an *isomorphism* (see also page 210). Thus we have proved that the set of vectors in the plane is *isomorphic* to the set of complex numbers.

As a special instance of the formula

$$[r_1(\cos\theta_1 + i\sin\theta_1)][r_2(\cos\theta_2 + i\sin\theta_2)]$$
$$= r_1 r_2[\cos(\theta_1 + \theta_2) + i\sin(\theta_1 + \theta_2)],$$
$$[r(\cos\theta + i\sin\theta)]^2 = r^2(\cos 2\theta + i\sin 2\theta).$$

Also,
$$[r(\cos\theta + i\sin\theta)]^3 = [r(\cos\theta + i\sin\theta)]^2\, r(\cos\theta + i\sin\theta)$$
$$= r^2(\cos 2\theta + i\sin 2\theta)\, r(\cos\theta + i\sin\theta)$$
$$= r^3(\cos 3\theta + i\sin 3\theta).$$

This suggests the more general theorem,

$$n \in N \Rightarrow [r(\cos\theta + i\sin\theta)]^n = r^n(\cos n\theta + i\sin n\theta)$$

which mathematicians call DeMoivre's theorem. [Abraham DeMoivre (1667–1754) was born in France but spent his adult life in England. His work in trigonometry and his work in probability theory make him a worthy contemporary of the better-known Isaac Newton.] As it applies to complex numbers, DeMoivre's theorem states that the nth power of a complex number is the complex number whose magnitude is the nth power of the magnitude of the complex number, and whose amplitude is n times the amplitude of the complex number.

We shall not discuss generalizations of DeMoivre's theorem in detail. We merely suggest, through examples, some leads you may want to follow. Exercises §907 give you opportunities to do this.

(1) Express the complex number $4 + 3i$ in polar form; then picture the power $(4 + 3i)^3$ (see Fig. 9–56 and Fig. 9–57). We have $r^2 = 4^2 + 3^2 = 25$; hence $r = 5$, $\cos\theta = \frac{4}{5}$, and $\sin\theta = \frac{3}{5}$. From the tables, $\theta \doteq 36.9°$.

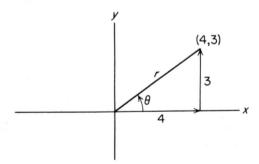

Fig. 9–56.

$$4 + 3i = 5\left(\frac{4}{5} + \frac{3i}{5}\right)$$

$$\doteq 5(\cos 36.9° + i\sin 36.9°)$$

$$(4 + 3i)^3 \doteq 125[\cos 3(36.9°) + i\sin 3(36.9°)]$$

$$= 125(\cos 110.7° + i\sin 110.7°).$$

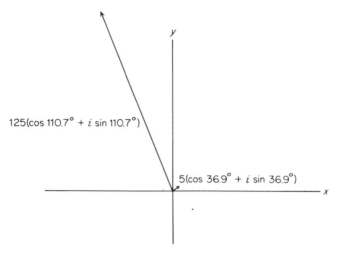

$125(\cos 110.7° + i \sin 110.7°)$

$5(\cos 36.9° + i \sin 36.9°)$

Fig. 9–57.

(2) Express the complex number $\sqrt{3} + i$ in polar form; then picture the fourth power and the fourth roots of $\sqrt{3} + i$ (see Fig. 9–58).

$$\sqrt{3} + i = \sqrt{3} + 1 \cdot i$$

$$r^2 = 3 + 1 = 4, \; r = 2, \; \cos \theta = \sqrt{3}/2, \; \sin \theta = \tfrac{1}{2}, \text{ and } \theta = 30°.$$

$$(\sqrt{3} + i)^4 = [2(\cos 30° + i \sin 30°)]^4$$
$$= 16(\cos 120° + i \sin 120°).$$

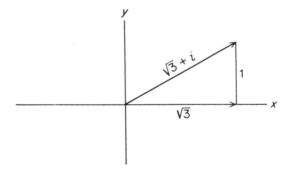

Fig. 9–58.

Draw a graph to show $\sqrt{3} + i$ and $(\sqrt{3} + i)^4$.

Would you dare to say

$$(\sqrt{3} + i)^{1/4} = [2(\cos 30° + i \sin 30°)]^{1/4},$$
$$= \sqrt[4]{2}(\cos 7.5° + i \sin 7.5°)?$$

This amounts to applying DeMoivre's theorem to an instance where the exponent is $\frac{1}{4}$. Surely the result, $\sqrt[4]{2}(\cos 7.5° + i \sin 7.5°)$, is a complex number; moreover,

$$[\sqrt[4]{2}(\cos 7.5° + i \sin 7.5°)]^4 = 2(\cos 30° + i \sin 30°) = \sqrt{3} + i.$$

It is a natural generalization of our previous ideas about roots to call $\sqrt[4]{2}(\cos 7.5° + i \sin 7.5°)$ a fourth root of $2(\cos 30° + i \sin 30°)$. Then the question arises whether there are other fourth roots of $2(\cos 30° + i \sin 30°)$.

We remove the restriction on θ, $0° \le \theta < 360°$, and write:

$$\sqrt{3} + i = 2(\cos 30° + i \sin 30°)$$
$$= 2[\cos(30° + k[360°]) + i \sin (30° + k[360°])]$$

where k is an integer. For examples,

$$\sqrt{3} + i = 2(\cos 30° + i \sin 30°) \qquad (k = 0)$$
$$= 2(\cos 750° + i \sin 750°) \qquad (k = 2)$$
$$= 2(\cos (-1050°) + i \sin (-1050°)). \qquad (k = -3)$$

Proceeding as before,

$$(\sqrt{3} + i)^{1/4} = \sqrt[4]{2}\left[\cos \frac{30° + k(360°)}{4} + i \sin \frac{30° + k(360°)}{4} \right]$$
$$= \sqrt[4]{2}[\cos (7.5° + k[90°]) + i \sin (7.5° + k[90°])].$$

As you assign to k the values $0, 1, 2, \ldots$, you get four distinct complex numbers, namely:

$$z_1 = \sqrt[4]{2}(\cos 7.5° + i \sin 7.5°) \qquad (k = 0)$$
$$z_2 = \sqrt[4]{2}(\cos 97.5° + i \sin 97.5°) \qquad (k = 1)$$
$$z_3 = \sqrt[4]{2}(\cos 187.5° + i \sin 187.5°) \qquad (k = 2)$$
$$z_4 = \sqrt[4]{2}(\cos 277.5° + i \sin 277.5°). \qquad (k = 3)$$

For $k = 4$, $\sqrt[4]{2}(\cos 367.5° + i \sin 367.5°) = z_1$; other integral values of k yield complex numbers equal to $z_1, z_2, z_3,$ or z_4.

The complex numbers z_1, z_2, z_3, z_4 are roots of the equation $z^4 = \sqrt{3} + i$; each is a fourth root of $\sqrt{3} + i$. But we shall not assign the symbol $(\sqrt{3}+i)^{1/4}$ to one of these numbers and define a *principal* fourth root of $\sqrt{3} + i$ as we previously defined principal roots of real numbers (page 193). Hence we shall not use symbols like $(\sqrt{3} + i)^{1/4}$ or $\sqrt[4]{\sqrt{3} + i}$; we avoid such ambiguous symbols. Draw a graph to show $\sqrt{3} + i$, $z_1, z_2, z_3,$ and z_4.

Notice that the equation $z^4 = \sqrt{3} + i$ has four distinct roots in the set C of complex numbers. It can be proved that a polynomial equation, $p(z) = 0$, of degree n, has exactly n roots in the set C. We illustrate with some further examples.

(3) Find the cube roots of unity. This means to solve the equation $z^3 = 1$. Since the equation is of degree 3, we expect to find exactly three cube roots of unity.

$$z^3 = 1 = 1 + 0 \cdot i = 1(\cos 0 + i \sin 0)$$
$$= 1[\cos (0 + 2\pi k) + i \sin (0 + 2\pi k)].$$

Hence
$$z = \sqrt[3]{1} \left(\cos \frac{2\pi k}{3} + i \sin \frac{2\pi k}{3} \right).$$

The three cube roots of unity are the complex numbers z_1, z_2, and z_3, where

$$z_1 = 1(\cos 0 + i \sin 0) = 1,$$

$$z_2 = 1 \left(\cos \frac{2\pi}{3} + i \sin \frac{2\pi}{3} \right),$$

and
$$z_3 = 1 \left(\cos \frac{4\pi}{3} + i \sin \frac{4\pi}{3} \right).$$

Draw a graph to show $z^3 = 1$, z_1, z_2, and z_3. Show that $z_1^3 = z_2^3 = z_3^3 = 1$. Express z_1, z_2, and z_3 in cartesian form as $z_1 = 1$, $z_2 = -\frac{1}{2} + \frac{1}{2}\sqrt{3}i$, $z_3 = -\frac{1}{2} - \frac{1}{2}\sqrt{3}i$.

(4) Solve the quadratic equation $z^2 - z + 1 = 0$. The discriminant $\Delta = 1 - 4 = -3$. Hence the equation $z^2 - z + 1 = 0$ is equivalent to

$$z = \frac{1}{2} + \frac{\sqrt{3}}{2}i \quad \text{or} \quad z = \frac{1}{2} - \frac{\sqrt{3}}{2}i.$$

Notice that this polynomial equation of degree 2 has exactly two roots. Its solution set is $\{z_1, z_2\}$, where

$$z_1 = 1 \left(\frac{1}{2} + \frac{\sqrt{3}}{2}i \right) = 1(\cos 60° + i \sin 60°)$$

$$z_2 = 1 \left(\frac{1}{2} - \frac{\sqrt{3}}{2}i \right) = 1(\cos 300° + i \sin 300°).$$

Substitute z_1 in the equation $z^2 - z + 1 = 0$, and notice that $z_1^2 - z_1 + 1 = 0$; repeat the substitution, using z_2.

We hope these examples arouse your curiosity and give you the urge to experiment further.

EXERCISES §907 (cont.)

12. Convert each complex number to polar form:
(a) $2 + 2i$ (b) $8i$ (c) $-5i$
(d) -12 (e) $2\sqrt{3} - 2i$ (f) $-5 + 12i$
(g) $6 + i$ (h) $-7 - 4i$ (i) $-13 - 13i$
(j) 54 (k) $1 - 5i$ (l) $-1 + 5i$.

Answers: (a) $2\sqrt{2}(\cos 45° + i \sin 45°)$;   (f) $13(\cos 112°37' + i \sin 112°37')$.

13. Convert each complex number to rectangular form:

(a) 6(cos 60° + i sin 60°)   (b) 5(cos 0° + i sin 0°)

(c) 12(cos 90° + i sin 90°)   (d) 4(cos 270° + i sin 270°)

(e) 2(cos π + i sin π)   (f) 3√2(cos $\frac{1}{4}\pi$ + i sin $\frac{1}{4}\pi$)

(g) 10(cos 27° + i sin 27°)   (h) 10(cos 207° + i sin 207°)

(i) 4(cos 142° + i sin 142°)   (j) 17(cos 304° + i sin 304°)

(k) 20(cos 450° + i sin 450°)   (l) 4(cos 5π + i sin 5π).

Answers: (a) $3 + 3\sqrt{3}i$;   (d) $-4i$;   (h) $-8.91 - 4.54i$.

14. Change the answer of Example (1) of the text to rectangular form; then carry out the multiplication of three factors of $4 + 3i$ in rectangular form and compare results.

15. Repeat the work of Example (1), estimating θ to the nearest tenth of a minute. Repeat Exercise 14 and note the improvement in the approximation.

Partial answer: $\theta = 36°52.2'$.

16. Carry out the indicated multiplications.

(a) [2(cos 90° + i sin 90°)][4(cos 180° + i sin 180°)]

(b) [6(cos 60° + i sin 60°)][5(cos 30° + i sin 30°)]

(c) [12(cos 45° + i sin 45°)][4(cos 225° + i sin 225°)]

(d) [3(cos 31° + i sin 31°)][2(cos 97° + i sin 97°)]

(e) [5(cos 216° + i sin 216°)][7(cos 144° + i sin 144°)]

(f) [2(cos 30° + i sin 30°)]³.

(g) [√2(cos 32° + i sin 32°)]¹².

Answers: (a) 8(cos 270° + i sin 270°) = $-8i$;   (g) 64(cos 24° + i sin 24°).

17. In Exercise 16, parts (a), (b), (c) and (f), change to rectangular form, then multiply and compare results.

18. Show that

$$\frac{1}{\cos \theta + i \sin \theta} = \cos (-\theta) + i \sin (-\theta).$$

Hint: Multiply numerator and denominator by

$$\cos \theta - i \sin \theta = \cos (-\theta) + i \sin (-\theta).$$

19. Show that

$$\frac{r_1(\cos \theta_1 + i \sin \theta_1)}{r_2(\cos \theta_2 + i \sin \theta_2)} = \frac{r_1}{r_2} [\cos (\theta_1 - \theta_2) + i \sin (\theta_1 - \theta_2)].$$

Hint: Use the results of Exercise 18.

20. Use Exercise 18 to prove that DeMoivre's theorem holds for negative integers.

21. Carry out the division $4i/(\sqrt{3} + i)$ in rectangular form, then convert numerator and denominator to polar form and apply Exercise 19. Compare results.

22. Determine the two square roots of i. First use the polar representation of i. Then draw a graph to show $z^2 = i$, z_1, and z_2.

23. Determine all the distinct solutions of each equation.

(a) $z^3 = -1$ (b) $z^4 = 1$ (c) $z^4 = -8 + 8\sqrt{3}i$

(d) $z^6 = -3 + i$ (e) $z^2 = -4 + 7i$ (f) $z^3 = 5 - 2i$.

Answers: (a) $\cos 60° + i \sin 60° = \frac{1}{2} + \frac{1}{2}\sqrt{3}i$, $\cos 180° + i \sin 180° = -1$, $\cos 300° + i \sin 300° = \frac{1}{2} - \frac{1}{2}\sqrt{3}i$; (d) $\sqrt[12]{10}(\cos 26°56' + i \sin 26°56') \doteq 1.080 + 0.549i$, $\sqrt[12]{10}(\cos 86°56' + i \sin 86°56') \doteq 0.065 + 1.210i$, etc.

24. (a) According to DeMoivre's theorem,

$$(\cos \theta + i \sin \theta)^3 = \cos 3\theta + i \sin 3\theta.$$

By direct multiplication,
$$
\begin{aligned}
(\cos \theta + i \sin \theta)^3 &= (\cos \theta + i \sin \theta)(\cos^2 \theta + 2i \cos \theta \sin \theta + i^2 \sin^2 \theta) \\
&= (\cos \theta + i \sin \theta)[(\cos^2 \theta - \sin^2 \theta) + i(2 \sin \theta \cos \theta)] \\
&= (4 \cos^3 \theta - 3 \cos \theta) + i(3 \sin \theta - 4 \sin^3 \theta).
\end{aligned}
$$

Hence, equating the real and imaginary parts of $\cos 3\theta + i \sin 3\theta$ and

$$(4 \cos^3 \theta - 3 \cos \theta) + i(3 \sin \theta - 4 \sin^3 \theta),$$
$$\cos 3\theta = 4 \cos^3 - 3 \cos \theta$$
$$\sin 3\theta = 3 \sin \theta - 4 \sin^3 \theta.$$

(b) Proceeding as in part (a), derive identities for $\cos 4\theta$ and $\sin 4\theta$.

908. Conditions that involve trigonometric ratios

You have already met conditions that involve trigonometric ratios. For example, $\cos x = 0.8$ is such a condition. You know how to solve this condition, to get an approximation for x, using tables of the trigonometric ratios. You find $x \doteq \pm 0.64 + k(2\pi)$, $k \in I$. You are usually limited to approximations to the solutions of trigonometric conditions; however, these approximations can be made as precise as you please by using precise enough tables of trigonometric ratios.

In Section 701 (page 291), we discussed graphical solutions of systems of conditions. Some of these systems of conditions involved trigonometric ratios. Our purpose in this section is to give you more experience with graphical solutions of conditions that involve trigonometric ratios; we shall also make use of identities derived in previous sections of this chapter to restate trigonometric conditions in more convenient forms. We proceed with examples that lead up to Exercises §908.

(1) Solve the condition $2 \sin^2 x - \cos x + 1 = 0$. We can express this condition as a polynomial in $\cos x$, as follows:

$$
\begin{aligned}
2 \sin^2 x - \cos x + 1 &= 2(1 - \cos^2 x) - \cos x + 1 \\
&= -2 \cos^2 x - \cos x + 3.
\end{aligned}
$$

Hence the condition $2 \sin^2 x - \cos x + 1 = 0$ is equivalent to the condition

$$2 \cos^2 x + \cos x - 3 = 0.$$

This new condition is a quadratic equation in the variable cos x. We find

$$2\cos^2 x + \cos x - 3 = (2\cos x + 3)(\cos x - 1) = 0$$

and $$\cos x = -\tfrac{3}{2} \quad \text{or} \quad \cos x = 1.$$

The condition $\cos x = -\tfrac{3}{2}$ has no solution in the set of real numbers, since $-1 \le \cos x \le 1$. The condition $\cos x = 1$ has the solution set $\{0 + k(2\pi)\} = \{2\pi k\}$, $k \in I$. As a check: $2\sin^2(2k\pi) - \cos(2k\pi) + 1 = 2(0)^2 - 1 + 1 = 0$.

This algebraic solution is much easier than the corresponding graphical solution. It would be tedious to graph $y = 2\sin^2 x - \cos x + 1$, and look for its x-intercepts. When algebraic methods fail, however, the graphic method is often a lifesaver.

(2) Solve the condition $\cos 3x + 0.6 = 0$. You could use the identity $\cos 3x = 4\cos^3 x - 3\cos x$ to reduce this condition to a polynomial condition in cos x. Then you could solve for cos x, using the methods of Chapter 6. You should remember, however, that you want to solve for x rather than for cos x. It is easier to proceed as follows (see Fig. 9–59):

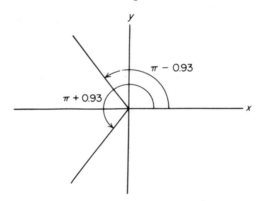

Fig. 9–59.

$$\cos 3x = -0.6$$
$$3x \doteq (\pi \pm .93) + k(2\pi)$$
$$= \pm 0.93 + (2k + 1)\pi.$$

Hence the set of approximate solutions is

$$\left\{ \pm 0.31 + (2k + 1)\frac{\pi}{3} \right\}, \quad k \in I.$$

(3) Solve the condition $\sin 2x - 2\cos x = 0$.
$$\sin 2x - 2\cos x = 2\sin x \cos x - 2\cos x$$
$$= 2\cos x (\sin x - 1).$$

The condition, $2 \cos x (\sin x - 1) = 0$, is equivalent to

$$\cos x = 0 \quad \text{or} \quad \sin x = 1.$$

If $\cos x = 0$, $x = \pm \dfrac{\pi}{2} + k(2\pi), \quad k \in I.$

If $\sin x = 1$, $x = \dfrac{\pi}{2} + k(2\pi), \quad k \in I.$

The solution set of $\sin 2x - 2 \cos x = 0$ is: $\{\pm\pi/2 + k(2\pi)\}, \ k \in I.$ As a check:

$$\sin \left(2 \left[\pm \frac{\pi}{2} + k(2\pi) \right] \right) - 2 \cos \left[\pm \frac{\pi}{2} + k(2\pi) \right]$$

$$= \sin \left[\pm\pi + k(4\pi) \right] - 2(0) = 0.$$

(4) Solve the condition $\sin x - 2 \cos x + 1 = 0$. This is equivalent to

$$\sin x + 1 = \pm 2\sqrt{1 - \sin^2 x}. \quad \text{(Why?)}$$

Squaring to eliminate the radical, we obtain

$$\sin^2 x + 2 \sin x + 1 = 4(1 - \sin^2 x)$$
$$5 \sin^2 x + 2 \sin x - 3 = 0.$$

This quadratic equation in $\sin x$ is equivalent to

$$\sin x = -1 \quad \text{or} \quad \sin x = .6.$$

Hence $x = \arcsin(-1) \quad \text{or} \quad x = \arcsin(.6).$

Direct substitution of $x = \arcsin(-1) = 3\pi/2 + 2k\pi$ in the given condition shows that $3\pi/2 + 2k\pi$ is a solution for each replacement of $k \in I$. For $x = \arcsin(.6)$, $\cos(\arcsin .6) = \pm.8$, and

$$\sin x - 2 \cos x + 1 = (.6) - 2(\pm.8) + 1.$$

Notice that $(.6) - 2(.8) + 1 = 0$, but $(.6) - 2(-.8) + 1 \neq 0$. Hence $x = \arcsin(.6)$ yields solutions of the given condition only when $\cos x > 0$; then $x \doteq .64 + 2k\pi$. The solution set is

$$\left\{ \frac{3\pi}{2} + 2k\pi, .64 + 2k\pi \text{ (approx.)} \right\}, \quad k \in I.$$

(5) Solve the condition $3 \sin x = 4 \cos x$. First we graph $y = 3 \sin x$ and $y = 4 \cos x$ (Fig. 9–60). Notice the intersections at approximately $\ldots, (-3\pi/4, -2), (\pi/4, 2), (5\pi/4, -2), \ldots$. Approximate solutions of the given condition are: $\ldots, -7\pi/4, -3\pi/4, \pi/4, 5\pi/4, \ldots$; that is, $\pi/4 + k\pi, \ k \in I.$

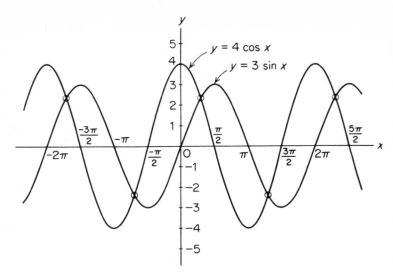

Fig. 9–60.

Next, we use polar coordinates to help visualize the problem. Consider the graphs of $r = 3 \sin \theta$ and $r = 4 \cos \theta$ (Fig. 9–61). The graphs seem to intersect at the pole. Actually, $r = 3 \sin \theta$ passes through the point $(0,0)$, and $r = 4 \cos \theta$ passes through the point $(0,\pi/2)$. In polar coordinates, the pole does not have a unique θ-coordinate; $(0,0)$ and $(0,\pi/2)$ are different number-pairs, although they correspond to the same point. The interesting

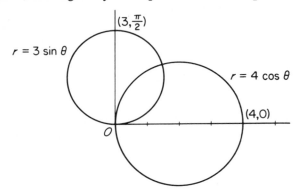

Fig. 9–61.

intersection is at a point that is roughly $(2,\pi/4)$. Recall that other coordinates of this point are $(-2,-3\pi/4)$, $(-2,5\pi/4)$, $(2,9\pi/4)$, etc.

To perform an algebraic solution, you could follow the method of

Example (4); but once you notice that a value of x that makes $\cos x = 0$ is not a solution, you may divide by $\cos x$ to obtain

$$\frac{3 \sin x}{\cos x} = 4$$

$$\tan x = \frac{4}{3}$$

$$x = \arctan \frac{4}{3}$$

$$\doteq .93 + k\pi, \quad k \in I.$$

Notice that this agrees with the crude solution, $\{\pi/4 + k\pi\}$, which we obtained by graphical methods ($\pi/4 \doteq 3.14/4 \doteq 0.8$).

Even these few examples are enough to suggest the great variety of conditions that involve trigonometric ratios. We can not hope to study such conditions exhaustively. Exercises §908 give you a chance to experiment further with them.

EXERCISES §908

1. Express each condition as a polynomial in $\sin x$, $\cos x$, or $\tan x$. Solve this polynomial condition for $\sin x$, $\cos x$, or $\tan x$ and then for x. Check your solutions by substitution in the given condition.

(a) $5 \cos^2 x + 4 \sin x - 4 = 0$ (b) $7 - 5 \cos x - \sin^2 x = 0$
(c) $3 \sec^2 x + \tan x - 5 = 0$ (d) $\cos^2 x - \sin x + 1 = 0$
(e) $2 \sin^2 x = 3 \cos x$ (f) $2 \cos^2 x = 5 \sin x + 3.$

Answers: (a) $5 \sin^2 x - 4 \sin x - 1 = 0$ is equivalent to $\sin x = -\frac{1}{5}$ or 1; hence the set of approximate solutions is

$$\{-.201 + 2k\pi, \; 3.343 + 2k\pi, \; \pi/2 + 2k\pi\}, \quad k \in I.$$

(c) $3 \tan^2 x + \tan x - 2 = 0$ is equivalent to $\tan x = \frac{2}{3}$ or -1; hence $x \doteq .588 + k\pi, \; 3\pi/4 + k\pi, \; k \in I.$

2. Solve each condition for x.

(a) $\tan 5x = .97$ (b) $\operatorname{ctn} 2x = 4.9$ (c) $\sin 2x = 4.8$ (d) $\cos (x/5) = .049.$

Answer: (b) $2x \doteq .20 + k\pi, \; k \in I$, yields $x \doteq .10 + k(\pi/2), \; k \in I.$

3. Solve each condition for x.

(a) $6 \sin x + \sin 2x = 0$ (b) $\sin x + 6 \sin 2x = 0$
(c) $\cos 3x + 3 \cos x + 2 = 0$ (d) $\cos 2x = \cos x$
(e) $\sin 2x = \cos 2x$ (f) $\tan \frac{1}{2}x = \sin x.$

Answer: (a) $x = k\pi$; (d) $x = 2k\pi$ or $\pm 2\pi/3 + 2k\pi.$

4. Solve Example (4) by changing to an equivalent condition involving only $\cos x$.

5. Use the methods of Example (4) to solve:

(a) $\sin x + \cos x - 1 = 0$ (b) $4 \sin x - 3 \cos x - 4 = 0$

(c) $4 \sin x + 3 \cos x - 4 = 0$ (d) $\sin 2x + \cos 2x - 1 = 0$.

Answer: (a) $x = 2k\pi$ or $x = \pi/2 + 2k\pi$.

6. Solve Example (5) by the methods of Example (4). Compare methods and answers.

7. Use the methods of Example (5) to solve

(a) $2 \cos x = 5 \sin x$ (b) $3 \sin x = \cos x$

(c) $2 \sin x + \cos x = 0$ (d) $13 \cos x + 50 \sin x = 0$.

Answer: (a) $x \doteq .38 + 2k\pi$ or $3.52 + 2k\pi$.

8. Show that the condition $\sin 3x + 3 \sin x - 5 = 0$ has no solution. *Hint:* $(\sin x \le 1 \text{ and } \sin 3x \le 1) \Rightarrow (\sin 3x + 3 \sin x \le 4)$.

9. Solve the following conditions:

(a) $\cos 3x + 5 \cos x + 2 = 0$ (b) $\cos 3x - 5 \cos x + 2 = 0$.

Suggestion for part (a): Use the identity $\cos 3x = 4 \cos^3 x - 3 \cos x$ to change this condition to the equivalent condition $2 \cos^3 x + \cos x + 1 = 0$. Replace $\cos x$ by s to secure the polynomial equation $2s^3 + s + 1 = 0$. Now use the methods of Chapter 6 to find roots of this equation. Ignore roots larger than 1 or less than -1. If s_1 is a root, then $\cos x = s_1$, or $x = \arccos s_1$. *Answer:* $x = \arccos(-.5898)$.

909. Further applications of the trigonometric ratios

We hope you have already sensed the usefulness of the trigonometric ratios and the trigonometric functions. Many people realize that surveyors, astronomers, and navigators use trigonometry. Fewer people realize that many branches of modern science rely heavily upon the trigonometric functions as convenient mathematical models.

We shall display well-organized logarithmic solutions of two oblique triangles. These problems are realistic; you use your knowledge of the trigonometric ratios to secure efficient solutions and checks.

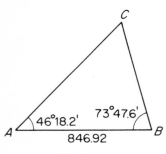

Fig. 9–62.

We shall also display sample formulas, from different fields of study, that involve the trigonometric ratios and their inverses. Of necessity we stop short of delving deeply into specialized problems. We hope to give you some little notion of the usefulness of the trigonometric ratios; we must rely upon you to find further applications to the fields of your special interest.

The following examples will prepare you for Exercises §909.

(1) The base line for a survey is 846.92 ft

long. The angles at the two ends of the base line (to the next station) are
73°47.6′ and 46°18.2′. Solve the triangle.

The first step is to sketch the triangle (Fig. 9–62). You already know how
to complete the solution using the law of sines. We organize this solution
conveniently as follows:

Formulas:

$$C = 180° - (A + B) \qquad \frac{a}{\sin A} = \frac{c}{\sin C} \qquad \frac{b}{\sin B} = \frac{c}{\sin C}$$

$$\sin C = \sin (A + B) \qquad a = \frac{c \sin A}{\sin (A + B)} \qquad b = \frac{c \sin B}{\sin (A + B)}$$

Computing Form:

$c = 846.92$	$\log c = 2.92784$	$\log c = 2.92784$
$A = 46°18.2′$	$\log \sin A = 9.85914 - 10$	
$B = 73°47.6′$		$\log \sin B = 9.98239 - 10$
$179°60.0′$		

$A+B = 120°05.8′ \quad -\log \sin (A+B) = 0.06289 \quad -\log \sin (A+B) = 0.06289$

$C = 59°54.2′$

$a = 707.73 \qquad \log a = 2.84987$

$b = 939.98 \qquad\qquad\qquad\qquad\qquad \log b = 2.97312$

First you make the computing form. If you must solve many triangles of the
same type, you print a form. Then you fill in the given data and calculate C.
Then you look up all the logarithms, avoiding unnecessary turning of pages
by skipping around in the computing form. Then you perform the calculations with the logarithms. Finally you get *a* and *b* by using the logarithm
table backwards.

Notice the use of sin $(A + B) = \sin C$ to avoid the chance of an error in
calculating C. Notice the use of $-\log \sin (A + B)$ to avoid subtraction.

Check: First you look back to the sketch to see if the computed values of
C, *a*, and *b* look right.

Then you use a formula that involves the parts of triangle *ABC* in a new
way. An excellent formula for this problem is

$$\frac{b + a}{c} = \frac{\cos \frac{1}{2}(B - A)}{\sin (\frac{1}{2}C)}.$$

This is one of *Mollweide's equations*, often used for checking purposes.
Notice that it involves *a*, *b*, *c*, *A*, *B*, and *C*. It is hard to imagine the possibility
of securing a check with this formula when there is an error in the solution

of triangle ABC. We use the formula first. Then we prove that the formula is an identity for the set of triangles in the plane.

$$b = 939.98$$
$$a = 707.73$$
$$b + a = 1647.71 \qquad\qquad \log (b + a) = 3.21688$$
$$c = 846.92 \qquad\qquad\qquad\quad \log c = 2.92784$$

$$\log \frac{b + a}{c} = 0.28904$$

$$B = 73°47.6'$$
$$A = 46°18.2'$$
$$B - A = 27°29.4'$$
$$\tfrac{1}{2}(B - A) = 13°44.7' \qquad \log \cos \tfrac{1}{2}(A - B) = 9.98738 - 10$$
$$C = 59°54.2'$$
$$\tfrac{1}{2}C = 29°57.1' \qquad\qquad \log \sin (\tfrac{1}{2}C) = 9.69833 - 10$$

$$\log \frac{\cos \tfrac{1}{2}(A - B)}{\sin (\tfrac{1}{2}C)} = 0.28905.$$

Notice that there is no need to calculate $(b + a)/c$ and $[\cos \tfrac{1}{2}(B - A)]/\sin (\tfrac{1}{2}C)$. The fact that their logarithms are equal, $0.28904 \doteq 0.28905$, is sufficient. We pause now to prove the identity,

$$\frac{b + a}{c} = \frac{\cos \tfrac{1}{2}(B - A)}{\sin (\tfrac{1}{2}C)}.$$

$$\frac{b + a}{c} = \frac{b}{c} + \frac{a}{c} = \frac{\sin B}{\sin C} + \frac{\sin A}{\sin C} \qquad \text{(law of sines)}$$

$$= \frac{\sin B + \sin A}{\sin C} \qquad\qquad \text{(adding fractions)}$$

$$= \frac{2 \sin \tfrac{1}{2}(B + A) \cos \tfrac{1}{2}(B - A)}{\sin C} \qquad \begin{array}{l}\text{(factoring } \sin B + \sin A \text{ as} \\ \text{in Section 904, page 445)}\end{array}$$

Since

$$\sin C = 2 \sin (\tfrac{1}{2}C) \cos (\tfrac{1}{2}C) \qquad\qquad (\sin 2\alpha = 2 \sin \alpha \cos \alpha)$$
$$= 2 \sin \tfrac{1}{2}C \cos \tfrac{1}{2}[180° - (B + A)] \qquad (C = 180° - (B + A))$$
$$= 2 \sin \tfrac{1}{2}C \cos [90° - \tfrac{1}{2}(B + A)] \qquad \text{(distributive law)}$$
$$= 2 \sin \tfrac{1}{2}C \sin \tfrac{1}{2}(B + A), \qquad\qquad (\cos (90° - \alpha) = \sin \alpha)$$

this reduces to

$$\frac{b + a}{c} = \frac{\cos \tfrac{1}{2}(B - A)}{\sin (\tfrac{1}{2}C)}.$$

This proof is typical. You use what you know about the special structure of the trigonometric ratios to write the expressions that appear on one side of an equation in other forms.

You may wish to prove another of Mollweide's equations in a similar way. This is

$$\frac{b - a}{c} = \frac{\sin \frac{1}{2}(B - A)}{\cos (\frac{1}{2}C)}.$$

When you divide the members of the two Mollweide equations, you get

$$\frac{b + a}{b - a} = \frac{\cos \frac{1}{2}(B - A)}{\sin (\frac{1}{2}C)} \div \frac{\sin \frac{1}{2}(B - A)}{\cos (\frac{1}{2}C)}$$

$$= \frac{\cos \frac{1}{2}(B - A) \cos (\frac{1}{2}C)}{\sin \frac{1}{2}(B - A) \sin (\frac{1}{2}C)}$$

$$= \frac{\cot (\frac{1}{2}C)}{\tan \frac{1}{2}(B - A)}$$

$$= \frac{\cot [90° - \frac{1}{2}(B + A)]}{\tan \frac{1}{2}(B - A)}$$

$$= \frac{\tan \frac{1}{2}(B + A)}{\tan \frac{1}{2}(B - A)}.$$

The identity, $\dfrac{b + a}{b - a} = \dfrac{\tan \frac{1}{2}(B + A)}{\tan \frac{1}{2}(B - A)}$, is called the *law of tangents*. We shall

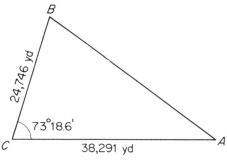

Fig. 9–63.

use it, in Example (2), to perform a logarithmic solution of a triangle in which two sides and the included angle are known. Recall, from Section 902, the need for such a formula to replace the law of cosines and gain the convenience of logarithms.

(2) Given $a = 24{,}746$ yd, $b = 38{,}291$ yd, and $C = 73°18.6'$, solve triangle ABC (see Fig. 9–63).

Formulas: *Check Formula:*

$$B + A = 180° - C \qquad \frac{a}{\sin A} = \frac{b}{\sin B} = \frac{c}{\sin C}$$

$$\tan \tfrac{1}{2}(B - A) = \frac{b - a}{b + a} \tan \tfrac{1}{2}(B + A)$$

$$B = \tfrac{1}{2}(B + A) + \tfrac{1}{2}(B - A)$$
$$A = \tfrac{1}{2}(B + A) - \tfrac{1}{2}(B - A)$$

$$c = \frac{a \sin C}{\sin A}.$$

Computing Form:

$179°60.0'$	
$C = 73°18.6'$	$\log \sin C = 9.98131 - 10$
$B + A = 106°41.4'$	

$\tfrac{1}{2}(B + A) = 53°20.7'$ $\log \tan \tfrac{1}{2}(B + A) = 0.12834$

$b = 38{,}291$

$a = 24{,}746$ $\log a = 4.39351$

$b - a = 13{,}545$ $\log (b - a) = 4.13178$

$b + a = 63{,}037$ $-\log (b + a) = 5.20040 - 10$

$\tfrac{1}{2}(B - A) = 16°06.4'$ $\log \tan \tfrac{1}{2}(B - A) = 9.46052 - 10$

$B = 69°27.1'$

$A = 37°14.3'$ $-\log \sin A = 0.21815$

$c = 39{,}172$ $\log c = 4.59297$

Check: First examine the original sketch as a check on the solution. Then,

$a = 24{,}746$ $\log a = 4.39351$

$A = 37°14.3'$ $\log \sin A = 9.78185 - 10$

$$\log \frac{a}{\sin A} = 4.61166$$

$b = 38{,}291$ $\log b = 4.58310$

$B = 69°27.1'$ $\log \sin B = 9.97145 - 10$

$$\log \frac{b}{\sin B} = 4.61165$$

$c = 39{,}172$ $\log c = 4.59297$

$C = 73°18.6'$ $\log \sin C = 9.98131 - 10$

$$\log \frac{c}{\sin C} = 4.61166$$

Examples (1) and (2) are typical of logarithmic solutions of oblique triangles. We shall not go into the solution of spherical triangles here; but astronomers and navigators make frequent use of calculation techniques like those illustrated above to solve spherical triangles. For example, a navigator measures the *altitude* above the horizon, and the *azimuth* angle (from true north) of a star. He uses star tables, and the time of his observations, to calculate a *line of position*. He uses a second set of observations to get a second line of position. The intersection of these two lines of position gives him his latitude and longitude.

(3) Find the width W (see Fig. 9–64) of a cutter for milling a splined shaft having 8 splines 0.223 in. wide, and a diameter, B, of 1.317 in. You may wish to prove for yourself the formula taken from *Machinery's Handbook*, Industrial Press, New York.

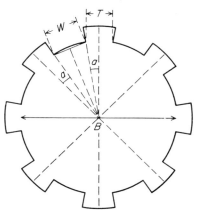

Fig. 9–64.

$$W = B \sin \left(\frac{360°/N - 2a}{2} \right).$$

N represents the number of splines; $360°/N$ is the angle used by 1 spline; $(360°/N - 2a)/2$ is the angle in the triangle we use to get $W/2$; in this triangle,

$$\frac{W/2}{B/2} = \sin \frac{360°/N - 2a}{2}.$$

For $N = 8$, $T = 0.223$, and $B = 1.317$,

$$\sin a = \frac{T/2}{B/2} = \frac{0.223}{1.317} \doteq .16932; \quad \text{hence} \quad a = 9°45'.$$

$$W \doteq 1.317 \sin \left(\frac{45° - 19°30'}{2} \right)$$

$$= 1.317 \sin 12°45'$$

$$\doteq .291 \text{ in.}$$

(4) Use Snell's law of refraction, $n = \sin i/\sin r = v/v'$, to calculate the velocity of light, v, in a plastic, from the velocity of light in air, $v' = 1.86 \times 10^5$ mi/sec, given $i = 28°$ and $r = 34°$ (see Fig. 9–65).

We have
$$v = v' \frac{\sin i}{\sin r} = 1.86 \times 10^5 \frac{\sin 28°}{\sin 34°}$$

$$\doteq 1.56 \times 10^5 \text{ mi/sec.}$$

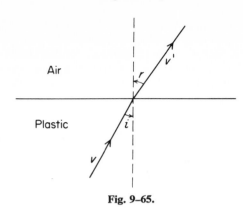

Fig. 9–65.

EXERCISES §909

1. Solve the following triangles. Check with one of Mollweide's equations.

(a) $B =$ 63°39.3' $C = 22°17.6'$ $a = 629.32$
(b) $B =$ 38°54.2' $a = 2964.6$ $c = 4276.3$
(c) $A = 117°21.8'$ $b = 21.326$ $c = 14.397$
(d) $A =$ 31°45.6' $a = 593.26$ $b = 347.61.$

2. A fire tower at point A is known to be 17396 yd from a second tower at B. A forest ranger at A sees the smoke of a fire in the direction of 42°18.3' north of the line from A to B, while the ranger at B finds the fire to be 58°24.6' north of the line from B to A. How far is the fire from each tower?

3. Two forces are acting on an object with an angle of 137°46.8' between their lines of action. If the magnitudes of the forces are 264.15 lb and 421.37 lb, what is the magnitude of the resultant? (*Suggestion:* Represent the forces with vectors. Then solve the triangle for the length of the vector sum.)

4. Two points A and B are separated by an impassable swamp. From a third point C it is possible to make the measurements: $CA = 1272.3$ ft, $CB = 1465.4$ ft, and angle $ACB = 67°21.8'$. What is the distance from A to B?

5. Prove Mollweide's second equation, $\dfrac{b - a}{c} = \dfrac{\sin \frac{1}{2}(B - A)}{\cos \frac{1}{2}C}$.

6. Sometimes it is useful to write a given formula in a different form. Show that the formula of Example (3) can be written as

$$W = \sqrt{B^2 - T^2} \sin \frac{180°}{N} - T \cos \frac{180°}{N} .$$

In this form you avoid calculating angle a; but you must calculate a square root. Use this formula to determine W for the data given in Example (3), and compare results. *Hint:*

$$B \sin \left(\frac{360°/N - 2a}{2} \right) = B \sin \left(\frac{180°}{N} - a \right) = B \left(\cos a \sin \frac{180°}{N} - \sin a \cos \frac{180°}{N} \right) .$$

Now use $\sin a = T/B$ with $\cos a = \sqrt{1 - \sin^2 a}$.

7. In Example (3), the distance along the arc, W_{arc}, is a good estimate for the length of the chord, W, when the angle subtending the arc is small. Show that

$$W_{\text{arc}} = B\frac{\pi}{N} - T.$$

Then estimate W for the data of Example (3), using W_{arc}.

Answer: $W_{\text{arc}} \doteq .294.$

8. A ray of light passes from alcohol to air with $i = 42°$. The angle r is found by measurement to be $65°$. Use Snell's law to determine the velocity of light in alcohol.

9. The number n in Snell's law is called the index of refraction of the second medium with respect to the first. The index of refraction of a flint glass with respect to air is $n = 1.754$. Determine i when $r = 10°, 20°, 30°, 34°$.

Answers: $(10°,17°44')$; $(20°,36°52')$; $(30°,61°17')$; $(34°,78°46')$.

10. The set of number-pairs, $\{(r,i)\}$, of Exercise 9 is a function. Solve for i in terms of r. Show that $r \le \arcsin 1/n$.

Partial answer: $i = \text{Arcsin}\,(n \sin r)$.

11. A ray of light passes from air through a piece of glass 0.5 in. thick (see Fig. 9–66). If $n = 1.754$ and $i = 60°$, determine r. The ray leaving the glass is parallel to the ray entering the glass, but displaced by an amount D. Calculate D.

Answers: $29°35'$; $0.291.$

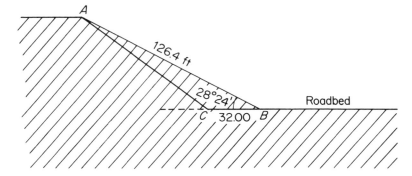

Fig. 9–66.

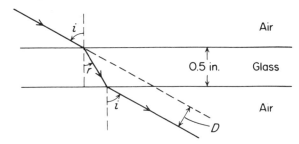

Fig. 9–67.

12. In widening a road, an embankment along the side must be cut away. The angle of elevation of the embankment is 28°24′, and the slant height is 126.4 ft (see Fig. 9–67). The roadbed is to be 32.00 ft wider. In order to estimate how much dirt must be removed, the area of a cross section is needed. Find this area.

13. To measure the height of an inaccessible object, a surveyor will sometimes use the following method. From a convenient distance, the angle of elevation of the top of the object is measured (angle α). Moving back a horizontal distance d, the angle of elevation is again measured (angle β). Prove that the height h is given by:

$$h = \frac{d}{\cot \beta - \cot \alpha}.$$

Hint: Determine DA in terms of α and h; $(DA + d)$ in terms of β and h; then eliminate DA.

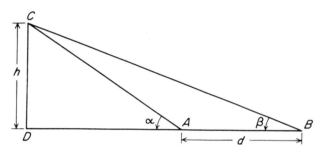

Fig. 9–68.

14. Use Exercise 13 to determine the height h of a smokestack when the following measurements have been made: $\alpha = 34°51′$, $\beta = 18°47′$, and $d = 281.2$ ft.

15. In regression analysis, a computer is frequently faced with the task of calculating $\sqrt{1 - r^2}$ when r is known. A table of the trigonometric functions can be used in the following manner. Determine θ so that $\sin \theta = r$. Then $\sqrt{1 - r^2} = \cos \theta$.

(a) Explain why this technique works.

(b) If $r = .65298$, find $\sqrt{1 - r^2}$.

10

Coordinate Geometry

Recall that the word *geometry* means earth-measurement. The early Greeks learned to measure distances, angles, areas, and volumes, and gradually built a mathematical model as a theoretical basis for these measurements. For example, they learned that the area of a triangle is half the product of its base and altitude (Fig. 10–1), $A = \frac{1}{2}ch$, as we would express it.

Of course there are no triangles in the world of experience. Mathematical triangles consist of *line segments*, and *points* where these line segments abut. The lines all lie in a *plane*. We think of points, lines, and planes as elements of an abstract system of mathematics. We treat points as ordered pairs of numbers, and lines as sets of points whose coordinates satisfy a first-degree equation; we treat a plane as a special set of points in a space of three dimensions. To earlier mathematicians, and many modern scientists, points, lines, and planes are abstractions based upon observations of the world of experience. They see what they call "triangles" in their physical surroundings. What they really do, of course, is to make approximations. They allow a pencil line to represent a mathematical line; they ignore the fact that the pencil line, unlike the mathematical line, may be $\frac{1}{200}$ in. wide. They allow a dot on a piece of paper to represent a mathematical point; they ignore the fact that the dot, unlike the mathematical point, has an area.

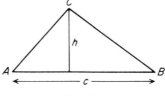

Fig. 10–1.

Euclid seems to have grasped some of the abstract quality of geometry as a mathematical model. He based his theorems upon proofs; these proofs depended, in the final analysis, upon assumptions about the way points, lines, and planes behave. Modern scholars are not entirely sure about Euclid's attitude toward the assumptions he made. Did he think that his assumptions were self-evident truths? Or did he think of them as rules of a game? Did Euclid think of points and lines as physical realities? Or did he think of them as names for ideas? We do not know.

Later scholars surely thought of Euclidean geometry as true. Only in the past 150 years has the nature of mathematical structures come to light, as mathematicians discovered useful mathematical systems based upon assumptions that contradict some of the assumptions that Euclid made. You have already met illustrations of this in your work with graphs.

In the *geometry of graphs* it is often convenient to use different units of measurement on the x- and y-axes. This geometry of graphs is certainly a convenient geometry, widely used in everyday affairs; but consider the triangle whose vertices are (0,0), (4,0) and (1,10) in Fig. 10–2.

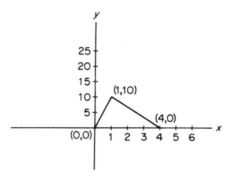

Fig. 10–2.

In Euclid's geometry, you can move the triangle without changing its size or shape; the same triangle in a new position looks the same. In the geometry of graphs, when you turn the triangle around the vertex, (0,0), through an angle of 90°, it looks like Fig. 10–3.

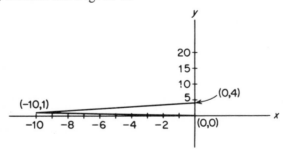

Fig. 10–3.

Recall, too, from Section 702 (page 307), how we turned circles into ellipses by stretching them in the direction of the x-axis or the y-axis. Euclid's geometry is a geometry of *rigid motions;* no such stretching of geometric figures is allowed; but there are other useful geometries that have different rules.

As modern mathematicians took a careful look at the nature of geometry, they realized how essential it is to agree in advance upon the rules of the game. We investigate first, in this chapter, a modern approach to Euclid's geometry. We examine properties of figures that remain unchanged as you perform rigid motions upon these figures; that is, as you move the figures so as to preserve both their size and shape. Then we suggest other simple geometries where the game is played by different rules.

1000. Rigid motions in the plane

You studied certain *transformations* in earlier chapters. For example, Fig. 10–4 suggests a *translation*. The circle $(x - 3)^2 + (y - 4)^2 = 4$ is the circle $x^2 + y^2 = 4$ with an alibi; its center has been moved to the point (3,4).

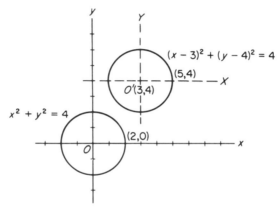

Fig. 10–4.

When you measure from the X- and Y-axes, the circle $(x - 3)^2 + (y - 4)^2 = 4$ takes on the alias $X^2 + Y^2 = 4$. The equations

(1)
$$\begin{cases} x = X + h \\ y = Y + k \end{cases}$$

express the xy-coordinates of a point P in terms of the XY-coordinates of P and the coordinates (h,k) of the origin of the XY-system. The equations

(2)
$$\begin{cases} X = x - h \\ Y = y - k \end{cases}$$

express the XY-coordinates of P in terms of the xy-coordinates of P and the coordinates (h,k) of the origin of the XY system. We call the systems of Equations (1) and (2) *equations of translation*.

We mentioned (page 318), but never developed, the transformation called rotation. The figure suggests a rotation of axes through an angle θ. From Fig. 10–5,

$$\sin \alpha = \frac{Y}{r}, \qquad \cos \alpha = \frac{X}{r}$$

$$\sin (\alpha + \theta) = \frac{y}{r}, \qquad \cos (\alpha + \theta) = \frac{x}{r}.$$

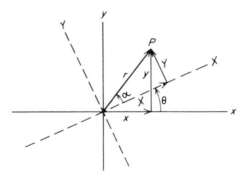

Fig. 10–5.

Identities from Chapter 9 yield:

$$\sin (\alpha + \theta) = \sin \alpha \cos \theta + \cos \alpha \sin \theta$$

$$\frac{y}{r} = \frac{Y}{r} \cos \theta + \frac{X}{r} \sin \theta$$

$$y = X \sin \theta + Y \cos \theta.$$

$$\cos (\alpha + \theta) = \cos \alpha \cos \theta - \sin \alpha \sin \theta$$

$$\frac{x}{r} = \frac{X}{r} \cos \theta - \frac{Y}{r} \sin \theta$$

$$x = X \cos \theta - Y \sin \theta.$$

The equations

(3)
$$\begin{cases} x = X \cos \theta - Y \sin \theta \\ y = X \sin \theta + Y \cos \theta \end{cases}$$

express the xy-coordinates of P in terms of the XY-coordinates of P and the angle θ from the x-axis to the X-axis. You can use the methods of Chapter 7 to solve these equations for X and Y. To do this, rewrite Equations (3):

$$\cos \theta \cdot X - \sin \theta \cdot Y = x$$

$$\sin \theta \cdot X + \cos \theta \cdot Y = y;$$

the determinant $D = \begin{vmatrix} \cos\theta & -\sin\theta \\ \sin\theta & \cos\theta \end{vmatrix} = \cos^2\theta + \sin^2\theta = 1$;

hence $\qquad X = \dfrac{1}{1}\begin{vmatrix} x & -\sin\theta \\ y & \cos\theta \end{vmatrix}, \qquad Y = \dfrac{1}{1}\begin{vmatrix} \cos\theta & x \\ \sin\theta & y \end{vmatrix}.$

Equations (4), $\qquad \begin{cases} X = x\cos\theta + y\sin\theta \\ Y = -x\sin\theta + y\cos\theta \end{cases}$

express the XY-coordinates of P in terms of the xy-coordinates of P, and the angle θ from the x axis to the X axis.

We call the systems of Equations (3) and (4) *equations of rotation*. Here are some examples of the application of the systems of Equations (3) and (4):

(1) The xy-coordinates of a point P are $(3,-2)$. What will the XY-coordinates of P be when you rotate the coordinate axes through an angle of $30°$ (that is, when the angle from the x-axis to the X-axis is $30°$)? For the replacement $\theta = 30°$, Equations (4) become:

$$X = x\cos 30° + y\sin 30° = \frac{\sqrt{3}}{2}x + \frac{1}{2}y$$

$$Y = -x\sin 30° + y\cos 30° = -\frac{1}{2}x + \frac{\sqrt{3}}{2}y.$$

The point whose xy-coordinates are $(3,-2)$ has XY-coordinates

$$X = \frac{\sqrt{3}}{2}(3) + \frac{1}{2}(-2) = \frac{3\sqrt{3}}{2} - 1$$

$$Y = -\frac{1}{2}(3) + \frac{\sqrt{3}}{2}(-2) = -\frac{3}{2} - \sqrt{3};$$

that is, $\left(\dfrac{3\sqrt{3}}{2} - 1, -\dfrac{3}{2} - \sqrt{3}\right).$

(2) The XY-coordinates of P are $(3/\sqrt{2}, 1/\sqrt{2})$. The XY axes were obtained by rotating the xy-axes through an angle of $45°$. That is, the angle from the x-axis to the X-axis is $45°$. What are the xy-coordinates of P? For the replacement $\theta = 45°$, Equations (3) become:

$$x = X\cos 45° - Y\sin 45° = \frac{1}{\sqrt{2}}X - \frac{1}{\sqrt{2}}Y$$

$$y = X\sin 45° + Y\cos 45° = \frac{1}{\sqrt{2}}X + \frac{1}{\sqrt{2}}Y.$$

The point whose XY-coordinates are $(3/\sqrt{2}, 1/\sqrt{2})$ has xy-coordinates

$$x = \frac{1}{\sqrt{2}}\left(\frac{3}{\sqrt{2}}\right) - \frac{1}{\sqrt{2}}\left(\frac{1}{\sqrt{2}}\right) = 1$$

$$y = \frac{1}{\sqrt{2}}\left(\frac{3}{\sqrt{2}}\right) + \frac{1}{\sqrt{2}}\left(\frac{1}{\sqrt{2}}\right) = 2;$$

that is, $(1,2)$.

(3) The equation of a straight line is $y = \sqrt{3}\,x + 6$. What is its equation when you rotate the coordinate axes through an angle of $\theta = 60°$? Equations (3) yield

$$x = X \cos 60° - Y \sin 60°$$

$$= \frac{1}{2}X - \frac{\sqrt{3}}{2}Y$$

$$y = X \sin 60° + Y \cos 60°$$

$$= \frac{\sqrt{3}}{2}X + \frac{1}{2}Y.$$

Substitution for x and y in the equation of the line yields:

$$\frac{\sqrt{3}}{2}X + \frac{1}{2}Y = \sqrt{3}\left(\frac{1}{2}X - \frac{\sqrt{3}}{2}Y\right) + 6$$

$$= \frac{\sqrt{3}}{2}X - \frac{3}{2}Y + 6.$$

This is equivalent to $2Y = 6$, or $Y = 3$. The equation of the line in XY-coordinates is $Y = 3$.

You should become thoroughly familiar with the equations of translation and rotation before you proceed to the study of Euclidean geometry as the set of properties that are preserved under translations and rotations. The following exercises will help you to do this.

EXERCISES §1000

1. Let $A(3, -5)$ be a point on the xy-coordinate system. An XY-coordinate system has its origin at A and axes parallel to the xy-axes.

(a) $(4,1)$, $(6,-2)$, $(-\frac{1}{2},-6)$, and $(1,-3)$ are coordinates of points on the xy-coordinate system. Determine the XY-coordinates of each point.

(b) $(1,1)$, $(-2,8)$, $(-3,5)$, and $(-6,-2)$ are coordinates of points on the XY-coordinate system. Determine the xy-coordinates of each point.

2. A triangle has its vertices at $A(-2,1)$, $B(4,-2)$, and $C(6,5)$. A translation is made to locate the new origin at A. Determine the new coordinates of the vertices. Draw a sketch.

3. The point $(-7,2)$ becomes $(2,-4)$ after a translation. What are the equations of the translation? How are the axes oriented?

4. An equation of a line is $y = -\frac{1}{2}x + 7$.

(a) Let A be the point $(3,2)$. Determine an equation of the line when the origin is translated to A.

(b) Repeat with $(10,2)$ for the coordinates of A.

Answer: (a) $Y = -\frac{1}{2}X + \frac{7}{2}$.

5. $(6,4)$, $(-2,4)$, $(-5,-1)$, and $(0,6)$ are coordinates of points on an *xy*-coordinate system. Determine the new coordinates of these points after:

(a) a rotation of $60°$

(b) a rotation of $90°$

(c) a rotation of Arctan $4/3$

(d) a rotation with $\cos\theta = -8/17$ and $\sin\theta = 15/17$.

Answers: (a) $(3 + 2\sqrt{3},\ 2 - 3\sqrt{3})$, etc.; (c) $(6.8, -2.4)$, etc.

6. The new coordinates of a set of points after a rotation of θ are $(2,6)$, $(0,-13)$, $(1,1)$, and $(-7,-2)$. Determine the old coordinates when θ is: (a) $45°$; (b) $120°$; (c) Arcsin $5/13$.

Answers: (a) $(-2\sqrt{2}, 4\sqrt{2})$, etc.; (c) $(-6/13, 82/13)$, etc.

7. The point $(5,5)$ becomes $(7,1)$ after a rotation. Write the conditions that the angle of rotation θ must satisfy. Solve for θ.

Answer: $\theta = $ Arcsin $(.6) \doteq 36°52'$.

8. An equation of a straight line is $y = -\frac{1}{2}x + 7$. What is its equation if the axes are rotated through an angle of $90°$?

9. Repeat Exercise 8 with $\theta = $ Arctan $3/4$ as the angle of rotation.

Answer: $Y = -2X + 14$.

10. Consider the set of points $\{(x,y) \mid y = x^2\}$. The axes are rotated $90°$. What is the new condition for this set of points? Is the set $\{(X,Y)\}$ a function?

11. Use the equations of rotation to show that the points on a circle with center at the origin satisfy the same equation before and after every rotation.

12. When the axes are rotated $45°$, what is the new equation of the set of points for which $y = 2/x$?

Answer: $X^2 - Y^2 = 4$.

We now define *rigid motions in the plane* to be translations, rotations, or combinations of translations and rotations. We set out to investigate the properties of geometric figures that are *invariant* under these transformations; that is, the properties that are preserved unchanged under translations and rotations.

First, you should think carefully about what it means to define rigid motions to be made up of translations or rotations. You begin with a set of points $\{(x,y)\}$. You *map* each point, (x,y) into a corresponding point (X,Y); this yields a set of points $\{(X,Y)\}$. Under translation:

$$\begin{array}{ccc} X = x - h & & x = X + h \\ Y = y - k & \text{or} & y = Y + k. \end{array}$$

Under rotation:

$$\begin{array}{ccc} X = x \cos\theta + y \sin\theta & & x = X \cos\theta - Y \sin\theta \\ Y = -x \sin\theta + y \cos\theta & \text{or} & y = X \sin\theta + Y \cos\theta. \end{array}$$

When you keep the axes fixed, you replace the set of points $\{(x,y)\}$ by a new set of points $\{(X,Y)\}$ that are the *images* of the old ones under translation or rotation. We have called this way of thinking *alibi*.

When you move the axes, you give each point in the set $\{(x,y)\}$ a new name; now you call the set of points $\{(X,Y)\}$. This amounts to translating or rotating the axes instead of the set of points. We have called this way of thinking *alias*.

Once you have defined rigid motions to be translations or rotations, you can forget about pictures. The equations of translation and rotation enable you to replace any condition involving x and y by a corresponding condition that involves X and Y. For example, the condition

$$y^2 = 7x$$

becomes, under translation,

$$(Y + k)^2 = 7(X + h),$$

and, under rotation,

$$(X \sin\theta + Y \cos\theta)^2 = 7(X \cos\theta - Y \sin\theta).$$

To emphasize the fact that you no longer need pictures, we rewrite the equations of rotation to eliminate any mention of the angle θ. We write

$$\begin{array}{ccc} X = cx + sy & & x = cX - sY \\ Y = -sx + cy & \text{or} & y = sX + cY. \end{array}$$

You may think $c = \cos\theta$, $s = \sin\theta$ if you wish. The essential thing is to think of c and s as symbols for real numbers that satisfy the condition $c^2 + s^2 = 1$. We shall need this condition upon c and s, which corresponds to $\cos^2\theta + \sin^2\theta = 1$, in what follows. You will find that the briefer forms of the equations of rotation save a great deal of writing.

Intuitively, measures of line segments and angles between lines are the basic invariants of a geometry of rigid motions. Two line segments are *equal* provided you can move one of the line segments to make it *coincide* with the other one. Two angles are equal provided you can fit one upon the other. We proceed to the analytical study of the effects of translations and rotations upon distances and angles.

We define the distance between $P_1(x_1,y_1)$ and $P_2(x_2,y_2)$ to be

(5) $$d = \sqrt{(x_2 - x_1)^2 + (y_2 - y_1)^2}.$$

You met this *distance formula* earlier, for example, when we discussed circles in Chapter 7. It is a basic formula of Euclidean coordinate geometry. People think of the distance d as a magnitude; hence d is a variable whose range is the set of positive real numbers. From our present point of view d is simply a number defined by (5).

To check the intuitive notion that distance is an invariant of the geometry of rigid motions, we calculate the distance $|P_1P_2|$ in xy-coordinates and in XY-coordinates. We study translations and rotations separately. The distance $|P_1P_2|$ in xy-coordinates is

$$\sqrt{(x_2 - x_1)^2 + (y_2 - y_1)^2}$$

in XY-coordinates is $\sqrt{(X_2 - X_1)^2 + (Y_2 - Y_1)^2}.$

For the translation $\begin{cases} X = x - h, \\ Y = y - k: \end{cases}$

$$\sqrt{(X_2 - X_1)^2 + (Y_2 - Y_1)^2}$$

$$= \sqrt{[(x_2 - h) - (x_1 - h)]^2 + [(y_2 - k) - (y_1 - k)]^2}$$

$$= \sqrt{(x_2 - x_1)^2 + (y_2 - y_1)^2}.$$

The distance formula yields the same answer in either coordinate system; hence the distance between two points is invariant under translation. For the rotation $X = cx + sy$, $Y = -sx + cy$;

$$\sqrt{(X_2 - X_1)^2 + (Y_2 - Y_1)^2}$$

$$= ([(cx_2 + sy_2) - (cx_1 + sy_1)]^2 + [(-sx_2 + cy_2) - (-sx_1 + cy_1)]^2)^{1/2}$$

$$= ((c^2 + s^2)[(x_2^2 - 2x_2x_1 + x_1^2) + (y_2^2 - 2y_2y_1 + y_1^2)]$$

$$+ (2cs - 2sc)(x_2y_2 + x_1y_1 - x_2y_1 - y_2x_1))^{1/2}$$

$$= \sqrt{(x_2 - x_1)^2 + (y_2 - y_1)^2}.$$

The distance formula yields the same answer in either coordinate system; hence the distance between two points is invariant under rotation.

To discuss the invariance of angles between lines, we must look critically at the ideas of angle and line. This is the topic of Section 1001.

EXERCISES §1000 (cont.)

13. Determine the distance between each pair of points:

(a) $(2,1)$; $(4,7)$ (b) $(-2,-1)$; $(4,7)$ (c) $(3,-2)$; $(-1,6)$

(d) $(4,-6)$; $(-1,6)$ (e) $(\sqrt{3},5)$; $(0,1)$ (f) $(0,-1)$; $(\sqrt{7},-2)$

(g) $(a,5)$; $(a,1)$ (h) (a,b); $(a+3, b+4)$ (i) (a,a); $(-a,-a)$.

14. Given $A(-3,-5)$ and $B(2,7)$, determine the distance $|AB|$. If a translation of the origin is made to $(1,-2)$, find the new coordinates of A and B. Use the new coordinates to determine the distance $|AB|$.

15. Find the distance between $A(4,2)$ and $B(-6,8)$. Rotate the axes $60°$, determine the new coordinates of these points and use them to find the distance $|AB|$.

16. The original coordinates of two points are $(-7,-4)$ and $(3,6)$. A translation of the origin to $(3,1)$ is made, followed by a rotation of Arctan $4/3$. Determine the distance between the points, first using the original coordinates, then using the final coordinates.

17. Show that a transformation that consists of a rotation followed by a translation can be expressed as a single transformation

$$X = cx + sy - h$$
$$Y = -sx + cy - k$$

where c, s, h, k are real numbers subject to the condition, $c^2 + s^2 = 1$.

18. The equations of Exercise 17 define the general *euclidean* transformation.

(a) What type of euclidean transformation will result when $c = 1$ and $s = 0$?
(b) What type of euclidean transformation will result when h and k are both zero?

19. Matrices provide a convenient tool to study euclidean transformations (see Section 706, page 361):

$$Z = \begin{pmatrix} X \\ Y \\ 1 \end{pmatrix}, \quad E = \begin{pmatrix} c & s & -h \\ -s & c & -k \\ 0 & 0 & 1 \end{pmatrix}, \quad \text{and} \quad z = \begin{pmatrix} x \\ y \\ 1 \end{pmatrix}.$$

(a) Show that the equations of Exercise 17 can be expressed with the matrix equation $Z = Ez$. (*Hint:* Carry out the matrix multiplication, then equate corresponding elements of the matrices on both sides of the matrix equation.)
(b) If, in the matrix E for the general euclidean transformation, we use $c = 1$ and $s = 0$, the transformation consists of a translation only. Thus

$$T = \begin{pmatrix} 1 & 0 & -h \\ 0 & 1 & -k \\ 0 & 0 & 1 \end{pmatrix}$$

is the matrix of a translation. What replacements of h and k would you use for a euclidean transformation consisting of a rotation only? Write the matrix R of a transformation consisting of a rotation only.

(c) Show that $E = TR$.

(d) Show that RT is a euclidean transformation, but, except in special cases, $RT \neq TR$ (that is, it makes a difference which you perform first, the rotation or the translation).

(e) Let

$$T_1 = \begin{pmatrix} 1 & 0 & -h_1 \\ 0 & 1 & -k_1 \\ 0 & 0 & 1 \end{pmatrix} \quad \text{and} \quad T_2 = \begin{pmatrix} 1 & 0 & -h_2 \\ 0 & 1 & -k_2 \\ 0 & 0 & 1 \end{pmatrix}.$$

Show that $T_1T_2 = T_2T_1$. What is the significance of this property?

(f) Write matrices for two rotations, R_1 and R_2, and show that $R_1R_2 = R_2R_1$.

(g) If

$$T = \begin{pmatrix} 1 & 0 & -h \\ 0 & 1 & -k \\ 0 & 0 & 1 \end{pmatrix},$$

show that

$$T^{-1} = \begin{pmatrix} 1 & 0 & h \\ 0 & 1 & k \\ 0 & 0 & 1 \end{pmatrix}.$$

(h) If

$$R = \begin{pmatrix} c & s & 0 \\ -s & c & 0 \\ 0 & 0 & 1 \end{pmatrix} \quad \text{with } c^2 + s^2 = 1,$$

show that

$$R^{-1} = \begin{pmatrix} c & -s & 0 \\ s & c & 0 \\ 0 & 0 & 0 \end{pmatrix}.$$

(i) Let E_1 and E_2 be two euclidean transformations. Show, by matrix multiplication, that E_1E_2 and E_2E_1 are both euclidean transformations; but that, except for special instances, $E_1E_2 \neq E_2E_1$.

(j) Show that the condition $c^2 + s^2 = 1$ is equivalent to the condition $|E| = 1$.

1001. Lines and angles

In Section 401 (page 102) you learned to work with the condition

(1) $$y = mx + b$$

for the set of linear functions $\{(x,y) \mid y = mx + b\}$. For each replacement of the parameters m and b, the graph of (1) is a straight line of slope m and y-intercept b.

Recall, also, the graph of the condition

(2) $x = a.$

For each replacement of a this is a straight line parallel to the y-axis. Such lines are *not* the graphs of functions, because they contain points (a, y_1) and (a, y_2) such that $y_1 \neq y_2$.

In this section we shall discuss the set of lines rather than the set of linear functions. We define a *straight line* to be a set of points

$$\{(x,y) \mid ax + by + c = 0, \text{ and not both } a \text{ and } b \text{ are zero}\}.$$

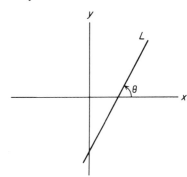

Fig. 10–6.

The condition

(3) $ax + by + c = 0$

is equivalent to $y = -ax/b - c/b$, provided $b \neq 0$. Hence its graph is a line of slope $-a/b$ and y-intercept $-c/b$. If $b = 0$ and $a \neq 0$, Equation (3) is equivalent to $x = -c/a$. Hence its graph is a line parallel to the y-axis.

If $a = b = 0$ and $c \neq 0$, Equation (3) defines the null set; if $a = b = c = 0$, it defines the entire plane. In neither of these cases is the graph of Equation (3) a line; hence the requirement that not both a and b are zero.

You can always write the equation of a particular line in the form

(4) $L: \quad ax + by + c = 0, \ a^2 + b^2 \neq 0.$

Since not both a and b are zero, $a^2 + b^2 \neq 0$.

Figure 10–6 displays the graph of an instance of Equation (4). We call the angle θ from the positive x-axis to L, the *inclination* of L. Notice that each line L has an inclination θ such that

(5) $0 \leq \theta < \pi.$

We define θ as a real number that you can calculate from (4) as follows:

(6)
$$b \neq 0 \Leftrightarrow \theta = \text{Arctan} \left(-\frac{a}{b} \right)$$

$$b = 0 \Leftrightarrow \theta = \frac{\pi}{2}.$$

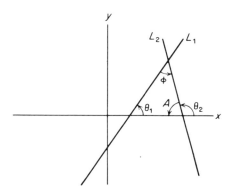

Fig. 10–7.

Now consider, in Fig. 10–7, the angle ϕ between L_1 and L_2. Since the sum of the interior angles of a triangle is $180° = \pi$ radians,

$$\phi + \theta_1 + A = \pi.$$

But
$$\theta_2 + A = \pi,$$
and, by subtraction,

$$(\phi + \theta_1) - \theta_2 = 0.$$

Hence
$$\phi = \theta_2 - \theta_1.$$

The angle ϕ between L_1 and L_2 in this figure is the difference in inclinations, $\theta_2 - \theta_1$.

We proceed to define the *directed angle* ϕ_{12} from L_1 to L_2. First, examine Fig. 10–8. To find the directed angle from L_1 to L_2 graphically, lay a pencil along L_1. Rotate the pencil until it lies along L_2. Call counterclockwise rotations positive and clockwise rotations negative. Choose the rotation ϕ_{12} such that

(7)
$$-\frac{\pi}{2} < \phi_{12} \leq \frac{\pi}{2}.$$

It is convenient to deal with an angle ϕ_{12} whose range is the same as the range of $y = \text{Arctan } x$. We shall often find ϕ_{12} from a knowledge of $\tan \phi_{12}$.

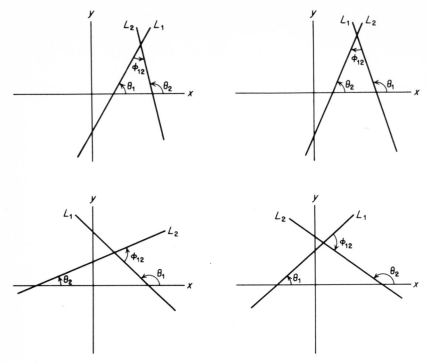

Fig. 10–8.

We now define the directed angle from L_1 to L_2 analytically to accomplish these same results. Thus

(8)
$$
\begin{cases}
-\vec{\pi} < \theta_2 - \theta_1 \leq -\dfrac{\pi}{2} \Leftrightarrow \phi_{12} = \pi + (\theta_2 - \theta_1) \\[2mm]
-\dfrac{\pi}{2} < \theta_2 - \theta_1 \leq \dfrac{\pi}{2} \Leftrightarrow \phi_{12} = \theta_2 - \theta_1 \\[2mm]
\dfrac{\pi}{2} < \theta_2 - \theta_1 < \pi \Leftrightarrow \phi_{12} = (\theta_2 - \theta_1) - \pi.
\end{cases}
$$

These definitions provide formulas for calculating ϕ_{12} from given values of θ_1 and θ_2. The range of ϕ_{12} is the range specified by Equation (7). The following examples illustrate this.

(1) Given $\theta_1 = 60°$ and $\theta_2 = 110°$, find ϕ_{12}. First calculate $\theta_2 - \theta_1 = 50°$ (see Fig. 10–9). Since

$$-90° < \theta_2 - \theta_1 \leq 90°$$

then $\phi_{12} = \theta_2 - \theta_1 = 50°$. This is a 50° counterclockwise rotation.

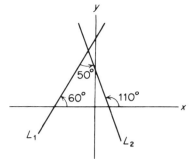

Fig. 10–9.

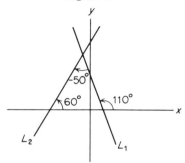

Fig. 10–10.

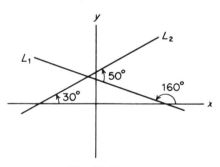

Fig. 10–11.

(2) Given $\theta_1 = 110°$ and $\theta_2 = 60°$, find ϕ_{12} (see Fig. 10–10).

$$\theta_2 - \theta_1 = -50°.$$

Since $-90° < \theta_2 - \theta_1 \leq 90°$, then

$$\phi_{12} = \theta_2 - \theta_1 = -50°.$$

This is a 50° clockwise rotation.

(3) Given $\theta_1 = 160°$ and $\theta_2 = 30°$, find ϕ_{12} (see Fig. 10–11).

$$\theta_2 - \theta_1 = -130°.$$

Since $-180° < \theta_2 - \theta_1 \leq -90°$, then

$$\phi_{12} = 180° + (\theta_2 - \theta_1) = 50°.$$

This is a 50° counterclockwise rotation.

(4) Given $\theta_1 = 30°$ and $\theta_2 = 160°$, find ϕ_{12} (see Fig. 10–12).

$$\theta_2 - \theta_1 = 130°.$$

Since $90° < \theta_2 - \theta_1 < 180°$, then

$$\phi_{12} = (\theta_2 - \theta_1) - 180° = -50°.$$

This is a 50° clockwise rotation.

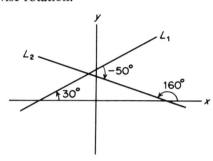

Fig. 10–12.

EXERCISES §1001

1. For each straight line, find the slope, $m = \tan \theta$, if it exists; use $\tan \theta$ to find the inclination, θ. Then graph the line to check your results:

(a) $-2x - 3y + 5 = 0$ $[m = \tan \theta = -2/3;\ \theta = \text{Arctan}\ (-2/3)]$
(b) $3x + 5y - 11 = 0$
(c) $-4x + 3y - 5 = 0$
(d) $6x - y - 3 = 0$
(e) $8x - 3 = 0$ $[m = \tan \theta$ is not defined; $\theta = \pi/2]$
(f) $3y + 5 = 0$ $[m = \tan \theta = 0;\ \theta = \text{Arctan}\ 0 = 0].$

2. Determine the inclination of each of the following lines, using Equations (6):

(a) $y = x + 4$ (b) $y = -\sqrt{3}x - 2$ (c) $y = \tfrac{1}{2}x + 1$
(d) $x = 3$ (e) $y = 7$ (f) $3x - 4y - 7 = 0$
(g) $2x + by + 13 = 0$ (h) $(2k)x + (4k)y - 5 = 0$
(i) $(\cos \alpha)x + (\sin \alpha)y - p = 0$

3. The inclination and one point are given for each of the following lines. Determine the equation of each line.

(a) $\theta = 45°$; $P(0,5)$ (b) $\theta = 135°$; $P(2,3)$ (c) $\theta = \pi/3$; $P(0,-2)$
(d) $\theta = 38°$; $P(0,3)$ (e) $\theta = .5$ rad; $P(0,6)$ (f) $\theta = .2$ rad; $P(3,1)$.

Hint for part (c): Since $\theta = \pi/3$, $m = \tan \theta = \sqrt{3}$; the equation of the line is $y + 2 = \sqrt{3}(x - 0)$ (Chapter 4, page 110), that is, $y = \sqrt{3}x - 2$.

4. Find ϕ_{12} for each of the following replacements of θ_1 and θ_2; that is, find the directed angle from L_1 to L_2 when given the inclinations of L_1 and L_2:

(a) $\theta_1 = 170°, \theta_2 = 5°$ (b) $\theta_1 = 5°, \theta_2 = 170°$
(c) $\theta_1 = 100°, \theta_2 = 40°$ (d) $\theta_1 = 40°, \theta_2 = 100°$
(e) $\theta_1 = 38°, \theta_2 = 38°$ (f) $\theta_1 = 20°, \theta_2 = 110°$
(g) $\theta_1 = 110°, \theta_2 = 20°$ (h) $\theta_1 = 130°, \theta_2 = 40°$
(i) $\theta_1 = 2.34, \theta_2 = 1.14$ (j) $\theta_1 = 1.14, \theta_2 = 2.34$.

Answers: (a) $15°$; (b) $-15°$; (i) -1.20.

It is usually easier to work with the tangent ratios than with the angles. We illustrate this fact now. First suppose that no one of the angles θ_1, θ_2, or ϕ_{12} is $\pi/2$; hence $\tan \theta_1$, $\tan \theta_2$, and $\tan \phi_{12}$ are defined. If, moreover, $\phi_{12} = \theta_2 - \theta_1$, then

(9)
$$\tan \phi_{12} = \frac{\tan \theta_2 - \tan \theta_1}{1 + \tan \theta_2 \tan \theta_1} \quad \text{(Chapter 9, page 442)}$$

$$= \frac{m_2 - m_1}{1 + m_2 m_1},$$

where m_1 and m_2 are the slopes of L_1 and L_2 respectively. This formula applies also when $\phi_{12} = (\theta_2 - \theta_1) \pm \pi$, because the tangent function has period π (page 158); that is,

$$\tan [(\theta_2 - \theta_1) \pm \pi] = \tan (\theta_2 - \theta_1).$$

Notice that the principal value of ϕ_{12}, as obtained from Equation (9), is the angle in the range $-\pi/2 < \phi_{12} \leq \pi/2$ required by Equation (7) (page 509). Hence

(10)
$$\phi_{12} = \text{Arctan} \left(\frac{m_2 - m_1}{1 + m_1 m_2} \right).$$

Equations (9) and (10) are convenient formulas when they apply, as the following examples show.

(5) Find ϕ_{12} for the lines $L_1: x - 3y + 5 = 0$ and $L_2: 2x + y - 3 = 0$. Rewrite $L_1: y = \frac{1}{3}x + \frac{5}{3}$, $L_2: y = -2x + 3$. This yields $m_1 = \frac{1}{3}$ and $m_2 = -2$. Applying Equation (9),

$$\tan \phi_{12} = \frac{(-2) - (1/3)}{1 + (-2)(1/3)} = -7.$$

Hence $\phi_{12} = \text{Arctan} (-7) \doteq -81°52'$. Figure 10–13 enables you to interpret and check this result.

(6) Find ϕ_{12} for the lines $L_1: x + 5y - 3 = 0$ and $L_2: 3x + 15y - 7 = 0$. Here $m_1 = m_2 = -\frac{1}{5}$, and, applying Equation (10),

$$\phi_{12} = \text{Arctan} \left(\frac{(-\frac{1}{5}) - (-\frac{1}{5})}{1 + (-\frac{1}{5})(-\frac{1}{5})} \right)$$

$$= \text{Arctan } 0 = 0.$$

You should draw a graph and interpret the fact $\phi_{12} = 0$ to mean that L_1 is parallel to L_2.

(7) Find ϕ_{12} for the lines L_1: $x + 2y + 3 = 0$ and L_2: $2x - y - 3 = 0$. Here $m_1 = -\frac{1}{2}$, $m_2 = 2$, and

$$\phi_{12} = \text{Arctan} \left(\frac{2 - (-\frac{1}{2})}{1 + 2(-\frac{1}{2})} \right)$$

$$= \text{Arctan} \left(\frac{2\frac{1}{2}}{0} \right).$$

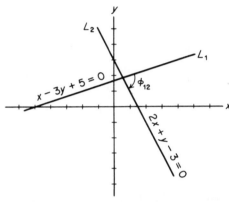

Fig. 10–13.

Since ϕ_{12} is an angle that does not have a tangent, the only possibility is $\phi_{12} = \pi/2$. You should draw a graph and interpret the fact $\phi_{12} = \pi/2$ to mean that L_1 is perpendicular to L_2.

(8) Find ϕ_{12} for the lines L_1: $x + y + 5 = 0$ and L_2: $3x + 2 = 0$. Here $m_1 = -1$, m_2 is not defined, and Equation (10) does not apply. Of course $\theta_1 = 135°$, $\theta_2 = 90°$, $\theta_2 - \theta_1 = -45°$; hence, by Equation (8), $\phi_{12} = -45°$.

EXERCISES §1001 (cont.)

5. Apply Equation (9) or (10), wherever possible, to find ϕ_{12} for each ordered pair of lines L_1 and L_2. Then draw a graph to interpret and check your results.

L_1	L_2
(a) $3y - x + 6 = 0$	$y = 2x + 4$
(b) $y = 2x$	$y = -5x$
(c) $x + 5y - 12 = 0$	$3x + 5y + 7 = 0$
(d) $3x - y + 5 = 0$	$y = 3x - 2$
(e) $3x - y + 5 = 0$	$y = -3x + 2$
(f) $3x - y + 5 = 0$	$y = -\frac{1}{3}x + 2$
(g) $3x + 5 = 0$	$y = 3x + 2$
(h) $3y + 5 = 0$	$y = 3x + 2.$

Answers: (a) $\phi_{12} = 45°$; (c) $\phi_{12} = \text{Arctan} (-10/28) \doteq -19°39'$; (e) $\phi_{12} = \text{Arctan} (.75) \doteq 36°52'$.

The special cases of parallel lines ($\tan \phi_{12} = 0$, or $\phi_{12} = 0$), and perpendicular lines ($\tan \phi_{12}$ undefined, or $\phi_{12} = \pi/2$), are especially important.

If $\theta_1 \neq \pi/2$ and $\theta_2 \neq \pi/2$ (so that $m_1 = \tan \theta_1$ and $m_2 = \tan \theta_2$ are defined), notice, in Equation (9), that $m_1 = m_2 \Rightarrow \tan \phi_{12} = 0$. Conversely, if $\tan \phi_{12} = 0$,

$$\frac{m_2 - m_1}{1 + m_2 m_1} = 0 \quad \text{and} \quad m_1 = m_2.$$

Hence, if m_1 and m_2 are defined,

(11) $$m_1 = m_2 \Leftrightarrow \phi_{12} = 0.$$

That is, two lines that have slopes are parallel if and only if their slopes are equal. Moreover, if both m_1 and m_2 are undefined, $\theta_1 = \theta_2 = \pi/2$, and $\phi_{12} = \theta_2 - \theta_1 = 0$ by Equation (8).

If $\theta_1 \neq \pi/2$ and $\theta_2 \neq \pi/2$, suppose, in Equation (9), that $1 + m_2 m_1 = 0$. If $m_2 = m_1$, $1 + m_1^2 = 0$; this is impossible for real values of m_1. Hence $m_2 \neq m_1$; $(m_2 - m_1)/(1 + m_2 m_1)$ is not defined, and $\phi_{12} = \pi/2$. Conversely, if $\tan \phi_{12}$ is not defined, $(m_2 - m_1)/(1 + m_2 m_1)$ is not defined, and $1 + m_2 m_1 = 0$. Hence, if m_1 and m_2 are defined,

(12) $$1 + m_2 m_1 = 0 \Leftrightarrow \phi_{12} = \frac{\pi}{2}.$$

That is, two lines that have slopes are perpendicular if and only if $1 + m_2 m_1 = 0$. Moreover, if $m_1 = 0$ and m_2 is undefined, or if m_1 is undefined and $m_2 = 0$, $\phi_{12} = \pi/2 - 0 = \pi/2$ or, by Equation (8),

$$\phi_{12} = \left(0 - \frac{\pi}{2} \right) + \pi = \frac{\pi}{2}.$$

It is often convenient to write the condition $1 + m_2 m_1 = 0$ as the equivalent condition $m_2 = -1/m_1$. This is always possible, since $1 + m_2 m_1 = 0 \Rightarrow m_1 \neq 0$. Hence, if m_1 and m_2 are defined,

(13) $$m_2 = -\frac{1}{m_1} \Leftrightarrow \phi_{12} = \frac{\pi}{2}.$$

We conclude that two lines with slopes are perpendicular if and only if their slopes are *negative reciprocals* ($m_2 = -1/m_1$ or $m_1 = -1/m_2$).

The following exercises provide further experiences with directed angles between lines.

EXERCISES §1001 (cont.)

6. For each pair of lines decide whether they are parallel, perpendicular, or neither.

(a) $2x + 4y - 7 = 0$, $y = -\frac{1}{2}x - 6$
(b) $4x + 3y - 8 = 0$, $3x - 4y + 2 = 0$
(c) $x + 6y = 9$, $y = 6x + 9$
(d) $2x + 5y = 8$, $5x + 2y = 8$
(e) $x + y = 2$, $x - y = 2$
(f) $14 - 6x - 9y = 0$, $15y + 10x = 21$
(g) $12x + 6y = 7$, $y = \frac{1}{2}x - 3$
(h) $y = \frac{1}{4}x + 6$, $4y + x + 6 = 0$.

7. Show that the triangle whose vertices are at $(-4, -4)$, $(1,6)$, and $(-2, -5)$ is a right triangle.

8. Write the equation of a line parallel to $y = 3x + 8$ passing through the point $(2,1)$.

9. Write the equation of a line perpendicular to $y = 3x + 8$ passing through the point $(2,1)$.

Answer: $x + 3y - 5 = 0$.

10. Determine $\tan \phi_{12}$ for the lines $y = x + 3$ and $y = 4x + 1$. Find new equations for the lines after a rotation of $60°$. Using the new slopes calculate $\tan \phi_{12}$ and compare with the first result.

Partial answer: After rotation, the slopes are $M_1 = \sqrt{3} - 2$ and
$$M_2 = \frac{17\sqrt{3} - 16}{47}.$$

11. Given the lines $y = m_1x + b$ and $y = m_2x + b$, show that, with suitable restrictions on the parameters m_1, m_2, and θ, $\tan \phi_{12}$ is invariant under a rotation. [*Suggestion:* Using the equations of rotation, the first equation becomes $(c + sm_1)Y = (cm_1 - s)X + b$; hence $M_1 = (cm_1 - s)/(c + sm_1)$. Determine M_2 in a similar fashion. Then, using $c^2 + s^2 = 1$, show that $(M_2 - M_1)/(1 + M_1M_2)$ reduces to $(m_2 - m_1)/(1 + m_1m_2)$. What about the cases where $c + sm_1$ or $c + sm_2$ equals zero?]

The fact that Equations (9) and (10) express $\tan \phi_{12}$ and ϕ_{12} in terms of the slopes m_1 and m_2 of L_1 and L_2 makes them convenient formulas. Equation (10) replaces the three separate Equations (8) by a single formula. In making general arguments (see Exercise 11) and dealing with cases in which m_1 or m_2 is not defined, Equations (9) and (10) are inconvenient; you must make exceptions for cases in which the tangent ratio is undefined.

We proceed to the proof that the directed angle between

$$L_1: \quad a_1x + b_1y + c_1 = 0$$

and
$$L_2: \quad a_2x + b_2y + c_2 = 0$$

is invariant under rigid motions. First we replace Equation (9) by a more convenient formula as follows:

(a) If $b_1 \neq 0$ and $b_2 \neq 0$, $\tan \theta_1 = -a_1/b_1$ and $\tan \theta_2 = -a_2/b_2$. Hence, if $\tan \phi_{12}$ is defined,

(14) $$\tan \phi_{12} = \frac{-a_2/b_2 + a_1/b_1}{1 + a_2/b_2 \cdot a_1/b_1} = \frac{a_1 b_2 - a_2 b_1}{a_1 a_2 + b_1 b_2}.$$

(b) If $b_1 = 0$ and $b_2 \neq 0$, $\tan \theta_1$ is not defined, $\theta_1 = \pi/2$, and $\tan \theta_2 = -a_2/b_2$. Hence, by Equation (8),

$$\phi_{12} = \left(\theta_2 - \frac{\pi}{2}\right) + k\pi,$$

where $k \in \{-1, 0, 1\}$. If $\tan \phi_{12}$ is defined,

$$\tan \phi_{12} = \tan \left(\theta_2 - \frac{\pi}{2}\right) \qquad \text{[the tangent function has period } \pi\text{]}$$

$$= -\tan \left(\frac{\pi}{2} - \theta_2\right) \qquad \text{[Chapter 9, page 442]}$$

$$= -\cot \theta_2 \qquad \text{[Chapter 9, page 442]}$$

$$= \frac{b_2}{a_2}.$$

If you substitute $b_1 = 0$ in Equation (14), $\tan \phi_{12} = a_1 b_2/a_1 a_2 = b_2/a_2$. Hence Equation (14) holds when $b_1 = 0$ and $b_2 \neq 0$.

(c) Similarly, you can prove that Equation (14) holds when $b_1 \neq 0$ and $b_2 = 0$ (see Exercise 12).

(d) If $b_1 = b_2 = 0$, $\theta_1 = \theta_2 = \pi/2$. Hence, by Equation (8), $\phi_{12} = 0$ and $\tan \phi_{12} = 0$. If you substitute $b_1 = b_2 = 0$ in Equation (14), $\tan \phi_{12} = 0/a_1 a_2$. Since $b_1 = 0 \Rightarrow a_1 \neq 0$, and $b_2 = 0 \Rightarrow a_2 \neq 0$, $\tan \phi_{12} = 0$. Hence Equation (14) holds when $b_1 = b_2 = 0$.

We conclude that Equation (14) holds for each pair of lines L_1 and L_2 provided $\tan \phi_{12}$ is defined.

To proceed: Under the translation $x = X + h$, $y = Y + k$,

$$L_1: \quad a_1(X + h) + b_1(Y + k) + c_1 = 0$$

$$L_2: \quad a_2(X + h) + b_2(Y + k) + c_2 = 0.$$

That is, $\qquad L_1: \quad a_1 X + b_1 Y + a_1 h + b_1 k + c_1 = 0$

$$L_2: \quad a_2 X + b_2 Y + a_2 h + b_2 k + c_2 = 0.$$

Applying Equation (14), the directed angle Φ_{12} between the transformed lines L_1 and L_2 has

$$\tan \Phi_{12} = \frac{a_1 b_2 - a_2 b_1}{a_1 a_2 + b_1 b_2} = \tan \phi_{12}.$$

Hence $\Phi_{12} = \phi_{12}$, and the directed angle between L_1 and L_2 is invariant under translation.

Under the rotation $x = cX - sY$, $y = sX + cY$,

$$L_1: \quad a_1(cX - sY) + b_1(sX + cY) + c_1 = 0$$
$$L_2: \quad a_2(cX - sY) + b_2(sX + cY) + c_2 = 0.$$

That is,
$$L_1: \quad (ca_1 + sb_1)X + (-sa_1 + cb_1)Y + c_1 = 0$$
$$L_2: \quad (ca_2 + sb_2)X + (-sa_2 + cb_2)Y + c_2 = 0.$$

Applying Equation (14), the directed angle Φ_{12} between the transformed lines L_1 and L_2 has

$$\tan \Phi_{12} = \frac{(ca_1 + sb_1)(-sa_2 + cb_2) - (ca_2 + sb_2)(-sa_1 + cb_1)}{(ca_1 + sb_1)(ca_2 + sb_2) + (-sa_1 + cb_1)(-sa_2 + cb_2)}$$

$$= \frac{(s^2 + c^2)(a_1b_2 - a_2b_1)}{(s^2 + c^2)(a_1a_2 + b_1b_2)} = \frac{a_1b_2 - a_2b_1}{a_1a_2 + b_1b_2}$$

$$= \tan \phi_{12}.$$

Hence $\Phi_{12} = \phi_{12}$, and the directed angle between L_1 and L_2 is invariant under rotation.

If $\tan \phi_{12}$ is not defined, $\phi_{12} = \pi/2$. Corresponding to the four cases listed above, we have:

(a)
$$1 + m_1m_2 = 1 + \left(-\frac{a_1}{b_1}\right)\left(-\frac{a_2}{b_2}\right) = 0.$$

Hence

(15)
$$a_1a_2 + b_1b_2 = 0.$$

(b)
$$\phi_{12} = \frac{\pi}{2} = \left(\theta_2 - \frac{\pi}{2}\right) + k\pi \quad \text{and} \quad 0 \le \theta_2 < \pi.$$

Hence
$$\theta_2 = 0$$

$$\tan \theta_2 = -\frac{a_2}{b_2} = 0 \Rightarrow a_2 = 0.$$

Then
$$(b_1 = 0 \text{ and } a_2 = 0) \Rightarrow a_1a_2 + b_1b_2 = 0.$$

(c) Similarly,
$$\phi_{12} = \pi/2, \; b_1 \ne 0, \text{ and } b_2 = 0 \Rightarrow a_1a_2 + b_1b_2 = 0.$$

(d) In this case, $\phi_{12} = 0$ and $\tan \phi_{12}$ *is* defined. We conclude that Equation (15) holds for each pair of lines L_1 and L_2 provided $\tan \phi_{12}$ is not defined.

It is readily shown that $a_1a_2 + b_1b_2$ is an invariant under translation and rotation. For example, under rotation

$$(ca_1 + sb_1)(ca_2 + sb_2) + (-sa_1 + cb_1)(-sa_2 + cb_2)$$
$$= (s^2 + c^2)(a_1a_2 + b_1b_2)$$
$$= a_1a_2 + b_1b_2.$$

This completes the proof that the length of a line segment (Section 1000) and the directed angle between two lines are invariants of translations and rotations, that is, that distances and directed angles are preserved under rigid motions. In the following sections you will investigate other invariants of rigid motions. In other words, you will study Euclidean geometry.

EXERCISES §1001 (cont.)

12. Show that Equation (14) holds when $b_1 \neq 0$ and $b_2 = 0$.

13. Repeat Exercise 5 using Formula (14).

14. Show that L_1 and L_2 are parallel (that is $\theta_1 = \theta_2$) if and only if $a_1b_2 - a_2b_1 = 0$.

15. Repeat Exercise 6 using Formula (15) and Exercise 14.

16. A triangle is formed by segments of the three lines:

$$L_1:\ 3x + 2y - 14 = 0$$
$$L_2:\ 4x - 5y + 12 = 0$$
$$L_3:\ 2x - y + \ 6 = 0.$$

Use Formula (14) to determine the three interior angles of the triangle.

Answer: 94°58′, 24°47′, 60°15′.

17. Find the coordinates of the vertex at the intersection of L_1 and L_2 of the triangle of Exercise 16. Then write the equation of the altitude to L_3.

Answer: (2,4); $x + 2y - 10 = 0$.

18. Let $P_1(x_1,y_1)$ and $P_2(x_2,y_2)$ be two points in the plane other than the origin. Show that:

(a) $(x_1y_2 - x_2y_1 = 0) \Leftrightarrow (P_1, P_2$ and the origin lie on the same line)
(b) $(x_1x_2 + y_1y_2 = 0) \Leftrightarrow ($the lines joining P_1 and P_2 with the origin are perpendicular).

19. Show that the points $(-9,6)$, $(2,3)$, and $(0,0)$ form a right triangle:

(a) Using Formula (12).
(b) Using Exercise 18(b).

1002. Plane loci—distances between points

In your previous dealings with graphs, you met straight lines, circles, polynomial graphs, and the like, as sets of points whose coordinates satisfy an equation. We define the *locus* of a condition as the set of points whose coordinates satisfy the condition. Every point on the locus has coordinates that satisfy the condition. No other point (not on the locus) can make this claim!

We turn now to the problem of finding an equation of a locus from a physical or geometric description of the locus. Suppose, for example, you ask: "What is the locus of points that are at a distance of 4 from the point $(2,-3)$?" We interpret this question as "Find an equation of the locus."

You already know how to graph an equation, that is, to find the locus of an equation (see Fig. 10–14).

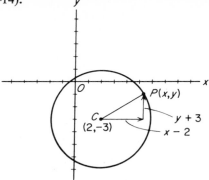

Fig. 10–14.

When you use the definition of distance you find: the distance between $C(2,-3)$ and $P(x,y)$ is

$$d = \sqrt{(x-2)^2 + (y+3)^2}.$$

By the physical, or geometric, condition expressed in the original question,

$$d = 4.$$

Hence an equation of the locus is $\sqrt{(x-2)^2 + (y+3)^2} = 4$, or

$$(x-2)^2 + (y+3)^2 = 16.$$

You can now identify the locus as a circle with center $(2,-3)$ and radius 4.

The answer to the original question is not always so easy as it was in the preceding example. Here are some further examples:

(1) What is the locus of points that are at the same distance from the point $(0,1)$ as from the line $y = -1$? In Fig. 10–15,

$$d_1 = \sqrt{(x-0)^2 + (y-1)^2},$$
$$d_2 = |y+1|.$$

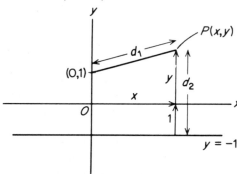

Fig. 10–15.

The geometric condition is $d_2 = d_1$, that is,

$$|y + 1| = \sqrt{x^2 + (y - 1)^2}$$
$$y^2 + 2y + 1 = x^2 + y^2 - 2y + 1,$$
$$4y = x^2$$
$$y = \tfrac{1}{4}x^2.$$

The locus is a parabola with vertex at $(0,0)$ and axis of symmetry the y-axis. It is an instance of the standard form $y = ax^2$, with $a = \tfrac{1}{4}$.

(2) What is the locus of points such that the sum of their distances from $(3,0)$ and from $(-3,0)$ is 10? In Fig. 10–16,

$$d_1 = \sqrt{(x + 3)^2 + y^2}$$
$$d_2 = \sqrt{(x - 3)^2 + y^2}.$$

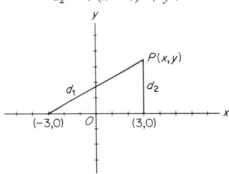

Fig. 10–16.

The geometric condition is $d_1 + d_2 = 10$, that is,

$$\sqrt{(x + 3)^2 + y^2} + \sqrt{(x - 3)^2 + y^2} = 10.$$

To identify the locus, we simplify this equation as follows. You should experiment with other procedures to appreciate the comparative simplicity of ours:

$$[\sqrt{(x + 3)^2 + y^2}]^2 = [10 - \sqrt{(x - 3)^2 + y^2}]^2$$
$$x^2 + 6x + 9 + y^2 = 100 - 20\sqrt{(x - 3)^2 + y^2} + x^2 - 6x + 9 + y^2$$
$$20\sqrt{(x - 3)^2 + y^2} = 100 - 12x$$
$$5\sqrt{(x - 3)^2 + y^2} = 25 - 3x$$
$$25(x^2 - 6x + 9 + y^2) = 625 - 150x + 9x^2$$
$$16x^2 + 25y^2 = 400$$
$$\frac{x^2}{25} + \frac{y^2}{16} = 1.$$

The locus is an ellipse with center at (0,0), major axis 10, and minor axis 8. It is an instance of the standard form

$$\frac{x^2}{a^2} + \frac{y^2}{b^2} = 1$$

with $a = 5$ and $b = 4$.

Notice, in each example above, that distance is the basic variable that appears in the physical or geometric condition that determines the locus. Since distance is invariant under translation and rotation, the locus you get will be invariant under translation and rotation. That is, circles become circles with new equations, parabolas become parabolas with new equations, etc. When you perform translations or rotations of axes, you get the same locus with a new name. When you use the same axes, but perform translations or rotations upon a locus, you get an identical locus in a new position. Thus the effect of a rigid motion upon a locus is to give it an alias or an alibi.

EXERCISES §1002

1. What is the locus of points that are the same distance from the point (0,3) as from the line $y = -3$?

Answer: $y = \frac{1}{12}x^2$.

2. Repeat Exercise 1, using the point (3,0) and the line $x = -3$. Can you predict the equation of this locus from the results of Exercise 1?

3. What is the locus of points that are the same distance from (0,2) as from the x axis? Compare with Example 1 in the text. Can you predict the result using a translation?

Answer: $y = \frac{1}{4}x^2 + 1$.

4. What is the locus of points such that the sum of their distances from (0,3) and from $(0,-3)$ is 10? Compare with Example (2) in the text. Explain the similarities and the differences.

5. What is the locus of points such that the sum of their distances from $(-1,3)$ and from (5,3) is 10? Notice that these two points are the result of moving the two points of Example (2) in the text to the right 2 units and up 3 units. What type of graph do you predict?

6. A point moves so that its distance to $A(-4,1)$ is always the same as its distance to $B(5,4)$. What is the equation of its locus? How is this locus related to the line segment AB?

Partial answer: $y = -3x + 4$.

7. Determine the equation of the perpendicular bisector of the line segment joining $A(2,-4)$ to $B(-3,6)$.

8. A point moves so that its distance to $(-4,1)$ is always twice its distance to (5,4). What is the equation of its locus?

Answer: $(x - 8)^2 + (y - 5)^2 = 40$.

9. What is the locus of points that are twice as far from (6,0) as from the y axis?

10. What is the locus of points that are half as far from (6,0) as from the y axis?

So far you have worked with conditions that specify a locus by giving you numbers that measure a property of the locus. There are important advantages to be gained by using parameters instead of numbers. When you do this, your solution of the locus problem yields a formula for solving a whole family of problems that have the same structure. The next examples illustrate this:

(3) What is the locus of points whose distances from a fixed point are equal to their distances from a fixed line?

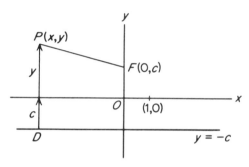

Fig. 10–17.

The algebra is simpler when you choose the fixed point and the fixed line to give the locus symmetry about the x-axis, the y-axis, or both. We follow the pattern of Example (1) (see Fig. 10–17). Think of c as a parameter whose range is the set L of real numbers. For the purposes of the problem in hand, you give c an arbitrary, fixed value. This means that the figure above is purely schematic; it represents the problem situation for just one value of the parameter c, and for just one of the possible ways of locating the fixed point and the fixed line with respect to the coordinate axes.

The geometric condition is $|PF| = |PD|$. We use the *absolute value* bars in the symbols $|PF|$ and $|PD|$ to mean that we are interested in the distances, rather than in the directed distances.

The algebraic equation is

$$\sqrt{(x - 0)^2 + (y - c)^2} = |c + y|$$
$$x^2 + y^2 - 2cy + c^2 = c^2 + 2cy + y^2$$
$$4cy = x^2$$

and if $c \neq 0$,
$$y = \frac{1}{4c} x^2.$$

The locus is a parabola with vertex at $(0,0)$ and with the y-axis as axis of symmetry. It is an instance of the standard form $y = ax^2$, with $a = 1/4c$.

If $c = 0$, the equation $4cy = x^2$ reduces to $x^2 = 0$, or $x = 0$. In this case the parabola is *degenerate*; it reduces to the y-axis. In the original problem, the fixed point is on the fixed line; the locus is the perpendicular to the fixed line at the fixed point.

Notice that we have solved a whole family of problems that have the same structure. Each value of c yields a particular problem of the family. For example, when $c = -\frac{1}{5}$, you get the problem in which the fixed point is $(0, -\frac{1}{5})$ and the fixed line is $y = \frac{1}{5}$. Mathematicians call the fixed point the *focus* and the fixed line the *directrix* of the parabola. The parabola whose focus is $(0, -\frac{1}{5})$ and whose directrix is $y = \frac{1}{5}$ has the equation

$$y = \frac{1}{4(-\frac{1}{5})} x^2 \quad \text{or} \quad y = -\tfrac{5}{4}x^2.$$

(4) What is the locus of points whose joins to two fixed points differ in length by a fixed amount?

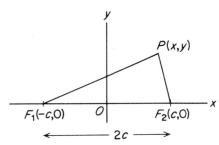

Fig. 10–18.

Your experience with previous examples suggests choosing the coordinate axes as in Fig. 10–18. We chose the two fixed points as $F_1(-c,0)$ and $F_2(c,0)$ on the x-axis and symmetrical about the y-axis. We may do this because any other placement of the fixed points can be changed into this one by translating or rotating axes. We chose $|PF_1| \geq |PF_2|$. Again this is a question of placing the coordinate axes so that this condition will hold.

Of course the figure is purely schematic. The parameter c is a variable whose range is the set of non-negative real numbers. For the purposes of the problem in hand you give c an arbitrary fixed value. Then, for any point $P(x,y)$ of the locus,

$$|PF_1| = \sqrt{(x+c)^2 + y^2}, \qquad |PF_2| = \sqrt{(x-c)^2 + y^2}$$

and $\quad |PF_1| - |PF_2| = \sqrt{(x+c)^2 + y^2} - \sqrt{(x-c)^2 + y^2} = 2a,$

where $2a$ represents the arbitrary fixed difference between $|PF_1|$ and $|PF_2|$.

The parameter a appears as a variable whose range is the set of non-negative, real numbers. A little reflection will show that the value of a is restricted by the condition $a \leq c$. From $|PF_1| - |PF_2| = 2a$, $|PF_1| = |PF_2| + 2a$; also, in triangle PF_1F_2, $|PF_1| < |PF_2| + 2c$, since each side of a triangle is less than the sum of the other two sides of the triangle. Of course you could place the point $P(x,y)$ as is done in Fig. 10–19. Then $|PF_1| = |PF_2| + 2c$; but for each location of $P(x,y)$,

$$|PF_1| \leq |PF_2| + 2c.$$

Hence $$|PF_2| + 2a \leq |PF_2| + 2c, \quad \text{and} \quad a \leq c.$$

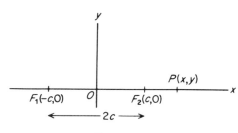

Fig. 10–19.

We proceed, as in Example (2), to simplify the equation of the locus. You should be on the lookout to find where the condition $a \leq c$ enters into the analysis:

$$[\sqrt{(x + c)^2 + y^2}]^2 = [\sqrt{(x - c)^2 + y^2} + 2a]^2$$

$$4cx - 4a^2 = 4a\sqrt{(x - c)^2 + y^2}$$

$$(cx - a^2)^2 = a^2(x^2 - 2cx + c^2 + y^2)$$

$$(c^2 - a^2)x^2 - a^2y^2 = a^2(c^2 - a^2).$$

We consider the various possibilities:

If $a = 0$ and $c = 0$, the equation reduces to $0x^2 - 0y^2 = 0$; the condition on $P(x,y)$ becomes an identity. In the original problem, the points F_1 and F_2 both coincide with the origin ($c = 0$); $|PO| - |PO| = 2a = 0$ is an identity, true of every point $P(x,y)$.

If $a = 0$ and $c \neq 0$, the equation reduces to $c^2x^2 = 0$, or $x = 0$. In the original problem, the points F_1 and F_2 are distinct points on the x-axis, symmetrically placed to the left and right of 0; the condition $|PF_1| - |PF_2| = 0$, or $|PF_1| = |PF_2|$, holds if and only if the point $P(x,y)$ lies on the y-axis, that is, the line $x = 0$.

If $a \neq 0$ and $a = c$, the equation reduces to $-a^2y^2 = 0$. This is equivalent to $y = 0$, the equation of the x-axis. In the original problem, $|PF_1| - |PF_2| = 2a = 2c$ defines the set of points on the x-axis to the right of F_2 (see Fig. 10–19, page 525). When we simplified the original equation of the locus by squaring both sides of the equation, we derived a new equation whose locus is the entire x-axis. This is like taking the equation $y = x$ (one line), and squaring both sides to get the equation $y^2 = x^2$ (two lines, $y = x$ or $y = -x$). The locus of the new equation contains the locus of the old equation and more besides.

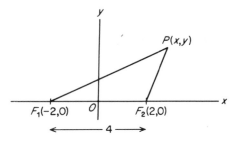

Fig. 10–20.

If $a \neq 0$ and $a < c$, the equation reduces to

$$\frac{x^2}{a^2} - \frac{y^2}{c^2 - a^2} = 1.$$

Since $c^2 - a^2 > 0$, we may let $c^2 - a^2 = b^2$, and get

$$\frac{x^2}{a^2} - \frac{y^2}{b^2} = 1.$$

This is the hyperbola with center at $(0,0)$, principal axis the x-axis, vertices $(-a,0)$ and $(a,0)$, and asymptotes $y = \pm bx/a$. The points $F_1(-c,0)$ and $F_2(c,0)$ are called *foci* of the hyperbola. In the original problem, $|PF_1| - |PF_2| = 2a > 0$; the locus is the branch of the hyperbola that lies to the right of the y-axis. When we simplified the original equation by squaring both sides of the equation, we derived a new equation whose locus is the entire hyperbola. Again the locus of the new equation contains the locus of the old equation and more besides.

Finally, if $a \neq 0$ and $a > c$, we let $c^2 - a^2 = -b^2$. The equation reduces to $-b^2x^2 - a^2y^2 = -a^2b^2$, or

$$\frac{x^2}{a^2} + \frac{y^2}{b^2} = 1.$$

This is the ellipse with center at $(0,0)$ and semi-axes of lengths a and b. In the original problem, $|PF_1| - |PF_2| = 2a > 2c$; we have already shown that there is no point $P(x,y)$ that satisfies this condition. Try, for example, $c = 2$

and $a = 3$. In Fig. 10–20, $P(x,y)$ must satisfy the conditions $|PF_1| = |PF_2| + 6$ (given), and $|PF_1| \leq |PF_2| + 4$ (one side of a triangle is less than the sum of the other two sides). These two conditions lead to the conclusion $6 \leq 4$. Hence they are inconsistent, and we conclude that the locus is the null set. When we simplified the original equation by squaring both sides of the equation, we derived a new equation whose locus is the ellipse

$$\frac{x^2}{a^2} + \frac{y^2}{b^2} = 1.$$

The locus of the new equation contains the locus of the original equation (the null set) and more besides.

You should read again the possible interpretations of the equation $(c^2 - a^2)x^2 - a^2y^2 = a^2(c^2 - a^2)$. Notice that this "simplified" equation is *not equivalent* to the equation $\sqrt{(x + c)^2 + y^2} - \sqrt{(x - c)^2 + y^2} = 2a$. Yet it helps you to interpret the original condition.

You may feel that Example (4) is complicated. Notice that there is a payoff to reward you for working out all the possible cases. You found that:

(a) The locus of points the difference of whose distances from one fixed point is zero is the whole xy-plane.

(b) The locus of points the difference of whose distances from two distinct, fixed points is zero is the perpendicular bisector of the line segment that joins the two fixed points.

(c) The locus of points the difference of whose distances from two distinct, fixed points equals the distance between the fixed points is the segment of the line joining the fixed points that lies to the right of one of the points.

So far, these results are rather evident when you study the geometry of the problem directly. The remaining results are less evident but come from our analysis of the problem:

(d) The locus of points the difference of whose distances from two distinct, fixed points is constant, and less than the distance between the fixed points, is one branch of the hyperbola that we have described above.

(e) The locus of points the difference of whose distances from two distinct, fixed points is constant, and more than the distance between the fixed points, is the null set.

You may be confident that this description covers all the possible cases. Any particular problem that has the structure of Example (4) may be treated as a special instance. For example: The locus of points whose distances to $(-3,0)$ and $(3,0)$ differ in length by 4 is shown in Fig. 10–21. $c = 3$, $2c = 6$, $2a = 4$, $a = 2$, $b^2 = c^2 - a^2 = 5$, $b = \sqrt{5}$. The locus is the hyperbola: $x^2/4 - y^2/5 = 1$. This is the locus of the conditions $|PF_1| - |PF_2| = \pm 4$.

The locus of points whose distances to $(3,4)$ and $(5,5)$ differ in length by 2 is shown in Fig. 10–22. Using the X- and Y-axes, $2c = \sqrt{(5 - 3)^2 + (5 - 4)^2} =$

$\sqrt{5}$, $c = \frac{1}{2}\sqrt{5}$, $2a = 2$, $a = 1$, $b^2 = c^2 - a^2 = \frac{5}{4} - 1 = \frac{1}{4}$, $b = \frac{1}{2}$. The locus is $X^2/1 - Y^2/\frac{1}{4} = 1$. The details of deriving an equation of the locus referred to the x- and y-axes, by translation and rotation, need not concern us here.

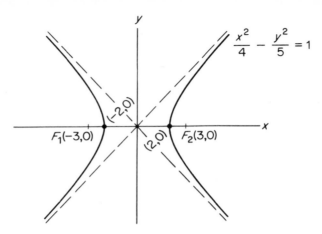

Fig. 10–21.

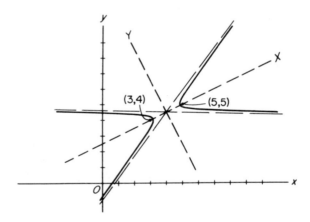

Fig. 10–22.

EXERCISES §1002 (cont.)

11. Write the equation of the parabola whose focus and directrix are:

(a) $F(0,4)$; $y = -4$ (b) $F(0,1)$; $y = -1$

(c) $F(0,-3)$; $y = 3$ (d) $F(0,-\frac{1}{4})$; $y = \frac{1}{4}$

(e) $F(0,3)$; $y = 1$ (f) $F(0,-4)$; $y = 2$.

Hint: Use the results of Example (3), page 523.

12. Derive the equation of a parabola whose vertex is at the origin and whose focus is on the x-axis.

Answer: $x = y^2/4c$, where c is the distance from the focus to the origin.

13. The parabola whose equation is $y - k = (1/4c)(x - h)^2$ has its vertex at (h,k), What are the coordinates of the focus? What is the equation of the directrix? *Answers:* $F(h,k + c)$ and $y = k - c$.

14. Locate the focus and directrix of each parabola.

(a) $y = \frac{1}{2}x^2$ (b) $y = -x^2$
(c) $4x = y^2$ (d) $y = x^2 - 4x + 7$
(e) $y = \frac{1}{2}x^2 + 3x + 6$ (f) $y = -\frac{1}{4}x^2 + x - 2$.

Answers: (a) $(0,\frac{1}{2})$, $y = -\frac{1}{2}$; (d) $(2,3\frac{1}{4})$, $y = 2\frac{3}{4}$.

15. What is the locus of points whose distances to $(-5,0)$ and to $(5,0)$ differ by 8? Use the results of Example (4) in the text and write the equation.

16. Show, for a hyperbola, that $c = \sqrt{a^2 + b^2}$. Locate the foci of the hyperbola $x^2 - y^2 = 1$. (Compare Chapter 7, page 311). Show that a circle with center at the origin that passes through the corners of the rectangle of Fig. 7–21 (page 313) intersects the x-axis at the two foci.

17. A hyperbola has its foci at $(-1,3)$ and $5,3)$. The difference between the distances from any point on the hyperbola to the foci is 2. Locate the center of the hyperbola, then write its equation with the help of the results of Example (4) in the text.

Answers: Center at $(2,3)$; $(x - 2)^2 - (y - 3)^2/8 = 1$.

18. A hyperbola has asymptotes $y = \pm 2x$ and foci at $(-4,0)$ and $(4,0)$. Find the vertices of the hyperbola and write the equation.

Answer: $a = 4/\sqrt{5}$; $20x^2 - 5y^2 = 64$.

19. The ratio c/a is called the *eccentricity* of the hyperbola. If $e = c/a$, show that

(a) $e > 1$ for all hyperbolas

(b) $e = \dfrac{\sqrt{a^2 + b^2}}{a} = \sqrt{1 + \left(\dfrac{b}{a}\right)^2}$

(c) $e = \sqrt{2}$ for an equilateral hyperbola

(d) When $1 < e < \sqrt{2}$ the hyperbola is "narrow"

(e) When $\sqrt{2} < e$ the hyperbola is "wide".

20. The locus of points the sum of whose distances to two fixed points is constant is an ellipse. Prove this by deriving the equation of the locus. Let the fixed points be $(-c,0)$ and $(c,0)$, and the constant sum be $2a$. Show that $a \geq c$. The equation, after squaring to eliminate radicals, has the form $(a^2 - c^2)x^2 + a^2y^2 = a^2(a^2 - c^2)$. Since $a^2 - c^2$ is non-negative it may be replaced by b^2.

21. Write the equation of the locus of points the sum of whose distances to $(-3,0)$ and $(3,0)$ is 12.

22. The fixed points in the ellipse of Exercise 20 are called *foci*. Show that the distance c from the center of an ellipse to one focus is given by $c = \sqrt{a^2 - b^2}$, where a is the semi-major axis and b is the semi-minor axis. Determine the co-ordinates of the foci of the ellipse $4x^2 + 25y^2 = 100$. If any point on this ellipse is joined to the two foci, what is the sum of the joins?

23. Find the locus of points such that their distances from the point $(6,0)$ divided by their distances from the line $x = \frac{3}{2}$ is constant and equal to 2.

Answer: $3x^2 - y^2 = 27$.

24. Find the locus of points such that their distances from the point $(2,0)$ divided by their distances from the line $x = 8$ is constant and equal to $\frac{1}{2}$.

Answer: $3x^2 + 4y^2 = 48$.

25. Prove that the locus of points whose distances from a fixed point are in a constant ratio e to their distances from a fixed line is a hyperbola when $e > 1$, and an ellipse when $0 < e < 1$.

Suggestions: The equation will be in simplest form if the coordinate system is placed so that the fixed point is $F(ae,0)$ and the fixed line is $x = a/e$. Then

$$\frac{\sqrt{(x - ae)^2 + y^2}}{|a/e - x|} = e, \quad \sqrt{(x - ae)^2 + y^2} = |a - ex|,$$

$$(1 - e^2)x^2 + y^2 = a^2(1 - e^2).$$

26. Show that when you use $F(-ae,0)$ and $x = -a/e$ in Exercise 25, the same locus results. The points $(ae,0)$ and $(-ae,0)$ are the *foci*, and the lines $x = \pm a/e$ are the *directrices* of the hyperbola or ellipse.

27. Show that the directrices are between the foci for a hyperbola ($e > 1$) and outside the foci for an ellipse ($e < 1$).

28. Determine the values of e and a for Exercises 23 and 24; then write the equations of these loci using the formula of Exercise 25.

Answer for Exercise 23: $e = 2$, $a = 3$.

1003. Plane loci—angles between lines

In Section 1002 the loci were defined in terms of one or more distances. Since distance is an invariant in the geometry of rigid motions, these loci are invariants in Euclidean geometry.

In other physical or geometric descriptions of loci, the basic variable is an angle. Again, we proceed through examples.

(1) What is the locus of points such that, when you join them to the point $(0,3)$, the join has slope 2? In Fig. 10–23, the directed distance from A to B is $x - 0$, and the directed distance from B to P is $y - 3$; this yields the slope $m = (y - 3)/(x - 0)$; by the physical condition given in the problem, $m = 2$. Hence $(y - 3)/x = 2$, $y - 3 = 2x$, $y = 2x + 3$.

The locus is a straight line of slope 2 and y-intercept 3. It is an instance of the standard form $y = mx + b$, with $m = 2$ and $b = 3$.

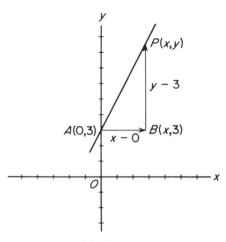

Fig. 10–23.

(2) What is the locus of points whose joins to the point $(4,1)$ are perpendicular to the line $y = -2x - 1$? In Fig. 10–24, the join of $A(4,1)$ to $P(x,y)$ has slope $m = (y - 1)/(x - 4)$. The line $y = -2x - 1$ has slope -2; a line perpendicular to $y = -2x - 1$ has slope $-1/-2 = 1/2$. By the physical

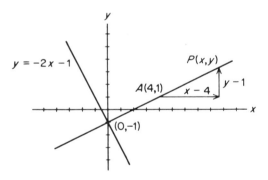

Fig. 10–24.

condition given in the problem, $m = \frac{1}{2}$. Hence the equation of the locus is

$$\frac{y - 1}{x - 4} = \frac{1}{2} \quad \text{or} \quad y - 1 = \frac{1}{2}(x - 4).$$

The locus is a straight line, of slope $\frac{1}{2}$, that passes through the point $(4,1)$.
(3) What is the locus of points whose joins to the points $(-2,0)$ and $(2,0)$

meet at right angles? In Fig. 10–25, the join of $A(-2,0)$ to $P(x,y)$ has slope $m_1 = y/(x + 2)$; the join of $B(2,0)$ to $P(x,y)$ has slope $m_2 = y/(x - 2)$. By the physical condition given in the problem, $1 + m_1 m_2 = 0$; that is,

$$1 + \frac{y}{x+2} \cdot \frac{y}{x-2} = 0,$$

$$\frac{y^2}{x^2 - 4} = -1,$$

$$x^2 + y^2 = 4.$$

The locus is a circle of radius 2 with center at the origin.

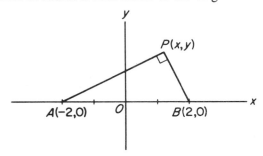

Fig. 10–25.

Notice in Examples (1), (2), and (3) that angle is the basic variable in the statement of the physical condition. Since angles are preserved under translations and rotations, so are the loci of these examples. The effect of rigid motions upon these loci is to give them aliases or alibis.

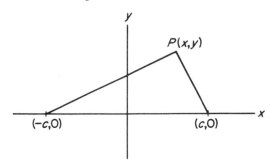

Fig. 10–26.

As in Section 1002, you may express a problem in terms of parameters and thereby develop a formula for solving a whole family of problems. The following example illustrates this:

(4) Find the locus of points whose joins to two fixed points meet at right angles.

You should notice that this question is a generalization of the question of Example (3). It is convenient to place the two fixed points as in Fig. 10–26. It is always possible to accomplish this arrangement by performing rigid motions.

As in Example (3),

$$1 + \frac{y}{x+c} \cdot \frac{y}{x-c} = 0,$$

$$x^2 + y^2 = c^2.$$

The locus is a circle of radius c with center at the origin.

EXERCISES §1003

1. What is the locus of points whose joins to the point $(-3,5)$ are perpendicular to the line $y = \frac{1}{4}x + 2$?

2. A point P moves so that the slope of its join to the point $(3,0)$ is one-half of the x coordinate of P. What is the locus of P?

Answer: $y = \frac{1}{2}x(x - 3)$.

3. The directed angle from the line $y = 2x + 4$ to a line through the point $(3, -2)$ is $45°$. What is the equation of the line?

Answer: $y = -3x + 7$.

4. The directed angle from a line through the point $(3, -2)$ to the line $y = 2x + 4$ is $45°$. What is the equation of the line?

5. What is the locus of points above the x-axis whose joins to the points $(-2,0)$ and $(2,0)$ meet at a $30°$ angle?

Answer: $x^2 + (y - 2\sqrt{3})^2 = 15$ and $y > 0$.

6. Given the points $A(2,0)$, $P(x,y)$, and $B(x + 4,0)$. The point P moves so that the directed angle from AP to PB is equal to the directed angle from PB to AB. Find the equation of the locus of P.

Answer: $y^2 = 8x$.

7. Given the lines L_1: $y = -7x + 11$ and L_2: $y = x + 3$. Find the equations of the lines that bisect the angles of intersection of L_1 and L_2. (*Hint:* If L represents one of the required lines, its slope m must be such that the directed angle from L_1 to L is equal to the directed angle from L to L_2.)

Answer: $y = 3x + 1$ and $3y + x = 13$.

8. Find the locus of points whose joins to the origin are perpendicular to the line $y = mx + b$.

Answer: $my + x = 0$.

9. A point P moves so that the slope of its join to the point (a,b) is one-half the x coordinate of P. What is the locus of P?

10. For each point of a locus the angle from the join to $(-c,0)$ to the join to $(c,0)$ is Arctan t. Find the equation of the locus.

Answer: $x^2 + (y - c/t)^2 = c^2(1 + 1/t^2)$. Compare with Exercise 5.

1004. Plane loci—polar coordinates

Several times we have found it simpler, or more convenient, to use polar coordinates than to use rectangular coordinates. Recall the convenience of the polar form of a complex number in Section 907 (page 473) and the simplicity of the polar graphs of the trigonometric functions in Section 906 (page 467). Now, again, we make use of polar coordinates to simplify certain problems. Some locus problems work out more easily when you use polar,

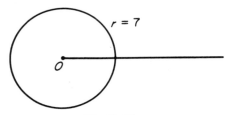

Fig. 10–27.

rather than rectangular coordinates. Again, we make use of examples:

(1) Find the locus of points whose distances from a fixed point are 7. When you choose the pole as the fixed point, the equation is $r = 7$ (see Fig. 10–27). This is simpler than the equation of the same circle, $x^2 + y^2 = 49$, in rectangular coordinates.

Of course you can use the equations $x = r \cos \theta$, $y = r \sin \theta$, to change the equation $x^2 + y^2 = 49$ into the polar form. Thus $x^2 + y^2 = 49$ becomes $r^2 \cos^2 \theta + r^2 \sin^2 \theta = 49$, $r^2 = 49$, $r = 7$.

You can use the equations $r = \sqrt{x^2 + y^2}$, $\theta = \arctan y/x$, to change the equation $r = 7$ into rectangular form. Thus $r = 7$ becomes $\sqrt{x^2 + y^2} = 7$ or $x^2 + y^2 = 49$.

Once you obtain an equation, in either the polar form or the rectangular form, you can change it into the other form.

(2) Find the locus of points whose distances from a fixed point are the products of their distances from a fixed line and a constant, $e > 0$. In Fig. 10–28, we chose the fixed line D as the perpendicular to the polar axis at the point $(c, 180°)$; c represents an element of the set L of real numbers. The fixed point is at the pole. The given condition is

$$d_1 = e d_2 \quad \text{and} \quad e > 0.$$

In polar coordinates, this is

$$r = e(c + r \cos \theta)$$

$$r(1 - e \cos \theta) = ce$$

$$r = \frac{ce}{1 - e \cos \theta}.$$

You learned in Section 1002 (page 530) that this locus is an ellipse, a parabola, or a hyperbola, according as $0 < e < 1$, $e = 1$, or $e > 1$. When $e = 1$, for example, the equation becomes

$$r = \frac{c}{1 - \cos \theta}.$$

This equation represents a parabola with focus at the pole and directrix the

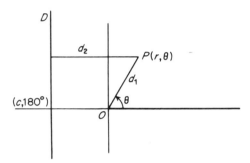

Fig. 10–28.

line D. To find the corresponding equation in rectangular coordinates: $r = \sqrt{x^2 + y^2}$ and $\cos \theta = x/\sqrt{x^2 + y^2}$ yield

$$\sqrt{x^2 + y^2} = \frac{c}{1 - x/\sqrt{x^2 + y^2}}$$

$$= \frac{c\sqrt{x^2 + y^2}}{\sqrt{x^2 + y^2} - x}.$$

Hence $\sqrt{x^2 + y^2}[\sqrt{x^2 + y^2} - x] = c\sqrt{x^2 + y^2}.$

Since $r = \sqrt{x^2 + y^2} \neq 0,$

$$\sqrt{x^2 + y^2} - x = c$$

$$\sqrt{x^2 + y^2} = x + c$$

$$x^2 + y^2 = x^2 + 2cx + c^2$$

$$y^2 = 2c\left(x + \frac{c}{2}\right).$$

You will recognize this as the equation of a parabola with vertex $(-c/2, 0)$, focus $(0,0)$, and directrix $x = -c$. For further experiences with the polar equations of conics, see Exercises 2 and 3 below.

(3) Find the locus of a point that moves outward from a fixed point at a constant speed of 3 ft/sec and revolves about the fixed point at a constant speed of 2 radians/sec.

We have stated this locus problem in physical language. Of course you cannot really move a point in the plane except in your imagination; but this way of stating the condition suggests using a small marble or other convenient object, to represent the point.

We begin with a table of values of t (seconds), r (feet), and θ (radians):

t (sec)	0	1	2	3	...
r (ft)	0	3	6	9	...
θ (rad)	0	2	4	6	...

Notice that we allowed the point to begin its motion, at time $t = 0$, from (0,0). In 1 sec the point moved away from the pole a distance of 3 ft and

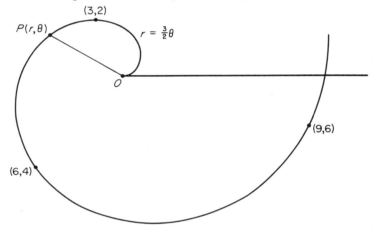

Fig. 10–29.

revolved about the pole through an angle of 2 radians; check the meaning of the other ordered number-triples, (t,r,θ).

In terms of the parameter t,

$$r = 3t$$
$$\theta = 2t.$$

You can eliminate the parameter t as follows: from $\theta = 2t$, $t = \theta/2$; substitution in $r = 3t$ yields $r = 3(\theta/2)$. Hence the polar equation of the locus is $r = 3\theta/2$.

The polar equation of this locus is much simpler than the corresponding rectangular equation, $\sqrt{x^2 + y^2} = 3/2 \arctan y/x$. Figure 10–29 shows the graph of the locus. Mathematicians call this graph a *spiral*. It is one of the several types of spirals that are useful to mechanical engineers.

Exercises §1004 provide further examples of plane loci that have simpler polar equations than rectangular equations.

EXERCISES §1004

1. Identify and sketch the polar graphs of the following conditions:

(a) $r = 4$ (b) $r = -2$ (c) $r = \sqrt{7}$
(d) $\theta = 30°$ (e) $\theta = 135°$ (f) $\theta = -45°$
(g) $\theta = \frac{1}{2}$ (h) $\theta = 1$ (i) $\theta = -2.5$.

2. Using Example (2), above, determine the eccentricity e and the distance c between the focus and the directrix of each conic. Identify the type of conic and make a sketch.

(a) $r = \dfrac{2}{1 - \cos \theta}$ (b) $r = \dfrac{4}{1 - \frac{1}{2} \cos \theta}$

(c) $r = \dfrac{5}{1 - 3 \cos \theta}$ (d) $r = \dfrac{7}{2 - 2 \cos \theta}$

(e) $r = \dfrac{16}{5 - 3 \cos \theta}$ (f) $r = \dfrac{6}{3 - 5 \cos \theta}$.

Answer: (e) $c = 16/3$, $e = 3/5$, ellipse.

3. Show that the equation of the locus of points whose distances from a fixed point are the products of their distances from a fixed line and a constant, $e > 0$, has the form $r = ce/(1 - e \sin \theta)$ when the fixed line is c units below and parallel to the polar axis, and the fixed point is at the pole.

4. Find the polar equation of the locus of points whose distances to the polar axis are equal to the squares of their distances to the pole. Sketch the graph. (See Fig. 9–43, page 467).

Answer: $r = \sin \theta$.

5. Use rectangular coordinates to derive the equation of the locus of points whose distances to the x-axis are equal to the squares of their distances to the origin. Change the equation to polar form and compare with Exercise 4.

Answer: $x^2 + y^2 - y = 0$.

6. A point moves so that its distance to the origin is the same as the ratio of its distance from the x-axis to its distance from the y-axis. Derive the equation of the locus in rectangular coordinates. Change the equation to polar form. Sketch the graph (see Fig. 9–45, page 467). Which equation is easier to graph?

Answers: $x^2(x^2 + y^2) - y^2 = 0$; $r = \tan \theta$.

7. Sketch the graph of:

(a) $r = \frac{1}{2}\theta$ (archimedean spiral)   (b) $r = e^{\theta/2}$ (logarithmic spiral)
(c) $r\theta = 3$ (hyperbolic spiral)   (d) $r^2 = 4\theta$.

8. Change the polar equations of Exercise 7 to rectangular form.

Answer: (b) $x \tan [\log (x^2 + y^2)] - y = 0$.

9. Let O be a fixed point and L a fixed line, a units from O. L' is a line through O that intersects L at point B. P is on L', b units from B in the direction of O. The locus of P, as L' rotates about O, is called the *conchoid of Nicomedes*. Show that the equation of this locus is $r = a \sec \theta - b$, when O is at the pole and L is perpendicular to the polar axis. Draw the graph of the locus when $a = 3$ and $b = 4$.

10. Let O be the pole of a polar coordinate system and B a point on the circle $r = 2a \cos \theta$. $P(r,\theta)$ is a point on the line OB extended so that BP is constant and equal to b. Derive the equation of the locus of P as B moves around the circle. Sketch the graph when $b = 2a$.

Answer: $r = 2a \cos \theta + b$.

11. (a) If the polar coordinate system is rotated through an angle θ_0, show that the point (r,θ) has coordinates (R,ϕ) when measured with respect to the new coordinate system where $R = r$ and $\phi = \theta - \theta_0$.

(b) Determine the new equation for each of the following sets of points after the rotation indicated.

(i) $r = 8 \cos \theta$; $\theta_0 = \dfrac{\pi}{2}$ (ii) $r = 8 \cos \theta$; $\theta_0 = \dfrac{\pi}{6}$

(iii) $r = 3 \sec \theta$; $\theta_0 = \pi$ (iv) $r = \dfrac{ce}{1 - e \cos \theta}$; $\theta_0 = \dfrac{\pi}{2}$.

1005. Distances from points to lines

You have been working with distances between points and angles between lines. These are the basic invariants of the geometry of rigid motions. As you recall your previous experiences in geometry you will think of other useful invariants. In this section you will study distances from points to lines. In Section 1006 you will study the division of a line segment in a given ratio. These are invariants of the geometry of rigid motions that depend upon the basic ones.

First, consider the distance from the origin to a line (Fig. 10–30). The line L in the figure is at a distance p from the origin, and in a direction that makes an angle α with the positive end of the x-axis; that is, the perpendicular from O to L meets L at a point N, with polar coordinates (p,α). Let $P(r,\theta)$ be any point on L. The polar equation of L is:

$$(1) \qquad p = r \cos (\theta - \alpha)$$

$$= r \cos \theta \cos \alpha + r \sin \theta \sin \alpha.$$

If the rectangular coordinates of P are (x,y), then $x = r \cos \theta$, and $y = r \sin \theta$. Hence, by substitution, you obtain a rectangular equation of L,

$$(2) \qquad x \cos \alpha + y \sin \alpha = p,$$

which displays the distance p from O to L.

Before going further, it is worthwhile to take a careful look at this *normal form* of the equation of a straight line. The parameters in the equation $x \cos \alpha + y \sin \alpha = p$ are α and p; α is the counterclockwise angle from the positive end of the x-axis to the *normal* (perpendicular) to L; p is the length of the normal from O to L, the so-called *normal intercept* of L. For each value of p, the equation $x \cos \alpha + y \sin \alpha = p$ represents a family of lines tangent to a circle of radius p with center at the origin. The range of α is $0 \leq \alpha < 2\pi$ (Fig. 10–31). For each value of α, the equation $x \cos \alpha + y \sin \alpha = p$

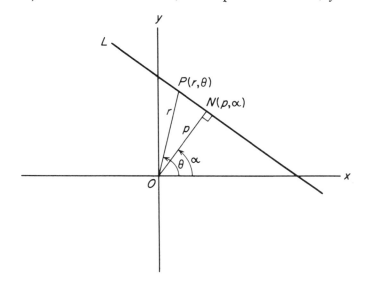

Fig. 10–30.

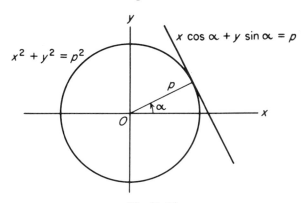

Fig. 10–31.

represents a family of lines at right angles to the half-line drawn in the direction α from the origin. The range of p is $p \geq 0$ (Fig. 10–32).

The question of finding the distance from the origin to a line reduces to the question of writing the equation of the line in normal form. Consider, then, the line $ax + by = c$. To rewrite its equation in the form $(\cos \alpha)x + (\sin \alpha)y = p$, recall (Sec. 703, page 326) that if two linear equations represent the same line, their coefficients are proportional. Hence

$$\cos \alpha = ka, \quad \sin \alpha = kb, \quad \text{and} \quad p = kc.$$

To determine the constant of proportionality k,

$$(ka)^2 + (kb)^2 = \cos^2 \alpha + \sin^2 \alpha = 1$$

(3) $$k = \pm \frac{1}{\sqrt{a^2 + b^2}}.$$

If $c < 0$, then you choose the negative sign, $k = -1/\sqrt{a^2 + b^2}$, to make

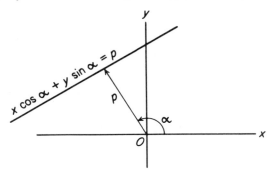

Fig. 10–32.

$p = kc > 0$. If $c > 0$, then $p = kc > 0$ requires $k = +1/\sqrt{a^2 + b^2}$. For a line passing through the origin, $c = 0$; then you choose the sign of k to agree with the sign of b; hence $\sin \alpha = kb > 0$, $0 < \alpha < \pi$, and α is the smaller of the two possible angles. In the trivial case, $b = c = 0$, the equation $ax = 0$, $a \neq 0$, represents the y-axis; the normal form of this equation is $x \cdot 1 + y \cdot 0 = 0$.
To summarize:

    (a) $c \neq 0$; choose the sign of k so that $p > 0$.
    (b) $c = 0$, $b \neq 0$; choose the sign of k so that $\sin \alpha > 0$.
    (c) $c = 0$, $b = 0$; choose the sign of k so that $\cos \alpha = 1$.

Examples will clarify the technique of rewriting equations of straight lines in normal form:
    (1) Express the equation of the line $3x - 4y = 9$ in normal form. Here $a = 3$ and $b = -4$; $\sqrt{a^2 + b^2} = \sqrt{25} = 5$; $c = 9 > 0$. Multiply by $k = +\frac{1}{5}$ to get the required equation:

$$\tfrac{3}{5}x - \tfrac{4}{5}y = \tfrac{9}{5}.$$

Hence $p = \tfrac{9}{5}$, $\cos \alpha = \tfrac{3}{5}$, and $\sin \alpha = -\tfrac{4}{5}$. Examine the graph, in Fig. 10–33, as the graph of $3x - 4y = 9$ and as the graph of $\tfrac{3}{5}x - \tfrac{4}{5}y = \tfrac{9}{5}$. The line $3x - 4y = 9$ passes through the points $(0,-\tfrac{9}{4})$ and $(3,0)$. Its graph is drawn.

Notice that the conditions $\cos \alpha = \frac{3}{5}$ and $\sin \alpha = -\frac{4}{5}$ determine an angle α in the fourth quadrant; notice that $p = \frac{9}{5}$ tells you where to draw the line at right angles to its normal. The graph coincides with the one drawn previously.

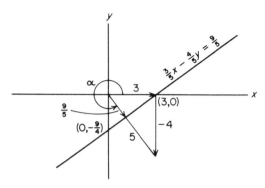

Fig. 10–33.

(2) Express the equation $y = -2x - 3$ in normal form. First, graph this line of slope -2 and y-intercept -3. Then rewrite the equation $y = -2x - 3$ as $2x + y = -3$. Here $a = 2$, $b = 1$, and $c < 0$. Multiply by $k = -1/\sqrt{5}$ to secure the normal form of the equation:

$$-\frac{2}{\sqrt{5}}x - \frac{1}{\sqrt{5}}y = \frac{3}{\sqrt{5}}.$$

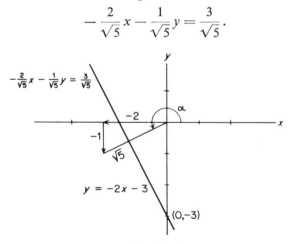

Fig. 10–34.

Hence $p = 3/\sqrt{5}$, $\cos \alpha = -2/\sqrt{5}$, $\sin \alpha = -1/\sqrt{5}$. The graph in Fig. 10–34 is the graph of $y = -2x - 3$ or $-2x/\sqrt{5} - y/\sqrt{5} = 3/\sqrt{5}$. The difference is merely a difference in the way you think about, and draw the two graphs.

To find the distance from the origin to a line L, you write the equation of L in the normal form; then the required distance is the value of p in the equation.

To find the distance from $O'(h,k)$ to the line L, you write the equation of L in the normal form; then you translate the origin of coordinates from O to O' by the equations

$$x = X + h$$

$$y = Y + k.$$

The equation $x \cos \alpha + y \sin \alpha = p$ becomes

$$(X + h) \cos \alpha + (Y + k) \sin \alpha = p$$

or $$X \cos \alpha + Y \sin \alpha = -(h \cos \alpha + k \sin \alpha - p).$$

The distance from $O'(h,k)$ to L is

(4) $$d = -(h \cos \alpha + k \sin \alpha - p).$$

Examples will clarify the technique of finding the distance from a given point to a given line:

(3) Find the distance from $(-2,3)$ to $x - 5y + 4 = 0$ (see Fig. 10–35).

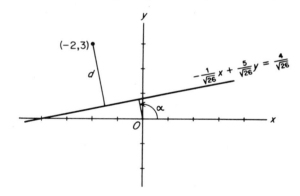

Fig. 10–35.

When you write $x - 5y + 4 = 0$ in the normal form, it becomes

$$-\frac{1}{\sqrt{26}}x + \frac{5}{\sqrt{26}}y = \frac{4}{\sqrt{26}}.$$

Then $h = -2$, $k = 3$, $\cos \alpha = -1/\sqrt{26}$, $\sin \alpha = 5/\sqrt{26}$, and $p = 4/\sqrt{26}$. Hence

$$d = -\left[(-2)\left(-\frac{1}{\sqrt{26}}\right) + 3\left(\frac{5}{\sqrt{26}}\right) - \frac{4}{\sqrt{26}}\right] = -\frac{13}{\sqrt{26}}.$$

Notice the distances to $-x/\sqrt{26} + 5y/\sqrt{26} = 4/\sqrt{26}$ from various points:

Distance from (0,0) is $-\left[0\left(-\dfrac{1}{\sqrt{26}}\right) + 0\left(\dfrac{5}{\sqrt{26}}\right) - \dfrac{4}{\sqrt{26}}\right] = \dfrac{4}{\sqrt{26}}$ (as you would expect);

Distance from (1,2) is $-\left[1\left(-\dfrac{1}{\sqrt{26}}\right) + 2\left(\dfrac{5}{\sqrt{26}}\right) - \dfrac{4}{\sqrt{26}}\right] = -\dfrac{5}{\sqrt{26}}$;

Distance from (6,2) is $-\left[6\left(-\dfrac{1}{\sqrt{26}}\right) + 2\left(\dfrac{5}{\sqrt{26}}\right) - \dfrac{4}{\sqrt{26}}\right] = 0$ (meaning that (6,2) lies on the line).

Experiment with other points, and with other combinations of lines and points, to test the theorem: The distance from $O'(h,k)$ to L is positive, negative, or zero according as O' lies on the same side of L as O, on the opposite side of L from O, or on the line L. In light of this theorem, the formula $d = -(h \cos \alpha + k \sin \alpha - p)$ yields the *directed distance, d,* from (h,k) to L.

We proceed to use these ideas about distances from points to lines to solve locus problems:

(4) Find the locus of points whose distances from $3x - 2y + 5 = 0$ are 4. As you examine Fig. 10–36 you should think: if 4 *is not* a directed distance,

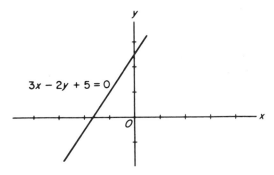

Fig. 10–36.

the locus is two lines parallel to $3x - 2y + 5 = 0$ and 4 units distant from it; if 4 *is* a directed distance from the line to the point, the directed distance from the point to the line is -4 and the locus is one line parallel to $3x - 2y + 5 = 0$ and further from the origin. We proceed to find these lines analytically:

Written in normal form, the equation $3x - 2y + 5 = 0$ becomes

$$-\frac{3}{\sqrt{13}}x + \frac{2}{\sqrt{13}}y = \frac{5}{\sqrt{13}}.$$

For a point $P(x,y)$ of the locus, we replace h by x and k by y in Equation (4). Then

$$-\left[-\frac{3}{\sqrt{13}}x+\frac{2}{\sqrt{13}}y-\frac{5}{\sqrt{13}}\right]=\pm 4.$$

The locus is the pair of lines whose equations in normal form are:

$$\frac{3}{\sqrt{13}}x-\frac{2}{\sqrt{13}}y=4-\frac{5}{\sqrt{13}}$$

and

$$-\frac{3}{\sqrt{13}}x+\frac{2}{\sqrt{13}}y=4+\frac{5}{\sqrt{13}}.$$

Complete the figure by drawing these lines. Notice how all three lines have the same normal; they differ in their normal intercepts; the lines of the locus are 4 units distant from the given line; the directed distance from $3x-2y+5=0$ to each point of $-3x/\sqrt{13}+2y/\sqrt{13}=4+5/\sqrt{13}$ is 4; the directed distance from each point of $-3x/\sqrt{13}+2y/\sqrt{13}=4+5/\sqrt{13}$ to $3x-2y+5=0$ is -4.

(5) Find the locus of points whose distances from $(-2,3)$ are equal to their distances from $x+y=5$.

As you examine Fig. 10–37, you should recall that the locus is a parabola

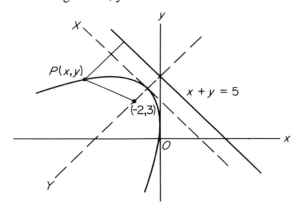

Fig. 10–37.

(page 523). Written in normal form, $x+y=5$ becomes

$$\frac{1}{\sqrt{2}}x+\frac{1}{\sqrt{2}}y=\frac{5}{\sqrt{2}}.$$

For a point $P(x,y)$ of the locus,

$$\sqrt{(x+2)^2+(y-3)^2}=\left|-\left[\frac{1}{\sqrt{2}}x+\frac{1}{\sqrt{2}}y-\frac{5}{\sqrt{2}}\right]\right|.$$

We take the absolute value of the distance from P to $x + y = 5$ because we are not interested in the directed distance.

You may wish to "simplify" this equation by squaring both sides. You obtain the equation $x^2 - 2xy + y^2 + 18x - 2y + 1 = 0$.

You may wish to compare your result with the equation of the parabola obtained by applying the results of Example (3) (page 523). Thus, using the X and Y axes of Fig. 10–37, c is one-half the distance from $(-2,3)$ to $x + y = 5$. Hence,

$$c = \frac{1}{2}\left(-\left[\frac{1}{\sqrt{2}}(-2) + \frac{1}{\sqrt{2}}(3) - \frac{5}{\sqrt{2}}\right]\right) = \sqrt{2}.$$

The equation of the parabola is $Y = X^2/4\sqrt{2}$. To refer the equation to the x- and y-axes, notice that the X- and Y-axes may be rotated through an angle of $-135°$ and then translated to intersect at O. The equations of the required transformation are

$$X = x \cos(-135°) - y \sin(-135°) - \frac{5}{\sqrt{2}} = -\frac{x}{\sqrt{2}} + \frac{y}{\sqrt{2}} - \frac{5}{\sqrt{2}}$$

$$Y = x \sin(-135°) + y \cos(-135°) + \frac{3}{\sqrt{2}} = -\frac{x}{\sqrt{2}} - \frac{y}{\sqrt{2}} + \frac{3}{\sqrt{2}}.$$

We shall return to transformations in Section 1008. Our present interest is in locus problems.

When you consult the section on formulas in your book of tables, you may find a statement like this: "To reduce $Ax + By + C = 0$ to normal form, divide by $\pm\sqrt{A^2 + B^2}$, where the sign of the radical is taken opposite to that of C when $C \neq 0$." You should test this statement against our discussion (page 540) of reducing the equation $ax + by = c$ to normal form.

Then you may find a statement like this: "The distance from the line $Ax + By + C = 0$ to the point $P_2(x_2, y_2)$ is

$$d = \frac{Ax_2 + By_2 + C}{\pm\sqrt{A^2 + B^2}}\text{,"}$$

Recall that Equation (4), above, states that the distance from (h,k) to $x \cos \alpha + y \sin \alpha = p$ is: $d = -(h \cos \alpha + k \sin \alpha - p)$. When written in normal form, the equation $Ax + By + C = 0$ becomes:

$$\frac{A}{\pm\sqrt{A^2 + B^2}}x + \frac{B}{\pm\sqrt{A^2 + B^2}}y = \frac{-C}{\pm\sqrt{A^2 + B^2}}.$$

Hence, Equation (4) yields the distance from (x_2, y_2) to $Ax + By + C = 0$ as:

$$d = -\left[x_2 \cdot \frac{A}{\pm\sqrt{A^2 + B^2}} + y_2 \cdot \frac{B}{\pm\sqrt{A^2 + B^2}} - \frac{-C}{\pm\sqrt{A^2 + B^2}}\right]$$

$$= -\left[\frac{Ax_2 + By_2 + C}{\pm\sqrt{A^2 + B^2}}\right].$$

Formula (4) yields the directed distance from the point to the line rather than the directed distance from the line to the point, hence the change of sign.

The following exercises will give you practice in working with questions that involve distances from points to lines.

EXERCISES §1005

1. Draw a figure for each line whose normal intercept p and inclination of the normal, α, are given. Then write the equation of the line.

(a) $p = 8$, $\alpha = 60°$ (b) $p = 5$, $\alpha = 90°$

(c) $p = 3$, $\alpha = 215°$ (d) $p = 15$, $\alpha = \text{Arccos } \frac{4}{5}$

(e) $p = 26$, $\alpha = \text{Arctan } (-\frac{12}{5})$ (f) $p = 4$, $\alpha = 162°$

(g) $p = 0$, $\alpha = 45°$.

Answers: (a) $x + \sqrt{3}y = 16$; (e) $5x - 12y = 338$.

2. Rewrite each equation in normal form. Determine p and α. Sketch the line.

(a) $x + y - 4 = 0$ (b) $5x - 12y + 52 = 0$

(c) $y = 7x - 10$ (d) $4x + 3y + c = 0$

(e) $3x + 6y + 25 = 0$ (f) $8x - 3y = 24$

(g) $5y = 12x$.

Answers: (a) $x/\sqrt{2} + y/\sqrt{2} = 2\sqrt{2}$, $\alpha = 45°$, $p = 2\sqrt{2}$; (e) $-x/\sqrt{5} - 2y/\sqrt{5} = 5\sqrt{5}/3$, $\alpha \doteq 243°26'$, $p = 5\sqrt{5}/3$.

3. Determine the distance of the line $5x - 12y + 52 = 0$ from each of the points: $(1,8)$, $(-1,5)$, $(2,-10)$, $(-4,-4)$, $(3,2)$.

Answers: -3, -1, etc.

4. The equation of a family of lines is $x \cos \alpha + y \sin \alpha = 6$, where α is a parameter. What do the members of this family have in common? Which members of the family will pass through the point $(0,12)$? (*Hint:* Determine α from the condition $(0) \cos \alpha + (12) \sin \alpha = 6$. Why?)

5. Write the equation of the family of lines that are tangent to the circle $x^2 + y^2 = 25$. Determine the lines tangent to this circle that pass through $(7,1)$.

Answer: $3x + 4y = 25$ and $4x - 3y = 25$.

6. The equation of a family of lines is $y = 7x + b$, where b is a parameter. What do these lines have in common? Which members of the family will be tangent to the circle $x^2 + y^2 = 8$? (*Hint:* Rewrite the equation in normal form; then set the normal intercept equal to $2\sqrt{2}$.)

7. The equation of a family of lines is $y = mx + 9$. What do these lines have in common? Write the equation of the family in normal form; then determine the members of the family that are tangent to $x^2 + y^2 = 9$.

Answer: $y = \pm\sqrt{8}x + 9$.

8. A triangle has its vertices at $A(2,3)$, $B(5,7)$, and $C(6,-8)$. Determine the length of the altitude from A to BC.

9. Show that the lines $3x - y + 7 = 0$ and $6x - 2y - 5 = 0$ are parallel; then find the distance between them. (*Hint:* Find the distance to one line from a point on the other.)

10. Determine the equations of the lines parallel to $y = \frac{1}{2}x + 3$ and 6 units away.

11. Find the locus of points whose directed distances to the lines $2x - y - 8 = 0$ and $x + 3y - 6 = 0$ are equal.

Answer: $(2\sqrt{2} - 1)x - (\sqrt{2} + 3)y + (6 - 8\sqrt{2}) = 0$.

Find the locus of points whose directed distances to these lines are negatives of each other. What is the geometric significance of these lines?

12. Work Exercise 7, page 533, using the method of Exercise 11.

13. Find the locus of points whose distances from $(4,-3)$ are equal to their distances to $2x - y - 3 = 0$.

Answer: $x^2 + 4xy + 4y^2 - 28x + 24y + 116 = 0$.

14. A point moves so that its distance to the line $x + y = 5$ is twice its distance to $(-2,3)$. Determine the equation of its path.

1006. Division of a line segment

Often in geometry it is fruitful to ask what are the coordinates of a point $P(x,y)$ that divides the line segment from $P_1(x_1,y_1)$ to $P_2(x_2,y_2)$ in the ratio t_1/t_2.

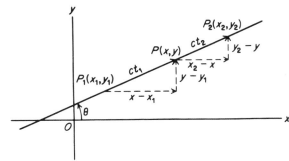

Fig. 10–38.

Figure 10–38 will help you to interpret this question. It means that $P_1P/PP_2 = ct_1/ct_2 = t_1/t_2$, $c \neq 0$, $t_1 \neq 0$, and $t_2 \neq 0$; we use the symbols P_1P and PP_2 for *directed line segments;* thus P_1P represents a vector that has magnitude $|ct_1|$ and is directed from P_1 to P.

Since P lies on the join of P_1 and P_2, the inclinations of the segments P_1P, and PP_2 are equal. Call this inclination θ. Then

$$\cos\theta = \frac{x - x_1}{ct_1} = \frac{x_2 - x}{ct_2} \quad \text{and} \quad \sin\theta = \frac{y - y_1}{ct_1} = \frac{y_2 - y}{ct_2}.$$

From the first of these equations, $c(t_2 x - t_2 x_1) = c(t_1 x_2 - t_1 x)$,

$$x(t_1 + t_2) = t_2 x_1 + t_1 x_2$$

$$x = \frac{t_2 x_1 + t_1 x_2}{t_1 + t_2}, \quad t_1 + t_2 \neq 0;$$

from the second of these equations,

$$y = \frac{t_2 y_1 + t_1 y_2}{t_1 + t_2}.$$

In the derivation of these formulas, notice that $c \neq 0$, $t_1 \neq 0$, $t_2 \neq 0$, and $t_1 + t_2 \neq 0$.

The following examples illustrate the application of these formulas:

(1) Find the coordinates of the point $P(x,y)$ that divides the line segment from $(-1,3)$ to $(2,5)$ in the ratio $3/2$.

In the formulas, $x_1 = -1$, $y_1 = 3$, $x_2 = 2$, $y_2 = 5$, $t_1 = 3$, and $t_2 = 2$. Hence

$$x = \frac{2(-1) + 3(2)}{3 + 2} = \frac{4}{5},$$

and

$$y = \frac{2(3) + 3(5)}{3 + 2} = \frac{21}{5} = 4\frac{1}{5}.$$

Study Fig. 10–39 to see how the formulas yield the coordinates of a point $P(\frac{4}{5}, 4\frac{1}{5})$, three-fifths of the way from $(-1,3)$ to $(2,5)$.

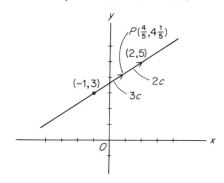

Fig. 10–39.

(2) Find the coordinates of points $P(x,y)$ that divide the line segment from $(2,-4)$ to $(-3,1)$ in various ratios:
   (a) Suppose $t_1/t_2 = 1/1$; then

$$x = \frac{1(2) + 1(-3)}{1 + 1} = -\frac{1}{2}, \qquad y = \frac{1(-4) + 1(1)}{1 + 1} = -\frac{3}{2}.$$

Draw a figure and notice that $t_1/t_2 = 1/1$ means that P is the *midpoint* of P_1P_2. In general, the midpoint of the line segment from $P_1(x_1,y_1)$ to $P_2(x_2,y_2)$ is $P(\frac{1}{2}[x_1 + x_2], \frac{1}{2}[y_1 + y_2])$.
   (b) Suppose $t_1/t_2 = -1/2$; then

$$x = \frac{2(2) + (-1)(-3)}{(-1) + (2)} = 7, \qquad y = \frac{2(-4) + (-1)(1)}{(-1) + 2} = -9.$$

Draw a figure and notice that $t_1/t_2 = -1/2$ means that P is exterior to P_1P_2, and as far from P_1 in one direction as P_2 is from P_1 in the opposite direction.
   (c) Suppose $t_1/t_2 = 1/-2$; then

$$x = \frac{(-2)2 + 1(-3)}{1 + (-2)} = \frac{-7}{-1} = 7, \qquad y = \frac{9}{-1} = -9.$$

The ratio $t_1/t_2 = 1/-2$ is, of course, the same as the ratio $-1/2$; hence the point P is the same as in (b).
   (d) Suppose $t_1/t_2 = -2/1$; then

$$x = \frac{1(2) + (-2)(-3)}{(-2) + 1} = \frac{8}{-1} = -8, \qquad y = 6.$$

Draw a figure and notice that P is exterior to P_1P_2, twice as far from P_1 as is P_2, and in the same direction.
   The previous examples suggest the generalization: To each value of the ratio t_1/t_2, $t_1 + t_2 \neq 0$, there corresponds a unique point on the join of P_1 and P_2; if $t_1/t_2 > 0$, P lies between P_1 and P_2; if $t_1/t_2 < 0$, P is exterior to P_1P_2, on the same side of P_1 as P_2 when $t_1/t_2 < -1$, and on the opposite side of P_1 from P_2 when $-1 < t_1/t_2 < 0$. Experiment with this generalization.
   What happens when $t_1/t_2 = -1/1 = -1$? Then $t_1 + t_2 = 0$ and the formulas break down. Try to interpret this situation geometrically.
   What happens when $t_1/t_2 = 0$? Suppose $t_1 = 0$ and $t_2 \neq 0$; then

$$x = \frac{t_2 x_1 + 0(x_2)}{0 + t_2} = x_1, \qquad y = y_1.$$

Hence P coincides with P_1.
   When $t_1 \neq 0$ and $t_2 = 0$, the ratio t_1/t_2 is not defined. The formulas yield $x = x_2$, $y = y_2$. Hence P coincides with P_2.
   You may be interested in experimenting further with special instances of these formulas. We apply them now to the solution of a locus problem:
   (3) Find the locus of the midpoints of the family of chords of the ellipse

$x^2/25 + y^2/9 = 1$ that have slope 1. In Fig. 10–40, we drew one member of the family of lines of slope 1; we wrote $y = x + c$, using the parameter c for the y-intercept. The chord is the line segment P_1P_2. For any point $P(x,y)$ of the locus,

$$x = \frac{x_1 + x_2}{2}, \qquad y = \frac{y_1 + y_2}{2}.$$

Since P_1 and P_2 lie on the ellipse $9x^2 + 25y^2 = 225$, and on the line

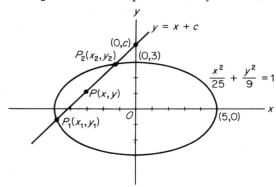

Fig. 10–40.

$y = x + c$, their coordinates satisfy the system of conditions:

$$9x^2 + 25y^2 = 225$$
$$y = x + c.$$

Substitution for y yields $9x^2 + 25(x + c)^2 = 225$, $34x^2 + 50cx + (25c^2 - 225) = 0$. The solutions are the x-coordinates of P_1 and P_2, namely,

$$x_1 = -\frac{50c}{68} - \frac{\sqrt{2500c^2 - 136(25c^2 - 225)}}{68}$$

and

$$x_2 = -\frac{50c}{68} + \frac{\sqrt{2500c^2 - 136(25c^2 - 225)}}{68}.$$

The x-coordinate of P is $x = \dfrac{x_1 + x_2}{2} = -\dfrac{50c}{68} = -\dfrac{25c}{34}$.

You use the equation $y = x + c$ to find

$$y_1 = -\frac{50c}{68} + c - \frac{\sqrt{2500c^2 - 136(25c^2 - 225)}}{68}$$

and

$$y_2 = -\frac{50c}{68} + c + \frac{\sqrt{2500c^2 - 136(25c^2 - 225)}}{68}.$$

The y-coordinate of P is

$$y = \frac{y_1 + y_2}{2} = -\frac{50c}{68} + c = \frac{9c}{34}.$$

For each value of c you get a definite midpoint, $(-25c/34, 9c/34)$, of the corresponding chord. The equations $x = -25c/34$, $y = 9c/34$ define the locus of $P(x,y)$ in terms of the parameter c. To derive the equation of the locus in a more familiar form, write $y = 9c/34$ as $c = 34y/9$; then substitute this value of c in the equation $x = -25c/34$ to obtain $x = (-25/34)(34y/9)$, or $x = -25y/9$. The required locus is the straight line $y = -9x/25$, of slope $-9/25$ through the origin. Hence the locus of the midpoints of the family of parallel chords of the ellipse is a straight line through the center of the ellipse.

Notice that the geometric meaning of the original problem limits the *extent* of the locus. The locus is the portion of the line $y = -9x/25$ whose elements are midpoints of the family of chords. You get real points P_1 and P_2 when and only when

$$2500c^2 - 136(25c^2 - 225) \geq 0$$

$$30{,}600 - 900c^2 \geq 0$$

$$c^2 \leq 34$$

$$-\sqrt{34} \leq c \leq \sqrt{34}.$$

You should find the range of x and y, using the conditions $x = -25c/34$ and $y = 9c/34$. Notice that $c = -\sqrt{34}$ and $c = \sqrt{34}$ yield tangent lines, $y = x - \sqrt{34}$ and $y = x + \sqrt{34}$, to the ellipse; each tangent line touches the ellipse at a point that lies on the line of midpoints, $y = -9x/25$.

EXERCISES §1006

1. Find the coordinates of the points that divide the line segment from $P_1(-4,1)$ to $P_2(5,-3)$ in each of the ratios: $1/3$, $-1/8$, $3/(-2)$, $99/1$. Draw a sketch and plot each point.

2. Determine the midpoint of each line segment.

(a) $P_1(-2,1)$ to $P_2(6,5)$ (b) $P_1(-7,-2)$ to $P_2(-1,8)$
(c) $P_1(3,-5)$ to $P_2(-2,3)$ (d) $P_1(0,b)$ to $P_2(a,0)$
(e) $P_1(a,b)$ to $P_2(-a,-b)$ (f) $P_1(a,b)$ to $P_2(b,a)$.

3. Determine the coordinates of the points that trisect the line segment from $P_1(-7,-2)$ to $P_2(-1,8)$.

   Answer: $(-5,\frac{4}{3})$ and $(-3,\frac{14}{3})$.

4. One end of a line segment is $P_1(3,-5)$ and the coordinates of the midpoint are $(-1,1)$. Find the coordinates of the other end of the line segment.

   Answer: $(-5,7)$.

5. Determine the coordinates of the centroid (intersection of the medians) of the triangle whose vertices are $A(1,3)$, $B(5,7)$, and $C(6,-8)$.

Answer: $(4,\tfrac{2}{3})$.

6. Show that the coordinates of the centroid of the triangle $A(x_1,y_1)$, $B(x_2,y_2)$, $C(x_3,y_3)$ are $\left(\dfrac{x_1 + x_2 + x_3}{3}, \dfrac{y_1 + y_2 + y_3}{3}\right)$.

7. Find the locus of the midpoints of the family of chords of the parabola $y = \tfrac{1}{2}x^2$ that have a slope of 1.

Answer: $x = 1$ and $y \geq \tfrac{1}{2}$.

8. $A(0,6)$ is a fixed point and $B(x_1,\tfrac{1}{4}x_1{}^2)$ is a point on the parabola $y = \tfrac{1}{4}x^2$. As B moves along the parabola, $P(x,y)$ is the midpoint of the line segment AB. Find the equation of the path of P.

Answer: $y = \tfrac{1}{8}x^2 + 3$.

9. Find the equation of the perpendicular bisector of the line segment from $P_1(-1,3)$ to $P_2(5,1)$ in two ways: (a) as the locus of points equidistant from P_1 and P_2, and (b) using the coordinates of the midpoint and the slope of P_1P_2.

1007. Plane loci—conditions in parametric form

Physical or geometric descriptions of loci often tell you how to find the two coordinates of each point on the locus in terms of a parameter. Recall, for example, finding the midpoints of a set of parallel chords of an ellipse in Section 1006 (page 550). We found the x- and y-coordinates of the midpoints in terms of a parameter, c, that represented the y-intercept of the chord. Also, in Section 1004 (page 536), it was convenient to express the θ- and r-coordinates of a point on the locus in terms of the parameter t. In this example t represented the time in seconds during which the point was allowed to move.

In this section you will meet further examples of the convenience of expressing the given conditions in *parametric form*. Often you will find it easier to derive separate equations for the coordinates of P than to find a single equation that describes the relation between the coordinates of P. The following examples illustrate this.

(1) A ball is thrown toward the east with an angle of elevation of $30°$ and an initial velocity of 60 ft/sec. Consider the ball as a point that moves in the plane under the action of gravity alone; that is, neglect air resistance, wind, air currents, etc. Find the locus of the point.

Figure 10–41 places the point from which the ball is thrown at the origin. The initial speed of the ball is $60 \cos 30° = 30\sqrt{3}$ ft/sec toward the east, and $60 \sin 30° = 30$ ft/sec upward. If no *forces* acted upon the ball, Newton's laws of motion would require it to move uniformly according to the equations $x = (30\sqrt{3})t$, $y = 30t$. You can eliminate t to get $y = 30x/30\sqrt{3} = x/\sqrt{3}$

as the equation of the locus; this is the line of slope $1/\sqrt{3}$ that passes through the origin; it is the line of inclination $30°$.

Actually, the ball falls, under the action of gravity, according to the law $s = \frac{1}{2}gt^2$, where g is the gravity constant. Although the value of g is slightly different at different points on the earth's surface, it is common to take $g = 32 \text{ ft/sec}^2$; that is, the speed of a freely-falling body increases by about 32 ft/sec in each second of its fall. This gives $s = 16t^2$.

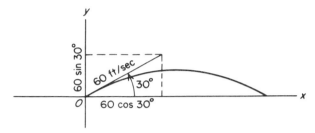

Fig. 10–41.

Hence the ball moves eastward according to the condition $x = 30\sqrt{3}t$, and *rises* according to the condition $y = 30t - 16t^2$. The y-coordinate of the ball (considered as a point) is the resultant of $30t$ ft of rise and $16t^2$ ft of fall during the first t seconds of flight.

The parametric equations of the *path* of the ball are

$$x = 30\sqrt{3}t$$
$$y = 30t - 16t^2.$$

These are parametric equations of the locus. They are convenient because they "fit" the problem. It seems easier, and more natural, to study the x- and y-coordinates of each point on the locus separately than to try to find the equation that expresses the relation between these x- and y-coordinates directly.

It is easy to eliminate t from these equations. Since $t = x/30\sqrt{3}$,

$$y = 30\left(\frac{x}{30\sqrt{3}}\right) - 16\left(\frac{x}{30\sqrt{3}}\right)^2 = \frac{1}{\sqrt{3}}x - \frac{4}{675}x^2.$$

The equation $y = -4x^2/675 + x/\sqrt{3}$ represents a parabola that passes through $(0,0)$. Hence the path of the ball is a parabola through the origin.

You can use the methods of Chapter 6 to find out more about this parabola. For example, the derivative of y is $y' = -8x/675 + 1/\sqrt{3}$; the value of y is a maximum when $y' = 1/\sqrt{3} - 8x/675 = 0$, that is, when $x = 675/8\sqrt{3}$. You should find the corresponding value of y, and hence the coordinates of the vertex of the parabola. You should also find the point where the ball hits the ground $(y = 0 \Rightarrow x = 0$ or $x = 675/4\sqrt{3})$. You should also ask some questions that involve time. For example, how far east does the ball travel in 1.5 sec? $[x = 30\sqrt{3}(1.5) = 45\sqrt{3}$ ft.] How high is the ball after 2 sec? $[y = 30(2) - 16(2^2) = -4$ ft.] It may be all right to neglect air-resistance. But it is scarcely fair to neglect mud-resistance. The ball does not go 4 ft into the ground. The answer is that the ball strikes the ground before 2 sec elapse. Hence, the ball is at ground-level after 2 sec.

Notice that the range of t is limited, $0 \le t \le t_g$, where t_g is the time when the ball strikes the ground. The range of x is limited in a similar way. The range of y is $0 \le y \le y_{max}$, where y_{max} is the maximum height of the ball. Experiment further with the parametric equations of the locus and with the equation $y = -4x^2/675 + x/\sqrt{3}$, which expresses the relation between x and y directly.

(2) A point revolves about the pole at an angular speed of $\frac{1}{2}$ radian/sec $(\theta = \frac{1}{2}t)$; it moves away from the pole according to the law $r = e^t/10$. Find the locus of the point. The polar coordinates of P are:

$$r = \frac{e^t}{10}, \qquad \theta = \tfrac{1}{2}t.$$

These are the parametric equations of the path of the point. To eliminate t, $t = 2\theta$, $r = e^{2\theta}/10$. Hence the equation $r = e^{2\theta}/10$ expresses the relation $\{(r,\theta)\}$ directly.

Figure 10–42 shows the graph of the parametric equations, or the equation $r = e^{2\theta}/10$. This curve is called a *logarithmic spiral*.

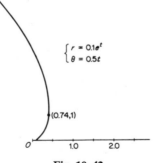

$$\begin{cases} r = 0.1e^t \\ \theta = 0.5t \end{cases}$$

(0.74,1)

t	r	θ
0.0	0.10	0.00
0.5	0.16	0.25
1.0	0.27	0.50
1.5	0.45	0.75
2.0	0.74	1.00
.	.	.
.	.	.
.	.	.

Fig. 10–42.

(3) An important tool for testing electronic equipment is the cathode-ray oscilloscope. To an amateur it appears to be a black box that contains a large picture tube, like those in TV sets, and various dials and adjustments. It is easy to feed alternating voltages of various amplitudes into the oscilloscope and to accomplish an effect like:

$$x = 5 \sin t, \qquad y = 3 \cos t.$$

This means that the beam of electrons in the tube shines on the point $P(x,y)$ at time t, where $x = 5 \sin t$ and $y = 5 \cos t$. The face of the tube is fluorescent, and a point continues to glow for a short time after the beam of electrons leaves it. What will the face of the tube look like? That is, where are all the points P located, or, what is the locus of P?

Notice that

$$\left(\frac{x}{5} = \sin t \text{ and } \frac{y}{3} = \cos t\right) \Rightarrow \left(\frac{x^2}{25} + \frac{y^2}{9} = \sin^2 t + \cos^2 t = 1\right).$$

Hence the locus of P is an ellipse with major axis 10, minor axis 6, and center at the origin. When the oscilloscope is properly adjusted, the whole ellipse appears on the face of the tube, although at any instant the beam of electrons is focused on one particular point.

EXERCISES §1007

1. Where is the ball of Example 1 after $\frac{1}{2}$ sec of flight? 1 sec? $1\frac{1}{2}$ sec? What is the highest distance above the ground reached by the ball? At what time does this occur? At what time does the ball strike the ground? Plot the path of the ball.

2. Make suitable replacements of the parameter t to determine about 12 number-pairs, (x,y), that belong to the relation of Example 3. Plot the graph.

3. An airplane is headed north with an airspeed of 7 nautical mi/min in the jet stream, a mass of air that moves east $1\frac{1}{2}$ nautical mi/min. Use the origin of a coordinate system to represent the original position of the plane, write equations to show the position of the plane after t min. Plot the path of the plane. What is the ground speed of the plane? What is the direction of travel?

Answer: $x = \frac{3}{2}t$ and $y = 7t$; 7.16 mi/min; about 12° east of north.

4. A ship is headed east at a speed of 15 knots in a 5-knot current that moves south. Write parametric equations for the path of the ship.

5. A projectile is fired with a muzzle velocity of 900 ft/sec from a gun whose barrel has a 45° degree angle of elevation. Write parametric equations for the path of the projectile, considering only the action of gravity. How long will the projectile be in the air? How far will it travel in the horizontal direction?

6. Find general formulas for the path of the projectile of Exercise 5 if v_0 is the muzzle velocity and θ is the angle of elevation.

Answer: $x = (v_0 \cos \theta)t$, $y = (v_0 \sin \theta)t - 16t^2$.

Find formulas for the time of flight and the range of the gun.

Answer: $t = (v_0 \sin \theta)/16$, $x = (v_0^2 \sin 2\theta)/32$.

7. The equations of the following loci are given in parametric form. Plot each graph by assigning values to the parameter to determine number-pairs (x,y) that belong to the relation. Then eliminate the parameter to write a single condition in x and y. Look out for restrictions on the range of x or y.

(a) $x = 4t$, $y = 3t - 2$

(b) $x = 2t - 5$, $y = \frac{1}{2}t + 4$

(c) $x = t + 1$, $y = t^2$

(d) $x = t^2 - 3t$, $y = 2t + 1$

(e) $x = 3 \sin t$, $y = 2 \sin t$

(f) $x = \cos t$, $y = 4 \sin t$

(g) $x = 2 + 3 \sin t$, $y = 3 + 2 \cos t$

(h) $x = t + 2$, $y = 1/t$

(i) $x = 3e^t$, $y = e^{-t}$

(j) $x = \sin t$, $y = \cos 2t$

(k) $x = 2 \sin t$, $y = 2 \csc t$

(l) $x = 1 + 3 \tan \theta$, $y = -2 + 4 \sec \theta$.

8. The graphs of some conditions are easier to plot from parametric form. Eliminate the parameter to write a single equation in x and y; then plot the graph using the form that appears to be more convenient.

(a) $x = 2 + t^3$, $y = t^2$

(b) $x = 8 \cos^3 t$, $y = 8 \sin^3 t$

(c) $x = \sin 2t$, $y = \cos t$

(d) $x = 2 \cos t$, $y = \cos 3t$

(e) $x = t - \sin t$, $y = 1 - \cos t$

(f) $x = 2 \cos t - \cos 2t$,

                                                   $y = 2 \sin t - \sin 2t$.

(g) $x = 2 \cos t$, $y = \cos \frac{1}{2}t$

(h) $x = \cos t + t \sin t$,

                                                   $y = \sin t - t \cos t$.

Answers: (a) $y = (x - 2)^{2/3}$; (b) $x^{2/3} + y^{2/3} = 4$; (e) $y^2 - 2y + [x - \arccos (1 - y)]^2 = 0$.

9. A circle of radius a rolls, without slipping, along a straight line. Find the locus of the path of a fixed point on the circumference of the circle. (*Suggestion:* Let the initial position of the point be the origin of a coordinate system. After the circle has turned through an angle t write equations for x and y in terms of t.)

Answer: $x = a(t - \sin t)$, $y = a(1 - \cos t)$.

Plot the locus of the point. This locus is called a *cycloid*.

10. A thread is held taut as it is unwound from a fixed circle of radius a. Find the locus of a fixed point on the thread when the circle has its center at the origin. [*Suggestion:* Let the initial position of the fixed point be at $(a,0)$. Write the coordinates of any other point on the locus in terms of the angle made by the radius of the fixed circle drawn to the tangent formed by the thread.]

Answer: $x = a(\cos t + t \sin t)$; $y = a(\sin t - t \cos t)$.

Plot the locus of the point. This locus is called the *involute* of a circle. [*Suggestion:* Draw this curve using an oatmeal box and a long piece of string.]

11. Two circles, with radii a and b, have their centers at the origin. A line L through the origin meets the first circle at Q and the second at R. $P(x,y)$ is located at the intersection of the perpendicular to the x-axis from R, and the line parallel to the x-axis through Q. Using the inclination of L as the parameter, derive parametric equations for the locus of P as L rotates about the origin. Show that the locus is an ellipse. Construct several points on the ellipse of Example 3, using the geometric conditions of this locus.

12. Let $P_0(a,b)$ be a point in the first quadrant. Let L be a line through P_0 intersecting the y-axis at M and the x-axis at N. Choose $P(x,y)$ so that $MP_0 = PN$. Find parametric equations for the path of P as the line rotates about P_0. *Suggestion:* Let the angle between L and the negative x-axis be the parameter (see Fig. 10–43). Then

$$y = RN \tan t = a \tan t$$
$$x = SN = b \cot t.$$

13. Eliminate the parameter in the parametric equations of Exercise 12 to show that the locus is the hyperbola $xy = ab$, passing through $P_0(a,b)$. Will the branch of the hyperbola in the third quadrant be included? Construct about five points of the hyperbola that passes through $(3,5)$; use the geometric conditions of Exercise 12.

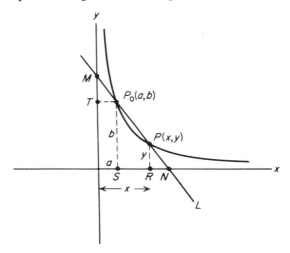

Fig. 10–43.

14. A ladder 20 ft long is leaning against the wall of a building, with a bucket of paint hanging on the middle rung. Find the path of the bucket of paint as the bottom end of the ladder slides on the ground away from the building. (*Suggestion:* Let the x-axis lie along the ground, and the y-axis along the wall of the building. Use the angle of the line joining the bucket of paint to the origin as the parameter.)

Answer: The circle $x = 10 \cos t$, $y = 10 \sin t$.

15. What will be the path of the paint in Exercise 14 if the bucket is on a rung 15 ft from the lower end of the ladder?

This concludes our presentation of plane loci that began in Section 1002. You should look back over Sections 1002 through 1007 at this point. We do not want you to lose the main idea among the details. Whenever you can express a physical or geometric condition upon a point analytically, you can derive an equation of the locus of the point. Then you can use algebraic methods to solve geometric problems.

1008. Rigid motions for conics

When you are free to choose the axes to use in a locus problem, you may get a simpler equation of the locus by placing the axes in a convenient place, with the origin at the center of an ellipse, at the vertex of a parabola, or the like. When you begin with an equation of a locus, sometimes you can simplify the equation by translation or rotation of axes.

If an equation is linear, it is easy to choose a convenient set of axes. For example, given the line $y = mx + b$, you can translate the origin to a point on the line; then you can rotate the axes until the x-axis or the y-axis coincides with the given line. For example:

$$(1) \qquad\qquad y = \tfrac{1}{2}x + 2.$$

Translate the origin to the point (0,2) by the equations

$$x = X, \qquad y = Y + 2.$$

The new equation is $Y = \tfrac{1}{2}X$. It is simpler than the given equation. Now rotate the axes through an angle θ, such that $\tan \theta = 1/2$; you may take $\cos \theta = 2/\sqrt{5}$ and $\sin \theta = 1/\sqrt{5}$ (see Fig. 10–44); The corresponding rotation is:

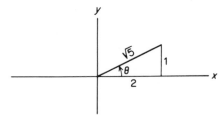

Fig. 10–44.

$$X = \bar{X}\left(\frac{2}{\sqrt{5}}\right) - \bar{Y}\left(\frac{1}{\sqrt{5}}\right), \qquad Y = \bar{X}\left(\frac{1}{\sqrt{5}}\right) + \bar{Y}\left(\frac{2}{\sqrt{5}}\right).$$

Substitution in $Y = \tfrac{1}{2}X$ yields

$$\left(\frac{1}{\sqrt{5}}\right)\bar{X} + \left(\frac{2}{\sqrt{5}}\right)\bar{Y} = \frac{1}{2}\left[\left(\frac{2}{\sqrt{5}}\right)\bar{X} - \left(\frac{1}{\sqrt{5}}\right)\bar{Y}\right]$$

$$\left(\frac{2}{\sqrt{5}} + \frac{1}{2\sqrt{5}}\right)\bar{Y} = 0$$

$$\bar{Y} = 0.$$

The given line is the $\bar{X}$ axis. Study Fig. 10–45 as you trace the effect of the two transformations.

Recall, from Section 702 (page 301), how we performed translations of axes to remove the x and y terms of equations of the form $Ax^2 + Cy^2 + Dx + Ey + F = 0$. We now use rotations to remove the xy-term in an equation of the form $Ax^2 + Bxy + Cy^2 + Dx + Ey + F = 0$. Combining these ideas, you can reduce any second degree equation in x and y to one of the standard forms of Section 702 (page 318).

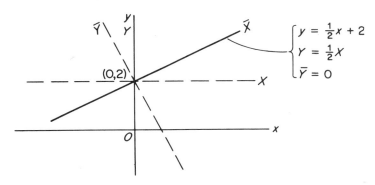

$$\begin{cases} y = \tfrac{1}{2}x + 2 \\ Y = \tfrac{1}{2}X \\ \bar{Y} = 0 \end{cases}$$

Fig. 10–45.

When you perform the rotation

$$x = X \cos \theta - Y \sin \theta$$
$$y = X \sin \theta + Y \cos \theta$$

upon the equation

I $\qquad Ax^2 + Bxy + Cy^2 + Dx + Ey + F = 0, \quad B \neq 0,$

you get the equation

II $\qquad A'X^2 + B'XY + C'Y^2 + D'X + E'Y + F' = 0,$

where $A' = A \cos^2 \theta + B \sin \theta \cos \theta + C \sin^2 \theta$

$\qquad B' = B(\cos^2 \theta - \sin^2 \theta) - 2A \sin \theta \cos \theta + 2C \sin \theta \cos \theta$

$\qquad C' = A \sin^2 \theta - B \sin \theta \cos \theta + C \cos^2 \theta$

$\qquad D' = D \cos \theta + E \sin \theta$

$\qquad E' = -D \sin \theta + E \cos \theta$

$\qquad F' = F.$

We wish to choose an angle of rotation, θ, such that

$$B' = B(\cos^2 \theta - \sin^2 \theta) - 2A \sin \theta \cos \theta + 2C \sin \theta \cos \theta = 0.$$

Using identities from Chapter 9:

$$\cos^2 \theta - \sin^2 \theta = \cos 2\theta, \quad \text{and} \quad 2 \sin \theta \cos \theta = \sin 2\theta.$$

Hence $B' = B \cos 2\theta - (A - C) \sin 2\theta = 0$

$$(A - C) \sin 2\theta = B \cos 2\theta.$$

If $A \neq C$, $\tan 2\theta = \dfrac{B}{A - C}.$

If $A = C$, $\cos 2\theta = 0,$

and we may choose $\theta = 45°$. Hence it is always possible to find an angle 2θ, and hence an angle θ, to make $B' = 0$. We shall choose the smallest positive value of 2θ in what follows.

Here are some examples to illustrate removing the xy-term of a second degree equation in x and y.

Through what angle, θ, can you rotate the axes to remove the xy-term of each equation?

(2) $3x^2 - 2xy + 5y^2 - 4y + 2 = 0$. Since $A - C = 3 - 5 \neq 0$,

$$\tan 2\theta = \frac{B}{A - C} = \frac{-2}{3 - 5} = \frac{-2}{-2} = 1;$$

we choose $2\theta = 45°$, $\theta = 22.5°$. For the rotation

$$x = X \cos 22.5° - Y \sin 22.5°$$

$$y = X \sin 22.5° + Y \cos 22.5°,$$

$B' = 0$. If you wish to check this statement, recall that

$$\sin \frac{\alpha}{2} = \pm\sqrt{\frac{1 - \cos \alpha}{2}}, \qquad \cos \frac{\alpha}{2} = \pm\sqrt{\frac{1 + \cos \alpha}{2}}.$$

Hence $\sin 22.5° = \sqrt{\dfrac{1 - \cos 45°}{2}} = \sqrt{\dfrac{1 - 1/\sqrt{2}}{2}} = \dfrac{1}{2}\sqrt{2 - \sqrt{2}},$

and $\cos 22.5° = \dfrac{1}{2}\sqrt{2 + \sqrt{2}};$

$$B' = -2[\tfrac{1}{4}(2 + \sqrt{2}) - \tfrac{1}{4}(2 - \sqrt{2})] - 6(\tfrac{1}{4})\sqrt{4 - 2} + 10(\tfrac{1}{4})\sqrt{4 - 2} = 0.$$

Of course you must use exact values of $\sin 22.5°$ and $\cos 22.5°$, rather than approximate values given in tables, to make $B' = 0$.

(3) $x^2 - 5xy + 2x - 6y + 5 = 0$. Since $A - C = 1 - 0 \neq 0$, $\tan 2\theta = -5/(1 - 0) = -5$; we choose

$$2\theta \doteq 101°, \qquad \theta \doteq 51°.$$

To get the exact rotation, $\tan 2\theta = -5$ and $90° < 2\theta < 180° \Rightarrow \cos 2\theta = -1/\sqrt{26}$ (see Fig. 10–46). Hence

$$\sin \theta = +\sqrt{\frac{1 + 1/\sqrt{26}}{2}} \quad \text{and} \quad \cos \theta = +\sqrt{\frac{1 - 1/\sqrt{26}}{2}}.$$

(4) $2x^2 + 3xy + 2y^2 - 5x + 2y = 0$. Since $A - C = 2 - 2 = 0$, $\tan 2\theta$ is not defined; $\cos 2\theta = 0$, and we choose

$$2\theta = 90°, \qquad \theta = 45°.$$

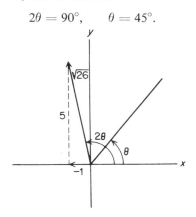

Fig. 10–46.

The rotation
$$x = \frac{1}{\sqrt{2}} X - \frac{1}{\sqrt{2}} Y$$

$$y = \frac{1}{\sqrt{2}} X + \frac{1}{\sqrt{2}} Y$$

makes $B' = 0$. This is a comparatively easy rotation to perform. Try it, and check to see that $B' = 0$.

EXERCISES §1008

1. Given the line $y - 3 = -2(x + 1)$; for what transformation of coordinate axes will this set of points be one of the new coordinate axes?

2. By substitution from the equations of transformation given for Example (2) in $3x^2 - 2xy + 5y^2 - 4y + 2 = 0$, write the equation of this set of points in the rotated coordinate system; notice that $B' = 0$.

Answer: $(4 - \sqrt{2})X^2 + (4 + \sqrt{2})Y^2 - 2\sqrt{2} - \sqrt{2}X - 2\sqrt{2} + \sqrt{2}Y + 2 = 0$.

3. Write the equation of the set of points in Example (4) after a rotation of 45°.

Answer: $7X^2 + Y^2 - 3\sqrt{2}X + 7\sqrt{2}Y = 0$.

4. Show that a rotation of $-45°$ will also make $B' = 0$ for Example (4).

5. Write the equation of the set of points in Example (3) after a rotation that makes $B' = 0$.

6. Find an angle of rotation, θ, that will result in a condition with $B' = 0$.

(a) $xy = 4$ (b) $x^2 + 2xy + y^2 = 5$

(c) $6x^2 + 3xy + 2y^2 = 8$ (d) $8x^2 - 12xy + 3y^2 - 2x - 10 = 0$

(e) $5x^2 + 7xy + 5y^2 - 14x + 2y - 15 = 0$

(f) $2x^2 - 5xy - 8y^2 + 4x - 3y - 7 = 0$.

Answers: (a) $\theta = 45°$; (c) $\theta \doteq 18°26'$; (d) $\theta \doteq 56°19'$.

7. Write the equations of transformation for each rotation of Exercise 6.

Answers: (a) $x = (X - Y)/\sqrt{2}$, $y = (X + Y)/\sqrt{2}$; (c) $x = (3X - Y)/\sqrt{10}$, $y = (X + 3Y)/\sqrt{10}$; (d) $x = (2X - 3Y)/\sqrt{13}$, $y = (3X + 2Y)/\sqrt{13}$.

8. Find the transformed equations of the conditions of Exercise 6.

Answers: (a) $X^2 - Y^2 = 8$; (c) $13X^2 + 3Y^2 = 16$;
(d) $-X^2 + 12Y^2 - 4X/\sqrt{13} + 6Y/\sqrt{13} - 10 = 0$.

9. Given the condition $2x^2 + \sqrt{3}xy + y^2 = 10$. Eliminate the xy-term by a rotation of coordinate axes. Draw both coordinate systems and sketch the graph on the new coordinate system, using the transformed equation.

Answer: $\theta = 30°$, $\frac{5}{2}X^2 + \frac{1}{2}Y^2 = 10$.

10. Repeat Exercise 9 with the condition $9x^2 + 24xy + 16y^2 + 40x - 30y = 0$.

Now that you know how to write Equation I in the form of Equation II with $B' = 0$, you can use the methods of Section 702 (page 301) to identify the locus of any equation of degree 2 in x and y as a parabola, an ellipse or circle, a hyperbola, or a degenerate form of one of these curves. Recall that a parabola may degenerate into parallel lines, an ellipse or circle into a point or an imaginary locus, and a hyperbola into a pair of intersecting lines.

It is a tedious job to find a rotation that will make $B' = 0$, to perform this rotation, and then to apply methods of Chapter 7 to identify the locus. We return to the idea of invariants and seek easier ways to identify the locus of a second-degree equation in x and y.

The equation

I $$Ax^2 + Bxy + Cy^2 + Dx + Ey + F = 0$$

is an equation of degree 2 in x and y. You have learned to rotate the x and y axes to get the equation

II $$(A\cos^2\theta + B\sin\theta\cos\theta + C\sin^2\theta)X^2$$
$$+ [B(\cos^2\theta - \sin^2\theta) - 2A\sin\theta\cos\theta + 2C\sin\theta\cos\theta]XY$$
$$+ (A\sin^2\theta - B\sin\theta\cos\theta + C\cos^2\theta)Y^2$$
$$+ (D\cos\theta + E\sin\theta)X + (-D\sin\theta + E\cos\theta)Y + F = 0,$$

that is, $A'X^2 + B'XY + C'Y^2 + D'X + E'Y + F' = 0.$

Now perform the translation

$$x = \bar{X} + h, \qquad y = \bar{Y} + k$$

upon the Equation I to get the equation

III $A\bar{X}^2 + B\bar{X}\bar{Y} + C\bar{Y}^2 + (2Ah + Bk + D)\bar{X} + (Bh + 2Ck + E)\bar{Y}$

$$+ (Ah^2 + Bhk + Ck^2 + Dh + Ek + F) = 0,$$

that is, $A''\bar{X}^2 + B''\bar{X}\bar{Y} + C''\bar{Y}^2 + D''\bar{X} + E''\bar{Y} + F'' = 0.$

Now we examine Equations I, II, and III to find invariants.

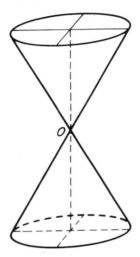

Fig. 10–47.

It can be proved that if one or more of the parameters A, B, C is not zero, then at least one of the parameters A', B', C', and at least one of the parameters A'', B'', C'' is not zero (see Exercise 15). In other words, an equation of degree 2 in x and y becomes, under rotation or translation, another equation of degree 2 with new variables. This suggests that all equations of degree 2 in x and y have a common geometric property. We call the graphs of all such equations *conic sections*. The Greeks thought of them as plane sections of circular cones; they imagined a cone, like the one suggested by Fig. 10–47, that extended infinitely far above and below its vertex, O. Experiment with such a cone to see how you can cut it to obtain the various conic sections. How do you get circles? ellipses? You get parabolas when you take a section of the cone parallel to one of the lines that passes through the vertex and lies in the surface of the cone. When you tilt this plane section one way you get ellipses; when you tilt it the other way you get hyperbolas.

How do you obtain the degenerate conics that are either a point or a pair of lines?

The fact that the degree of a second-degree equation in x and y is invariant under translation or rotation corresponds to the geometric property that a second-degree equation in x and y represents a conic section.

To find other invariants of the second-degree equation: First examine Equations I and III, and notice that $A'' = A$ and $C'' = C$; hence $A'' + C'' = A + C$. Then examine Equations I and II, and notice that

$$A' = A \cos^2 \theta + B \sin \theta \cos \theta + C \sin^2 \theta, \text{ and}$$

$$C' = A \sin^2 \theta - B \sin \theta \cos \theta + C \cos^2 \theta;$$

hence $A' + C' = A + C$. This means that the sum of the coefficients of x^2 and y^2 is an invariant under rotation and translation of axes. The knowledge that $A + C$ is invariant often saves calculation, as you will see in later examples.

Next you may wish to try your hand at proving the identity

$$(B'')^2 - 4A''C'' = (B')^2 - 4A'C' = B^2 - 4AC.$$

Of course,

$$A'' = A, \ B'' = B, \text{ and } C'' = C \Rightarrow (B'')^2 - 4A''C'' = B^2 - 4AC.$$

Also, $\begin{cases} A' = A \cos^2 \theta + B \sin \theta \cos \theta + C \sin^2 \theta \\ B' = B(\cos^2 \theta - \sin^2 \theta) - 2A \sin \theta \cos \theta + 2C \sin \theta \cos \theta \\ C' = A \sin^2 \theta - B \sin \theta \cos \theta + C \cos^2 \theta \end{cases} \Rightarrow$

$$\{(B')^2 - 4A'C' = B^2 - 4AC\}$$

although it takes skillful use of the identities of Chapter 9 to prove it (see Exercise 14 or 15). We conclude that the expression $\Delta = B^2 - 4AC$ is an invariant under translation and rotation of axes.

The invariant Δ enables you to identify the type of graph that corresponds to a particular second-degree equation in x and y:

(a) By our definition of an ellipse, $x^2/a^2 + y^2/b^2 = 1$ represents an ellipse with center at the origin and major and minor axes parallel to the coordinate axes. In this equation, $A = 1/a^2$, $B = 0$, $C = 1/b^2$, $D = E = 0$, and $F = -1$; $\Delta = B^2 - 4AC = -4/a^2b^2 < 0$. When you translate, or rotate, the coordinate axes, Δ is invariant. Hence, for an ellipse, $\Delta < 0$.

(b) By our definition of a hyperbola, $x^2/a^2 - y^2/b^2 = 1$ represents a hyperbola with its center at the origin and principal axis the x-axis. In this equation $\Delta = B^2 - 4AC = -4\left(\dfrac{1}{a^2}\right)\left(\dfrac{-1}{b^2}\right) = \dfrac{4}{a^2b^2} > 0$. When you translate, or rotate, the coordinate axes, Δ is invariant. Hence, for a hyperbola, $\Delta > 0$.

(c) By our definition of a parabola, $y = ax^2$ represents a parabola with vertex at the origin and symmetrical about the y-axis. In this equation, $\Delta = B^2 - 4AC = 0$. Hence, for a parabola, $\Delta = 0$.

These facts enable you to decide, about a particular second-degree equation in x and y, whether its locus is an ellipse ($\Delta < 0$), a hyperbola ($\Delta > 0$), or a parabola ($\Delta = 0$). The question as to whether the locus is a degenerate form is still an open question. Here are some examples to help you assimilate these new ideas. Identify the locus that each equation represents:

(5) $2x^2 - 3xy + 5y^2 - 2x + 3y - 17 = 0$.

$$\Delta = B^2 - 4AC = (-3)^2 - 4(2)(5) < 0.$$

The locus is an ellipse that may be degenerate; that is, the graph may be a point or imaginary.

(6) $2x^2 - 7xy + 5y^2 - 2x + 3y - 17 = 0$.

$$\Delta = B^2 - 4AC = 9 > 0.$$

The locus is a hyperbola that may be degenerate; that is, the graph may be a pair of intersecting straight lines.

(7) $3x^2 - 6xy + 3y^2 - 2x + 3y - 17 = 0$.

$$\Delta = B^2 - 4AC = 0.$$

The locus is a parabola that may be degenerate; that is, the graph may be two straight lines that are parallel or coincident.

You may be wondering whether there are other invariants. How would a person go about discovering all of the invariants of a second-degree equation in x and y? One answer lies in the extension of the matrix theory, which you met in Chapter 7 (page 349), to the study of *quadratic forms*. We mention one other invariant, which arises naturally in the study of quadratic forms. It is:

$$R = \begin{vmatrix} 2A & B & D \\ B & 2C & E \\ D & E & 2F \end{vmatrix}.$$

The proof that R is an invariant under rotation and translation can be made to depend upon the identities of Chapter 9. We omit it because it is neither easy nor mathematically elegant.

The invariant R enables you to tell whether or not the locus is degenerate.

(d) For an ellipse, $\Delta = B^2 - 4AC < 0$; hence $AC > B^2/4 > 0$. A and C must be either both positive, or both negative. You can always make the coefficient of x^2 positive, by multiplying the terms of the condition by -1 if necessary. Hence, if the equation $Ax^2 + Bxy + Cy^2 + Dx + Ey + F = 0$ represents an ellipse, we may assume that $A > 0$ and $C > 0$. When you transform the equation by rotation or translation, $A + C$ is invariant. Hence $A' + C' > 0$ in any transformed equation. You can choose translations or rotations that transform the given equation into the equation

$$\frac{1}{a^2}X^2 + \frac{1}{b^2}Y^2 - M = 0, \quad \text{with} \quad \frac{1}{a^2} + \frac{1}{b^2} > 0;$$

you *cannot* choose translations or rotations that transform the given equation into the equation

$$-\frac{1}{a^2}X^2 - \frac{1}{b^2}Y^2 - M = 0, \quad \text{with} \quad -\frac{1}{a^2} - \frac{1}{b^2} < 0.$$

There are three cases, namely:

$M > 0$ corresponds to a non-degenerate ellipse
$M = 0$ corresponds to a point ellipse
$M < 0$ corresponds to an imaginary ellipse.

Since R is an invariant, and

$$R = \begin{vmatrix} \dfrac{2}{a^2} & 0 & 0 \\ 0 & \dfrac{2}{b^2} & 0 \\ 0 & 0 & -2M \end{vmatrix} = \frac{-8M}{a^2b^2},$$

we conclude that, when $A > 0$ and $\Delta < 0$, you have an ellipse that is non-degenerate, a point, or imaginary, according as $R < 0$, $R = 0$, or $R > 0$.

(e) For a hyperbola, you can always choose translations or rotations that transform the given equation into the equation

$$\frac{1}{a^2}X^2 - \frac{1}{b^2}Y^2 - M = 0.$$

There are two cases, namely:

$M \neq 0$ corresponds to a non-degenerate hyperbola
$M = 0$ corresponds to a pair of intersecting lines.

Since R is an invariant, and

$$R = \begin{vmatrix} \dfrac{2}{a^2} & 0 & 0 \\ 0 & -\dfrac{2}{b^2} & 0 \\ 0 & 0 & -2M \end{vmatrix} = \frac{8M}{a^2b^2},$$

we conclude that when $\Delta > 0$ you have a hyperbola that is non-degenerate, or a pair of intersecting straight lines, according as $R \neq 0$ or $R = 0$.

(f) For a parabola, you can always choose translations or rotations that transform the given equation into the equation

$$X^2 - MY - N = 0.$$

There are two cases, namely:

$M \neq 0$ corresponds to a non-degenerate parabola
$M = 0$ corresponds to a pair of parallel lines, real and distinct when $N > 0$, coincident when $N = 0$, and imaginary when $N < 0$.

Since R is invariant, and

$$R = \begin{vmatrix} 2 & 0 & 0 \\ 0 & 0 & -M \\ 0 & -M & -2N \end{vmatrix} = -2M^2,$$

we conclude that when $\Delta = 0$, you have a parabola that is non-degenerate, or a pair of parallel lines (real or imaginary), according as $R \neq 0$ or $R = 0$.

The following table summarizes the results of (a) through (f) above:

Δ	R	Locus
$A > 0$ and $\Delta < 0$	$R < 0$	Non-degenerate ellipse
	$R = 0$	Point ellipse
	$R > 0$	Imaginary ellipse
$\Delta > 0$	$R \neq 0$	Non-degenerate hyperbola
	$R = 0$	Pair of intersecting lines
$\Delta = 0$	$R \neq 0$	Non-degenerate parabola
	$R = 0$	Pair of parallel lines (real or imaginary)

The following examples will help you learn to use the invariants Δ and R to classify the graphs of second-degree equations in x and y.

(8) $2x^2 - 3xy + 5y^2 - 2x + 3y - 17 = 0$. In Example (5) we found that $\Delta < 0$. This identifies the graph as an ellipse that may or may not be degenerate. Now we have $A > 0$ and

$$R = \begin{vmatrix} 4 & -3 & -2 \\ -3 & 10 & 3 \\ -2 & 3 & -34 \end{vmatrix} = -1094 < 0.$$

We know that the ellipse is non-degenerate.

(9) $2x^2 - 3xy + 5y^2 - 2x + 3y + 17 = 0$. We have $\Delta = B^2 - 4AC < 0$, $A > 0$, and

$$R = \begin{vmatrix} 4 & -3 & -2 \\ -3 & 10 & 3 \\ -2 & 3 & 34 \end{vmatrix} > 0.$$

We identify the graph as an imaginary ellipse.

This concludes our discussion of rigid motions for conics. You will realize, as you finish reading this section, that actual rotations and translations of conics may involve tedious calculations. It is possible to use your knowledge of the invariants $A + C$, Δ, and R, to shorten some of the calculations. We give you a chance to explore these possibilities in Exercises 21 and 22, below. However, we are more interested in having you realize the importance of the idea of invariants that you have met. As you continue to study geometry, whether the geometry of rigid motions or one of the many other important geometries, you will find that a geometry is basically a study of the invariants of a chosen set of transformations.

EXERCISES §1008 (cont.)

11. Verify that $A' + C' = A + C$ for whichever of the Exercises 2 to 9 of this section you have done. (Remember to use A' and C' as found after the rotation before both sides of the condition are multiplied by a constant to simplify coefficients.)

12. Verify that $(B')^2 - 4A'C' = B^2 - 4AC$ for those of Exercises 2 to 9 that you have done.

13. Verify that R is invariant for those of Exercises 2 to 9 that you have done.

14. Use A', B', and C' as given in the text to prove that Δ is invariant for every rotation θ; use direct substitution and trigonometric identities. (Warning! Have several sheets of paper available.)

15. Prove that Δ is an invariant for every rotation by carrying out the steps outlined below:

(a) Show that
$$B' = B \cos 2\theta - (A - C) \sin 2\theta$$
$$A' - C' = B \sin 2\theta + (A - C) \cos 2\theta$$

(b) Use the results of part (a) to show that
$$(B')^2 + (A' - C')^2 = B^2 + (A - C)^2$$

(c) Since you know that $A' + C' = A + C$, subtract $(A' + C')^2$ from the left side and $(A + C)^2$ from the right side; then simplify the results.

16. If $B \neq 0$ and at least one of A or C is zero, show that the graph must be a hyperbola.

17. If A and C have opposite signs, show that the graph must be a hyperbola.

18. Calculate Δ and R for each equation to determine the type of graph and whether it is a degenerate form.

(a) $2x^2 + xy - 5 = 0$
(b) $x^2 + xy + y^2 + 9 = 0$
(c) $x^2 + xy + y^2 - 9 = 0$
(d) $x^2 - 4xy + 4y^2 - 3x + 5 = 0$
(e) $5x^2 - 7xy + 3y^2 + x - 2y - 4 = 0$
(f) $x^2 + 2xy + 3y^2 + 2x + 2y + 1 = 0$
(g) $2x^2 + xy - y^2 - 7x - y + 6 = 0$
(h) $9x^2 - 12xy + 9y^2 - 16 = 0$
(i) $3x^2 + 12xy + 12y^2 - 5x + 12y + 10 = 0$
(j) $8x^2 - 3xy + 2y^2 - 4x - 12 = 0.$

Answers: (a) hyperbola; (b) imaginary ellipse; (d) parabola; (e) ellipse; (g) intersecting lines.

19. For an ellipse or hyperbola, a translation to eliminate the linear terms will place the new origin at the center of the conic. To make $D'' = 0$ and $E'' = 0$, solve

$$2Ah + Bk + D = 0$$
$$Bh + 2Ck + E = 0$$

for (h,k). The coefficients of the second-degree terms are unaltered in a translation. F'' can be determined by replacing x by h and y by k in the left side of the original equation. (Why?) Determine the center and the new equation after a translation to eliminate the linear terms for each conic.

(a) $3x^2 + 2xy - 4y^2 + 8x + 46y - 129 = 0$
(b) $x^2 - 4xy + 2y^2 + 4x + 4y + 10 = 0$
(c) $4x^2 - 3xy - y^2 - 2x - 3y = 0$
(d) $6xy + 5y^2 - 6x + 4y - 13 = 0$
(e) $3x^2 - 2xy - y^2 - 13x - 3y + 4 = 0$
(f) $x^2 - 4xy + 4y^2 + 5x - 3y + 7 = 0.$

Answers: (b) $(4,3)$, $F'' = 24$; (f) impossible, parabola has no center.

20. Show that the linear equations of Exercise 19 can always be solved for h and k except when $\Delta = 0$. In this case the equations are inconsistent. Why should there be no center for the conic when $\Delta = 0$? See Exercise 19(f).

21. Show that after a translation to eliminate linear terms, $F'' = -R/2\Delta$.

Hint: Since R is an invariant under a translation,

$$R = \begin{vmatrix} 2A'' & B'' & 0 \\ B'' & 2C'' & 0 \\ 0 & 0 & 2F'' \end{vmatrix}.$$

Evaluate the determinant and solve for F''. Use this method to calculate F'' for the problems in Exercise 19 that you have previously worked by the other method, and compare results.

22. To sketch the graphs of central conics (hyperbolas and ellipses) you need only to know where the center is located, what angle to rotate the coordinate system, and the equation in standard form with respect to the final coordinate system. You can determine the coefficients for the final equation by using the invariants. You proceed as follows: Calculate Δ and R so that you know what kind of graph to expect. Locate the center, (h,k), using the methods of Exercise 19. Draw the translated coordinate system. Determine the angle of rotation, θ. Draw the rotated coordinate system with center at (h,k). Calculate F'', after the translation, by the methods of Exercise 21. F'' does not change when you rotate the axes. To determine A' and C' after the rotation, recall from Exercise 15 that $(B')^2 + (A' - C')^2 = B^2 + (A - C)^2$. Since you chose θ to make B' zero, you can solve

$$A' - C' = \pm\sqrt{B^2 + (A - C)^2}$$

$$A' + C' = A + C$$

simultaneously for A' and C'. The sign before the radical should be the same as the sign of B in the original equation, since

$$A' - C' = B \sin 2\theta + (A - C) \cos 2\theta$$

$$= B \sin 2\theta + \frac{B}{\tan 2\theta} \cos 2\theta \quad \text{(Why?)}$$

$$= B\left(\sin 2\theta + \frac{\cos^2 2\theta}{\sin 2\theta}\right) = \frac{B}{\sin 2\theta},$$

and $0 < 2\theta < \pi$. After you solve the above equations for A' and C', plot the graph of $A'\bar{X}^2 + C'\bar{Y}^2 + F'' = 0$ on the final coordinate system.

Sketch the graph of each equation using this method.

(a) $12x^2 + 12xy + 7y^2 - 12x + 34y + 55 = 0$
(b) $5x^2 - 3xy + y^2 + 6x - 3y + 7 = 0$
(c) $x^2 - 2xy - 3y^2 + 12x + 20y - 48 = 0$
(d) $2x^2 + 6xy + 2y^2 + x - 11y + 19 = 0$
(e) $x^2 - 8xy + 3y^2 + 3x - 4y + 5 = 0$
(f) $2x^2 - 3xy + 6y^2 - 5x + y - 17 = 0$

Answers: (a) center $(3,-5)$, $\theta \doteq 33°41'$, $16\bar{X}^2 + 3\bar{Y}^2 = 48$; (c) center $(-2,4)$, $\theta \doteq 77°$, $(-\sqrt{5} - 1)\bar{X}^2 + (\sqrt{5} - 1)\bar{Y}^2 = 20$.

23. Sketch the graph of $x^{1/2} + y^{1/2} = 1$. (*Hints:* Investigate symmetry. What is the range of x and y? Square to eliminate the radicals; then determine the type of graph.)

1009. Analytic proofs of geometric theorems

You have already met analytic proofs of geometric theorems. Each locus problem leads to a theorem of geometry. Recall, for example, that the locus of points whose distances from two fixed points are equal is the right bisector of the segment that joins the fixed points. This is a theorem of the geometry of rigid motions whose analytic proof you met in Section 1002 (page 527).

In this section you will study further examples of analytic proofs of geometric theorems. You will find that analytic proofs are straightforward although sometimes very long. Often they are easy. Even when they are harder, the difficulty lies in the algebraic treatment and not, as in the "synthetic" proofs of elementary geometry, in finding the right combination of geometric facts to use. We proceed with examples:

(1) The line segment joining the midpoints of two sides of a triangle is parallel to the third side of the triangle, and half as long as the third side of the triangle.

Notice the statement of this theorem. It refers to any plane triangle. In elementary synthetic geometry, you focus attention upon a particular

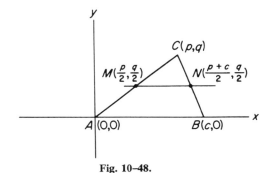

Fig. 10–48.

triangle *ABC*, which represents any plane triangle. Then you try to prove the theorem by assuming only the *given* facts and *previously-proved* facts of geometry.

Analytic geometry gives you the additional advantages of a coordinate system. Study Fig. 10–48 and the proof that follows, to see how this works.

In the geometry of rigid motions you may place the origin of coordinates at any point (by translation) and orient the axes in any direction (by rotation). It is convenient to place the origin of coordinates at the vertex *A*, to make the coordinates of *A* $(0,0)$; orient the axes to place the *x*-axis along the line *AB*, to make the coordinates of *B* $(c,0)$; then the third vertex of triangle *ABC* is a point *C*(p,q). Notice that *C* may be any point in the plane; you are not free to place *C* in some special way, on the *y*-axis, for example. Such a special placement of *C* would amount to dealing with a special triangle *ABC*, with a right triangle, for example.

The midpoint *M* of the side *AC* has coordinates $([p + 0]/2, [q + 0]/2)$ (page 547), that is, *M*$(p/2, q/2)$. Similarly, the coordinates of *N* are $([p + c]/2, q/2)$. The line that joins *M* and *N* has slope

$$m = \frac{q/2 - q/2}{\dfrac{p + c}{2} - \dfrac{p}{2}} = \frac{0}{\dfrac{c}{2}} = \frac{0}{c} = 0,$$

provided $c \neq 0$. The assumption $c \neq 0$ amounts to supposing that A and B are distinct points, that is, that triangle ABC is not degenerate. Hence, for a non-degenerate triangle ABC, MN is parallel to the x-axis and, therefore, to AB. The distance between M and N is

$$\sqrt{\left(\frac{p+c}{2} - \frac{p}{2}\right)^2 - \left(\frac{q}{2} - \frac{q}{2}\right)^2} = \sqrt{\left(\frac{c}{2}\right)^2} = \frac{c}{2}.$$

Hence $MN = \frac{1}{2}AB$.

We shall not repeat, each time we use it, the argument that justifies a convenient choice of coordinate axes. We shall use previously proved formulas of the analytic geometry of rigid motions without referring each time to the theorems that justify their use. The effect will be to make our proofs seem quite informal. You should make it a habit to ask: Why? You will find your answers in the algebra of real numbers and its application to coordinate geometry.

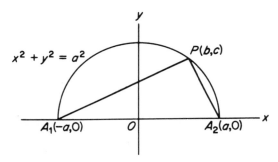

Fig. 10–49.

(2) The angle inscribed in a semi-circle is a right angle. In Fig. 10–49, the slope of A_1P is $m_1 = (c - 0)/(b + a)$; the slope of A_2P is $m_2 = (c - 0)/(b - a)$. Hence

$$m_1 m_2 = \frac{c}{b + a} \cdot \frac{c}{b - a} = \frac{c^2}{b^2 - a^2}.$$

Since $P(b,c)$ lies on the circle $x^2 + y^2 = a^2$, then $b^2 + c^2 = a^2$ and $b^2 - a^2 = -c^2$. Substitution yields

$$m_1 m_2 = \frac{c^2}{-c^2} = -1.$$

Hence A_1P is perpendicular to A_2P, and angle A_1PA_2 is a right angle.

You should go over this proof and ask questions like: Is the semi-circle A_1PA_2 really *any* semi-circle? Might one of the denominators $b + a$, $b - a$, or $b^2 - a^2$ be zero? If so, would this destroy the proof as given? Why does $m_1 m_2 = -1$ make angle $A_1PA_2 = 90°$?

(3) An arc of a circle is measured by twice the angle that the chord, on which the arc stands, subtends at any point on the circumference of the circle that is on the same side of the chord as the center of the circle.

In Fig. 10–50 we placed the center of a circle of radius a at the origin. We placed the end points of the chord A_1A_2 on the line $y = b$. This justifies a choice of coordinates, $A_1(p,b)$, $A_2(q,b)$. We have

$$p^2 + b^2 = a^2 \quad \text{and} \quad q^2 + b^2 = a^2.$$

By subtraction,

$$p^2 - q^2 = 0, \quad p^2 = q^2, \quad \text{and} \quad p = \pm q.$$

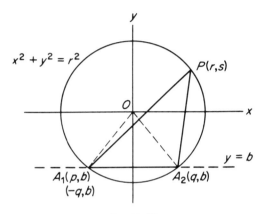

Fig. 10–50.

This justifies a choice of coordinates $A_1(-q,b)$, $A_2(q,b)$, where we choose $q > 0$, to correspond to the placement of A_1 and A_2 in the figure.

By definition, the arc A_1A_2 is measured by the angle A_1OA_2 that it subtends at the center of the circle.

The slope of OA_1 is $(b - 0)/(-q - 0)$. The slope of OA_2 is $(b - 0)/(q - 0)$. Hence

$$\tan(A_1OA_2) = \frac{b/q - (-b/q)}{1 + (b/q)(-b/q)} = \frac{2b/q}{1 - b^2/q^2} = \frac{2bq}{q^2 - b^2}.$$

The slope of A_1P is $(s - b)/(r + q)$. The slope of A_2P is $(s - b)/(r - q)$. Hence

$$\tan(A_1PA_2) = \frac{\dfrac{s - b}{r - q} - \dfrac{s - b}{r + q}}{1 + \dfrac{s - b}{r - q} \cdot \dfrac{s - b}{r + q}} = \frac{(s - b)(r + q) - (s - b)(r - q)}{(r - q)(r + q) + (s - b)(s - b)}$$

$$= \frac{(s - b)[(r + q) - (r - q)]}{r^2 - q^2 + s^2 - 2bs + b^2} = \frac{2q(s - b)}{r^2 + s^2 - 2bs - q^2 + b^2}.$$

We have $r^2 + s^2 = a^2$, and $b^2 + q^2 = a^2$ yields $q^2 = a^2 - b^2$. Hence, by substitution,

$$\tan(A_1PA_2) = \frac{2q(s-b)}{a^2 - 2bs - (a^2 - b^2) + b^2}$$

$$= \frac{2q(s-b)}{-2bs + 2b^2} = \frac{2q(s-b)}{-2b(s-b)}$$

$$= \frac{-q}{b}.$$

To prove that twice angle $A_1PA_2 =$ angle A_1OA_2, we investigate

$$\tan 2(A_1PA_2) = \frac{2\tan(A_1PA_2)}{1 - \tan^2(A_1PA_2)}$$

$$= \frac{2(-q/b)}{1 - q^2/b^2} = \frac{-2bq}{b^2 - q^2}.$$

But $$\tan(A_1OA_2) = \frac{2bq}{q^2 - b^2} = \tan 2(A_1PA_2).$$

$$\tan(A_1OA_2) = \tan 2(A_1PA_2) \Rightarrow A_1OA_2 = 2(A_1PA_2) + k\pi, \quad k \in I.$$

Since $0 < A_1OA_2 \leq \pi$, we conclude that $A_1OA_2 = 2(A_1PA_2)$.

As you re-read this proof, you should investigate special instances that lead you to zero denominators. You should also notice how mechanical the proof is, how directly it attacks the problem in hand. Notice, then, that analytical proofs replace the special insights that characterize synthetic proofs by the skillful use of a few geometric ideas. Analytical proofs lean heavily upon the algebra of real numbers.

There is one more feature of analytical proofs that you should notice. In Example (3), a special case arises when the points A_1 and A_2 are the end points of a diameter of the circle. Figure 10–50 then becomes Fig. 10–49. Angle $A_1OA_2 = \pi$. By Example (2), angle $A_1PA_2 = \pi/2$. As you examine the proofs in Examples (2) and (3), you will find that Example (2) is an instance of Example (3). Example (2) arises when, in Example (3), you take $b = 0$.

As you work Exercises §1009, notice how often an important special instance of a theorem comes to your attention as you try to prove the theorem. For example, your proof will require the assumption that a denominator is different from zero. As you think about the requirement you may be led to discover an interesting *corollary* to the theorem. Thus analytical proofs of geometric theorems suggest interesting special theorems. They also suggest generalizations of theorems. You will find yourself asking what happens if you try to get along without one of the special assumptions you are making in this proof. Often you will be led by these questions to discover more general theorems.

Keep in mind, as you work the exercises, the possibility of discovering special instances (corollaries) and generalizations of the theorems you are asked to prove.

EXERCISES §1009

Prove each theorem analytically. Make a sketch for each exercise, keeping in mind that a judicious placement of the figure on the coordinate system may simplify the algebra of the proof.

1. The midpoint of the hypotenuse of a right triangle is equidistant from the three vertices.

2. The angles opposite the equal sides of an isosceles triangle are equal. [*Suggestion:* Place the triangle so that the base is on the x-axis with the vertices at $(a,0)$, $(-a,0)$, and $(0,b)$. Be sure to show that this represents the general isosceles triangle.]

3. The sum of the lengths of the perpendiculars drawn from any point on the base to equal sides of an isosceles triangle is equal to the length of an altitude drawn to one of the equal sides.

4. The figure formed by joining the midpoints of consecutive sides of any quadrilateral is a parallelogram.

5. The line joining the midpoints of the non-parallel sides of a trapezoid is parallel to the bases and has a length that is half the sum of the lengths of the bases.

6. The line segment joining the midpoints of the diagonals of a trapezoid has a length that is half the difference of the lengths of the bases.

7. If the length of an altitude of a triangle is the mean proportional between the lengths of the segments cut off on the base to which it is drawn, the triangle is a right triangle. (*Suggestion:* Place the triangle so that the base is on the x-axis and the altitude lies on the y-axis.)

8. State and prove the converse of the theorem of Exercise 7.

9. The medians of a triangle meet in a point that is two-thirds the distance from a vertex to the midpoint of the opposite side. This point is called the *centroid* of the triangle.

10. The altitudes of a triangle meet in a point called the *orthocenter* of the triangle.

11. The perpendicular bisectors of the sides of a triangle meet in a point called the *circumcenter* of a triangle.

12. The centroid, orthocenter, and circumcenter of a triangle lie on the same line called *Euler's line*.

13. A point moves so that the sum of the squares of its distances to the four vertices of a square is constant. Show that the locus of the point is a circle with center at the intersection of the diagonals of the square. What constant sum will give a point circle? an imaginary circle? a non-degenerate circle? a circle lying outside the square?

14. The length of a perpendicular from any point on a circle to a diameter is the mean proportional between the lengths of the segments cut off on the diameter.

15. Two points are on a diameter of a circle, equidistant from the center. Show that the sum of the squares of the distances from each point on the circle to these points is the same constant.

16. Two circles are tangent to each other, with a diameter of the smaller circle coinciding with a radius of the larger. Prove that the midpoint of any chord of the larger circle, drawn from the point of tangency, lies on the smaller circle.

17. From a point on a parabola, a tangent line is drawn. Prove that the point of intersection of the tangent line with the axis of the parabola and the foot of the perpendicular from the point of tangency to this axis are equidistant from the vertex of the parabola. (Does this theorem suggest a method of constructing a tangent line at any point on the parabola?)

18. Let T be a tangent line to a parabola, L the line joining the point of tangency to the focus, and M a line through the point of tangency parallel to the axis of the parabola. Prove that the angle from L to T is equal to the angle from T to M.

19. A line segment of constant length moves so that one endpoint is always on one of two perpendicular lines, while the second endpoint remains on the other line. Show that the locus of a point P on the line segment is an ellipse. For what point on the line segment is the locus a circle?

20. The product of the distances from a point P to two intersecting lines is constant. Show that the locus is a hyperbola. (*Suggestion:* Let the intersecting lines be $y = mx$ and $x = 0$.)

1010. Other geometries in the plane

Early in this chapter we mentioned the geometry of graphs as one example of a geometry that is not the geometry of rigid motions. In this section we shall mention several other geometries, and explore one of them briefly.

The names of Gauss (1777–1855), Lobachevski (1793–1856), and Bolyai (1802–1860) are associated with the development of the first non-euclidean geometry. The work of these men climaxed the efforts of their predecessors to prove that through a given point, not on a given line, there can be drawn one and only one line parallel to the given line. This is the famous fifth postulate of Euclid, which seemed, to his successors, more a theorem to be proved than an arbitrary assumption upon which to build plane geometry.

Lobachevski showed conclusively that the fifth postulate must remain an arbitrary assumption, independent of the other postulates of Euclid. He accomplished this by inventing a geometry in which the other postulates were assumed but the fifth postulate was denied. In this geometry, through a given point, not on a given line, infinitely many straight lines can be drawn parallel to the given line. Mathematicians had to make room for a new and different, but equally logical, geometry. Before long, Riemann (1826–1866) gave them a third geometry in which through a given point, not on a given line, no straight line can be drawn parallel to the given line.

For a time it was common to consider non-euclidean geometries as mathematical curiosities. People still thought of euclidean geometry as the "true" geometry. Then the physicists began to look for mathematical models to use in describing the space-time world of modern physics. Several models presented themselves, and the geometries of Lobachevski and Riemann have both contributed to the mathematical treatment of the physics of relativity.

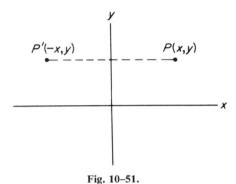

Fig. 10–51.

Mathematicians have stopped their search for the "true" geometry. They are concerned only with logically consistent geometries. They leave to the scientists the task of applying these geometries to describe observations.

Even an introductory study of the geometries of Lobachevski and Riemann would deflect us from our present goal. You may wish to follow up this study on your own. If so, you will find Chapter IV of *What is Mathematics?*, by Courant and Robbins, Oxford University Press, 1941, a good place to start. Readers interested in the geometry of drawing and painting will find the discussion of projective geometry of special interest. We leave these interesting sidelines now, and proceed to use some comparatively simple geometries as illustrations of geometries that are not the geometry of rigid motions.

First, recall, from Chapter 7 (page 366), the transformation

$$X = -x,$$
$$Y = y$$

as a reflection of the plane in the y-axis (see Fig. 10–51). In the sense of alibi, the point $P(x,y)$ is mapped by the transformation into the point $P'(X, Y)$ where $X = -x$ and $Y = y$. The geometry of reflections in a straight line is not the geometry of rigid motions. It does not preserve directed angles, as Fig. 10–52 shows. Notice that $\phi'_{12} = -\phi_{12}$. It does, however, preserve many of the same properties of figures as does the geometry of rigid motions.

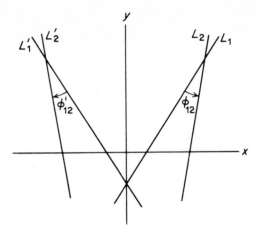

Fig. 10–52.

We consider now a more novel transformation that is a kind of reflection in the unit circle. Under this transformation, the inside of the unit circle (with the exception of the center) is mapped upon the outside of the unit circle, the outside of the unit circle is mapped upon the inside of the unit circle, and points on the unit circle are mapped into themselves. We call this transformation an *inversion* of the plane in the unit circle (see Fig. 10–53).

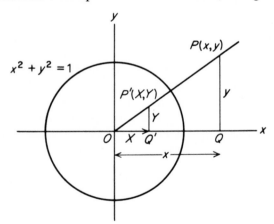

Fig. 10–53.

We define the *image* of the point $P(x,y)$ (other than O) to be the point $P'(X,Y)$, such that

    (a) P' lies on OP

    (b) $OP \cdot OP' = 1$.

Clearly, the triangles OPQ and $OP'Q'$ of the figure are similar; and, since $OP \cdot OP' = 1$,

$$\frac{x}{X} = \frac{y}{Y} = \frac{OP}{OP'} = \frac{OP \cdot OP'}{(OP')^2} = \frac{1}{(OP')^2} = \frac{1}{X^2 + Y^2}.$$

This gives us the equations of the transformation:

$$x = \frac{X}{X^2 + Y^2},$$

$$y = \frac{Y}{X^2 + Y^2}.$$

Recall, from Section 702 (page 304) that the graph of

I $\qquad\qquad Ax^2 + Ay^2 + Dx + Ey + F = 0$

may be a circle ($A \neq 0$) or a straight line ($A = 0$).

Inversion of this graph in the unit circle yields

$$A\frac{X^2}{(X^2 + Y^2)^2} + A\frac{Y^2}{(X^2 + Y^2)^2} + D\frac{X}{X^2 + Y^2} + E\frac{Y}{X^2 + Y^2} + F = 0.$$

The first two terms on the left yield

$$A\left[\frac{X^2 + Y^2}{(X^2 + Y^2)^2}\right] = \frac{A}{X^2 + Y^2}; \quad \text{provided } X^2 + Y^2 \neq 0.$$

($X^2 + Y^2 \neq 0$ excludes the origin as the image of a point.) Substitution for the first two terms and multiplication by $X^2 + Y^2$ yields

$$A + DX + EY + F(X^2 + Y^2) = 0.$$

That is

II $\qquad\qquad FX^2 + FY^2 + DX + EY + A = 0.$

It may be a circle ($F \neq 0$) or a straight line ($F = 0$).

We conclude that the image of a straight line or a circle is either a straight line or a circle. More specifically, if

(1) $A \neq 0$ and $F \neq 0$: the graph of I is a circle not through the origin; its image, II, is a circle not through the origin. Hence the image of a circle not through O is a circle not through O.

(2) $A \neq 0$ and $F = 0$: the graph of I is a circle through O; its image is a straight line not through O. Hence the image of a circle through O is a straight line not through O.

(3) $A = 0$ and $F \neq 0$: the graph of I is a straight line not through O; its image is a circle through O. Hence the image of a line not through O is a circle through O. (Notice how Cases (2) and (3) illustrate the inverse character of the transformation.)

(4) $A = 0$ and $F = 0$; both graphs are the straight line $(DX + Ey = 0)$ through O. (The two graphs are identical straight lines through the origin, as is obvious from the fact that the image, P', of P lies on OP. But of course the points are rearranged on this line.)

The following exercises give you a chance to find the inverses of particular straight lines and circles.

EXERCISES §1010

1. If P' is the image of P, show that P must be the image of P'.

2. Use the idea of Exercise 1 to show that

$$X = \frac{x}{x^2 + y^2}, \qquad Y = \frac{y}{x^2 + y^2}.$$

3. Give an analytic proof of Exercises 1 and 2 by solving algebraically the equations of transformation given in the text for X and Y in terms of x and y.

4. Determine the coordinates of the image of each point. Plot the point and its image and note the relation to the unit circle.

(a) (1,3)   (b) $(\frac{1}{2},0)$ (c) (1,1)
(d) (0,−4)   (e) $(-\frac{1}{4},\frac{1}{2})$ (f) $(\frac{3}{5},\frac{4}{5})$.

In Exercises 5 to 11, find the inverse of each graph. Sketch the graph and its inverse. Fit each exercise into the appropriate case, (1) through (4), as listed above.

5. $y = 3x + 2$ **6.** $x = 5$

7. $y = 2x$ **8.** $x^2 + y^2 = 3$

9. $(x - 3)^2 + y^2 = 4$ **10.** $(x - 2)^2 + (y + 2)^2 = 5$

11. $(x - 2)^2 + (y + 2)^2 = 8$.

12. Show that if P is a point on the unit circle $x^2 + y^2 = 1$, then P is its own image point.

13. If a circle passes through O (Case 2) and intersects the unit circle at two points, show that its image is the straight line through the two intersection points. (*Hint:* See Exercise 12.)

14. With a compass, draw the circle through O with center at (1,1). Illustrate Exercise 13 by constructing the image of this circle.

15. Show that the image of any circle inside the unit circle lies entirely outside the unit circle.

So far, you have studied the geometry of inversion in the unit circle from the point of view of alibi. The coordinate axes remain the same. Except for the points on the unit circle, each point of the plane moves to a new position.

You may also think of the geometry of inversion in the unit circle from the point of view of alias. Notice what the transformation

$$x = \frac{X}{X^2 + Y^2}, \qquad y = \frac{Y}{X^2 + Y^2}$$

does to the grid lines of an ordinary sheet of graph paper. The family of lines $x = a$, $a \neq 0$, is mapped into a family of circles $X/(X^2 + Y^2) = a$, that

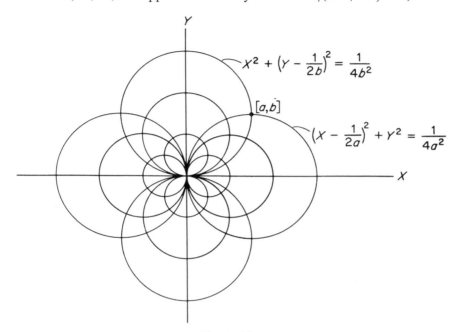

Fig. 10–54.

is, $aX^2 + aY^2 = X$, or $(X - 1/2a)^2 + Y^2 = 1/4a^2$; the family of lines $y = b$, $b \neq 0$, is mapped into the family of circles $X^2 + (Y - 1/2b)^2 = 1/4b^2$. Figure 10–54 shows the resulting grid of circles.

You may think of a new-type coordinate system in which the point $[c,d]$ is the point, other than the origin, where the circle $(X - 1/2c)^2 + Y^2 = 1/4c^2$ intersects the circle $X^2 + (Y - 1/2d)^2 = 1/4d^2$. This amounts to giving the point (a,b) a new name $[c,d]$, where the number-pair $[c,d]$ is found by

$$c = \frac{a}{a^2 + b^2}, \qquad d = \frac{b}{a^2 + b^2}.$$

For example, $(2,2)$, which is located at the intersection of $x = 2$ and $y = 2$, gets the new name $[\frac{1}{4},\frac{1}{4}]$ and is plotted by determining the intersection of the circles above with $c = \frac{1}{4}$ and $d = \frac{1}{4}$.

We hope you find the idea of a coordinate system where you locate points as intersections of circles, rather than as intersections of perpendicular lines, a fascinating idea. We hope it suggests to you a new freedom of thought in your approach to geometry.

EXERCISES §1010 (cont.)

16. On an xy-coordinate system, draw the grid lines $x = a$ and $y = b$ for a and b replaced by $\pm\frac{1}{4}$, $\pm\frac{1}{2}$, ±1, ±2. On an XY-coordinate system, use a compass to draw the grid circles $(X - 1/2a)^2 + Y^2 = 1/4a^2$ and $X^2 + (Y - 1/2b)^2 = 1/4b^2$ for each of the same replacements of a and b. (*Warning*: Choose the unit distance large, say about 1 in. on both coordinate systems.)

17. Plot the following pairs of points on the respective coordinate systems of Exercise 16. Compare positions of the points.

(a) $P(2,2)$ and $P[\frac{1}{4},\frac{1}{4}]$

(b) $Q(-\frac{1}{2},\frac{1}{2})$ and $Q[-1,1]$

(c) $R(-1,-1)$ and $R[-\frac{1}{2},-\frac{1}{2}]$

(d) $S(\frac{1}{4},-\frac{1}{4})$ and $S[2,-2]$.

18. Plot the following pairs of points on the respective coordinate systems of Exercise 16. You may have to estimate locations between grid lines and grid circles.

(a) $T(\frac{2}{5},-\frac{4}{5})$ and $T[\frac{1}{2},-1]$

(b) $U(\frac{1}{2},1)$ and $U[\frac{2}{5},\frac{4}{5}]$

(c) $V(-\frac{1}{3},-\frac{1}{3})$ and $V[-\frac{3}{2},-\frac{3}{2}]$

(d) $W(1.2,.4)$ and $W[.75,.25]$.

19. What are the images of the families $y = mx$ and $x^2 + y^2 = a^2$ (the grids of a polar coordinate system)?

20. Show that the image of the point (r,θ) in polar coordinates is (R,Θ) where $R = 1/r$ and $\Theta = \theta$.

When you begin to think about the invariants of the geometry of inversion in the unit circle, you may have trouble at first. Certainly distance is not preserved. Are any of the familiar geometric properties preserved? Clearly the image of $x^2 + y^2 = 1$ is $X^2 + Y^2 = 1$; that is, the unit circle is an invariant of the transformation. Recall also that circles and straight lines always yield circles or straight lines. Hence being a circle or a straight line is an invariant of the transformation. But you may feel that this is a rather weak sort of invariant.

What about angles? Is the angle between two curves equal to the angle between the inverses of those two curves? To test this, we must define clearly what we mean by the angle between two curves. We suppose that each curve has a definite tangent line at the point of intersection. Then Fig. 10–55 suggests a usable definition: The directed angle from C_1 to C_2 is defined to be the directed angle from T_1 to T_2, where T_1 is the tangent to C_1 and T_2 is the tangent to C_2 at the point of intersection of C_1 and C_2. Hence, in the figure, the directed angle from C_1 to C_2 is ϕ_{12}.

Let us experiment now with straight lines and circles as a partial test of the hypothesis that inversion in the unit circle preserves the angle between two curves.

Consider the lines $y = \frac{1}{3}x + 2$ and $y = 2x - 3$ (Fig. 10–56). They intersect at (3,3). Since $m_1 = \frac{1}{3}$ and $m_2 = 2$,

$$\tan \phi_{12} = \frac{2 - \frac{1}{3}}{1 + 2(\frac{1}{3})} = 1, \quad \text{and} \quad \phi_{12} = (+45°).$$

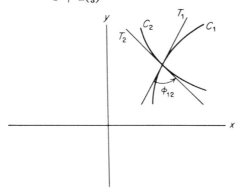

Fig. 10–55.

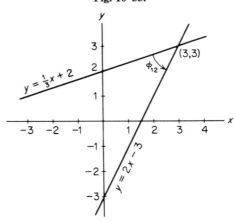

Fig. 10–56.

The image of $y = \frac{1}{3}x + 2$ is $6X^2 + 6Y^2 + X - 3Y = 0$, or $(X + \frac{1}{12})^2 + (Y - \frac{1}{4})^2 = \frac{10}{144}$. This is a circle with center at $(-\frac{1}{12}, \frac{1}{4})$ and radius $\sqrt{10}/12$.

The image of $y = 2x - 3$ is $3X^2 + 3Y^2 - 2X + Y = 0$, or $(X - \frac{1}{3})^2 + (Y + \frac{1}{6})^2 = \frac{5}{36}$. This is a circle with center at $(\frac{1}{3}, -\frac{1}{6})$ and radius $\sqrt{5}/6$ (Fig. 10–57).

The circle C_1: $6X^2 + 6Y^2 + X - 3Y = 0$ intersects the circle C_2: $3X^2 + 3Y^2 - 2X + Y = 0$ at the points $(0,0)$ and $(\frac{1}{6}, \frac{1}{6})$.

The slope of R_1 joining $(-\frac{1}{12},\frac{1}{4})$ and $(\frac{1}{6},\frac{1}{6})$ is $-\frac{1}{3}$; hence the slope of T_1 (perpendicular to R_1) is 3. The slope of R_2 joining $(\frac{1}{3},-\frac{1}{6})$ and $(\frac{1}{6},\frac{1}{6})$ is -2; hence the slope of T_2 is $\frac{1}{2}$. The angle between T_1 and T_2 (and hence the angle between C_1 and C_2) is Φ_{12}, and

$$\tan \Phi_{12} = \frac{\frac{1}{2} - 3}{1 + (\frac{1}{2})(3)} = \frac{-5}{5} = -1.$$

Hence $\Phi_{12} = -45°$. Notice that the angle between the inverses of the two lines has the same magnitude as the angle between the two lines. Notice

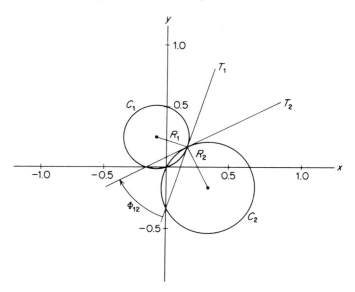

Fig. 10–57.

that it has the opposite direction. It requires more advanced techniques than we have presently available to establish this as a general theorem. It can be proved that the directed angle between the inverses of any two curves is the negative of the directed angle between the two curves.

We hope that you have derived some satisfaction from this section on other geometries in the plane. More than that, we hope you have caught a glimpse of the possibilities of a modern approach to a geometry as *the study of the invariants of a chosen set of transformations.* This modern approach to geometry frees the mathematician of the concept of *trueness to the world of experience.* With this new freedom the geometer can explore the consequences of a wide variety of geometric assumptions; and already the payoff in mathematical models for modern physics and the social sciences is becoming apparent.

EXERCISES §1010 (cont.)

21. Show that $\tan \phi_{12}$ for the lines $y = \frac{1}{2}$ and $y = \frac{1}{2}x + \frac{1}{2}$ is numerically equal, but opposite in sign, to $\tan \Phi_{12}$ for the image circles.

Partial answer: C_1 has center at $(0,1)$; C_2 at $(-\frac{1}{2},1)$. The circles intersect at $(0,2)$.

22. Since $x = a$ and $y = b$ meet at right angles, then their images should meet at right angles. Prove analytically that each member of the family $(X - 1/2a)^2 + Y^2 = 1/4a^2$ meets each member of the family $X^2 + (Y - 1/2b)^2 = 1/4b^2$ at right angles.

Hint: Since the lines intersect at (a,b), the circles will intersect at the image point $\left(\dfrac{a}{a^2 + b^2}, \dfrac{b}{a^2 + b^2} \right)$.

23. Using the equations of transformation, determine the image of the parabola $y = 2x^2$.

Answer: $Y^3 + (Y - 2)X^2 = 0$.

The graph of the image is called a cissoid. From the coordinates of several points on the parabola, find the coordinates of several points on the cissoid. Show that they satisfy the equation of the cissoid. Sketch the graph of the parabola; then sketch the graph of the cissoid from your knowledge of inversion.

24. Determine the equation of the inverse curve of the equilateral hyperbola $x^2 - y^2 = \frac{1}{4}$. Change to polar coordinates and show that it is a lemniscate.

Answer: $(X^2 + Y^2)^2 = 4(X^2 - Y^2)$; $r^2 = 4 \cos 2\theta$.

Sketch the two curves on the same graph paper.

25. Determine the equation of the inverse curve of the parabola $y = x^2 - \frac{1}{4}$. Change to polar coordinates and show that it is a cardioid.

Answer: $(X^2 + Y^2 + 2Y)^2 = 4(X^2 + Y^2)$; $r = 2 - 2 \sin \theta$.

Sketch the graphs.

26. Draw the unit circle and a triangle with no side through the origin. From your knowledge of inversion, what kind of a figure will the set of points that are inverse to the points on the triangle form? Sketch the inverse figure.

27. A mechanical device can be constructed to locate the image of a given point under inversion. Two bars of equal length, OA and OB, are fixed at O (the center of inversion). A deformable rhombus $APBP'$ is fastened to OB and OA at A and B. $(OA)^2 - (AP)^2$ is taken for the unit distance. Show that P and P' are images of each other under inversion. Construct a model from cardboard.

28. If a bar MP is fastened to the linkage of Exercise 27, one end at P on the rhombus and the other end, M, fixed so that the distance from M to O is equal to MP, then P must move along a circle through O. How must P' move? This linkage to generate straight line motion is known as *Peaucellier's inversor* (Fig. 10–58).

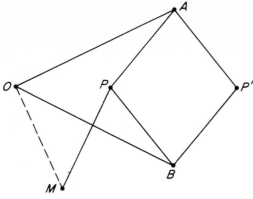

Fig. 10–58.

1011. Higher-dimensional geometries

You now realize that there are several geometries in the plane. What about geometries in *spaces* of more than two *dimensions*? That is, what if you locate a *point* by three coordinates (x,y,z), four coordinates (x,y,z,w), or, as in Section 706 (page 361) by n coordinates $(x_1, x_2, x_3, ..., x_n)$?

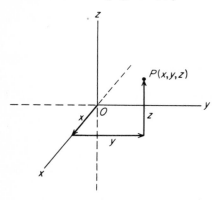

Fig. 10–59.

Again we shall think of a geometry as a study of the invariants of a chosen set of transformations. But we shall limit ourselves to rigid motions, translations of the origin, and rotations about the origin. We shall not explore the geometries associated with other sets of transformations.

In a space of three dimensions it is common to label the axes x, y, and z and to speak of the point (x,y,z) (see Fig. 10–59). It is conventional to choose a *right-handed* system. You think of a screw placed at the origin and pointed along the z-axis. In a right-handed system, when you turn the screw in the direction from the x-axis toward the y-axis, the screw moves in the positive direction along the z-axis. Study the figure to see how the coordinates (x,y,z) locate the point P in one of the (8) *octants* about O.

It is not helpful to set up a coordinate system for a space of four dimensions by adding a fourth axis. People can visualize a three-dimensional world, but find it hard to picture a four-dimensional world. Yet, algebraically, you can work with a *point* $P(x,y,z,w)$, or a *point* $P(x_1, x_2, x_3, ..., x_n)$. You can carry over the language of geometry to talk about a space of more than three dimensions even though you find such a space hard to picture.

We define the distance between $P_1(x_1,y_1,z_1)$ and $P_2(x_2,y_2,z_2)$ to be $d = \sqrt{(x_2 - x_1)^2 + (y_2 - y_1)^2 + (z_2 - z_1)^2}$. You may wish to study Fig. 10–60 to see that this distance formula is a generalization of the distance formula of the geometry of rigid motions in the plane.

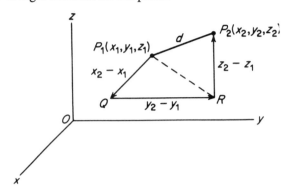

Fig. 10–60.

Triangle P_1QR lies in a plane parallel to the XOY-plane; it is a right triangle in which

$$|P_1R|^2 = (x_2 - x_1)^2 + (y_2 - y_1)^2.$$

Triangle P_1RP_2 lies in a plane perpendicular to the XOY-plane; it is a right triangle in which

$$|P_1P_2|^2 = |P_1R|^2 + (z_2 - z_1)^2;$$

that is, $\quad\quad d^2 = (x_2 - x_1)^2 + (y_2 - y_1)^2 + (z_2 - z_1)^2.$

Hence, when you begin by assuming the theorems of euclidean geometry, you can prove that the distance d between $P_1(x_1,y_1,z_1)$ and $P_2(x_2,y_2,z_2)$ is

$$d = \sqrt{(x_2 - x_1)^2 + (y_2 - y_1)^2 + (z_2 - z_1)^2}.$$

Of course, when you begin to develop the geometry of rigid motions, you reverse this procedure. You define d by this equation. Then you prove the theorems of euclidean geometry as consequences of this, and other definitions and assumptions.

For the geometry of rigid motions in a space of n dimensions, the definition of distance between $P_1(x_1, x_2, ..., x_n)$ and $P_2(x'_1, x'_2, ..., x'_n)$ is

$$d = \sqrt{(x'_1 - x_2)^2 + (x'_2 - x_2)^2 + ... + (x'_n - x_n)^2}.$$

To define the direction of the vector P_1P_2 in a space of three dimensions, it is conventional to give the cosines of the angles this vector makes with the three coordinate axes. Thus, in Fig. 10–61, the direction of the vector P_1P_2 is given by the number-triple $[\cos \alpha_1, \cos \alpha_2, \cos \alpha_3]$. The definitions,

$$\cos \alpha_1 = \frac{x_2 - x_1}{d}, \quad \cos \alpha_2 = \frac{y_2 - y_1}{d}, \quad \cos \alpha_3 = \frac{z_2 - z_1}{d},$$

involve the directed distances $x_2 - x_1$, $y_2 - y_1$, $z_2 - z_1$, and the distance d. Hence the idea of angle is based upon purely analytical definitions, rather than upon geometric ideas like amount of rotation.

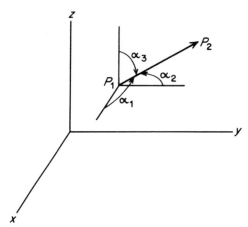

Fig. 10–61.

For the geometry of rigid motions in a space of n dimensions, the direction of the vector from $P_1(x_1, x_2, ..., x_n)$ to $P_2(x_1', x_2', ..., x_n')$ is given by the number n-tuple

$$[\cos \alpha_1, \cos \alpha_2, ..., \cos \alpha_n]$$

where $\qquad \cos \alpha_i = \dfrac{x_i' - x_i}{d}, \quad i = 1, 2, ..., n.$

These definitions of distance and direction make it possible to develop the geometry of rigid motions for a space of n dimensions. We avoid the kind of details that you met for plane geometry in Sections 1000 and 1001.

We complete this chapter by examining a few important sets of points in a space of three dimensions. It is interesting and useful to generalize the ideas of straight line, circle, parabola, and the like to discover their counterparts in 3-space.

First, think of the cartesian product $(L \times L) \times L$. To each ordered pair of real numbers (x,y) in $L \times L$, we assign a real number z to obtain an ordered triple of real numbers (x,y,z). In terms of coordinate geometry, this amounts to locating a point (x,y,z) in a space of three dimensions.

Now consider relations in the cartesian product $(L \times L) \times L$; consider, for example, the subset of $(L \times L) \times L$, such that

$$x^2 + y^2 + z^2 = 1.$$

When you rewrite the condition $x^2 + y^2 + z^2 = 1$ in the form

$$(x - 0)^2 + (y - 0)^2 + (z - 0)^2 = 1$$

and recall the distance formula

$$(x_2 - x_1)^2 + (y_2 - y_1)^2 + (z_2 - z_1)^2 = d^2,$$

you recognize the point $P(x,y,z)$ as a point whose distance from the origin, $(0,0,0)$, is 1. It seems natural to call the set of points whose coordinates satisfy the condition $x^2 + y^2 + z^2 = 1$ a *sphere* with center at $(0,0,0)$ and radius 1.

More generally, the set of points whose coordinates satisfy the condition $x^2 + y^2 + z^2 = r^2$ is a sphere with center at $(0,0,0)$ and radius r; the set of points whose coordinates satisfy the condition $(x - a)^2 + (y - b)^2 + (z - c)^2 = r^2$ is a sphere with center at (a,b,c) and radius r.

What, now, of the set of points whose coordinates satisfy the condition $x^2/a^2 + y^2/b^2 + z^2/c^2 = 1$? When $z = 0$, you get the ellipse $x^2/a^2 + y^2/b^2 = 1$, which lies in the xy-plane; when $x = 0$ you get the ellipse $y^2/b^2 + z^2/c^2 = 1$, which lies in the yz-plane; when $y = 0$, you get the ellipse $x^2/a^2 + z^2/c^2 = 1$, which lies in the xz-plane (see Fig. 10–62). We define the set of points whose coordinates satisfy the condition $x^2/a^2 + y^2/b^2 + z^2/c^2 = 1$ as an *ellipsoid* with center at $(0,0,0)$ and semi-axes of lengths a, b, and c.

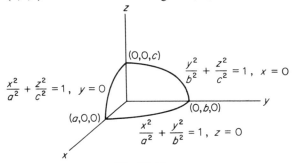

Fig. 10–62.

Exercises §1011 give you an opportunity to work with paraboloids and hyperboloids as generalizations of parabolas and hyperbolas. We speak of *surfaces* in a space of three dimensions as we speak of *curves* in a space of two dimensions. Of course there are also curves in a space of three dimensions. When two surfaces intersect one another, the points common to the two surfaces lie on a curve. Such a curve of intersection may be a *plane* curve or a *skew* curve; that is, all the points of the curve may lie in one plane, or the curve may twist in space as in the case of the thread of a screw.

We have left for last a discussion of planes in 3-space. We define a plane as a set of points whose coordinates satisfy an equation of the form

$$ax + by + cz = d$$

with at least one of the parameters a, b, c, not zero. (Compare the definition of a straight line, (page 508).

As a special case, $a = b = 0$ and $c \neq 0$ yields

$$z = \frac{d}{c}.$$

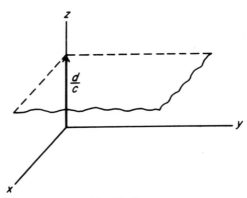

Fig. 10–63.

This is a plane parallel to the xy-plane at a directed distance d/c from the xy-plane (see Fig. 10–63). Similarly, $x = p$ is a plane parallel to the yz-plane, and $y = q$ is a plane parallel to the xz-plane.

The condition $ax + by + cz = 0$ defines the family of planes through the origin. The condition $x \cos \alpha_1 + y \cos \alpha_2 + z \cos \alpha_3 = d$ defines the family of planes at a distance d from the origin. Study Fig. 10–64 as you consider the plausibility of this last statement. Here, $x \cos \alpha_1$ is the projection of the directed line segment OQ on the line ON, whose direction is defined by the number-triple $[\cos \alpha_1, \cos \alpha_2, \cos \alpha_3]$; $y \cos \alpha_2$ is the projection of QR on this same line segment; $z \cos \alpha_3$ is the projection of RP on this same line segment. The condition $x \cos \alpha_1 + y \cos \alpha_2 + z \cos \alpha_3 = d$ states that the sum of these projections is d. This means that $P(x,y,z)$ lies in a plane at a distance d, in the direction defined by $(\cos \alpha_1, \cos \alpha_2, \cos \alpha_3)$, from $(0,0,0)$.

We hope that this brief look at the geometry of rigid motions in 3-space will stimulate you to work Exercises §1101 and to begin to make further generalizations. Notice that geometries in a space of two dimensions are studies of the behavior of sets of points. When you define a point in n-space as an ordered n-tuple $(x_1, x_2, \ldots, x_n)$, you can proceed to develop a geometry of n-space just as we have developed a corresponding geometry of 2-space.

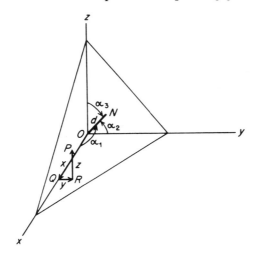

Fig. 10–64.

EXERCISES §1011

1. Find the distance in a three-dimensional space between P_1 and P_2 for:

(a) $P_1(2,1,5)$ and $P_2(5,13,9)$ (b) $P_1(4,0,-2)$ and $P_2(5,3,6)$

(c) $P_1(0,0,0)$ and $P_2(x,y,z)$ (d) $P_1(2,6,-1)$ and $P_2(x,y,z)$.

2. Show that the points $P_1(3,-4,2)$, $P_2(2,3,-4)$ and $P_3(-4,2,3)$ are the vertices of an equilateral triangle.

3. By computing three distances, show that the points $P_1(5,0,3)$, $P_2(8,1,1)$, and $P_3(-1,-2,7)$ are on the same straight line.

4. Find the distance in a four-dimensional space between P_1 and P_2 for:

(a) $P_1(0,0,0,0)$ and $P_2(2,6,1,4)$ (b) $P_1(6,5,-1,2)$ and $P_2(0,2,3,3)$

(c) $P_1(0,0,0,0)$ and $P_2(x,y,z,w)$ (d) $P_1(2,3,-1,5)$ and $P_2(x,y,z,w)$.

5. Determine the direction cosines for the vector P_1P_2, using the data of Exercise 1(a); using the data of Exercise 1(b).

6. Show that the sum of the squares of the direction cosines of any vector in a three-dimensional space is 1. (*Hint:* Use the definition of $\cos \alpha_i$ together with the definition for distance.) Would this property hold for a space of n dimensions?

7. If $\cos \alpha_1 = \frac{1}{2}$ and $\cos \alpha_2 = \frac{1}{2}\sqrt{3}$, determine $\cos \alpha_3$ (see Exercise 6). Draw a vector from the origin with these direction cosines.

8. The graph of the condition $x^2 + y^2 + z^2 = 9$ in a three-dimensional space is the set of points on a sphere with center at the origin and radius 3. What set of points belongs to the graph of the condition $x^2 + y^2 + z^2 < 9$?

9. Show that the graph of the condition $(x - 3)^2 + (y - 1)^2 + (z + 2)^2 = 9$ is the set of points on the surface of a sphere with radius 3 and center at $(3,1,-2)$. (*Hint:* Use the distance formula.)

10. In a space of four or more dimensions, the set of points that are equidistant from a fixed point is called a *hypersphere*. What is the center and radius of the hypersphere

$$(x - 3)^2 + (y - 1)^2 + (z + 2)^2 + (w - 5)^2 = 9 ?$$

11. Make a sketch of the part of the ellipsoid $x^2/4 + y^2/25 + z^2/49 = 1$ that is in the first octant.

12. Describe the set of points in 3-space determined by:

(a) $y = 3$ (b) $x = -5$ (c) $z = 2$

(d) $x = y$ (e) $z = 3x$ (f) $z = \frac{1}{2}y + 4.$

13. Write and simplify the algebraic condition that expresses the geometric condition that a point (x,y,z) is equidistant from $(4,3,0)$ and $(6,7,2)$. What is the graph of this condition?

14. A plane is perpendicular to the vector from $P_1(3,-1,0)$ to $P_2(7,11,3)$ and is 2 units from the origin. What is its equation?

Answer: $4x + 12y + 3z = 26.$

15. If $P_1(x_1,y_1,z_1)$, $P_2(x_2,y_2,z_2)$, and $P_3(x_3,y_3,z_3)$ are any three points not on a straight line, show that

$$\begin{vmatrix} x & y & z & 1 \\ x_1 & y_1 & z_1 & 1 \\ x_2 & y_2 & z_2 & 1 \\ x_3 & y_3 & z_3 & 1 \end{vmatrix} = 0$$

is the equation of the plane passing through P_1, P_2, and P_3. (*Hint:* If you expand the determinant by the top row you find a linear condition; hence this is the equation of some plane. By direct substitution, you can show that the coordinates of each point satisfy the condition, since the value of a determinant is zero when two of its rows are identical.)

16. Determine the equation of the plane passing through $P_1(2,-2,0)$, $P_2(1,0,2)$, and $P_3(-2,1,4)$. (See Exercise 15.)

Answer: $2x - 4y + 5z = 12.$

17. If a line in the plane has a normal intercept of r and the angle of the normal is α_1 (see Section 1005), then the equation of the line is $x \cos \alpha_1 + y \sin \alpha_1 = r$. Let α_2 be the angle from the y-axis to the normal of the line. Then $\alpha_2 = \alpha_1 - \pi/2$ or $\alpha_2 = \alpha_1 + 3\pi/2$. Show that the equation of the line becomes $x \cos \alpha_1 + y \cos \alpha_2 = r$. The elements of the number-pair $[\cos \alpha_1, \cos \alpha_2]$ are called direction cosines of the normal to the line. Compare this form of the equation of a line in a space of two dimensions with the equation of a plane in a space of three dimensions.

You can sketch a surface in three dimensions by considering the curves formed by the intersections of the surface with planes parallel to the coordinate planes. For example, the replacement $z = k$ in the condition defining the surface yields the set of points in the intersection of the surface and a plane perpendicular to the z-axis (parallel to the xy-plane), k units from the origin. Determine each type of surface in Exercises 18 through 23 and make a sketch:

18. $x^2 + y^2 - z^2 = 0$ (right circular cone)

19. $x^2 + y^2 - 4z = 0$ (paraboloid of revolution)

20. $2x + 6y - 5z = 9$ (plane)

21. $x^2 + y^2 = 16$ (right circular cylinder)

22. $4x^2 + z^2 = 16$ (elliptical cylinder)

23. $x^2 + y - 4 = 0$ (parabolic cylinder).

You can represent a curve in 3-space as the intersection of two surfaces. In Exercises 24 through 28 identify each curve and make a sketch:

24. $4x - 5y - 2z = 6$ and $z = 0$ (straight line)

25. $x + y = 4$ and $z = x$ (straight line)

26. $x^2 + y^2 = 25$ and $z = x$ (ellipse)

27. $x^2 + y^2 = 25$ and $y = 3$ (parallel lines)

28. $x^2 + y^2 = 9$ and $y^2 + z^2 = 9$ (two ellipses).

A second way to represent a curve in 3-space is to give the coordinates of points on the curve as functions of a parameter (compare Section 1007, page 552). For the curves of Exercises 29 and 30, determine the coordinates of a few points on the curve, replacing the parameter t by each of several real numbers. Investigate the type of curve.

29. $x = 2 + t$
$y = -3 + 3t$
$z = 5 - 2t$

(Eliminating the parameter t between two different pairs of equations results in two linear conditions in x, y, and z. Hence graph is intersection of two planes, or a straight line.)

30. $x = 3 \cos t$
$y = 3 \sin t$
$z = \frac{1}{2}t$

(Eliminating the parameter between the first two equations yields $x^2 + y^2 = 9$. Hence all points of the curve lie on the cylinder $x^2 + y^2 = 9$. As t increases, the point moves around the cylinder, but z increases directly as t to give a spiral in 3-space, known as a *helix*.)

11

Mathematical Structures

You have worked with the set L of real numbers and the set C of complex numbers. For a time, in Chapters 7 and 10, you worked with matrices whose elements are real numbers, and thought of these matrices as elements of a mathematical system somewhat like the systems of real numbers and complex numbers. The time has come to look back over what you have done, and to look ahead to glimpse some of the mathematical things you have not yet done.

Recall our use of the word *structure* to describe the system of real numbers, complex numbers, or $n \times n$ square matrices whose elements are real numbers. We propose, in this final chapter, to ask: "What is a mathematical structure?" and: "What do some of the modern mathematicians mean when they say that mathematics is a study of structures?"

1100. An order structure

Rather than attempt to discuss the mathematical idea of structure in a general way, we prefer to proceed through examples. We begin with what is perhaps the simplest sort of mathematical structure, a so-called *order structure*.

We have used the sentence $a < b$ as we spoke of real numbers. We say *a is less than b* and understand this sentence as a condition upon the real numbers that you may use as replacements for the variables a and b.

Now suppose we look at the way people use the phrase *less than*; suppose we try to pick out its essential characteristics; suppose we try to express these characteristics by a few simple assumptions. Mathematicians who have done this came up with the following scheme:

Assume a set K: $\{x, y, z, ...\}$ and a connective phrase, $<$, which you may use only in accordance with the postulates:

P 1 $\qquad\qquad (x \neq y) \Rightarrow (x < y \text{ or } y < x)$

P 2 $\qquad\qquad (x < y) \Rightarrow (y \nless x)$

P 3 $\qquad\qquad (x < y \text{ and } y < z) \Rightarrow (x < z)$.

Notice that we have used some symbols and ideas from your previous work. We suppose that $x = y$ means that the symbols x and y are names for the same element of K; then $x \neq y$ means that the symbols x and y are *not* names for the same element of K. Similarly $y \not< x$ means: "It is not the case that $y < x$." It is convenient to make use of these familiar symbols; but we shall avoid assuming that we know anything about them except what the postulates tell us.

We now *define* the symbol ">" as follows:

D 1 $$(x > y) \Leftrightarrow (y < x).$$

We shall now prove three theorems that are logical consequences of these assumptions:

T 1 $$x \not< x.$$

Proof: Suppose $$x < x.$$

Then $$x \not< x. \qquad \text{(P 2)}$$

The assumption $x < x$ leads to the contradictory conclusion $x \not< x$; hence this assumption must be rejected. Hence it is not the case than $x < x$; that is, $x \not< x$.

T 2 $$(x = y) \quad \text{or} \quad (x < y \text{ or } x > y).$$

Proof: Suppose it is *not* the case that $(x = y)$ or $(x < y \text{ or } x > y)$. Then by D 1, it is not the case that $(x = y)$ or $(x < y \text{ or } y < x)$. Hence $(x \neq y)$ and it is not the case that $(x < y \text{ or } y < x)$. This contradicts P 1. Hence the assumption must be rejected, and it *is* the case that $(x = y)$ or $(x < y \text{ or } x > y)$.

T 3   (a) It is not the case that $(x = y \text{ and } x < y)$
         (b) It is not the case that $(x = y \text{ and } y < x)$
         (c) It is not the case that $(x < y \text{ and } x > y)$.

Proof (a): Suppose $x = y$ and $x < y$. Since $x = y$, we may substitute y for x. Then $x < y$ becomes $x < x$, which contradicts T 1. Hence it is not the case that $(x = y \text{ and } x < y)$
Proof (b): The proof of (b) is similar to the proof of (a).
Proof (c): Suppose $x < y$ and $x > y$. Then, by D 1, $x < y$ and $y < x$. Hence by P 3, $x < x$. This contradicts T 1 and the proof of (c) is complete.

Notice that we said nothing about the physical meaning of the elements $x, y, z, \ldots$ of the set K. Notice, also, that the properties of the connective phrase, $<$, are just the properties we laid down in the postulates or proved in the theorems. Hence we are now free to look for interpretations of the connective phrase, "$<$," in the world of experience. Such interpretations must obey the postulates P 1, P 2, and P 3.

(1) Consider first the set of English words and the connective phrase alphabetically precedes. The postulates become:

P 1: If x and y stand for different words then x alphabetically precedes y or y alphabetically precedes x.

P 2: If x alphabetically precedes y then y does not alphabetically precede x.

P 3: If x alphabetically precedes y and y alphabetically precedes z then x alphabetically precedes z.

Since the postulates do apply, we conclude that the set of English words with the phrase "alphabetically precedes" has the structure of the set K with the phrase "$<$." Hence we may assume that T 1, T 2, and T 3 are true for English words relative to the phrase "alphabetically precedes." For example,

T 2: x and y stand for the same word or (x precedes y or y precedes x).

As further examples try:

(2) The set of all subsets of the set {Jane, Mary, Tom}, and the connective phrase, "contains elements not contained in."

The set of all subsets of $\{J, M, T\}$ is

$$\Big\{\{J, M, T\}, \{J, M\}, \{J, T\}, \{M, T\}, \{J\}, \{M\}, \{T\}, \{\ \ \}\Big\}.$$

Including the null set, { }, there are 8 subsets of $\{J, M, T\}$.

Now test this interpretation to see whether the postulates apply:

P 1: (x is not the same subset as y) $\Rightarrow$ (x contains elements not in y or y contains elements not in x). No trouble here.

P 2: (x contains elements not in y) $\Rightarrow$ (y does not contain elements not in x). One contrary example is enough to prove that this postulate does *not* apply. Let $x = \{J\}$ and $y = \{M\}$. Then x contains elements not in y ($J \in x$ and $J \notin y$), and y contains elements not in x ($M \in y$ and $M \notin x$).

The failure of P 2 is sufficient to eliminate this interpretation of our order structure. You may wish to experiment with P 3 and find that (x contains elements not in y and y contains elements not in z) $\nRightarrow$ (x contains elements not in z). Take for example, $x = \{J\}$, $y = \{M\}$ and $z = \{J\}$.

(3) The set of weights of all packages mailed at post offices in the United States, and the connective phrase "is lighter than."

As you test this interpretation, you will find that the postulates do apply. Of course there are practical limitations. It may not be easy to decide which of two packages is lighter. Their weights may differ by only a few thousandths of a pound. Still, your theoretical concept of relative weights of packages does fit the postulates.

(4) The set of girls in a sorority and the connective phrase "is envious of."

As you test this interpretation of the order structure, you will find that some of the postulates do not fit. For example, P 3 becomes: If Jane envies Lenore and Lenore envies Mary then Jane envies Mary. Of course this is not necessarily true.

We have used a simple order structure to illustrate a point about mathematics in general. Mathematicians take an idea like "less than." They try to formulate its essential characteristics into a set of assumptions. The assumptions are purposely abstract. They do not refer to any one particular interpretation. Thus the mathematicians build a *structure* with abstract elements, one or more undefined phrases, definitions, and theorems. This structure then becomes available to people who want to investigate and describe the world of experience. Hence mathematics is, in this sense, a study of structures.

In the remainder of this chapter you will explore some of the important structures from the *storehouse of structures* called mathematics. Meanwhile, Exercises §1100 give you opportunities to experiment with the simple order structure that we described above.

EXERCISES §1100

1. Let K be the set of points on a line, and interpret " $<$ " as "to the left of." Are the postulates satisfied?

2. Let K be a set of 16 basketball teams that have just completed a tournament where a team is dropped out if it loses one game. Interpret " $<$ " as "has eliminated." Which of the postulates are not satisfied?

3. Let K be a set of persons consisting of a boy, his father, his father's father, etc. That is, for each person in the set, his father is also in the set. If you interpret " $<$ " as "is a descendant of," are the postulates satisfied?

4. Nine persons are equally spaced around a circular table; $x < y$ means that the shortest distance from x to y is in the clockwise direction. Which of the postulates are satisfied?

5. Let K be the set of real numbers and interpret, $x < y$ as There exists a positive real number, p, such that $x = y + p$. (Notice that this is not the usual concept of "less than" in the real number system.) Are the postulates satisfied? Are the theorems valid?

6. Let K be the set of complex numbers and interpret $(a + bi) < (c + di)$ as Either (a is less than c) or ($a = c$, and b is less than d). Are the postulates satisfied?

1101. A simple algebraic structure

The mathematical structures that you met in Chapters 2, 5, and 7 are too complicated for our present purposes. They combine order structure with algebraic structure and ideas about continuity that involve basic mathematical difficulty. We begin to build toward such structures now; but we begin with comparatively simple structures.

A simple algebraic structure involves a set of elements, one or more *binary operations*, and some assumptions about how the elements of the set behave when you perform the operations.

As before, equality of two elements of the set means identity of these elements; in symbols, $x = y$ means that x and y are symbols for the same element. Consequently, if $x = y$ you may replace x by y in any mathematical expression.

The word *operation* is a primitive term that we make no attempt to define. When we speak of a binary operation, we mean that to each pair of elements of the set there corresponds a third element. Examples of binary operations are addition (given 2 and 3, addition yields 5), multiplication (given 2 and 3, multiplication yields 6), and combining successive transformations (a rotation of 40° followed by a rotation of −10° yields a rotation of 30°). We assume that the operation is *well-defined* in the sense that the third element is unique; you may get different symbols when you perform a binary operation, for example,

$$2 + 3 = 5, \quad \text{and} \quad 2 + 3 = \frac{10}{2};$$

$$2 \times 3 = 6, \quad \text{and} \quad 2 \times 3 = 10 - 4;$$

40° rotation followed by −10° rotation yields 30° rotation

and　　40° rotation followed by −10° rotation yields −330° rotation;

but these different symbols are symbols for the same element.

We proceed to an example of a simple algebraic structure.

Consider a set K: $\{a, b, c, ...\}$, a well-defined binary operation $*$, and the postulates:

P 1　$(x \in K$ and $y \in K) \Rightarrow$ (there is an element $z \in K$ such that $x * y = z$)
(In words, the set K is *closed* under the operation $*$.)

P 2　$(x \in K, y \in K,$ and $z \in K) \Rightarrow [x * (y * z) = (x * y) * z]$
(In words, the operation $*$ is *associative*.)

P 3　There is an element $e \in K$ such that $(x \in K) \Rightarrow x * e = e * x = x$.
(In words, the set K contains an *identity element e* for the operation $*$.)

Notice that the elements $a, b, c, ...$ of K are abstract. We have said nothing about the physical meaning of these elements. You are assured that there is at least one element of K called e, and a well-defined *operation* called $*$. The postulates tell you what you may do with the elements of the set. The fact that you can perform operations upon the elements of K (just the operation, $*$, here) makes this an *algebraic structure*. This fits the common idea of algebra as a subject where you manipulate symbols like a, b, c, ... according to certain rules.

Notice that the set of postulates for this algebraic structure is not very restrictive. For example, we have not required that $x * y = y * x$, in words, that the operation be *commutative*. It should be easy to find interpretations of this structure. We list some:

(1) The set N of natural numbers, with $e = 1$ and $*$ as multiplication.

(2) The set of natural numbers and zero, with $e = 0$ and $*$ as addition.

(3) The set of even natural numbers and zero, with $e = 0$ and $*$ as addition. Notice that P 1 holds because the sum of two even numbers is an even number.

(4) The set of 4×4 matrices whose elements are natural numbers or zero, with

$$e = \begin{pmatrix} 1 & 0 & 0 & 0 \\ 0 & 1 & 0 & 0 \\ 0 & 0 & 1 & 0 \\ 0 & 0 & 0 & 1 \end{pmatrix},$$

and $*$ as matrix multiplication. Recall that matrix multiplication is not commutative. To require that $x * y = y * x$ would eliminate this example.

(5) The set of all subsets of a given set S with e the null set and $*$ as the word "or." We check the three postulates for this interpretation of our algebraic structure.

P 1: (A is a subset of S and B is a subset of S)

$\Rightarrow$ [there is a subset C of S such that $(A$ or $B) = C$]

We interpret $(A$ or $B)$ as the set whose elements are elements of A or elements of B or elements of both A and B. Recall our frequent use of this idea since Chapter 2. For example, the graph of $(y = x + 2$ or $y > x^2)$ is the set of points that belong to the graph of $y = x + 2$, or belong to the graph of $y > x^2$, or belong to both the graphs of $y = x + 2$ and $y > x^2$. Mathematicians call the set $(A$ or $B)$ the *union* of the sets A and B. They write this $A \cup B$, and speak of the union of A and B. Clearly $A \cup B$ is a subset of S provided A and B are subsets of S. Hence P 1 holds for this interpretation of our algebraic structure.

P 2: If A, B, and C are subsets of S, then

$$A \cup (B \cup C) = (A \cup B) \cup C.$$

You should think about the meaning of this postulate. Figure 11–1 may help you to visualize its meaning. You may also see directly that *A* or (*B* or *C*) = (*A* or *B*) or *C*.

P 3: There is a subset of ϕ of *S* (ϕ is commonly used as a symbol for the null set), and if *A* is a subset of *S*, then

$$A \cup \phi = \phi \cup A = A.$$

We leave you to study P 3 and to see that it does apply to this interpretation of our algebraic structure.

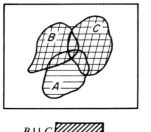
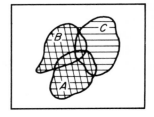

$B \cup C$ ▨▨▨▨
A ∪ (*B* ∪ *C*) is the
entire shaded area

$A \cup B$ ▧▧▧▧
(*A* ∪ *B*) ∪ *C* is the
entire shaded area

Fig. 11–1.

This simple algebraic structure serves its purpose here if you see how its set of elements, its binary operation, and its postulates may be interpreted in several different ways. Each theorem that you can prove for this structure will apply to each of its interpretations.

In the next two sections you will investigate two important algebraic structures. Notice that we deal with algebraic structures apart from order structures. In Section 1104 you will combine an algebraic structure with an order structure.

EXERCISES §1101

For each of the following systems determine which of the postulates, P 1, P 2, and P 3, are satisfied.

1. The set of integers, *I*, with *e* = 0 and * as addition.

2. The set of negative integers and zero with *e* = 0 and * as addition.

3. The set of odd integers with *e* = 1 and * as multiplication.

4. The set of odd integers and zero with *e* = 0 and * as addition.

5. The set of all 2 × 2 matrices whose elements are real numbers with

$e = \begin{pmatrix} 0 & 0 \\ 0 & 0 \end{pmatrix}$ and * as matrix addition.

6. The set of integers, I, with $e = 0$ and $*$ as subtraction.

7. The set of rational numbers with $e = 1$ and $*$ as multiplication.

8. The set of rational numbers with $e = 0$ and $*$ as addition.

9. The set of integral multiples of 3 with $e = 3 \cdot 0 = 0$ and $*$ as addition.

10. The set of all subsets of a given set, S, with $e = S$ and $*$ as the word "and."

11. The set of complex numbers $\{1, -1, i, -i\}$ with $*$ as multiplication and $e = 1$.

12. The set of 2×2 matrices of the form $\begin{pmatrix} a & -b \\ b & a \end{pmatrix}$, $a \in I$, $b \in I$, with $e = \begin{pmatrix} 1 & 0 \\ 0 & 1 \end{pmatrix}$ and $*$ as matrix multiplication.

13. The set of polynomials of the form $p(x) = ax + b$, $a \in I$, $b \in I$, with $e = 0 \cdot x + 0$ and $*$ as addition of polynomials.

14. The same set of polynomials as in Exercise 13 with $e = 0 \cdot x + 1$ and $*$ as multiplication of polynomials.

15. The set of integers, I, with $x * y = (2 + x + y)$ and $e = -2$.

16. The set of integers, I, with $x * y = (2xy)$ and $e = \frac{1}{2}$.

1102. Groups

Modern mathematicians have chosen simple-looking words that are easy to spell and easy to pronounce; these words mean exactly what mathematicians make them mean. As a case in point, a *group* is an algebraic structure defined as follows: a set K: $\{a, b, c, \ldots\}$, a well-defined binary operation $*$, and the postulates:

P 1 $(x \in K$ and $y \in K) \Rightarrow$ (there is an element $z \in K$ such that $x * y = z$)
P 2 $(x \in K, y \in K,$ and $z \in K) \Rightarrow [x * (y * z) = (x * y) * z]$
P 3 There is an element $e \in K$ such that $(x \in K) \Rightarrow (x * e = e * x = x)$
P 4 $(x \in K) \Rightarrow$ (there is an element $x' \in K$ and $x * x' = e$).

You have already met many systems that have the structure of a group. We remind you of a few such systems:

(1) The set of integers, I, with $e = 0$, $*$ as addition. Notice, particularly, the effect of P 4. x' is the inverse for addition of x. For $x = 7$, $x' = -7$; for $x = -3$, $x' = 3$; for $x = 0$, $x' = -0 = 0$. The only element of I that is its own inverse is the element $e = 0$.

Notice that the set of natural numbers is *not* a group under addition. The set N does not include the identity element $e = 0$. Notice that the set of natural numbers and zero is *not* a group under addition. Although this set contains the identity element 0, it does not include the inverses for addition of each of its elements. For example, for the element 5, the inverse element -5 is *not* a member of the set of natural numbers and zero.

(2) The set of even integers (this includes 0) under addition. Check each of the postulates for a group. Recall that the sum of two even integers is an even integer, and that the negative of an even integer is an even integer.

Notice that the set of odd integers under addition is *not* a group; this set does not include the identity element $e = 0$. Even when you use the set of odd integers and zero you do not get a group; the set is not *closed* under addition, since the sum of two odd integers is not an odd integer.

(3) The set of remainders obtained in the division of natural numbers by 6. This set of remainders is $\{0,1,2,3,4,5\}$. The operation, $*$, is ordinary addition combined with the idea of casting out multiples of 6 that you met in Section 706 (page 361). Recall the language that we introduced. Two elements are said to be *congruent modulo 6* if they differ by a multiple of 6. Thus, in this system, $6 = 0$, $7 = 1$, $8 = 2$, etc. This definition of $*$ yields closure of the set $\{0, 1, 2, 3, 4, 5\}$ under addition. To see how this works, examine the addition table:

+ (Mod 6)	0	1	2	3	4	5
0	0	1	2	3	4	5
1	1	2	3	4	5	0
2	2	3	4	5	0	1
3	3	4	5	0	1	2
4	4	5	0	1	2	3
5	5	0	1	2	3	4

You should interpret this table as follows: Select a number from the left-hand column, say 3; select a number from the top row, say 4; then the sum, $3 + 4$, appears in the cell opposite 3 and below 4. Notice that $3 + 4 = 1$.

Clearly, P 1 and P 2 hold in this system. In P 3, you take $e = 0$. In P 4, you seek the inverse for addition modulo 6 of each element of the set $\{0,1,2,3,4,5\}$. From the addition table, $0' = 0$ since $0 + 0 = 0$, and $1' = 5$ since $1 + 5 = 0$; in this way you continue to find that $2' = 4$, $3' = 3$, $4' = 2$, and $5' = 1$.

Since all four postulates hold for this system, we conclude that the set of natural numbers modulo 6 is a group under addition modulo 6.

(4) The set of fractions of arithmetic, with $e = 1$, $*$ as multiplication. Notice, particularly, the effect of P 4. x' is the inverse for multiplication of x. Hence $(\frac{2}{3})' = \frac{3}{2}$, $(\frac{1}{7})' = 7$, and $1' = 1$. The only element of the set that is its own inverse is 1.

Notice that the set of natural numbers is *not* a group under multiplication. The set N contains the identity element $e = 1$; but it does not contain the inverses for multiplication of each of its elements. Neither is the set I a group under multiplication. The number 5 is an element of the set I, but its inverse for multiplication is not an element of I.

The set of rational numbers (including zero) is not a group under multiplication. All of the postulates except P 4 hold; but the element $0 \in R$ has no inverse for multiplication. Recall that $1/0$ is not defined. If you exclude the number zero, and work with the set of rational numbers with zero excluded, you will find that this set is a group under multiplication.

(5) The set of non-zero remainders obtained in the division of natural numbers by 5. This set of non-zero remainders is $\{1,2,3,4\}$. The operation, $*$, is ordinary multiplication combined with the idea of casting out multiples of 5.

Examine the multiplication table for this set:

$\times$ (Mod 5)	1	2	3	4
1	1	2	3	4
2	2	4	1	3
3	3	1	4	2
4	4	3	2	1

Notice that the set is closed under multiplication; $e = 1$; $1' = 1$, $2' = 3$, $3' = 2$, $4' = 4$.

It is interesting to contrast this set with the set of non-zero remainders obtained in the division of natural numbers by 6. This set of natural numbers modulo 6, with zero excluded, is $\{1,2,3,4,5\}$. The multiplication table is

$\times$ (Mod 6)	1	2	3	4	5
1	1	2	3	4	5
2	2	4	0	2	4
3	3	0	3	0	3
4	4	2	0	4	2
5	5	4	3	2	1

Notice that this set is *not* closed under multiplication; for example, $2 \cdot 3 = 0$ and 0 is not an element of the set. It has an identity element, $e = 1$, but 2, 3, and 4 do not have inverses; that is, the conditions $2y = 1$, $3y = 1$, and $4y = 1$ have no solutions in the system.

It is possible to prove that the set of natural numbers modulo m, with zero excluded, is a group under multiplication if and only if m is a prime number. Thus $m = 5$ yields a group, but $m = 6$ does not.

(6) The set $\{1,i,-1,-i\}$, where $i^2 = -1$, with $e = 1$ and $*$ as multiplication, is a group.

The multiplication table is:

×	1	i	−1	−i
1	1	i	−1	−i
i	i	−1	−i	1
−1	−1	−i	1	i
−i	−i	1	i	−1

Notice that this system obeys our postulates and hence has the structure of a group. It has many different physical interpretations. Consider, for example, a 4-spoke wheel as pictured in Fig. 11–2.

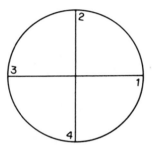

Fig. 11–2.

Symbolize a 90° counterclockwise rotation of the wheel by i; let $i^2 = i \cdot i = -1$ represent a 180° counterclockwise rotation; let $i^3 = i \cdot i \cdot i = -i$ represent a 270° counterclockwise rotation; and let $i^4 = i \cdot i \cdot i \cdot i = 1$ represent a 360° counterclockwise rotation. If, now, we consider as equal any two rotations that turn the wheel into the same final position, we have, for a rotation a, $a = a + k(360°)$, $k \in I$. With this understanding, the multiplication table above represents the combination of any two of the rotations into a single equal rotation. For example, $i \cdot (-i)$ represents a 270° rotation, $-i$, followed by a 90° rotation, i; the effect is a 360° rotation, which is equivalent to a 0° rotation, 1; that is, $i \cdot (-i) = 1$.

Exercises §1102 give you opportunities to interpret this group of four elements in other ways. Mathematicians call it a *cyclic group of order 4*; it has four elements that can all be produced from the single element i by repeating the group operation. Thus $i = i$, $i^2 = -1$, $i^3 = -i$, and $i^4 = 1$; the elements of the group can be *generated* in a kind of cycle from one of the elements of the group.

Each of the six examples that we have given thus far is an example of a special type of group that mathematicians call *commutative*. They all obey a fifth postulate, namely,

P 5 $(x \in K \quad \text{and} \quad y \in K) \Rightarrow (x * y = y * x)$.

They are called *commutative groups*, or sometimes *abelian groups*, in honor of the Norwegian mathematician Abel (1802–1829). Abel and Galois (1811–1832), a French mathematician, laid the foundations for the study of groups. The group structure has proved to be a unifying idea for pulling together a great deal of the pre-19th century mathematics, and a question-raising idea that has led modern mathematicians to invent much that is new in mathematics.

Not all groups are commutative. We give you now two examples of non-abelian groups:

(7) Consider the set of 4×4 matrices with elements in the set L. We take

$$e = \begin{pmatrix} 1 & 0 & 0 & 0 \\ 0 & 1 & 0 & 0 \\ 0 & 0 & 1 & 0 \\ 0 & 0 & 0 & 1 \end{pmatrix},$$

and $*$ as matrix multiplication. Not all such matrices have inverses, but some of them do. Consider, then, the subset whose elements are matrices that have inverses; thus in this subset, each element has an inverse. It can be proved that if A and B are $n \times n$ matrices, with inverses for multiplication A^{-1} and B^{-1} respectively, then $(AB)^{-1} = B^{-1}A^{-1}$. That is, the inverse of a product is the product of the inverses taken in the reverse order. This means that the set of 4×4 matrices that have inverses for multiplication is closed under multiplication. It means that this set of so-called *non-singular* matrices is a group under matrix multiplication. But it is not an abelian group; there are pairs of non-singular matrices that do not obey P 5 (see page 352).

(8) Recall the set T of translations of the euclidean plane. This set of translations forms an abelian group under the operation of combining successive translations into a single equivalent translation. Thus a translation of 2 units to the right and one unit down, followed by a translation of 3 units to the right and 3 units up, is equivalent to a translation of 5 units to the right and 2 units up. The set T is closed under the operation of combining translations in this way; e is the translation that moves the origin zero units to the right and zero units up; the inverse of t is the translation that undoes what t does. Hence the set T is a group under the operation of combining successive translations; it is an abelian group because $t_1 * t_2 = t_2 * t_1$; that is, t_2 followed by t_1 has the same effect as t_1 followed by t_2.

The set R of rotations of the euclidean plane is likewise an abelian group under the operation of combining successive rotations into a single, equivalent rotation.

But the set E of euclidean transformations of the plane is a non-abelian group. We noticed, in Section 1000 (page 507) that $e_1 * e_2$ may be different from $e_2 * e_1$; for example, a translation followed by a rotation may have an effect different from the rotation followed by the translation.

We shall not prove theorems based upon the postulates for a group. The theory of groups is a very extensive branch of modern mathematics. We pause only to re-emphasize our point about structures. The group structure, with its large body of theorems, is available to anyone who finds a physical situation to which it applies; that is, a physical situation in which there is a set K and a binary operation, $*$, that obey the postulates P 1 through P 4. If P 5 also holds, the physical interpretation will have, besides, the special properties of an abelian group.

Exercises §1102 give you opportunities to explore group structure further and to identify a variety of instances of group structure in the world of experience.

EXERCISES §1102

1–16. Determine which of the systems in Exercises §1101 are groups; abelian groups.

17. Investigate each of the following sets of numbers to see if it is a group with respect to the operation of addition; with respect to the operation of multiplication.

(a) The set of natural numbers, N
(b) The set of integers, I
(c) The set of rational numbers, R
(d) The set of complex numbers, C.

18. The complex numbers of the set, $\{a + bi \mid a \in I \text{ and } b \in I\}$, are called gaussian integers. Are the gaussian integers a group with respect to addition? With respect to multiplication?

19. Is the set of the three cube roots of unity, $\{1, -\frac{1}{2} + \frac{1}{2}\sqrt{3}i, -\frac{1}{2} - \frac{1}{2}\sqrt{3}i\}$, a group with respect to multiplication? Write the multiplication table.

20. Write the addition and multiplication tables for the set of natural numbers modulo 7. Is this set a group with respect to addition? If the zero is excluded, is it a group with respect to multiplication?

21. Repeat Exercise 20 with the modulus 8.

22. The elements of the set, $\{a, b, c, d\}$, are combined with respect to $*$ according to the following table

$*$	a	b	c	d
a	d	c	a	b
b	c	d	b	a
c	a	b	c	d
d	b	a	d	c

Is it a group? Is it an abelian group? Which element is the identity? Give the inverse of each element.

23. An element of a group always commutes with its inverse, whether the group is abelian or not. Supply the reasons for the following proof that $x' * x = x * x'$.

Steps	*Reasons*

$$x' * x = (x' * x) * e$$
$$= x' * (x * e)$$
$$= x' * \{x * [x' * (x')']\}$$
$$= x' * \{[x * x'] * (x')'\}$$
$$= x' * [e * (x')']$$
$$= x' * (x')'$$
$$= e$$
$$= x * x'.$$

24. Prove that $(x')' = x$, that is, the inverse of the inverse of an element of a group is the element itself.

1103. Fields

Another of the easy-to-say and easy-to-spell words of modern mathematics is *field*. Mathematicians work with both commutative and non-commutative fields; but we shall limit our discussion to a *commutative field*.

A commutative field is an algebraic structure defined as follows: a set K, $\{a, b, c, ...\}$, two well-defined binary operations, $+$ and $\cdot$, and the postulates;

For $+$	*For* $\cdot$
K is an abelian group under $+$. We designate the identity for $+$ by 0; the inverse of x with respect to $+$ by $-x$.	With the element 0 excluded, K is an abelian group under $\cdot$. We designate the identity for $\cdot$ by 1; the inverse of x with respect to $\cdot$ by $1/x$.

For $+$ *and* $\cdot$

$$(x \in K, y \in K, \text{ and } z \in K) \Rightarrow x \cdot (y + z) = (x \cdot y) + (x \cdot z).$$

That is, $\cdot$ is *distributive* over $+$.

In this definition of a commutative field, we have used the familiar symbols $0, 1, +, \cdot$. In place of "$x \cdot y$" we often write merely "xy." This should help you to identify field structure with familiar structures of number systems. You should be careful, however, to maintain the abstract point of view. A symbol like $+$ means exactly what we make it mean. As we proceed, you will use these symbols in unfamiliar ways.

We suggest a few examples of field structure. Then we prove two theorems that hold in any commutative field. We hope this will reinforce the ideas that we have planted in your mind. Mathematics is a storehouse of structures. A single structure may serve as a mathematical model for many different-appearing applications.

(1) The set of integers modulo 5: $\{0,1,2,3,4\}$.

Addition: *Multiplication:*

+ (Mod 5)	0	1	2	3	4
0	0	1	2	3	4
1	1	2	3	4	0
2	2	3	4	0	1
3	3	4	0	1	2
4	4	0	1	2	3

(Mod 5)	1	2	3	4
1	1	2	3	4
2	2	4	1	3
3	3	1	4	2
4	4	3	2	1

Identity element: 0   *Identity element:* 1

Inverses: $-0 = 0$ (since $0 + 0 = 0$)   Inverses: $\frac{1}{1} = 1$ (since $1 \cdot 1 = 1$)

$-1 = 4$ (since $1 + 4 = 0$) $\frac{1}{2} = 3$ (since $2 \cdot 3 = 1$)

$-2 = 3$ (since $2 + 3 = 0$) $\frac{1}{3} = 2$ (since $3 \cdot 2 = 1$)

$-3 = 2$ (since $3 + 2 = 0$) $\frac{1}{4} = 4$ (since $4 \cdot 4 = 1$)

$-4 = 1$ (since $4 + 1 = 0$)

Notice that each of the groups is closed (P 1); associative (P 2); has an identity (P 3); has an inverse for each element (P 4); and is commutative (P 5). It can be shown that $\cdot$ is distributive over $+$.

Recall that the set of integers modulo 6 is *not* a field. When you exclude 0 from the set of integers modulo 6, the set $\{1,2,3,4,5\}$ is not a group with respect to multiplication.

(2) The set of rational numbers. Recall that the set of positive integers and zero is not a group under addition. This set does not contain inverses for addition or multiplication. The set of all integers is a group under addition; but the set of integers with zero excluded is not a group under multiplication; it does not contain inverses for multiplication. The set of positive rational numbers is not a group under addition; it is a group under multiplication. The set of all rational numbers is a commutative field. The identity for addition is 0; the identity for multiplication is 1. Each element x has an inverse for addition, $(-x)$, and each element except 0 has an inverse for multiplication, $(1/x)$.

The set of rational numbers is the "smallest" field that contains the natural numbers as a subset. This set of rational numbers is the set you get by extending the idea of number, beginning with the natural numbers and building a system of numbers in which subtraction (that involves inverses for addition) and division except by zero (that involves inverses for multiplication) are always possible.

(3) The set of numbers of the form $a + b\sqrt{2}$, where a and b are rational numbers.

For addition:	*For multiplication:*

P 1 $(w + x\sqrt{2}) + (y + z\sqrt{2})$
$= (w + y) + (x + z)\sqrt{2}.$

$(w + x\sqrt{2})(y + z\sqrt{2})$
$= (wy + 2xz) + (wz + xy)\sqrt{2}.$

The sum of two numbers of the form $a + b\sqrt{2}$ is a number of the form $a + b\sqrt{2}.$

The product of two numbers of the form $a + b\sqrt{2}$ is a number of the form $a + b\sqrt{2}.$

P 2 and P 5 Hold for real numbers, and hence for real numbers of the form $a + b\sqrt{2}$, under both addition and multiplication.

P 3 The identity for addition is:

$$0 + 0 \cdot \sqrt{2} = 0.$$

The identity for multiplication is:

$$1 + 0 \cdot \sqrt{2} = 1.$$

P 4 $-(w + x\sqrt{2}) = (-w) + (-x)\sqrt{2};$

$$\frac{1}{w + x\sqrt{2}} = \frac{w - x\sqrt{2}}{w^2 - 2x^2}$$

$(w + x\sqrt{2}) + [(-w) + (-x)\sqrt{2}]$

$$= \frac{w}{w^2 - 2x^2} + \frac{-x}{w^2 - 2x^2}\sqrt{2};$$

$= [w + (-w)] + [(x + (-x)]\sqrt{2}$

$$(w + x\sqrt{2}) \cdot \frac{1}{w + x\sqrt{2}} = 1.$$

$= 0 + 0\sqrt{2}.$

The inverse for addition of $w + x\sqrt{2}$ is a number of the form $a + b\sqrt{2}$, namely, $-(w + x\sqrt{2}) = (-w) + (-x)\sqrt{2}.$

The inverse for multiplication of $w + x\sqrt{2}$ is a number of the form $a + b\sqrt{2}$, namely, $\dfrac{1}{w + x\sqrt{2}}$

$$= \frac{w}{w^2 - 2x^2} + \frac{-x}{w^2 - 2x^2}\sqrt{2}.$$

In the same way, you can show that the set of numbers of the form $a + b\sqrt{3}$, where a and b are rational numbers, is a commutative field. Such fields are *algebraic fields;* students of algebra like to build up the "smallest" possible field in which they can solve a certain class of problems; for example, an algebraic field can be constructed especially for the purposes of solving a given quadratic equation; you calculate the discriminant, $D = b^2 - 4ac$, for the given equation; for cases in which $D > 0$, you construct the field $m + n\sqrt{D}$, where m and n are rational numbers.

(4) The real numbers. When you look back to the properties of real numbers that we assumed in Chapter 2 (page 63), you will realize that the system of real numbers is a commutative field. As we have used the field of real numbers, we assumed other properties beyond the field properties.

We assumed that the real numbers also comprise an order structure. We assumed other properties that can be summarized under the ideas of *continuity*. We mention these ideas briefly in Section 1104.

(5) The complex numbers. When you look back to the properties of complex numbers that we assumed in Chapter 5 (page 212), you will realize that the system of complex numbers is a commutative field. There are other systems that bear a close resemblance to the system of complex numbers. An Irish mathematician, Sir William Hamilton (1805–1865) recognized the first such system that is a non-commutative field. He called these new numbers *quaternions*. These quaternions, and their generalizations in matrix fields, have played an important part in the development of modern physics.

At this point, we prove two theorems that depend only upon the postulates for a commutative field. Hence these theorems hold good for any instance of a commutative field. They are not merely theorems about rational numbers, or real numbers. They are theorems about the abstract structure that we have called a commutative field.

T 1 $x \cdot 0 = 0$.

Since
$$a + 0 = a, \qquad \text{(P 3 for +)}$$
$$x \cdot (a + 0) = x \cdot a. \qquad \text{(Equality)}$$
But
$$x \cdot (a + 0) = x \cdot a + x \cdot 0, \qquad \text{(Distributive law)}$$
and hence
$$x \cdot a + x \cdot 0 = x \cdot a. \qquad \text{(Equality)}$$
Since
$$x \cdot a = z \text{ is an element of } K, \qquad \text{(P 1 for ·)}$$
there is an element
$$-z \in K \qquad \text{(P 4 for +)}$$
and
$$z + (-z) = 0.$$
Since
$$z + x \cdot 0 = z, \qquad \text{(Equality)}$$
$$(-z) + [z + x \cdot 0] = (-z) + z. \qquad \text{(Equality)}$$
Hence
$$[z + (-z)] + x \cdot 0 = z + (-z), \qquad \text{(P 2 and P 5 for +)}$$
and
$$0 + x \cdot 0 = 0. \qquad \text{(P 4 for +)}$$
Since
$$0 + x \cdot 0 = x \cdot 0, \qquad \text{(P 3 for +)}$$
$$x \cdot 0 = 0. \qquad \text{(Equality)}$$

T 2 $ab = 0 \Leftrightarrow (a = 0 \text{ or } b = 0)$.

First we prove that $(a = 0 \text{ or } b = 0) \Rightarrow ab = 0$.

Suppose $a = 0$ or $b = 0$.

If $a \neq 0$, then $b = 0$ and $ab = a \cdot 0 = 0$.   (T 1)

If $b \neq 0$, then $a = 0$ and $ab = 0 \cdot b = b \cdot 0 = 0$.   (P 5 for · and T 1)

If $a = 0$ and $b = 0$, then $ab = 0 \cdot 0 = 0$.   (T 1)

Hence $(a = 0 \text{ or } b = 0) \Rightarrow (ab = 0)$.

Second we prove that $ab = 0 \Rightarrow (a = 0 \text{ or } b = 0)$.

Suppose $ab = 0$.

If $a \neq 0$, then $\dfrac{1}{a} \in K$ and $a \cdot \dfrac{1}{a} = 1$.   (P 4 for $\cdot$)

$$\frac{1}{a}(ab) = \frac{1}{a} \cdot 0 = 0.$$ (Equality and T 1)

$$\frac{1}{a}(ab) = \left(\frac{1}{a} \cdot a\right) \cdot b = \left(a \cdot \frac{1}{a}\right) \cdot b = 1 \cdot b = b.$$

(P 2, P 5, P 4, and P 3 for $\cdot$)

Hence $b = 0$.   (Equality)

If $b \neq 0$, a similar argument leads to the conclusion $a = 0$. Hence

$$ab = 0 \Rightarrow (a = 0 \quad \text{or} \quad b = 0).$$

Combining the two parts of the proof, we conclude

$$ab = 0 \Leftrightarrow (a = 0 \quad \text{or} \quad b = 0).$$

The list of theorems that mathematicians have proved for commutative fields is long. Perhaps the two theorems that we have proved are enough to illustrate the possibilities. Exercises §1103 provide further examples of fields and an opportunity to prove several more theorems that apply to any commutative field.

EXERCISES §1103

1. Show that the set of integers modulo 7 is a field. Give the inverses of each element with respect to both operations.

2. Show that the set of numbers $\{a + b\sqrt{5}\}$, where $a \in R$ and $b \in R$, is a field.

3. Let K be the set of 9 elements of the form $a + bi$, where a and b belong to the set of integers modulo 3. To add or multiply in K, the elements are combined as in the set of complex numbers; then the coefficients are reduced modulo 3. Make an addition table and a multiplication table. Is K a field?

4. Determine which of the following are fields:
(a) The set of numbers $\{a + bi\}$, $a \in I$ and $b \in I$.
(b) The set of numbers $\{a + bi\}$, $a \in R$ and $b \in R$.
(c) The set of multiples of 3, $\{3m\}$, with $m \in I$.
(d) The set of numbers $\{a + b\sqrt{7}\}$, $a \in R$ and $b \in R$.
(e) The set of numbers $\{a\sqrt{7}\}$, $a \in R$.
(f) The set of 2×2 matrices whose elements are real numbers.
(g) The set of 2×2 matrices of the form $\begin{pmatrix} a & -b \\ b & a \end{pmatrix}$, where $a \in L$ and $b \in L$.

5. Fill in the reasons for each step in the proof that $(-a)b = -(ab)$ in a field.

$$[a + (-a)]b = 0 \cdot b = b \cdot 0 = 0.$$

$$[a + (-a)]b = ab + (-a)b.$$

Hence $\qquad ab + (-a)b = 0 \quad \text{and} \quad (-a)b = -(ab).$

6. In a field every equation of the form $x + a = b$ has a solution. Prove that

$$x + a = b \Leftrightarrow x = b + (-a).$$

7. In a field, every equation of the form $ax = b$, with $a \neq 0$, has a solution. Prove that for $a \neq 0$,

$$ax = b \Leftrightarrow x = \frac{1}{a} \cdot b.$$

8. Does an equation of the form $ax + b = c$, with $a \neq 0$, have a solution in a field?

9. Determine the solutions of the following equations in the field indicated:

(a) $(\sqrt{5} + 2)x + 3 = 2 - \sqrt{5}$ in the field of Exercise 2.

(b) $3x + 5 = 4$ in the field of Exercise 1.

(c) $6x + 6 = 5$ in the field of Exercise 1.

(d) $(1 + 2i)x + (1 + i) = 5 + 4i$ in the field of Exercise 4(b)

(e) $(1 + 2i)x + (1 + i) = 2 + i$ in the field of Exercise 3.

(f) $\begin{pmatrix} 3 & -2 \\ 2 & 3 \end{pmatrix} x = \begin{pmatrix} 14 & -5 \\ 5 & 14 \end{pmatrix}$ in the field of Exercise 4(g).

(g) $\begin{pmatrix} 1 & 1 \\ -1 & 1 \end{pmatrix} x + \begin{pmatrix} -5 & -2 \\ 2 & -5 \end{pmatrix} = \begin{pmatrix} 8 & -3 \\ 3 & 8 \end{pmatrix}$ in the field of Exercise 4(g).

Answers: (a) $-3 + \sqrt{5}$; (b) 2; (d) $2 - i$; (f) $\begin{pmatrix} 4 & 1 \\ -1 & 4 \end{pmatrix}$; (g) $\begin{pmatrix} 6 & -7 \\ 7 & 6 \end{pmatrix}$.

1104. Real numbers as ordered fields

You have observed that the set L of real numbers has the structure of a commutative field. As we have used them, the real numbers have also the order structure of Section 1100. Mathematicians call a set that has this order structure a *linearly ordered* set. Hence the set of real numbers is a linearly ordered set.

A linearly ordered set may have additional properties relating to order. For example, if every non-empty subset S of a set M has a smallest member, the set M is said to be *well-ordered*. In symbols:

$(S \subset M, S \neq \phi, \text{ and } x \in S) \Rightarrow$ (there is an element $a \in S$ such that $a \leq x$).

Notice that the set of natural numbers is well-ordered, but the sets of rational numbers and of real numbers are not. For example, $\{x \mid x > 1\}$ is a non-empty subset of R that has no smallest member. However, R and L have the following property:

$$(x \in M, \ y \in M, \text{ and } x < y) \Rightarrow (\text{there is an element } b \in M$$
$$\text{such that } x < b < y),$$

between each two distinct elements, there is another element of the set. Sets with this property are said to be *dense*.

To connect the field structure with the order structure, we use the postulates for:

Linear Ordering of a Commutative Field

$$(x < y) \Rightarrow (x + z < y + z)$$
$$(x < y \text{ and } 0 < z) \Rightarrow (xz < yz)$$
$$(x < y \text{ and } z < 0) \Rightarrow (yz < xz)$$

Actually this last postulate is redundant, since it can be proved from the preceding ones.

Taken together, the postulates for a commutative field, linear ordering, denseness, and linear ordering of a commutative field are a sufficient basis for much of what you have done with the set L, but they do not completely characterize the set L. Ideas related to continuity of a function, and limit of a variable, still remain as intuitive notions that depend upon pictures, rather than upon mathematical postulates.

To put the ideas of continuity and limit upon a postulational footing, modern mathematicians use axioms like the following:

Axiom of continuity. $(S \subset L$ and $S \neq \phi$ and S is *bounded above*$) \Rightarrow$ (there is an element $u \in L$ such that u is a *least upper bound* of S). The term *bounded above*, as applied to the set S, means that there is an element $b \in L$, such that for each element $x \in S$, $x \leq b$. The term *least upper bound*, as applied to the set S, means that there is an element $u \in L$ that is itself an upper bound of S and is less than or equal to all other upper bounds of S.

Perhaps you sense the connection between postulating the existence of least upper bounds of subsets of L and finding the limit of a variable, like the slope of a secant line in Section 603 (page 257). It would be out of place here to follow up the consequences of the axiom of continuity. It is enough for you to know that, besides algebraic structures and order structures, mathematics deals with *topological structures*. Modern mathematicians are concerned about removing space-perception from the realm of intuition. As they examine ideas about continuity and limit, beginning with postulates, they make available a whole storehouse of structures that they call topological.

In summary, the set L, with which you have worked, is a complex mathematical structure. It is a combination of order, algebraic, and topological structures.

EXERCISES §1104

1. Show that R is not a well-ordered set. (*Hint:* Consider the subset of R defined by the condition $x > 2$. Does this subset have a smallest member?)

2. Since $R \subset L$, explain why Exercise 1 implies that L is not a well-ordered set.

3. Show that N is not a dense set.

4. Show that R is a dense set. [*Hint:* Given $x < y$, with $x \in R$ and $y \in R$. Let $b = \frac{1}{2}(x + y)$. Show first that $b \in R$; then show that $x < \frac{1}{2}(x + y) < y$.]

5. Show that L is a dense set.

6. Show that the axiom of continuity does not hold in R. (*Hint:* Consider the subset of R defined by the condition $x^2 < 2$. Is there an element in R that is a least upper bound?)

7. A linearly ordered set in which the continuity axiom holds is said to be *complete*. Show that:

    (a) N is a complete, linearly ordered set but it is not dense.
    (b) R is a dense, linearly ordered set but it is not complete.
    (c) L is a dense, complete, and linearly ordered set.

1105. Mathematics is the study of structures

As we write this last section, we do not wish to depreciate the specific things you have learned as you studied elementary analysis; at the same time we want to leave you with a broad outlook.

We hope you have learned to view mathematics as a storehouse of structures. Questions of truth and falsity become, in mathematics, questions of *validity*. A statement that involves the primitive terms either is or is not a valid statement; that is, it is or is not a logical consequence of the postulates.

When you try to apply mathematics, you ask: "Does the system to which I wish to apply this mathematical structure fit the postulates of the structure?" If it does, you proceed with confidence. If it does not, this mathematical structure is not the one for you. If you are not sure, you investigate further to try to decide.

Index

Date Due

JAN 31 '61		
FEB 19 62		
NOV 3 0 1963		
NOV 2 1964		
MAY 19 1969		
MAY 29 1969		
OCT 1 9 1970		
JAN 3 1 1972		
DEC 4 1972		
JUN 0 6 1975		
OCT 1 8 1977 pd		
AUG 2 7 1986		
PRINTED IN U. S. A.		